Systems Engineering Design Renaissance

by
Walter Sobkiw

Published by

C~B
CassBeth, Cherry Hill, NJ

Published by Cassbeth, Cherry Hill, New Jersey, USA

For information contact www.cassbeth.com

First Edition

Library of Congress Control Number: 2014911869

ISBN: 978-0-9832530-7-5 (hardcover)

Dedicated to our Parents whose values and hard work allowed us to become a space faring civilization.

It is for my children, their families, and their world.

Preface

In my last text I focused on systems practices and I asked a fundamental question: If you had the opportunity to write a book on systems practices what would you focus on? Would you identify the most important and trendy processes, methods, techniques and describe them or would you try to teach how to develop processes, methods, and techniques? My goal was to broaden the discussion and try to show how to develop processes, methods, and techniques that are needed for the next generation. I thought that the reader should have a view of what happened in the past, appreciate the struggle, and be somewhat proficient in many different processes, methods, and techniques, which I arbitrarily grouped into practices.

In this book I hope to describe and teach design, more specifically systems engineering design. This thing called design is the miracle of starting with nothing and creating something. I am not sure if great designers are born or can be taught but I will do my best to try and teach this thing called systems engineering design.

This effort was born from my experience of going back to the universities in 2008 as an advisor on senior class systems engineering projects. From that point forward I have been involved as an adjunct systems engineering professor, course developer, and someone helping to establish and shape the direction of university level systems engineering degrees and curriculum.

This book uses the phrase systems engineering design. However the content of this book is not limited to systems engineers. This book is appropriate for all that are engaged in systems, especially large systems. We may be systems users, managers, administrators, policy makers, architects, designers, builders, testers, teachers, doctors, etc in fields as diverse as healthcare to spaceships. But these systems engineering design teachings can apply and should be considered when trying to make existing systems better or design new systems. They should become our design common sense in what I now view as Renaissance.

This book is an attempt to introduce systems engineering design in a semi academic text. In many ways it is based on a format of an advisor sitting at the table with students. It includes the mechanics of executing a design practice, offers examples, but then departs from the traditional textbook format and offers opinions. I have tried to delineate where my opinions start but the line is not always clearly drawn. I also included exercises at the end of each chapter to stimulate thinking beyond the content of the chapter. They represent what might be found in a high quality work setting or student advisor session.

Fundamentally the purpose of this book is to introduce my children and future generations to this work. I wrote a less formal book on systems engineering[1], a

---

[1] Sustainable Development Possible with Creative System Engineering, Walter Sobkiw, 2008, ISBN 0615216307.

textbook[2] on systems engineering, and suggest that you consider all my texts as you enter the systems space and make your contributions. I invite others to improve upon this work and offer their own texts.

My motivation for entering this space is because of my concern for our future. I have placed great emphasis on the importance of a systems education in my professional dialog. This is driven by my views as follows.

Our world today is very different from the world of our parents. Whether we like it or not we live in a complex high technology society that surfaced only recently. We take for granted our water, sewage, power, transportation, communications, social, and other systems. These systems were established by the previous generation through hit or miss and usually became successful when early systems practitioners became involved. These practitioners were grown out of necessity in the vast collection of nonprofit organizations, for profit companies, and government national labs. The body of systems knowledge grew and until recently was only found in a few universities.

Today we now know that systems are the essence of our modern high tech world. So we must prepare a generation of systems people to not only maintain and improve our existing systems but develop new systems that will be needed if we are to gracefully live in this new century. We are also finding that what we viewed as single standalone systems are now becoming interconnected as the level of needed services increases. So the systems are growing more complex needing not just a few systems practitioners in isolated organizations but many systems practitioners found in all organizations. These are powerful words and you may be asking why the emphasis on systems and the need for so many systems practitioners?

There will be systems. These systems will be good and provide needed benefits with no negative unintended consequences or they will be bad and provide some benefits but with massive negative unintended consequences. So the trick is to avoid the bad systems. In many ways this is tied to the recent trends in sustainability. Somehow we always practiced sustainability otherwise how did we arrive at a point in our history where we have billions of people? So why change?

The difference today is that our systems and the technologies they use are so powerful that the unintended consequences of these systems can devastate our lives in our time and our children's lives in the future. It doesn't matter if the issue is water, energy, sanitation, transportation, communications, or other systems – errors or mistakes in these systems could have devastating consequences and we as a people sense this and so we discuss sustainability.

So the importance of a systems education from the broader social perspective is intimately tied to not only the quality of our life but to the quality of the life of future generations. There are no governments, institutions, companies, management

---

[2] Systems Practices as Common Sense, by Walter Sobkiw, CassBeth, 2011, ISBN 978-0983253082.

techniques, political dogma, ideologies or other engineering scientific or technical approaches that will get us through the next 100 years of peaceful sustainable development except for systems engineering and thinking practiced by people with a solid systems education.

This brings me to the topic of education and why a systems education is needed. Before I move into education let me briefly talk about training. The point being – is there a difference between training and an education.

In training a task is narrowly defined. It is fully understood. It is also something that needs to be repeated. Occasionally legal ramifications may be associated with the task, so a certificate or license is issued to someone who will perform the highly structured, well defined, well understood, repeatable task. Training is what is provided to the individual or team of individuals so that they can perform these tasks with no errors. Sometimes the training is classroom, sometimes it is computer based, sometimes simulators are used, and then there is on the job training. The goal is to always imprint the repeatable tasks so that there are no errors.

In an education students are immersed in a body of knowledge for the specific purpose of entering into an unknown task such as developing a new product, opening new markets, establishing a new company, or developing a new system. An education attempts to transfer the knowledge, skills, and values, to positively shape the mind and character of the next generation. It is something that will allow students to enter unknown space and emerge with a viable sustainable solution.

So a systems education is needed because the problems for this new generation are new. They can not be solved using the approaches from the past. Yes the past needs to be known, understood and appreciated. Also following some steps, no matter how brilliant those steps may appear to the originators, can not solve the new problems facing our future. Only a solid education, which exposes the student to previous work, existing practices, and current thoughts on new ideas, will allow this new generation to develop the new systems for their time.

Deciding on the final content for this book was challenging because I produced a textbook and a pop culture book. Also I am working on other books. While these books have overlapping content they do not focus on the singular goal of systems engineering design. While this book has unique content attempting to offer the magic sauce associated with systems engineering design, it needs to offer content found in the other books. So a major decision was needed. Should this text be standalone or build from the previous texts forcing the readers to buy the other books. I did not think the latter was appropriate, so this text is standalone. So there is some content from my previous books, with updates. Sometimes the depth and breadth will be less or more than in my previous texts. In many ways this is an example of the systems challenge. There are different stakeholders, audiences, and perspectives. The result is overlap and completely new elements to consider.

This book is one entry into the extremely important education foundation. I hope you enjoy the rest of the book. Our focus is systems engineering design.

Figures

Tables

Examples

1 Systems Engineering Design

There is systems thinking, practices, and management but how does one actually perform systems engineering design? Also what is meant by the phrase "Systems Engineering Design". Are not engineering and design redundant? Let's start with the basics by examining the dictionary definitions of engineering, design, and systems engineering and then progress beyond those definitions.

Engineering tends to have a relatively simple definition. These are some dictionary definition items associated with engineering:

- Application of scientific and mathematical principles to practical ends such as the design, manufacture, and operation of efficient and economical structures, machines, processes, and systems.
- Profession of applying scientific principles to the design, construction, and maintenance of engines, cars, machines, etc. (mechanical engineering), buildings, bridges, roads, etc. (civil engineering), electrical machines and communication systems (electrical engineering), chemical plant and machinery (chemical engineering), or aircraft (aeronautical engineering).
- Practical application of science and mathematics, as in the design and construction of machines, vehicles, structures, roads, and systems.
- Application of science to practical uses such as the design of structures, machines, and systems. Engineering has many specialties such as civil engineering, chemical engineering, and mechanical engineering

Design has different meanings depending on the audience or context. There are the artist's, engineer's, and philosopher's views. There are overlaps and common elements between these views.

From the artists point of view engaged in the fine arts, visual arts, and art in general their designs can be granted a patent. It is called a design patent. A Design Patent is granted to anyone who creates an ornamental design of an item that can be manufactured. The appearance of the article is protected. Examples include ornamental designs of jewelry, furniture, kitchen tools, computer icons and other objects with distinctive shapes, colors, textures, size, and other attributes. Some dictionary definitions of design from the artists' perspective are:

- Sketch or drawing
- Arrangement or pattern or features of an artistic or decorative work
- An artistic or decorative creation

Engineers are granted Utility Patents. They are granted to anyone who invents or discovers any new and useful process, machine, manufacture, or compositions of matter, or any new and useful improvement of those elements. Process means a process or method; new industrial or technical processes may be patented. Manufacture refers to articles, which are made. Composition of matter relates to chemical compositions and may include mixtures of ingredients as well as new chemical compounds. Yet those machines, processes, and compositions are the result of what everyone would call design. Some dictionary definitions of design from the engineers' perspective are:

- Create, fashion, execute, or construct according to plan, devise, contrive
- Form or conceive in the mind, invent
- Plan out in mind, conceive or execute a plan, make artistically or skillfully
- Have as a purpose, intend, plan
- Devise for a specific function or end
- Make a drawing, pattern, or sketch, lay out, draw the plans for
- Work out structure or form, by making a sketch, outline, pattern, or plans

In systems engineering design concepts are driven by:

- Functions
- Performance
- Technology

Then there is the philosophers' view of design: a coherent or purposeful pattern, as opposed to chaos. So Chaos is the antithesis of design. This suggests something bringing order to chaos, but what is that something if not the art of design.

Systems' engineering also has many definitions, but they too point to some common overlapping themes. From a dictionary point of view the word systems comes from the word systema circa 1603. The word systema is defined as:

- A complex of anatomical structures functionally related

This makes sense given the time frame and the focus people had on trying to understand how the human body works. Additional definitions of systems engineering are:

- Discipline that concentrates on the design and application of the whole (system) as distinct from the parts. It involves looking at a problem in its entirety, taking into account all the facets and all the variables and relating the social to the technical aspect[3].

- Interdisciplinary approach and means to enable the realization of successful systems. It focuses on defining customer needs and required functionality early in the development cycle, documenting requirements, and then proceeding with design synthesis and system validation while considering the complete problem: operations, cost and schedule, performance, training and support, test, manufacturing, and disposal. It considers both the business and the technical needs of all customers with the goal of providing a quality product that meets the user needs[4].

Notice that the second definition starts to list what is done when engaged in systems engineering. I prefer the first definition of systems engineering primarily because the list of what one would do when engaged in systems engineering is extensive[5] and changes with time. Also it is succinct. However there are some core elements that are needed when engaged in systems engineering.

Imagine a place where you can create things and make decisions where there are no hidden agendas and all stakeholders are treated equally. How would potential approaches surface, how would they be narrowed and selected, how would decisions be made? What tools and techniques would be used if they were not the greatest moneyed interests, the most politically powerful, or the most dangerous?

How about using logical methods based on reasonable techniques understood by reasonable people in a process that is fully transparent and visible to everyone. Everyone has a view of all the alternatives. Everyone has a view of all the decision paths. Everyone has an opportunity to impact the alternatives and decision paths.

Do not fall for the rhetoric that this is mob rule or design by committee. These are reasonable people using thousands of years of tools, techniques, processes, and methods to make informed decisions. There are no hidden agendas with vested interests or people who just give up and go silent or worse compromise. Everyone is comfortable with the decision because it is intuitively obvious to all. Everyone obviously has responsibility in such an endeavor. No one can ignore that responsibility. That in a nutshell is Systems Practice.

The reality is many of us engage in systems practices in our everyday lives when we reject fate and try to control our destinies. We use whatever tools we have at our disposal to make these decisions everyday of our lives. Everyone engaged in our

---

[3] From Simon Ramo, left Hughes Aircraft, Founder of TRW, Source from International Council on Systems Engineering (INCOSE) Systems Engineering Handbook 2011.

[4] International Council on Systems Engineering (INCOSE) Systems Engineering Handbook 2011.

[5] This author, Walter Sobkiw attempted to identify and describe how to perform many of these systems practices in the text: Systems Practices as Common Sense, by Walter Sobkiw, CassBeth, 2011, ISBN 978-0983253082.

modern world should have some say in its evolution and that say should be from the system perspective of his or her view. So we can start at this point by saying that you as a systems practitioner do the following:

1. Always broaden your horizons and perspective. Just when you think you have it, move to a broader view.
2. Reject the status quo. If you find yourself in that mix, step out of it and look for truth. It takes time for a valid solution to solidify.
3. Reject all vested interests including hidden interests.
4. Try to see the forest from the trees but always zoom in onto the leaf of a particular tree and find the cute bug sitting on the edge.
5. Avoid the trap of being set only at one abstraction level, the high level. You must be able to scale all abstraction levels simultaneously. This is hard.

So design appears to be the miracle that happens when someone or a team attempts to create something from nothing. Systems engineering is an extension of that concept of creating something from nothing. If it is difficult to develop design, then the complexity suggested by a system suggests even more difficulty.

When the patent process is examined there are some insights that are offered on the subject of design. For example a design patent is associated with a work of art which has shape, color, texture, size, weight and other attributes. For example a unique coffee cup can be associated with a design patent. This is in contrast to a utility patent that is associated with a device or process, which is the result of a design effort. They use design to bring them into being, but they are not granted a design patent. So the term design has multiple meanings. In our case to be clear we are addressing the design of a device or process and in our case a system.

Author Comment: There are those who do not want to take the time to read the long definition of systems engineering just offered. In those instances I offer the following definition of systems engineering:

- I like Ramo's definition
- Systems engineering is the effective application of different practices to surface the needs of all the stakeholders, define and understand the relevant architecture alternatives, select the most effective architecture, codify the necessary requirements, ensure the design and implementation support the original architecture vision, verify the requirements are satisfied, validate that the system needs are met and will not degrade over its expected life time, and when the system reaches its end of life it is effectively shutdown and disposed of with minimal impact to all stakeholders.

The second item tends to list items that most can relate to if they are not part of the systems engineering community. It also tries to capture the spirit of the succinct Ramo definition, especially the second part of the Ramo definition, which has been lost to time: **"relating the social to the technical aspect"**.

1.1 Great System Designs

Can great designs be created by anyone in any organization or are there attributes of organizations and people that need to be in place before great designs can be created? This is an interesting question.

Author Comment: Hughes Aircraft produced great designs. Everyone in the world recognized they produced outstanding systems. They had a culture that was unique and that culture eventually transferred to the new people as they entered that culture. That culture was based on the following ingredients or formula:

1. **Symbol:** Howard Hughes mystique and values of breaking the boundaries, doing it with outstanding quality, don't tell anybody what you are doing, non conflict of interest compensation, no stock holding, no shared equity everyone working for non profit medical foundation.
2. **Cold War:** Unlimited funds.
3. **Private Ownership:** It was a cocoon, technology first, profits second, no quarterly stockbrokers to answer to and disrupt operations.
4. **Recruit Superb Talent:** Recruited from Universities especially those on the Ph.D. tracks or orientation and pay them more than others would pay.
5. **Unique Management Style:** Modeled after Bell Labs, key word is labs, invent, ask people to do things that have never done before, have people be unbounded, just go for it, find experts across company, family sharing. Provide extremely stable work environment[6] and pay more than anyone else in the industry pays.

These attributes made the company extremely successful and prized by the world in its time. It is difficult to find these attributes in most companies.

Developing a design has some extremely important attributes. For example a design that duplicates an existing design is not a new design. This seems like it is stating the obvious but within this concept is the idea that time should not be wasted recreating the wheel. If it exists, just use it with modifications as needed. So design suggests breaking new ground. A new design should always push one or more envelopes if it is addressing an existing need with current solutions. It also must push the quality envelope of existing designs, again otherwise why bother. Buried in this environment are the sponsor, user, and or market. They will not move to a

---

[6] Hughes never had a layoff.

lower quality solution or a worse design unless they are driven by an external factor such as extremely lower costs, regulation, or rising ignorance.

So the attributes of great designs go back to the attributes found within the Hughes Mystique:

- Breaking the existing performance and functional boundaries
- Doing it with outstanding quality

These attributes however need an environment where they can be nurtured and grown. No one is willing to break new boundaries, do things they have never done before unless they feel extremely secure and are not worried about damaging their careers, reputations, or finding their next paying position[7].

Systems are multi dimension. To understand a system, multiple views must be considered. This means there are different kinds of pictures, analysis, and words all grouped into some cohesive set so that all can understand the system. For example most individuals will attempt to view a system from a financial point of view. But there are also functional and performance points of views in which a system can be optimized.

The reality is a system with a given set of functional and performance characteristics will be at a given cost. The designers can choose to reduce performance or functionality to reduce costs, but then they run the risk of creating a useless system from the user point of view, those that must rely on the system. In some cases this reduced functionality and or performance can lead to loss of life. Most focus on examples of airplanes falling from the sky, bridges falling down, or cars killing needlessly. However, we should never forget that people have died from bad water, bad food, bad sanitation, bad drugs, bad health care, and even bad cities that result in crime and destruction of human spirit.

Author Comment: There are many traps that people can fall into when they first enter the systems engineering design space. For example most believe systems engineering will result in the perfect optimized solution, architecture, or design – the system. The reality is that multiple architecture approaches will work, but these architectures must be born from the fire of systems engineering. Each architecture or system will shine in a particular area and be weak in another area. Money can be applied to the weak architecture areas to bring it into the desired performance level. Also any of these architectures will cost about the same in the end. This realization

---

[7] This is traceable to Maslow's Hierarchy of Needs. Abraham Maslow proposed this in a paper in 1943. A.H. Maslow, A Theory of Human Motivation, Psychological Review 50(4), 1943.

was born from empirical data at Hughes Aircraft[8], Fullerton, California circa 1982 and communicated to me by a very senior Hughes person. He had worked with Howard Hughes in the early years. His name was also Howard and yes he was brilliant.

1.2 Design and Architecture

Systems architects are typically associated with the entire system and designers are associated with the elements that make up a system. They both engage in the same miracle of creating something from nothing. Once systems architects and designers establish the systems architecture and design anyone can then produce, distribute, sell, buy, use, maintain, and eventually dispose of the system. If the systems architects and designers are successful then each of the recipients of the systems architecture and design are able to effortlessly execute their roles.

The systems architects and designers are the visionaries that develop the new architecture and design. There are many others who support their vision and engage in the mechanics of many design practices to ensure the architecture and design are captured and understood for all stakeholders. For example there are people who engage in analysis and developing the detailed specifications. But it is the systems architects and designers that maintain and drive the system vision and ensure it is properly reflected in the information products[9].

Author Comment: Some suggest that complex designs always start with an architecture phase before there is movement into what most would view as design. However the act of developing the architecture is design. Some suggest that architecture is a new pattern that emerges that all other designers then follow with their unique designs. All these observations are valid.

1.2.1 Fashion Design

As the few thousand years of civilization have clicked by we have become very proficient at doing some things and designing our clothing or fashion design is one of those marvelous wonders. We take it for granted and we should not at our peril. There is significant knowledge, expertise, care, technology, complexity, and innovation in the design, production, distribution, and retirement of our clothing just like in all our other complex systems.

The fashion designer needs to balance function, performance, and esthetics in each new design. The design may be a single product like a shirt with a single

---

[8] Hughes Aircraft is now owned by Raytheon, See the University of Las Vegas Howard R. Hughes College of Engineering archives.

[9] Information products will be discussed later in this text. For now it is as the name suggests, anything that captures and communicates information about the architecture and design in this case.

pattern and material choice or what some outside the fashion industry would call a product line, or even multiple product lines with multiple patterns, colors, materials, and uses (shirt, blouse, pant, dress, undergarment, etc). When addressing function the expected user setting is considered. These considerations factor into the choice of materials, cut, and esthetic design. Some of the considerations are:

- Casual, professional, vacation, formal user settings
- Infant, child, adult
- Male, female
- Spring, summer, winter, fall
- Geographic location and climate

Fashion designers can start with a sketch using chalk, pencil, pen, or computer. The sketch can expand to include colors and rough pattern ideas. Some fashion designers work like sculptors and assemble their prototype designs on mannequins using pins. The point is they start with a concept and mature it to a point so that pattern making then can be performed. From the pattern the first prototype garment is produced. The first garment is then checked for fit, operation, and acceptance. This is essentially a research and development prototype. As the design is modified and matured with all colors, patterns, materials, fasteners, sizes, and other key elements the process eventually translates into pre-production prototypes, market test runs, and then full scale production.

This industry produces one of the most important things we need (food, clothing, and shelter are basic needs). It is functional, performs well, is high quality (lasts through multiple wear sessions and wash cycles), and is aesthetically pleasing and uplifting.

Author Comment: Could you imagine what would happen if clothing were to be converted into an investment as happened to housing in the USA circa 1979 to 1981. Instead the fashion industry maintains 3 categories of clothing, each at their own respective costs. Haute Couture is expensive custom fitted clothing made to order for a specific customer, uses high quality expensive fabric and is sewn by the most experienced and capable seamstresses in a time-consuming hand-executed manufacturing process. Ready-to-Wear clothing is the most current fashion trend that is factory made using standard sizes but may require alternation to complete the final fit. Mass-Market clothing is the least expensive, is not intended for alteration and tends to be a proven fashion trend rather than a new fashion release. This suggests that what some may view as a new architecture (a new fashion trend) is establish in Haute Couture or Ready-to-Wear, but that is not always the case.

1.2.2 Interior Design

Interior design is like fashion design where we take the design activities and system complexity for granted. The building architect working with the civil, mechanical, and other engineers develops the architecture, which may include elements of the interior design such as walls, windows, doors, lighting, acoustics, ventilation, materials, structures, etc. Then interior designers work with the architects' vision to select furniture, fixtures, window treatments, floor treatments, etc. However some structures developed by the architect are devoid of all interior elements except for load bearing structures, basic window openings, and entrances. The interior designer then has full control over the entire interior including elements such as walls, ceilings, lighting, materials, structures, etc.

When the interior designer works they need to balance function, performance, and aesthetics just like fashion designers. The choice of colors, materials, patterns, and physical layout in terms of privacy walls, stairs, and other elements are considered. They can begin with a sketch using pencil, pen, or chalk. The sketch can be enhanced with color and patterns as the concept matures. It can be rendered in 2-dimensional or 3-dimensional computer imagery. There can be a scale model or even a like size model. A physical space with no interior elements that has all utilities and supporting structures in place can be used to stage and visualize interior design alternatives. Examples include furniture stores, kitchen and bathroom showrooms, and unfinished industrial spaces.

For interior designers working with finished spaces the design elements are presented in photographic samples of what could be a design approach. Samples are offered of material, color, texture selection for wall, floor, and ceiling treatments. Samples are also offered of lighting, kitchen, bathroom, office, industrial fixtures, devices, appliances, machinery, etc[10]. This is all provided for visualization so that the interior designer can balance available space, function, performance, needs, and aesthetics.

Author Comments: Many people in the USA participate in design as part of the home ownership process. Most engage in the interior design activities but shortly after WW-II many Americans also engaged in the process of building their own houses. They were introduced to all elements of complex design as they engaged in building their homes. Without knowing it they needed to evaluate their needs, decide on location, select the house architecture (ranch, colonial, bi-level, etc), and then implement and produce the final result either as a participant with other team members or as a sponsor funding the team. The very act of forcing so many people to become designers elevated the ability of society to understand complex systems

---

[10] In the United States when we purchase a house and begin to make it our space we engage in this process and take the entire supporting infrastructure for our design choices for granted.

and design. Home ownership helps to build a very aware, responsible, and sustainable society.

1.3 Design Theory Philosophies and Art

Is there a theory of design? How does design relate to philosophy and art? These are interesting topics and worth considering when trying to understand how we develop systems engineering designs.

We know that as part of our formal and informal education we are introduced to many different topics. These topics tend to fall into the liberal arts and the sciences. As very young children before we start school we are introduced to colors, shapes, texture, size via coloring books, blocks, clay, and finished toys of all forms and function. During all our years we are exposed to film, music, writings, art, theatre, etc which expose us to more liberal arts and sciences as part of informal education.

When we enter school our formal education begins. In liberal arts we study literature, history, the mechanics of language and writing, music, painting, drawing, and even sculpting with clay and paper mache. In the sciences we study the earth, our solar system, biology, chemistry, physics, and mathematics. Many who may be interested in engineering take mechanical drawing, drafting, software programming, and other engineering related classes before university.

Everyone engages in building and modifying various things long before they enter the university to study engineering and or design. Some build structures to play in while others may create paintings. Some may draw, others may write. Still others may modify home machines like lawn mowers, televisions, stereos, automobiles, etc. Others may cook and develop new eating delights and some modify or write software, websites, or music.

So long before we enter the engineering space we have a broad foundation that allows us to design even though we may not view it as design. The reality is that to design is human. We just do what comes naturally when we have the freedom and time to express ourselves. So when we discuss design theory philosophies and art we are just trying to explain some part of our universe.

1.3.1 Art

Art exists everywhere you look. Art takes a medium like paint and canvas and transforms those fundamental building elements into a finished item, a work of art. This is design - from nothing comes something. In order to bring this design into being knowledge is needed of the medium and its limitations. For example working with paint and canvas will not result in sound. It is a visual image. This seems obvious but if the artist is trying to express a vision and have it become a final design with physical attributes that vision may require a different medium, such as stone which has texture and is 3 dimensional. So perhaps the vision may be implemented with paint, canvas and stone in motion.

In art the final vision is always modified by the medium. There is only so much you can do with paint and canvas when trying to express colors, brightness, contrast, shape, and perspective. So perhaps the artist needs to distort one element of the artwork so that another element of the artwork or design becomes prominent.

Many tend to equate beautiful buildings as works of art rather than works of engineering. Also some may view the architecture of the building as a subset of art. These are excellent examples of the medium affecting the vision and the medium being understood via the engineering discipline.

When an artist produces multiple copies of the same item there are always differences. When multiple artists produce the same item there are differences. For example when multiple software programmers write code to solve the same problem, the solution is always different except in the rarest and most simple cases. The same is true of designers. Multiple teams will rarely develop the exact same design. However, when a work of art or design is subjected to a manufacturing process those differences become significantly smaller. Depending on the manufacturing process even machines may be unable to detect the differences between multiple copies.

In art just like any discipline one can study art or one can do art. The study can include history, mediums, techniques, artists and what they did and or do, etc. Art can be a tiny logo or very large as in the case of the layout of an entire city. This small treatment of art may not do justice to artists but the key elements for designers are visible. They are:

- The medium needs to be selected
- The medium modifies the designers' visions
- The designer must respect and use the medium for maximum effectiveness
- There may be unexpected wonderful emergence as the designer works with the medium, this might be called great art

Author Comment: Hand eye coordination is a critical skill that is developed in early childhood education. It is at that time when children engage in their art projects that make their way to the kitchen refrigerator. Many unfamiliar with the basics of child development do not know or understand the importance of a simple crayon drawing or strange shape formed from paper mache or clay. They don't realize some may be getting nurtured and matured to one day become great designers.

Author Comment: With the rise of computer technology many are missing the chance to develop important hand eye coordination skills. The simple act of being able to write letters clearly on a straight-line help to build spatial relations, printing and cursive writing are just as important as drawing and sculpting. Today we are at a crossroads where a generation that had the opportunity to develop these skills and use computers is disappearing. There is a fundamental question we need to address - how is the computer medium with its software helping or hindering our ability to capture our visions. There has been a large trend in reuse across disciplines. Could that be because it is difficult to capture original visions on a computer? What does this mean? It may suggest that all great design organizations should include artists who are capable of expressing visions without using the computer. This could be via drawings, sketches, graphics, line art, cartoons, physical mockups, physical model structures, animations, etc.

Author Comment: Conversely the computer is a new medium and as such should be able to lead to new designs if we believe that the medium impacts the designers' vision. This suggest that the computer needs to be effectively applied and not used to compromise the design in the name of expediency and or cost. The computer has also allowed the user to perform tasks not possible in the past without other resources. For example:

- It is easy to develop and print a book with hundreds of pages
- It is possible to produce interesting animations without an art department and slow turn around time medium like film
- It is possible to quickly author and preview music including compositions with an entire orchestra

We just need to ensure we don't use the computer to destroy our art when computers cannot meet the challenge of capturing the vision.

1.3.2 Designers and Medium

When designers work, they need to work with the available "medium". The term Medium is a broad reference to the materials, tools, practices, and technologies. This suggests the designers are not only familiar with the medium but also understand the ramifications of their use under various conditions. Materials is also a broad term that includes fundamental physical material such as wood, stone, metals to abstract materials such as software. Material also can include what we view as an aggregation such as a subsystem. So when we are designing an automobile at one abstraction level the mechanical engineer designing the engine may focus on different metals, ceramics, and composites to use for the engine components. At a different abstraction level the system designer may be focusing on the types of engines, such as gas, electric, or diesel to use in the design of the automobile.

In all cases the materials, tools, practices, and technologies need to be fully understood so that appropriate design choices can be selected. For example an electric engine may be desired however technology may need to be matured in one or more areas before the electric engine can be considered for the particular automobile application.

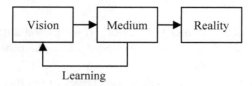

Figure 1 Designers and Medium

This concept can be represented using a block diagram. The block diagram is a visualization and just like any other medium it has limitations that will impact the final reality.

1.3.3 Critical Thinking

Educators take great pride in being able to produce critical thinkers. But what is critical thinking and why is it important to systems engineering design? The following are some definitions of critical thinking:

- Disciplined thinking that is clear, rational, open-minded, and informed by evidence
- Mental process of actively and skillfully conceptualizing, applying, analyzing, synthesizing, and evaluating information to reach an answer or conclusion

Critical thinking is a situation where someone is able to filter out all the irrelevant elements and get to the heart of a situation very quickly and explain their thought process so that everyone understands the conclusion, its lineage, and it is the correct conclusion with no bias or agenda. This requires a well-trained and disciplined mind that is challenged to engage in critical thinking throughout their formal education from first grade through to the university, work, and life experiences. The idea is that practice makes perfect.

Critical thinking is extremely important in the liberal arts and is constantly addressed. That is why some with liberal arts backgrounds can enter the high technology systems arena. Their ability to think critically and get a team off of a dead end or stalled position is invaluable. They are able to challenge accepted doctrines from the technologists and defend their positions because of the clarity of their thinking possible because of their critical thinking skills. It is a given that technical team members also must be able to think critically. However they have the luxury of falling back on quantitative aspects of a situation using math and logic. The interesting scenario is when qualitative elements are all that are available. This is a scenario where again liberal arts inspired team members using their critical thinking skills can move the situation forward. Some of the key elements of critical thinking and its results are:

- Clarifies goals, examines assumptions, discerns and articulates the relevant from the irrelevant, offers evidence through observation, evaluates evidence, assesses conclusions
- Enters into the logic of problems and issues to see them for what they are without egocentric, social, financial, organizational, personal, or other bias
- Does not shift context to deflect into wrong or useless thinking leading to wrong conclusions or abandonment of finding a solution
- Uses logic and criteria such as clarity, credibility, accuracy, precision, relevance, depth, breadth, significance, and fairness
- Fair-minded, intellectual humility, empathy, integrity, perseverance, courage, and autonomy - without these key traits the results may be clever, but manipulative and often unethical
- Enables analysis, evaluation, explanation, and restructuring of thinking to prevent adopting, acting on, or thinking with a false belief
- Identifies prejudice, bias, propaganda, deception, self-deception, distortion, misinformation

Some of the attributes of critical thinkers are:

- Wants to engage problems and decisions using critical thinking skills
- Raises important questions and problems
- Formulates questions and problems clearly and precisely
- Recognizes problems, wants to find solutions to those problems
- Understands prioritization and order of precedence in problem solving
- Gathers, assesses, and offers relevant information
- Interprets information effectively
- Recognizes unstated assumptions and values
- Comprehends and uses language with accuracy, clarity, and discernment
- Interprets data, to appraise evidence and evaluate arguments
- Recognizes existence or non-existence of logical relationships
- Thinks open-mindedly within alternative systems of thought, recognizing and assessing, assumptions, implications, and practical consequences
- Draws warranted conclusions and generalizations
- Comes to well-reasoned conclusions, solutions, and generalizations
- Tests conclusions, solutions and generalizations using relevant criteria
- Renders accurate judgments
- Reconstructs beliefs on basis of wider experience

From a systems engineering design perspective the team members must always ask themselves if they are engaged in critical thinking as they discuss and address their respective design areas.

Author Comment: Some suggest that individuals can have intellectual skills without critical thinking skills. I disagree. It may be a matter of context but being able to execute a math problem without being able to critically think about the nature of the problem and its elements is in my view being devoid of intellectual skill. Computers have that luxury people do not have that luxury. We all must embrace and enhance our critical thinking skills especially when engaged in systems, which by their very nature have large impacts and many consequences.

Author Comment: Those who come from a biased position will attempt to shutdown or discredit critical thinking and its activities. A common method to compromise critical thinking is to de-scope the problem or change the context so that the problem goes away. In this manner a naïve manager may believe they have successfully managed the situation and closed out the activity. Many times this leads to terrible consequences and injustices. An example is a jury that is instructed to disregard physical evidence or events, which are actually the only items that matter for the final obvious conclusion. We can become victims to rules that really do not need to be followed but are set by those interested in their exclusive agenda. Thus critical thinking is attacked and shut down. This can and should never be tolerated, including in systems engineering design.

1.3.4 Scientific Method

In order for students to be accepted to a university engineering program typically they must be exposed to science course material in high school. Why is there this emphasis on science courses? Let's step back and examine the scientific method.

Author Comment: Many people do not understand that engineering requires significant education including the liberal arts, science, and mathematics. This is especially true of people who have less formal education or come from cultures where these foundations are not known, understood, and appreciated.

The scientific method is used for acquiring knowledge and investigating phenomena. We soon learn there are basic steps in the scientific method:

- Define a question
- Gather information
- Form a hypothesis

16

- Develop a reproducible experiment to test the hypothesis
- Collect the data
- Analyze the data
- Interpret the data
- Draw conclusions that prove or disprove the hypothesis
- Publish the results
- Have others duplicate the experiment
- Proven hypothesis then becomes a theory

Within the scientific method are certain key elements. Scientists think in terms of cause and effect. The cause and effect is framed in terms of data. The data is usually quantitative to avoid misinterpretation of results. The data analysis uses mathematics and logic to understand the results. This can be presented in graphical format using charts and table formats. The hypothesis selected tends to follow Occam's razor[11] where the simplest explanation is usually the correct one. This can be viewed as succinctness, fewest assumptions, and economy. The conclusion also tends to follow Occam's razor. This is especially important when the conclusion shows the hypothesis is incorrect.

Author Comment: Contrary to what many think who refused to take science classes, disproving a hypothesis is just as important as proving a hypothesis. This is especially important if the failed hypothesis is a significant surprise.

So the scientific method transfers to engineering and design. Our initial design starts out as hypothetical design. As we perform analysis, especially systems engineering analysis, the design quickly starts to fall apart and so we move into a space of multiple design alternatives. The designs just like the scientific method hypothesis and conclusion tend to follow Occam's razor. The simplest most elegant designs[12] tend to survive the analysis findings. The analysis tends to be rooted in quantitative data using mathematics and logic. The analysis itself is similar to a reproducible experiment where the design is tested by the analysis.

The structure of the experiment in the scientific method has several important elements. It needs to be easily and consistently[13] reproducible. It should be as simple as possible without compromising the experiment. It should have the

---

[11] William of Ockham (1287 – 1347) was an English Franciscan friar and scholastic philosopher and theologian.

[12] This is also known as the KISS principle - Keep it Simple Stupid. One of the measures of elegance in a design is simplicity.

[13] Reproducible suggests consistency. Some claim one reproduction is all that is needed and that is incorrect. In the scientific method the experiment always must be reproducible or the error in the experiment must be detected and corrected.

following fundamental steps:

1. Tester names and date
2. Hypothesis statement
3. Purpose of experiment (prove or disprove hypothesis)
4. Expected results
5. Materials
6. Test Steps
7. Observations
8. Data collected
9. Data analysis
10. Conclusions and next steps

When our designs are implemented and produced they are subjected to tests. The design tests follow the basic principles in a scientific method experiment:

1. Purpose of test
2. Test materials
3. Test steps
4. Data collected
5. Tester and witness names and date

We then prepare a test report, it includes:

1. Observations
2. Data collected
3. Data analysis
4. Conclusions and next steps

As we engage in systems engineering design we should appreciate the scientific method and what it brings to the party.

1.3.5 Deductive and Inductive Reasoning

Deductive reasoning or thinking is a top down approach. The starting point is to find the most broad level general statement or facts about a situation and logically proceed to lower levels until they reach a logical conclusion. This suggests:

- There are no errors in the logic
- No statements are flawed or missing
- The full set of statements or facts are known
- All statements are precise and accurate

The problem is that there are always assumptions mixed in with the givens that form the set of statements. There is also the issue of introducing invalid assumptions and or givens. A formal systems engineering design analysis practice that uses deductive reasoning is Fault Tree Analysis (FTA).

Inductive reasoning or thinking is a bottom up approach where very specific statements are aggregated to form a conclusion. Although inductive reasoning descriptions typically use examples to lead to general propositions with limited or no assumptions, there is always reality where assumptions enter into the inductive conclusion. Just like in deductive reasoning, the assumptions, givens, examples and the resulting propositions can be flawed, missing, or not available thus leading to a wrong conclusion. A formal systems engineering design analysis practice that uses inductive reasoning is Failure Mode Effects Analysis (FMEA).

In the scientific method inductive reasoning is used to develop the hypothesis and deductive reasoning is used to develop the experiment and conclusion. In this scenario the inductive reasoning hypothesis is tested by the deductive reasoning experiment / conclusion while the deductive reasoning experiment / conclusion is tested by the inductive reasoning hypothesis. The ultimate goal is to prove or disprove the hypothesis in the scientific method. In systems engineering design analysis when FTA and FEMA is performed on the same aspect of the system they complement and check each other to add more confidence to the conclusion.

Deductive reasoning is much easier to practice. The biggest issue is ensuring all the facts and assumptions are known, then a logical path to an ultimate conclusion can be traced. Inductive reasoning is difficult because all the detailed facts and assumptions can be known but the pattern is not detected. Part of this is actually being able to find the relevant detailed set of facts and assumptions, but the connections are not made or the wrong connections are made resulting in a flawed conclusion. When teaching inductive reasoning simple examples are offered of a few statements. In practice there are dozens or even thousands of items to consider, such as when FMEA is used or a major go no go decision is needed for a new technology, product, or system.

1.3.6 Socratic Method

The Socratic method is a form of dialog between individuals based on asking and answering questions. It can be used in the design process. For example you propose this design. I ask this question, how do you respond.

It is used to stimulate critical thinking and further development of ideas. Typically the discussion involves defense of a point of view. One participant asking a series of questions may lead another into contradiction thus weakening the point of view being defended and strengthening an alternative point of view. This should result in a modification of the compromised point of view so that it is strengthened. So as questions are asked failure is detected and modification occurs - the modification then strengthens the idea, point of view, or in our case a design.

This method also tends to surface important elements of different points of views that not only become key discriminators between the points of views, but also become the key strengths of each point of view. Once applied to design, alternative designs also start to rise and fall with key discriminators and strengths surfacing as the questions are being asked.

Many who engage in the Socratic method tend to work in a real time mode, such as a classroom setting where a teacher is engaging their students. In these settings the questions and responses happen on the spot, there is no time delay. The same can be done when addressing design, where the technical director questions the team and the team questions itself. However in the design setting there comes a point in the dialog where a break needs to happen and the participants go to their respective work settings to perform research, investigation, and reflection to address outstanding unanswered questions. The dialog break can be a few hours, days, weeks, months, and perhaps years.

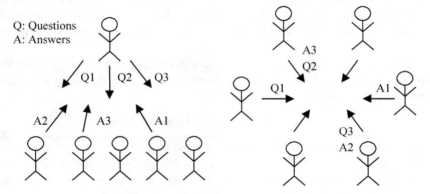

Socratic discourse in teacher student setting   Socratic discourse in peer to peer setting

Figure 2 Socratic Discourse Alternatives

In many ways engineering processes based on design reviews, such as Preliminary Design Review (PDR) and Critical Design Review (CDR) are based on the Socratic method as they have expectations that translate into key questions that must be answered at the design reviews. If the questions can not be adequately answered then the designers must go back to the drawing board and mature and or correct the designs. So designers can pull the standard questions asked at PDR, CDR[14], and other reviews and start to ask them on the first day of the design activity. These standard questions can form the basis of their unique questions associated with their unique need and the unique designs trying to fulfill the unique

---

[14] MIL-STD-1521, Technical Reviews and Audits, June 1995, lists a standard set of topics, which are easily interpreted as questions that can be asked at PDR, CDR, and other systems engineering design major milestones.

need.

Socratic questioning is used to explore complex ideas, find truth, surface issues and problems, find assumptions, explore concepts, and determine known from unknown elements. Some believe the questions need to be systematic, disciplined, and deep however that tends to create an intimidating environment where the most important question may never be asked. Some also believe the questions should focus on fundamental concepts, principals, theories, issues, or problems. However a detailed question that most initially view as noise may push the discourse into a new level and result in a major breakthrough.

Author Comment: I always make a point of asking questions or moving the conversation into left field. Most participants view this as a distraction. Some get angry and naive management wants to stop the activity. However, as the discourse continues and the redirection is followed, massive creativity is unleashed. It's at this point that innovation takes place and new technologies, approaches, systems, products, etc are born. I was first exposed to this design technique at Hughes Aircraft. Few follow this path and that is why few organizations can truly innovate.

There have been attempts to identify general categories of questions to consider while engaged in the Socratic method. When reviewing the following list think in terms of questions that the root word suggests.

Table 1 Socratic Method General Questions

- **Purpose:** forces the team members to define the task
- **Information:** what is the source and quality of the information
- **Interpretation:** examine how the team members organize and give meaning to the information, consider alternative meanings
- **Assumptions:** what is being taken for granted, what is being missed
- **Implications:** force team members to follow where the thinking is going
- **Point of View:** state the point of view then consider other points of views as offered by other team members
- **Relevance:** what matters and what is noise
- **Accuracy:** force team to test for correctness
- **Precision:** force team to provide details and be specific
- **Consistency:** look for contradictions
- **Logic:** challenging team to put it all together, make sense, make reasonable
- **Clarification:** close areas open to significant interpretation
- **Evidence:** request examples, analogies, data, information
- **Consequence:** challenge team to address where current logic path is going
- **Questions:** the most important question is questions about the questions, have they all been asked and addressed

Author Comment: The answers are irrelevant. It is all about the questions. Are the all questions being asked? As the right questions surface the answers become self-evident. If someone is suppressing the asking of questions they must be removed from the mix, they are anti-civilization. A good technical director will practice the Socratic method with the team and good management will allow, encourage, and facilitate this process.

1.3.7 Rational and Action Centric Design Models

Software engineering is a relatively new discipline. Many tend to forget the struggle of first understanding different computing architecture possibilities, different operating systems, and different languages. These three items alone can consume a career. Yet it has been acknowledged that software engineering must exist and mature as a discipline. This has yielded many new discussions, which many traditional engineers find to be spins on existing engineering concepts and ideas. For example agile methods are easily equated to maturing prototypes from initial research to a fielded implementation. We see that software has this luxury because it is easily changed while the implementation of a office building is difficult if not impossible to change. You can not argue that after the first floor is built you will learn more about the challenge and then build a better second floor.

Yet there are design ideas that should be discussed. Because software is easy to change, its design process are both positively and negatively impacted. It is much more accepting of the art concept where the medium shapes the final solution. So there tends to be a rejection of what some might suggest hard core engineering. This is engineering driven by rational principles, or a rational centric model. This is in contrast to an action centric model where an action is taken and then an observation is made. This is like striking the chisel on a stone sculpture or making a brush stroke on a painting.

The action centric model is influenced by empiricism, where knowledge comes from sensory experience. This is analogous to science, which is based on evidence discovered in experiments. In the scientific method all hypotheses and theories must be tested against observations rather than relying solely on a priori reasoning, intuition, or revelation. So the process of science can find its application in the design process. This is a way to view the action centric model.

Proponents of the action centric model point to extremely high quality software as viewed as by users. This software is developed with the user closely connected to the design process. Using software it is easy to develop user interactions and immediately get feedback that then results in appropriate changes.

However, even though this software design may be viewed as spectacular in terms of effectiveness, which includes use and stability, internally it may be a design nightmare. The internal design may be such that no one knows how it works, changes may be impossible, changes may have massive negative ripple effects, or a latent design defect may be present that can cause significant harm when surfaced months or years later.

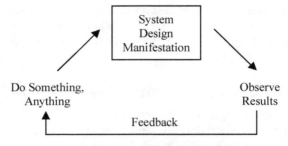

Figure 3 Action Centric Model

Yet the action centric model does have significant merits if it is acknowledged that a production ready system needs to be developed from the prototype, even if the prototype is already in field operations. This is the advantage of software; the next release is always possible.

However if we examine the design process closely we see the action centric model is not only relegated to software. All design starts at the concept stage. The artifacts in the form of documents, presentations, and models are all relatively easy to change. So all engineering engages in the action centric model early in the effort. There are always questions asked, elements proposed, and observations made. The observations may be formal or informal analysis. They can be on the spot during a technical interchange or somewhat delayed via an action item response. The point is that elements of a design are offered and then observed by the design team. Based on those observations, the design elements are modified and matured.

This brings the discussion back to the Socratic method of discourse. When a question is asked a response is anticipated. The question and response modify the solution space. The question or questions can be in the form of words, a spin through a software increment with immediate user feedback, outputs from models, mockups, prototypes, etc.

The rational and action centric models exist in a design activity. If the team is free to express themselves during design, these models will naturally emerge. They then need to be recognized for their strengths and effectively managed.

1.3.8 Linear and Nonlinear Thinking

Linear thinking is an approach where a starting point is selected and then using logic a selected path is followed to a conclusion. The starting point is critical. Non linear thinking is contrasted by changing the starting point and departing from the context or even logic to the next point in the thought process.

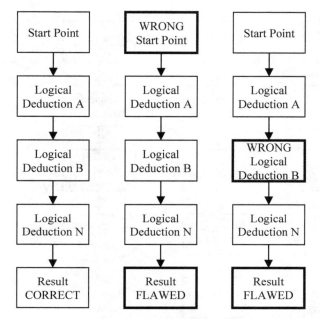

Figure 4 Linear Thinking

Linear thinking is easily seen and practiced when solving simple problems such as might be presented in mathematics. When complex problems are encountered people get stuck and they are unable to proceed to the next step of a particular thread of reason. So they jump to a related area in the problem space, back track to find a different logical path or even change the starting point.

When solving complex problems, jumping to a different aspect of a problem when stuck and unable to make progress can be viewed as following the path of least resistance. As the focus changes to an area where the path and its logic are easily seen and addressed, there is time for the mind to internalize the other aspects of the problem. No problem or aspect of a complex problem is solved before its time. In this way progress is always made.

Some people fear nonlinear thinking especially if they come from simple management settings. This is viewed by some as chaotic with no end in sight. If managers have no background in this area, new design can quickly be shutdown. So it is important to understand when nonlinear thinking surfaces in a team and to allow for its natural progression.

Linear and nonlinear thinking are not labels that are applied to people. Instead they are practices that anyone can apply individually or in a team setting. They each have their advantages and should be respected when they naturally emerge as complex problems are being addressed.

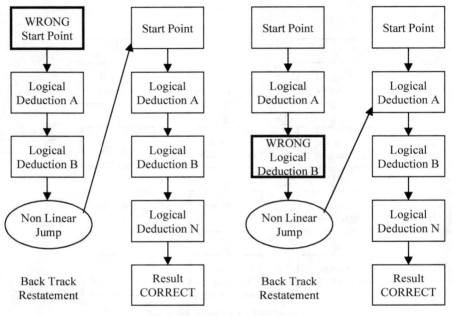

Figure 5 Nonlinear Thinking

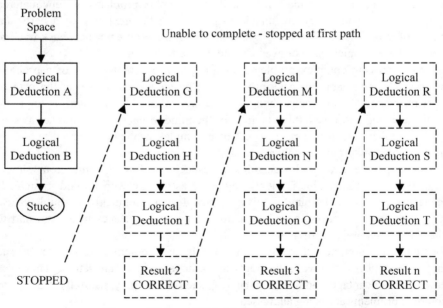

Figure 6 Linear Thinking Complex Problem

The STOP[15] approach is ideal for capturing design concepts because it easily fits into and acknowledges non-linear thinking. Even though STOP requires that the design be mature before writing begins, it can be used to capture the design as it unfolds. First in storyboard format and then on finished white papers that represent key topics and issues associated with the designs. What we think of as the slide presentation has its roots in these basic practices.

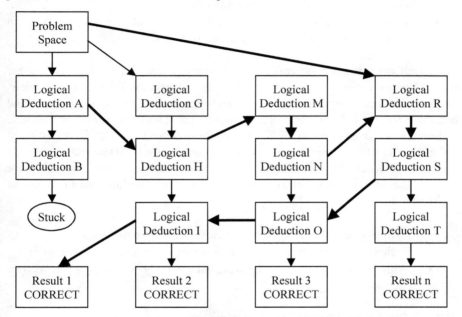

Figure 7 Nonlinear Thinking Complex Problem

1.3.9 Systems Thinking

Systems' thinking is the opposite of reductionism. Systems' thinking views the system as a whole within the context of its environment. Systems' thinking is in contrast with other forms of thinking. These other approaches frame the arguments and set the starting points in their favor. This is why practicing nonlinear thinking is important to the systems thinking process. Examples of other forms of thinking that drive enterprises and solutions are:

- **Financial:** Driven by finance and accounting with little or no knowledge in what the enterprise or system is doing.

---

[15] Sequential Thematic Organization of Publications (STOP), Hughes Aircraft Fullerton, 1963. Also discussed in Systems Practices as Common Sense, by Walter Sobkiw, CassBeth, 2011, ISBN 978-0983253082.

- **Marketing:** This goes beyond the traditional marketing boundary and has marketing dictating all system decisions as they see it at this instant in time, including day to day operations. There is also little or no knowledge in how the enterprise or system is executed other than through organizational titles.
- **Product:** All problems are modified so that all solutions match the in house or pre selected product or products.
- **Technology:** All problems are modified so that all solutions match the in house or pre selected technology or technologies.

Not all engineers are systems oriented. Many prefer to specialize. Others are new to the profession and may not have a full appreciation for the systems view. However as time progresses most engineers move into the systems space and become very valuable to their organizations. The paths are varied but include exposure to other engineering disciplines on large projects via design reviews and technical interaction. There is also movement into proposal and marketing areas. At some point, leadership roles surface where the systems perspective is critical for success. If engineers work their respective areas with no consideration to the rest of the system the risk is:

- Each engineering area optimizes their solution from their point
- Each area may compromise the solutions of the other engineering areas
- With one or more engineering areas unknowingly compromised the system may not work

1.3.10 Systems Theory Thoughts

Many engineering students are introduced to systems in classes associated with control theory[16]. A black box is drawn, inputs and outputs are labeled and then the question is asked: what happens at the output as the input passes through the system, how is the input transformed into an output. The term transfer function is used to describe how the input is processed to yield the output. The system is characterized by its transfer function. This is an important concept as we move the discussion away from quantitative into qualitative analysis.

The transfer function is determined using science with experimentation then mathematics to characterize a device. For example an inductor or capacitor that behave in certain ways as a function of input and time can be measured. The behavior is easily duplicated. The behavior then can be mathematically characterized. The process of characterizing a device and capturing its transfer function allows us to build passive filters. The filters can be different types (high

---

[16] Modern Control Systems, Richard C. Dorf, Addison-Wesley Publishing Company, 1967, 1974, Library of Congress CCN 67-15660, ISBN 0201016060.

pass, low pass, band pass, notch, and complex) with different characteristics (frequency cutoff and drop off).

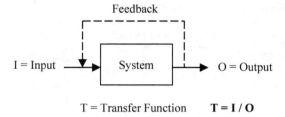

Figure 8 System Transfer Function with Feedback

A more complex system is associated with what is termed a valve. A valve can be implemented as a tube or transistor. This is an active device that also can be characterized in a lab setting and then modeled using mathematical equations. In this way different amplifiers can be designed in terms of the desired output and the devices' transfer function.

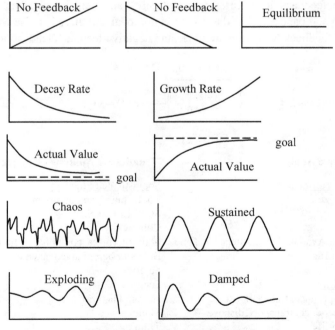

Figure 9 Potential System Outputs

These systems have feedback. The feedback tends to introduce non-linearity and unexpected results in the system output. The system output is tracked over time. An unstable system is characterized by an exploding output.

The term system starts to surface when the amplifier or active device is represented in an ideal form. This is called an operational amplifier (op amp) and it has infinite gain and bandwidth with zero noise.

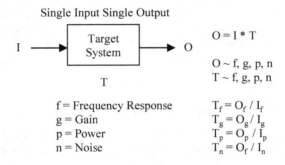

Figure 10 Single Input Single Output System

Using the op amp it is possible to study the effects of feedback. We quickly see that positive feedback leads to system instability and negative feedback leads to reduced gain and bandwidth. If the system is not ideal and there is noise we also see that positive feedback leads to more noise and negative feedback leads to less noise.

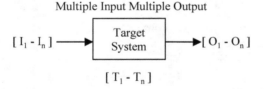

Quantitative Analysis

Generic Performance
Physical Size
Weight
Heat
Reliability, Availability Maintenance Time
Expected Life

Sustainability
Energy to produce, transport, use
Waste to produce, transport, dispose
Waste half life

Human Performance
Number of staff to operate, manage, maintain

Qualitative Analysis - Complex

Sophisticated Practices
Tools: management, maintenance, training
Staff skill levels
Complexity
(# of interfaces, components, functions, etc)
Behavior across unexpected events
Safety
Security
Human Factors
Maintenance
Training
Support
Quality

Figure 11 Multiple Input Multiple Output Complex Systems

Using math and the models of idealized components the performance of an analog electrical system can be understood in terms of gain, power output, frequency response, and noise. This begs the question: can any system be understood in terms of its inputs and transfer function if the inputs and transfer function could be found and understood?

A complex system is more than a single input and single output with a transfer function. A system has many inputs, many interacting transfer functions, and many outputs. A system is also more than just one view of a black box with its input, output, and transfer function. A system is a collection of black boxes that need to be understood on their own terms and how they might interact with each other.

For example in the amplifier case there may be a single transfer function that can capture the frequency response, gain, power output, and noise. However the amplifier has weight, physical size, generates heat, has reliability characteristics and an expected life. These can be quantitatively calculated. There are also sustainability performance characteristics that can be calculated such as energy to produce, transport, use, dispose and then waste to production, transport, use, dispose. There are also qualitative elements associated with the amplifier such as safety, maintenance, training, human factors, testability, etc which can be understood using logic and quantitative elements. These are sophisticated practices usually applied to more complex systems but they still need to be addressed in even the simplest systems.

The transfer function for complex systems is captured both in quantitative and qualitative analysis. One analysis may impact another analysis and the impact may not be known in the accepted literature and reduced to a universally known equation representing a model.

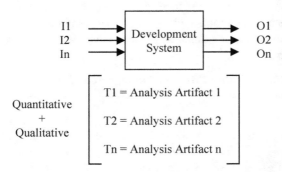

Goal: Remove and or mitigate negative emergence

Figure 12 System Development as a System

For a system that is used to develop a system (the process) this suggests that the transfer function is distributed into the humans engaged in the system development. So the transfer function of the target system is captured in the body of artifacts that represent the system analysis. The artifacts are the result of a system that was used to develop the target system. This is the development system. It too has a transfer function and that transfer function includes process, tools, artifacts, and management.

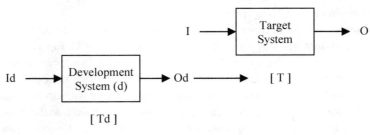

[Td]

Td ~ process, tools, artifacts, management

Artifacts ~ documents, presentations, prototypes, models, specifications, blueprints, manuals, websites, etc

Done by Learning Organization

Figure 13 System Solution

This suggests that a learning organization is engaged in the system design activity because the target system is a function of the development system suggesting the development system is modified or tuned by the target system solution. The relationship between the target system and development system suggests that there might be generic practices that can apply to any system. The variable might be system complexity where less complex systems may not need the breadth and depth of the systems practices that are needed for complex system.

The development system tools include engineering and management tools. They are varied and a function of the domain. These management tools also include what many may consider analysis.

Table 2 System Management Tools

• Requirements	• Requests for Information	• Certifications
• Specifications		• Artifacts
• Systems Requirements Databases	• Requests for Proposal	• Evidence
• Blueprints	• Proposals	• Decisions Analysis
• Drawings	• Statements of Work	• Tradeoffs
• Traceability	• Business Plans	• Analytical Hierarchy Process
• Plans	• Goals	
• Milestones	• Schedules	• Life Cycle Cost
• Technical Interchange Meetings	• PERT Charts	• Design to Cost
	• Earned Value Management Systems	• Return on Investment
• Working Groups	• Verifications	• Measure of Effectiveness

Table 2 System Management Tools

• Reviews and Audits	• Validations	

Continuing down the transfer function path, there are many additional items that apply to the development system. They also are varied and a function of the domain.

Table 3 What Applies to All Systems

• System Boundaries	• Physical Structure	• Certifications
• Stakeholders	• Human Factors	• Training
• Architecture	• Safety	• Installations
Descriptions	• Security	• Switch on
• Key Performance	• Reliability Availability	• Sustainment
• Key Functions	• Maintenance	• Shutdown
• Requirements	• Design	• Decommissioning
• Specifications	• Implementation	• Disposal
• Complexity Analysis	• Production	• Internal Sustainability
• Technologies	• Verifications	• External Sustainability
• Allocations	• Validations	• Operations
• Interface Analysis		

The goal of the development system or process is to surface all the emergent properties of the system. That means all views and analysis practices should be considered until a point of diminishing returns is reached.

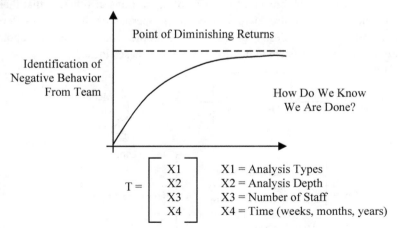

Figure 14 Mitigating Negative Emergence

At some point placing more people on an effort, doing more analysis, doing different analysis yields no more insights about the system. This can and should be measured. When that point is discovered, it is the point of diminishing returns and the system has its lowest risk of unexpected negative emergence.

Author Comment: It's not just the parts. It's not just the interfaces. It's about the infinite possibilities when the parts and interfaces come together. This begs the question of how can emergent properties be detected. Is the human brain (neural network performing math, logic, plus magic) the infinite pattern matcher that can detect emergent properties of a system? What prepares the human, with their brain to become a wondrous detector of emergent properties?

A system starts with a need and then progresses through various phases of development, operation, and eventual shutdown. It is this characteristic that makes a system theory complex. In many ways it might be a collection of theories that connect in a way that eventually leads to a unifying theory.

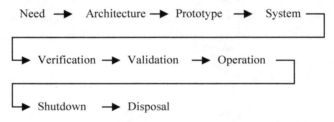

Figure 15 System Evolution

Putting together the black box control theory of input, transfer function that then yields an output with the desire to find emergent properties of the system offers some insight into a possible design process. For example what can be said about architecture, prototype, or system validation if we apply theses ideas?

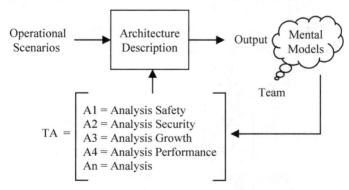

Figure 16 Architecture Validation

Using the same control theory concepts of inputs, outputs, and complex transfer function [TA] an architecture or design might be validated. The validation includes various operational scenarios with a transfer function of various analyses that feeds architecture descriptions that are then compared against various mental models. As this system for the design of architecture is permitted to unfold mental models from the team check the various approaches and issues surface. These issues are then used to iterate the analysis and architecture descriptions of the various alternatives until the preferred architecture design surfaces.

Prototype validation might follow the same approach as architecture validation. However, the information products will be different. The TA from the architecture validation might be part of the TP for the prototype validation.

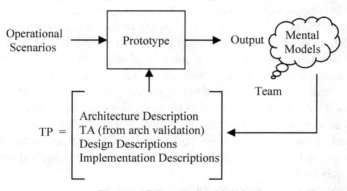

Figure 17 Prototype Validation

System validation might follow the same approach as architecture and prototype validation. However, the information products will be different. The TA from the architecture validation and TP from the prototype validation might be part of the TS for the system validation.

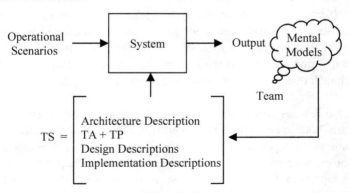

Figure 18 System Validation

The systems theory needs to lead to a practical representation of the systems engineering design process. This systems engineering design process is usually captured and described in the Systems Engineering Management Plan (SEMP).

Example 1 Transfer Function and Corporate Incentives

The transfer function coupled with the system boundary can be used to understand a system from a qualitative point of view. For example assume we are looking at a company as a system. The transfer function can include the parameters of profit, tax rate, tax deductions, and anti trust legislation.

If the tax rate is very high such as 90% and the tax law allows for deductions for the cost of doing business, a company can either pay the 90% tax on profits or use the profits to invest. The investment can be in tools, personnel, and material, for existing or future operations and or research and development.

If suddenly the tax rate is lowered to 15% or eliminated the company can decide to accumulate cash that then can be used to buy out their competition. Eventually this will allow a company to enjoy monopoly or oligopoly status unless antitrust legislation exists and is enforced. Once all the reasonable companies are bought then there is cash sitting on the sidelines. If the condition also exists in the transfer function that executive bonuses are also based on earnings per share the executives can purchase company stock, reducing the number of shares, increasing their bonuses and maintaining the stock price in a changing environment[17]. The investment in the future is delayed or not funded at the same level if the tax rate were extremely high.

In this scenario the people are not bad; it is just that the system has a transfer function that will result in a certain output under certain input conditions. The issue with complex systems is that the transfer function is always complex. For example what if the executives were not driven by immediate self-interest? What if they were driven by trying to benefit all stakeholders so that everyone wins[18]?

In the absence of relying on higher ideals of the system participants and accepting self-interest as a driver, the system transfer function could change. For example the tax rate could change to 90% or anti trust laws, could be enforced, or both. This was the situation for most of the post WW II time frame up until the 1980s. The question is why was the system changed in the 1980s and allowed to exist even though many realized its flaws and resulting damages?

One of the reasons why there is no unified systems theory is because transfer functions are both quantitative and qualitative. Also the quantitative transfer functions are stove piped unable to easily cross connect across boundaries of analysis. For example what are the training impacts on the frequency response of a reel to reel tape recorder. This is not easy to see or quantitatively address. The frequency response can be quantitatively measured over time. However if it

---

[17] Personal author experience. This practice was well established in the 1980s shortly after the US corporate tax rates were changed and continues as of the writing of this book..

[18] Many movies in the 1980's were made where this was the main struggle. The movies as most art were a reflection of society, in this case the results of lowering corporate tax rates.

degrades there needs to be an understanding of when and why it degrades. This translates into a maintenance activity where the tape heads are cleaned and demagnetized to ensure that the maximum frequency response is offered by the tape recorder. This analysis is obvious now, but extremely complex when first performed. It falls into the category of preventative maintenance to ensure peak system performance.

Qualitative elements are based on logic and set theory but the considered elements and parameters vary between people. That is why assumptions are so important when addressing qualitative aspects of the system analysis. Two people will design and implement the same system differently regardless of the level of detail offered in the analysis, specifications, and design. So verification and validation are critical process elements and are used because people will implement the same system differently.

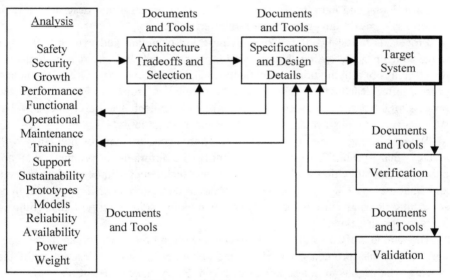

Figure 19 Potential SEMP Diagram

So in the absence of a unified system theory we have previous experience, knowledge, and some basic techniques or practices captured in the SEMP. We engage in these practices to surface, develop, maintain, and eventually dispose of our systems.

1.4 Process

DeMarco[19] provides a definition of *methodology*: "A general systems theory of

---

[19] Peopleware, DeMarco, Tom, Yourdon Press, 1987. Second edition, Dorset House Publishing Company, Inc, ISBN: 0932633439

how a whole class of thought-intensive work ought to be conducted." A *technique,* on the other hand, may be regarded as less encompassing or comprehensive than a methodology. A methodology is comprised of one or more techniques, together with concept or theory that makes it cohesive[20].

Process, method, and methodology terminology is used frequently. Many use process and method interchangeably and state that they are a series of steps to accomplish a task. Many use the term methodology to house the description of the approach to be used in an analysis. Methodology is usually viewed as something that is static and does not change.

For this text a process consists of multiple methods. Some will use methodology to represent the collection of methods to accomplish a task. I prefer to use process in place of methodology because a process suggests feedback loops, automation using tools where practical, and change[21]. In systems design practices it is critical that feedback loops and iteration exist in the thing (the process) that describes how to perform systems design practices for a selected system.

Process is not static. It is like a living thing changing and evolving as other things in the process setting change. Organizations change because they also display the attributes of a living thing, continually changing and evolving. Organization and process affect each other, they cannot be created in isolation. For example the process might state that the test team must be independent. The implications of that statement are that the test team reports to an external authority[22].

When offering a system solution the team needs to identify how they will create[23] that system. They need to identify the information products that are produced, how they tie together, what tools and techniques will be used or created, and what the issues are in building the system. It does not matter if it is a re-spin of something that has existed for 100 years or building something new like going to Mars for the first time.

Day one identify how the job will tackled, write it down, start doing it, if it does not work or has problems, modify it, then change the written description of the process. The trick is to not do this in isolation. Every stakeholder needs to own the process. They have to agree to the process, love the process, and make it work. It is not the job of management to force a process on those that will implement the process. However management is an equal stakeholder in the process. The best way

---

[20] Sandia Software Guidelines Volume 5; Tools, Techniques, and Methodologies; Sandia Report, SAND85–2348 1 UC–32, Reprinted September 1992.

[21] Systems Practices as Common Sense, by Walter Sobkiw, CassBeth, 2011, ISBN 978-0983253082.

[22] The question is how independent: company president, division president, physical location general manager, engineering head, business area manager, or project manager.

[23] Some suggest that create is not appropriate, instead design should be used. Create is used here to represent design and art in the broadest sense possible, not just some limited phase of engineering or artistic pursuit.

to make management a stakeholder in the process is to give them technical tasks that feed the process.

1.4.1 Idealized Process

The process discussion could start with a general process that some refer to as the waterfall model. It has its roots in environments where change is prohibitively costly or impossible. Examples are manufacturing and construction. The implication is that there is no feedback mechanism for change beyond perhaps just the previous level.

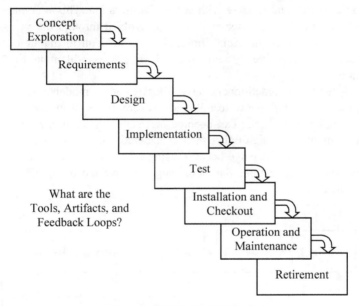

Figure 20 Waterfall Model

Although this may be a simplified idealization of a process, the reality is that these steps are iterated with different feedback loops to any other level[24]. For example before there is a final production facility, there are multiple pre-production prototypes and test production runs. Before there is a building or bridge there are several mockups and scale models before construction begins. Many early software practitioners coming from computer science backgrounds were not exposed to these engineering principals and have misunderstood this simplified ideal process.

Engineering disciplines use ideal representations to support engineering analysis

---

[24] Winston W. Royce recognized the issues and proposed a modified waterfall model for software. Managing The Development Of Large Software Systems, Winston W. Royce, Technical Papers of Western Electronic Show and Convention (WesCon), Los Angeles, USA, 1970.

that is based on logical and mathematical representations. This same concept applies to the waterfall process representation. It is an idealized representation of a more complex world.

The key issue associated with this model is the number of iterations. In the case of a physical building or manufacturing line there is no degradation with iteration. The iterations are performed on elements not part of the final solution; they are prototypes, mockups, and scale models. With software, the iterations usually happen on the final product unless the team is willing to go through all the code and create a final clean version[25]. The problem is this code eventually will become less maintainable, stable, and flexible with successive iteration. This was known by the late 1970's, with software based systems that evolved through the years and that were then believed to be unstable, inflexible, and difficult to maintain. So in the case of software intensive systems there is a process dilemma that is more significant than other systems[26].

Recently software practitioners have adopted other models, which basically represent passing through the waterfall model several times. With each pass through there is the risk that the code can become less stable as additions are attached to earlier versions of the design rather than considered holistically at the early stages of the effort. This is a challenge because using the waterfall model in its idealized state adds other complications that some suggest have led to significant software project failures.

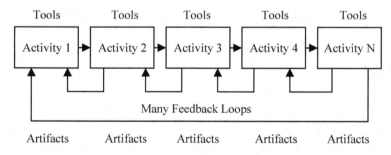

Figure 21 Process Basic Elements

So, the team must be able to create process, methods, methodology and it must match the proposed system solution. Not only are the sequence of activities important, but also the tools and artifacts are key to the process. The tools are unique to each domain and change with time. The process is not complete until all the tools are identified and related to the process elements. Also the process is not complete until all the artifacts are identified and related to the process elements.

---

[25] The spiral model suggests multiple iteration based on prototypes.

[26] This was a major reason the Federal Aviation Administration (FAA) used in the 1980's to justify the Advanced Automation System (AAS) Program.

Finally the feedback loops must be present.

1.4.2 System V-Diagram

Variants to the idealized process are often shown using the V-Diagram. Initially the V-Diagram was used to show the relationship between different levels of test and the baseline requirements of the system. Over time the V-Diagram was modified and is used to represent an idealized system engineering process.

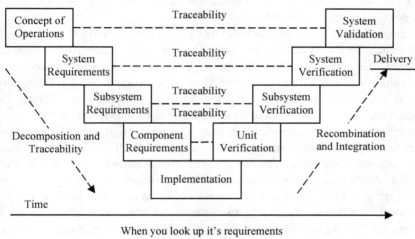

When you look up it's requirements
When you look down it's design

Figure 22 Test V-Diagram

The Test V-Diagram[27] was created to show a new approach to test and integration for a new system that would start to automate the cognitive processes of its system operators. It was driven by the new challenge to surface latent defects in the software. It was recognized that software could be untested using existing test approaches. So to offer full test coverage of the software the concept of bottom up integration and test was suggested. It was later modified and adopted by others[28] to represent systems engineering at a high level[29].

---

[27] Test V-Diagram first appeared at Hughes Aircraft circa 1982 on the Federal Aviation Administration (FAA) Advanced Automation System (AAS) program pre-proposal effort.

[28] The reason the V is such a powerful and enduring image comes from the Hughes culture of coupling all text to powerful multidimensional images. This was the foundation of Sequential Thematic Organization of Publications (STOP) invented at Hughes in 1963.

[29] The Relationship of System Engineering to the Project Cycle, Kevin Forsberg and Harold Mooz, National Council On Systems Engineering (NCOSE) and American Society for Engineering Management (ASEM), 21–23 October 1991.

It is unclear if the Test V-Diagram originated with the VEE Heuristic[30]. It would make sense because so many people from education, psychology, cognitive processing, knowledge management, etc were working with computer systems in the 1970's. A side oriented V appeared in DOD-STD-2167 circa 1982 to represent the software development cycle. In this case it showed parallelism between established hardware development and emerging software development. It suggested an approach for building the next generation software systems and showed the different abstraction levels of the design associated with the major milestones used to manage the effort.

Decomposition as a top down activity was fully accepted at that time. Test as a bottom up activity was obvious in most cases but not fully articulated. The thought process was that the bottoms up test approach would complement the top down decomposition and offered an alternative view of the system. Strong traceability would be used between the tests and the associated requirements. Strong bi-directional traceability also would be used between the various specifications.

The bottoms up activity blended well with the natural progression of integration. So tests would be performed at the lowest levels so that all conditions and cases could be evaluated and not hidden or prevented from stimulation by a higher level abstraction. Also as the integration continues the interfaces could be fully tested.

The System V-Diagram as it is occasionally referred to is used to communicate some aspect of systems engineering to systems and non-system practitioners. It shows traceability through the various specification levels and the links to the associated, verification, validation and integration levels. One of the primary messages is that decomposition is from the top down while test and integration is from the bottom up. It also shows when system handoff or delivery occurs so that system validation can proceed. It tends to be modified to show some particular aspect of systems engineering such as sustainability

In this extended view of the life cycle of the system the operations, shutdown and disposal are added resulting in the Sustainable System V-Diagram. This extended view suggests a need for one or more information products associated with "community sustainability". This is not unlike what happened with the rise of the environmental movement and the introduction of environmental impact studies when new or modified structures are proposed in a community[31].

The V-Diagram also has been used to show a systems process at a very high level. The V diagrams tend to lose the traceability information between the left and

---

[30] Educating, Gowin, D.B., Ithaca, N.Y., Cornell University Press. 1981. Gowin developed the VEE heuristic to help students understand knowledge structure (relational networks, hierarchies, and combinations) and understand the process of knowledge construction. It assumes knowledge is not absolute but depends on concepts, theories, and methodologies used to view the world.

[31] Community is the collection of stakeholders that are impacted by the system.

right side of the V but they still tend to preserve the decomposition view on the left side and aggregation view on the right side.

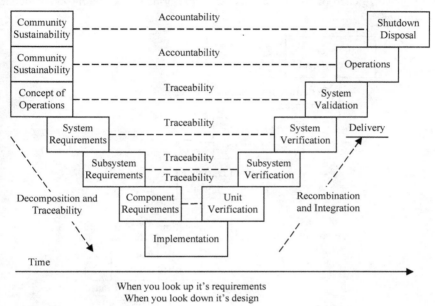

Figure 23 Sustainable System V-Diagram

Irrespective of the diagram and even the words in each diagram element we can all relate to these implied activities and sequence even though they appear to be different. What needs to happen is the team needs to reflect the "process" and fully document it in the plan document or documents.

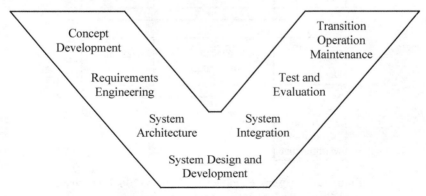

Figure 24 Systems Engineering V-Diagram

In all instances the V diagrams can be unwound and shown in waterfall layout. If we unwind the Systems Engineering V-Diagram we start to see that the process tends to be from the acquisition perspective with an emphasis on architecture. It is easy to visualize each of the process elements performed by different independent organizations.

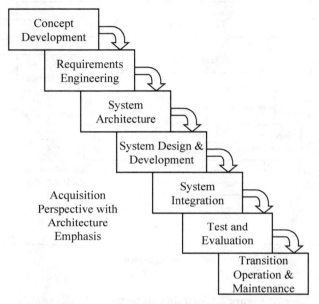

Figure 25 Systems Engineering Waterfall Process Depiction

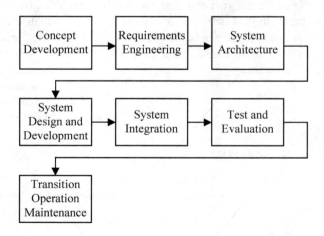

Figure 26 Systems Engineering Process block Diagram

They also can be shown as a process block diagram where is block is a process element and the left to right top to bottom orientation with connecting arrows shows sequence. The later for of representing the process is very effective and allows for significant annotation to show artifacts tools and other key process elements such as milestones, phases, etc.

1.4.3 Successive Refinement and Abstraction Levels

In the past many who engaged in systems engineering design viewed the process as one of discovery. There are techniques, practices, tools, process steps and some form of control but essentially the need evolves into a solution as the problem and solution progress from a broad perspective and high level abstractions to lower levels of abstractions and perspectives.

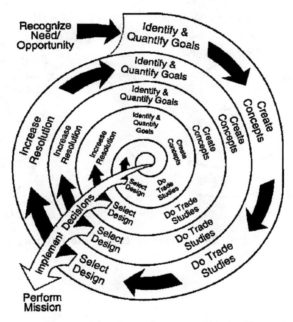

Figure 27 Successive Refinement[32]

Many view systems engineering design like pealing an onion, with the analogy appropriately carried over to include the associated tears. This idea was widely promulgated at Hughes Aircraft in Fullerton[33] and is somewhat captured in the early NASA Systems Engineering Handbooks[34] as Successive Refinement.

The idea of using circles or spirals to show movement from general to specific

---

[32] NASA Systems Engineering Handbook, SP-6105, June 1995. NASA Systems Engineering Handbook (DRAFT), September 1992.

[33] This was observed by Walt Sobkiw, author of this text, circa 1982, while supporting various systems engineering activities at Hughes Aircraft Fullerton, California.

[34] NASA Systems Engineering Handbook, SP-6105, June 1995. NASA Systems Engineering Handbook (DRAFT), September 1992.

was a common depiction in the late 1970's early 1980's. It is easy to draw and clearly represented the concept. It probably originated from the automation systems at that time where they would extend the senses such as sight via RADAR and then reduce the information to high level summaries using computer processing.

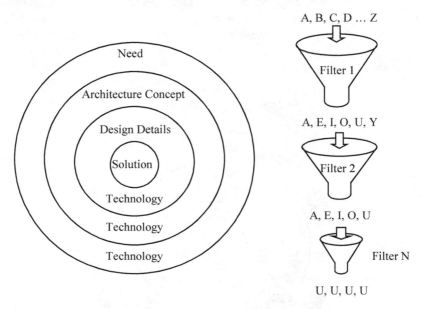

Figure 28 Abstraction Levels and Filtering

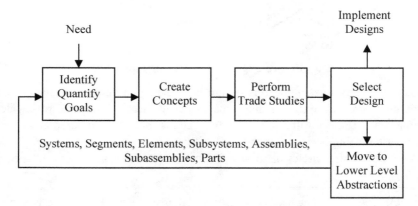

Figure 29 Successive Refinement Systems Engineering Design

This was accomplished using algorithms that would examine broad areas of information such as a 10-mile view of airspace and then home into a smaller area such as a 1-mile area of airspace. This was referred to as large search areas and small search areas in RADAR tracking algorithms. Meanwhile data would be subjected to filtering techniques where there would be progressively smaller funnels receiving outputs from larger funnels until the final key information was offered.

Pealing the onion, going from general to specific and moving from a high abstraction level to a low abstraction level was everyday thinking in these very high technology organizations. These ideas have sadly been lost and they are key findings that surfaced with the rise of systems engineering after WWII.

The spiral representation of Successive Refinement can be easily translated to a process block diagram. The block diagram then can be used as a building block for a complete end to end process for performing systems engineering design.

Author Comment: It is not possible to engage in proper meaningful systems engineering without these ideas being part of the everyday culture in an organization. Many do not understand these ideas were a key ingredient that separated high technology operations from everyday organizations. Many today trying to engage in high technology and or systems engineering are running obsolete unworkable operations because they refuse to accept these ideas, usually using cost and schedule as an excuse not realizing they do not have workable processes to get to viable solutions.

1.4.4 Creativity and Innovation Process

There is a simple formula that can be applied by anyone to spur creativity and innovation. Herman Helmholtz (1821 to 1894) studied creativity and introduced the idea that there are 3 stages to creativity: saturation, incubation, and illumination. Graham Wallas expanded on these ideas and offered them in his work, Art of Thought, 1926. The Wallas stage model, creative insights and illuminations, has 4 or 5 stages. The additional stage is called Intimation and may be viewed as part of Incubation or Illumination.

1. **Preparation:** initial work on problem, focusing mind on problem, exploring problem space
2. **Incubation:** problem is internalized, unconscious mind, nothing externally is happening, 2a. Intimation: sub-stage, person gets feeling solution close
3. **Illumination:** insight or idea bursts into conscious awareness
4. **Verification:** idea is verified, elaborated, and applied

For this text the formula for personal creativity and innovation is Saturate, Incubate, Synthesize, Optimize, and Select[35].

---

[35] This author was exposed to these ideas in elementary school and has practiced them since that time. These ideas were periodically reintroduced in middle and high school.

1. **Saturate**: Exactly as the word implies. Immerse yourself in the material, no matter how mundane or irrelevant it may seem in the beginning. Talk to everyone about the material and dialog if possible.
2. **Incubate**: Exactly as the word implies. Sleep on it and let the miracle of the human mind go to work on the problem.
3. **Synthesis**: Happens after incubation. You can't stop it; it is human. Eventually approaches will start to surface. Mature these approaches as you continue to saturate and incubate.
4. **Optimize**: As the word implies, take each viable approach and move it to its most elegant limit.
5. **Select**: You guessed it, pick your best approach.

The personal creativity model can be expanded to teams engaged in systems engineering design.

1. **Saturate**: Immerse the team in the material, no matter how mundane or irrelevant it may seem in the beginning. The entire team is engaged and meets regularly to exchange findings. Humans are left and right brain creatures. To fully understand a situation, words and pictures are needed. The words backed up with mathematics, logic, set theory and a picture born of true inspiration are the heart of communicating our visions. Essentially these all represent different perspectives of a problem and are associated with saturating our minds with the problem.
2. **Incubate**: Exactly as the word implies where the team sleeps on it and we let the miracle of the human minds go to work on the problem. A team of people needs time to incubate a problem. It is at this point that a gestalt surfaces and the team starts to become more than the sum of its individual minds. You will not know when incubation will start but you will detect it as the team members start to offer parts of a solution. Gradually more solution parts emerge then someone or some members start to put the whole picture together. These people are typically the systems architects. They emerge with the system solution; you cannot appoint the system architects.
3. **Synthesis**: Just like for the personal case, this happens after team incubation. You can't stop it; it is human. Eventually various approaches start to surface from within the team. Mature these approaches as you continue to saturate and incubate. In many ways systems engineering is purely about synthesis rather than reduction. Throw all kinds of things on the table and start to put them together. Putting together the non-obvious pieces can lead to major breakthroughs. It is at this point that the natural systems architects that emerged start to inspire the team. The rest of the team starts to find their comfort zones in various specialization areas.
4. **Optimize**: Just like for the personal case and is as the word implies where

the team takes each viable approach and moves it to its most elegant limit. The specialists really start to take on the load at this time as the system architects maintain the vision and adjust the vision based on the specialists' findings.

5. **Select**: Just like for the personal case the team picks the best approach. The selection is born from intense tradeoff analysis using the Measure of Effectiveness (MOE) equation[36]. The selection is fully transparent and understood by all the stakeholders. It is born of reason and common sense.

When this model is applied to a team, different team members progress through the model stages at different times. Some move very quickly through the stages and they try to pull everyone along with their ideas. Others lag behind. Both these two groups, the leaders and laggards, are important because they challenge the team.

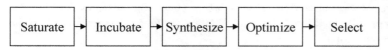

Figure 30 Creativity Innovation Event

So, how does the team know it is done? Does everyone need to come to the same ending conclusion? Is there any iteration or is this just a series of events with feedback affecting previous stages?

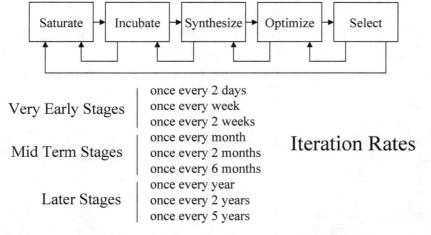

Figure 31 Creativity Innovation Iteration

Obviously this needs to be a process not a series of events that just translate into an event. There should be feedback loops with iteration and iteration rates. One approach to determining closure is to measure the point of diminishing returns. For

---

[36] Discussed in detail in this text as part of architecture tradeoff and decision making.

example, have there been no new additions to the ideas or arguments and have the open issues become relatively benign. However, care needs to be taken because the team just may not be effective. Adding new team members and determining if new insights surface can check if the process has reached a natural conclusion and was not artificially shutdown.

As this creativity innovation process is executed tools and artifacts should be identified and used to support the process.

Author Comments: With the rise of software some have started to offer alternative theories of design. What has been suggested is that there is a Rational Centric Model (RCM) and an Action Centric Model (ACM). The RCM is based on traditional science, engineering, and discourse ideas and practices associated with the Socratic method. The ACM is based taking action and then viewing the result. Examples are then offered in software where code is initially developed and then it is beaten or fashioned into a final solution much like an artist might beat a piece of bronze into a goblet.

What is missing from the RCM and ACM discussion is the concept of art. All engineering education acknowledges that engineering design is a combination of science, engineering, and art. In art the medium modifies the original ideal vision of the artist. The same is true in engineering design, the science and what is possible from an engineering point of view given the medium and its technologies shapes the final solution.

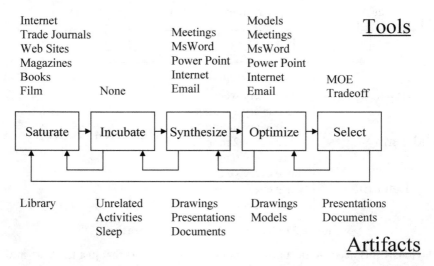

Figure 32 Creativity and Innovation Process

Design is a creative process that acknowledges art. There is a process that can be used to spur creativity that naturally couples with the RCM. The creative process is really what the ACM tries to describe. However the ACM by itself is not a reasonable explanation of design, it is only an observation of what may be occurring in some settings such as simple software development efforts.

Author Comment: Many suggest using a morphological matrix to help spur creativity and innovation. I disagree with that approach because it limits ones choices. The mind is an amazing tool for searching through unstructured information to detect patterns. Those who use regular expressions to search through vast amounts of unstructured text (Internet) understand that a 9x9 matrix is silly.

1.4.5 Process Table

In addition to the waterfall and V-Diagram views the process also can be reflected in a table. The table and waterfall views allow for the depiction of artifacts and tools, which is critical to defining a clear unambiguous process. The waterfall diagram is able to show feedback, which many immature managers reject. However feedback is a given and it can go back to any previous level including the very first starting point in the process. The V-Diagram however is very effective at showing traceability between information products with their respective system abstraction levels and test levels.

Table 4 Process Table of Systems Engineering V-Diagram

Process Steps	Artifacts	Tools
Concept Development	Presentations, Mockups, Surveys	Office Automation, Modeling, Simulations
Requirements Engineering	Specifications	Database
Systems Architecture	Document, Presentations	Office Automation
System Design and Development	Documents, Product Brochures, Blue Prints, Models, Drawings	Office Automation, Design Tools
System Integration	Plans, Schedules	Office Automation, Configuration Management
Test and Evaluation	Procedures, Reports	Office Automation, Test & Evaluation
Transition Operation Maintenance	Documents	Office Automation

Table 5 Process Table of Idealized Process

Process Steps	Artifacts	Tools
Concept Exploration	Presentations, Mockups, Surveys	Office Automation, Modeling, Simulations
Requirements	Specifications	Database
Design	Documents, Product	Office Automation, Design

Table 5 Process Table of Idealized Process

Process Steps	Artifacts	Tools
	Brochures, Blue Prints, Models, Drawings	Tools
Implementation	Documents, Blue Prints, Drawings	Manufacturing Tools
Test	Procedures, Reports	Office Automation, Test & Evaluation
Installation and Checkout	Documents	Office Automation
Operation and Maintenance	Documents	Office Automation
Retirement	Documents	Office Automation

The Systems Engineering V-Diagram process table is very similar to the Idealized process table. In the Systems Engineering V-Diagram process we see the "Architecture" elements pulled out from "Design" in the Idealized Process table. In the Idealized Process table we see "Installation and Checkout" and Retirement pulled out from "Transition Operation and Maintenance" in the Systems Engineering V-Diagram process table. So it is a matter of emphasis - what does the team think is important at a given abstraction level. The activities still will be performed, however there is less need to communication certain activities at a higher abstraction level. This also suggests some risk perception and emphasis perception and will translate to funding and staffing levels during project planning.

Example 2 NASA Process Converted to Process Tables

The following pages capture a NASA engineering process initially shown as an annotated block diagram. In this text it is converted to process tables. The original NASA process is one of the earliest NASA systems engineering process description documents[37]. There is significant text that is written to try and capture the details of a process. The process descriptions are augmented with various visualizations:

- Process flow charts
- Block diagrams with annotations
- IDEF
- Text and free form graphics
- Process table

A process is designed just like a device, subsystem, product, organization etc. The process just like any other design can be abstracted to three different levels:

---

[37] NASA Systems Engineering Handbook, SP-6105, June 1995.

- Concept
- Physical structure
- Implementation

They all start with the need statement which can be referred to as:

- Mission
- Market
- Needs

So what can we observe about the NASA process? We observe that they are tailored to the specific needs of NASA. We also see that there are details that start to provide further information about the process. We also see that there is duplication and inconsistencies in the process. Even though this is a very early work, future releases attempted to address the duplication and inconsistencies yet they are still in the process descriptions. The question is why?

Inconsistencies and duplication in process descriptions surface when there is an attempt to develop a universal process description for all activities in an organization. There is no way to avoid the situation. The reality is a universal process is only a guide that can be used to develop the actual process to be used on a specific activity. The activities may be a program, project, research and development, etc.

Table 6 Mission Feasibility Process Table

1 Mission Feasibility	
• Define mission objectives and top level functional performance Reqs • Ensure mission technical and programmatic feasibility • Confirm mission need	
Input	**Output**
• Start with nothing • Mission needs • Goals and objectives • Programmatic guidelines	• Mission Concept Review • Report Proposal • System Specification
Tools	**General Information Products**
• Office Automation: Word Processing, Spreadsheet, Presentation, Email • Systems: Modeling	• Plan Documents • Analysis Documents • Specification Documents
Activities	**Artifacts**
Understand the Customer	1.12 Mission needs 1.12 Goals and objectives 1.12 Programmatic guidelines

Table 6 Mission Feasibility Process Table

1.12 Refine User Needs and Objectives	
1.12 Refine Constraints and Assumptions	1.12 Assumptions guidelines constraints
1.12 Develop Top Level Mission Reqs	1.12 Functional mission concept
1.4 Develop Top Level Functional Mission Concept	1.12 Science Reqs
1.5 Develop Evaluation Criteria	1.12 Mission Reqs
	1.4 Functional mission concept
	1.5 Evaluation criteria
	1.5 Reference missions
	1.5 Technical Performance Measures (TPM)
	1.6 System Segment Reqs
Identify Possible Alternatives	
1.6 Flowdown Top Level System Requirements	1.7 System concept and architecture
1.7 Develop Feasible System Concept(s)	1.7 Design disclosures
1.8 Allocate Requirements	1.7 Product baseline structure
1.9 Analyze and Evaluate	1.7 Operations concept
1.10 Synthesize and Downselect	
1.11 Technical Planning and Management	1.8 Allocated Reqs
1.12 Develop Tools and Methods	1.8 TPM Budgets Margins
	1.9 Cost effectiveness analysis
	1.9 Environment assessment
	1.9 Safety engineering studies
	1.9 Specialty engineering studies
	1.9 Life cycle cost estimates
	1.9 Trade and analysis results
	1.10 Report / proposal
	1.10 System specification
	1.11 Program management plan
	1.11 Project management plans
	1.11 Engineering master plan
	1.11 Master schedule
	1.11 Lessons learned
	1.12 Analysis models
	1.12 Systems engineering tools
Additional Information	**Deliverables**
• NASA Feasible Concept	• Report Proposal

Table 6 Mission Feasibility Process Table

• NASA Phase A • DOD Pre Milestone / not defined	• System Specification

Table 7 Mission Definition Process Table

2 Mission Definition	
• Establish validated (segment level Reqs) which meet mission objectives • Establish architectural and top level operations concept • Identify technology risks and mitigation plan • Refine programmatic resource need estimates	
Input • Mission Concept Review • Report Proposal • System Specification	**Output** • Mission Definition Review • Technical Development Reqs • System Specification
Tools • Office Automation: Word Processing, Spreadsheet, Presentation, Email • Systems: Modeling	**General Information Products** • Plan Documents • Analysis Documents • Specification Documents
Activities	**Artifacts**
Analyze Mission Requirements 2.1 Refine Top Level Mission Requirements 2.2 Refine Mission Concept(s) and Operations 2.3 Develop & Refine Evaluation Criteria 2.4 define Refine System Requirements 2.5 Develop Alternative System Architectures & Concepts 2.6 Allocate Requirements to Segments / Elements 2.7 Analyze and Evaluate Architecture(s) & Concepts 2.8 Synthesize and Downselect 2.9 Technical Planning and Management 2.10 Develop Tools and Methods	2.1 Mission needs 2.1 Goals and objectives 2.1 Programmatic guidelines 2.1 Assumptions guidelines constraints 2.2 Mission concept(s) 2.2 Operational concept(s) 2.3 Evaluation criteria 2.3 Reference missions 2.3 TPM)s 2.4 Science Reqs 2.4 Mission Reqs 2.4 Disposal Reqs 2.4 Verification Reqs 2.5 System concept and architecture' 2.5 Design disclosure 2.5 Product breakdown structure 2.5 Operations concept

Table 7 Mission Definition Process Table

	2.6 Performance Reqs 2.6 TPMs Budgets and margins 2.7 Cost effectiveness analysis 2.7 Environment assessment 2.7 Feasibility assesment 2.7 Specialty engineering studies 2.7 LCC estimates 2.7 Trade and analysis results 2.8 System specification 2.8 Technical development Reqs 2.9 Program management plan 2.9 Project management plans 2.9 Engineering master plan 2.9 Master schedule 2.9 Systems engineering management plan 2.9 Technology development plan 2.9 Integrated logistics plan 2.9 Configuration management plan 2.9 Information management plan 2.9 Lessons learned 2.10 Analysis models 2.10 Systems engineering tools 2.10 Test faculties and equipment
Additional Information • NASA Alternative Architectures • NASA Top Level Architecture • NASA Phase A • DOD Concept Exploration and Definition	**Deliverables** • Technical Development Reqs • System Specification

Table 8 System Definition

3 System definition
• Establish validated Reqs for end items (complete functional baseline) • Complete architecture level of design • Mitigate technical risk; critical technology, long lead items • Establish firm estimates of programmatic and technical resources • Mitigate programmatic risks

Table 8 System Definition

• Demonstrate system can be built within cost schedule performed constraints	
Input	**Output**
• Mission Definition Review	• System Definition Reviews
Tools	**General Information Products**
• Office Automation: Word Processing, Spreadsheet, Presentation, Email • Systems: Modeling	• Plan Documents • Analysis Documents • Specification Documents
Activities	**Artifacts**
Analyze System Requirements 3.1 Mission and requirements analysis 3.2 Develop system evaluation criteria 3.3 Flow down and refine Reqs 3.4 Develop and refine prime / critical item concepts 3.5 Allocate requirements to end items 3.6 Evaluate and analyze end system item concepts 3.7 Integrate segments 3.8 Synthesize / select optimal option 3.9 Develop technology 3.10 Technical management and planing 3.11 Develop refine tools and methods	3.1 Applicable Standards 3.1 Refined mission Reqs 3.1 System Reqs 3.1 Verification Reqs 3.2 Acceptance criteria 3.2 Evaluation criteria 3.2 Reference missions 3.2 Technical Performance Measures (TPM) 3.3 Assumptions guidelines constraints 3.3 Lower Level Reqs 3.3 3.5 Verification Reqs Matrix 3.4 Design disclosure 3.4 Integration and assembly 3.4 Interface Control Documentation 3.4 Launch Operations 3.4 Operations 3.5 Design to specification 3.5 Interface reqs 3.5 System specification 3.5 TPM Budgets Margins 3.6 Cost effectiveness analysis 3.6 Life cycle cost 3.6 Logistics Support 3.6 Producibility 3.6 Reliability & Maintainability 3.6 Reliability program plan 3.6 Safety hazard analysis 3.6 Specialty engineering studies 3.6 Trade analysis and results 3.9 Development test results 3.9 Engineering Items 3.10 Analysis models 3.10 Configuration management plan

Table 8 System Definition

	3.10 Document tree
	3.10 Drawing tree / engineering drawing list
	3.10 EMI / EMC Control plan
	3.10 Engineering master plan
	3.10 Information management plan
	3.10 Integrated logistics support program plan
	3.10 Integration and assembly Plan
	3.10 Lessons learned
	3.10 Manufacturing plan
	3.10 Master schedule
	3.10 Payload to carrier integration plan
	3.10 Program management plan
	3.10 Project management plans
	3.10 Quality assurance plan
	3.10 Reliability control plan
	3.10 Risk Management Plan
	3.10 Statement of work
	3.10 System safety plan
	3.10 Systems engineering management plan
	3.10 Technology development plan
	3.10 Test faculties and equipment
	3.10 Verification Plans
	3.11 Systems engineering tools
Additional Information	**Deliverables**
• NASA Functional Baseline	• Technical Development Reqs
• NASA Phase B	• System Specification
• DOD Demonstration and Validation	

Table 9 Preliminary Design

4 Preliminary Design	
• Establish a design solution that fully meets mission needs	
• Complete test and verification plan	
• Establish design dependent requirements and interfaces	
• Complete implementation level of design	
Input	**Output**
• System Definition Reviews	• Preliminary Design Reviews
Tools	**General Information Products**
• Office Automation: Word Processing, Spreadsheet, Presentation, Email	• Plan Documents
	• Analysis Documents

Table 9 Preliminary Design

• Systems: Modeling	• Specification Documents
Activities	**Artifacts**
Preliminary design	4.1 Disposal Reqs
4.1 Analyze and refine requirements	4.1 Flow down reqs
4.2 Perform design analysis	4.1 Interface reqs
4.3 Perform engineering development tests	4.1 Specification updates
4.4 Define interfaces	4.1 Verification Reqs
4.5 Perform preliminary design	4.2 Design analysis reports
4.6 Evaluate verify and validate design	4.2 Trade analysis and results
4.7 Complete plans and doc for qual items	4.3 Development test results
4.8 Integrate system segments elements	4.3 Engineering Items
4.9 Technical planning and management	4.4 Integrated schematics
	4.4 Interface Control Documentation
	4.5 Design disclosure
	4.5 Electronics parts list
	4.5 Hardware / Software list
	4.5 Instrument Pom & Commands
	4.6 Cost effectiveness analysis
	4.6 Environmental
	4.6 Failure Modes and Effects
	4.6 Life cycle cost
	4.6 Logistics Support
	4.6 Nuclear
	4.6 Producibility
	4.6 Reliability control plan
	4.6 Safety hazard analysis
	4.6 Specialty engineering studies
	4.7 Qualification item plans
	4.9 Configuration management plan
	4.9 Document tree
	4.9 Drawing tree / engineering drawing list
	4.9 Engineering master plan
	4.9 Information management plan
	4.9 Integrated logistics support program plan
	4.9 Integration and assembly Plan
	4.9 Lessons learned
	4.9 Manufacturing plan
	4.9 Master schedule
	4.9 Materials and process control plan
	4.9 Payload to carrier integration plan
	4.9 Program management plan

Table 9 Preliminary Design

	4.9 Project management plans 4.9 Reliability program plan 4.9 Risk Management Plan 4.9 Specification tree 4.9 Statement of work 4.9 System safety plan 4.9 Systems engineering management plan 4.9 Verification Plans 4.10 EMI / EMC Control plan 4.10 Quality assurance plan
Additional Information • NASA Design to Baseline • NASA Phase B • DOD Engineering and Manufacturing Deployment	**Deliverables** • Technical Development Reqs • System Specification

Table 10 Final Design

5 Final design • Establish complete validated detailed design • Complete all design specialty audits • Establish manufacturing process and controls • Finalize and integrate interfaces	
Input • Preliminary Design Reviews	**Output** • Critical Design Reviews
Tools • Office Automation: Word Processing, Spreadsheet, Presentation, Email • Systems: Modeling	**General Information Products** • Plan Documents • Analysis Documents • Specification Documents
Activities	**Artifacts**
5.1 Define and control detailed I/F 5.2 Perform detailed design 5.3 Perform engineering tests 5.4 Fabricate / test qualification items 5.5 Evaluate verify and validate design 5.6 Complete detail design and production plans 5.7 Integrate system segments elements 5.8 Technical management and planning	5.1 Interface Control Documentation 5.1 Payload to carrier integration plan 5.2 Design disclosure 5.2 Integration and assembly 5.2 Materials and process control plan 5.3 Development test results 5.3 Engineering Items 5.4 Qualification items 5.4 Qualification results 5.5 Cost effectiveness analysis

Table 10 Final Design

	5.5 Environmental
	5.5 Failure Modes and Effects
	5.5 Life cycle cost
	5.5 Logistics Support
	5.5 Maintainability
	5.5 Nuclear
	5.5 Producibility
	5.5 Reliability & Maintainability
	5.5 Safety hazard analysis
	5.5 Specialty engineering
	5.6 Build to specification
	5.6 Verification Reqs and specifications
	5.8 Engineering master plan
	5.8 Lessons learned
	5.8 Master schedule
	5.8 Program management plan
	5.8 Project management plans
	5.8 Revised updated parts list
Additional Information • NASA Build to Baseline • NASA Phase C • DOD Engineering and Manufacturing Deployment	**Deliverables** • Technical Development Reqs • System Specification

Table 11 Fabrication and Integration

6 Fabrication and Integration	
• Produce items that conform to specifications and acceptance criteria • Assemble and integrate system • Verify and validate system • Develop capability to use systems to perform mission • Prepare facilities for production, maintenance and operations	
Input • Production Readiness Reviews	**Output** • Test Readiness Reviews
Tools • Office Automation: Word Processing, Spreadsheet, Presentation, Email	**General Information Products** • Plan Documents • Analysis Documents • Specification Documents • Test Documents
Activities	**Artifacts**

Table 11 Fabrication and Integration

	6.2 End Item
<u>Manufacturing and Assembly</u>	6.2 Quality assurance plan results
6.1 Ready production facilities	6.2 Spares
6.2 Fabricate assemble end item	6.2 Support Item
6.3 Complete end item verification test	6.3 Test faculties and equipment
preparations	6.3 6.7 Verification Procedures and data
6.4 Compare plans / documentation for end	6.4 As build documentation
items	6.4 Technical manuals and data
6.5 Test verify end item	6.4 Users manuals
	6.5 Compliance
<u>Integration and Test</u>	6.5 V&V evaluation results
6.6 Assemble and physically integrate system	6.5 Verification Reqs
6.7 Complete test plans and docs for system	6.5 Verified HW
6.8 Complete plans and docs for system	6.6 Integrated system
	6.6 Support equipment
<u>Verification and Acceptance</u>	6.7 In flight checkout plans
6.9 Test verify system	6.8 Final as built documentation
6.10 Perform acceptance testing	6.8 Operations procedures
6.11 Integrate system and control and verify	6.9 Tested system
interfaces	6.9 V&V SW
6.12 Train	6.9 Verification Reqs compliance
6.13 Technical management and planning	6.10 Acceptance Data
	6.10 Delivered system
	6.12 Trained personnel
	6.12 Training facilities equipment
	material
	6.13 Engineering master plan
	6.13 Lessons learned
	6.13 Master schedule
	6.13 Problem / failure reports
	6.13 Program management plan
	6.13 Project management plans
	6.13 Revised updated plans
	6.13 Wavers
Additional Information	**Deliverables**
• NASA Build to Baseline	• V&V Evaluation Results
• NASA As Built Baseline	• Tested System
• NASA Phase D	
• DOD Production and Deployment	

Table 12 Preparation for Deployment

7 Preparation for Deployment

Table 12 Preparation for Deployment

• Configure system for launch deploy • Establish readiness to launch / deploy	

Input	Output
• System Acceptance Review	• Flight Readiness Review

Tools	General Information Products
• Office Automation: Word Processing, Spreadsheet, Presentation, Email	• Plan Documents • Analysis Documents

Activities	Artifacts
	7.1 deliver installed system 7.1 Final system documentation
Prepare for deployment	
7.1 Deliver intact all system 7.2 Configure Hardware 7.3 Configure Software 7.4 Configure support system 7.5 Prepare personnel 7.6 Update mission ops plans and procedures 7.7 Complete integrated pre operations checkout	7.5 Trained personnel 7.6 Operations data 7.6 Go no go data 7.6 operational readiness criteria 7.7 Readiness reports 7.7 incidents reports 7.7 Problem failure reports

Additional Information	Deliverables
• NASA As Built Baseline • NASA Phase D • DOD Production and Deployment	• Trained personnel • Problem reports • Deployment recommendations

Table 13 Deployment and Operation Verification

8 Deployment and Operation Verification • Launch / deploy system • Establish operational envelop of system • Establish system logistics	

Input	Output
• Flight Readiness Review	• Operational Readiness Review

Tools	General Information Products
• Office Automation: Word Processing, Spreadsheet, Presentation, Email • Systems: Modeling	• Plan Documents • Analysis Documents • Specification Documents

Activities	Artifacts

Table 13 Deployment and Operation Verification

8.1 Launch / Deploy 8.2 Configure for checkout and operations 8.3 Demonstrate operational capability	8.3 Operational evaluation results 8.3 In-flight checkout results
Additional Information • NASA As Deployed Baseline • NASA Phase D • DOD Production and Deployment	**Deliverables** • Reports

Table 14 Mission Operations

9 Mission Operations • Perform mission • Sustain mission • Improve / augment system	
Input • Operational Readiness Review	**Output** • Decommissioning Review
Tools • Office Automation: Word Processing, Spreadsheet, Presentation, Email	**General Information Products** • Reports
Activities	**Artifacts**
Operations 9.1 Configure for operations 9.2 Conduct mission 9.3 Train personnel 9.4 Maintain system 9.5 Support system 9.6 Distribute mission products 9.7 Asses trends 9.8 Update design and documentation 9.9 Improvement block changes 9.10 Sequential production	9.2 Mission products 9.3 Trained personnel 9.5 Spares 9.7 Problem failure reports 9.7 Readiness reports 9.7 Learned lessons 9.9 Product improvement requirement modifications 9.10 Sequential production
Additional Information • NASA As Deployed Baseline • NASA Baseline Evolution • NASA Phase E • DOD Operations and Support	**Deliverables** • Reports

Table 15 Disposal

10 Disposal • Decommission / dispose of system items	
Input • Decommissioning review	**Output** • None
Tools • Office Automation: Word Processing, Spreadsheet, Presentation, Email	**General Information Products** • None
Activities	**Artifacts**
10.1 Decommission dispose 10.1 Store / monitor	10.1 Disposed items 10.1 Decommissioned items 10.1 Recycled items 10.1 Waster
Additional Information • None	**Deliverables** • None

1.4.6 Major Milestones and Artifacts

Major milestones are a good way to frame the key phases of a design. They represent a logical collection of a body of work that includes artifacts and even progress payments from a sponsor.

Just like process, there really is no universal set of milestones. The milestones are a function of the stakeholders' perspectives and the unique system under development. For example the key milestones from a sponsors' perspective are different than from a developers perspective. There may be overlap and even significant alignment however the sponsor usually comes from the perspective of – should money be paid for work performed and or should money be released for the next phase. The designer however is coming from the perspective of – are we ready for the next abstraction level to be understood or next steps to be performed.

One approach to identifying major milestones[38] is to examine the idealized process and establish major milestones at the start and or end of each idealized process element.

---

[38] Technical Reviews And Audits Systems Equipments And Computer Software, MIL-STD-1521A and B June 1976 June 1995.

Table 16 Potential Major Milestones

MIL-STD-1521B Milestones A	Potential System Design Milestones B
System Requirements Review (SRR)	System Needs Analysis (SNA)
System Design Review (SDR)	System Conceptual Architecture (SCA)
System Software Review (SSR)	System Physical Architecture (SPA)
Hardware Requirements Review (HRR)	System Implementation Architecture (SIA)
Preliminary Design Review (PDR)	System Requirements Description (SRD)
Critical Design Review (CDR)	System Design Implementation (SDI)
Test Readiness Review (TRR)	System Verification & Validation (SVV)
Functional Qualification Test (FQT)	
Functional Configuration Audit (FCA)	
Physical Configuration Audit (PCA)	

MIL-STD-1521B maps somewhat to the idealized process. However when we examine the work associated with developing a system design we see significant engineering activity during concept exploration. We also see significant activity in the form of needs analysis prior to concept exploration.

Table 17 Process and Major Milestone Gaps

Idealized Process	Milestones A	Milestones B
- - - none defined - - -	- - - none defined - - -	SNA (needs analysis)
Concept Exploration	SRR	SCA, SPA, SIA
Requirements	SDR, SSR, HRR	SRD
Design	PDR, CDR	SDI
Implementation	- - - none defined - - -	SDI
Test	TRR, FQT, FCA, PCA	SVV
Installations & Checkout	- - - none defined - - -	- - - none defined - - -
Operation & Maintenance	- - - none defined - - -	- - - none defined - - -
Retirement	- - - none defined - - -	- - - none defined - - -

Sponsor independent organizations that develop their own technologies, products, product lines, and systems are engaged long before the Milestone A sequence starts. When new participants enter the system space they see this disconnect and get confused. What they may not realize is that another organization may have performed the Needs Analysis and Concept Exploration that eventually leads to a request for proposal that includes completing the design and may also include implementation and production.

The reason for this split is to ensure as much competition as possible in the most expensive part of the system development. The idea of a few architecture companies or organizations that explore needs and conceptual architectures versus detailed design, implementation, and production companies exists both in government and industry. But the concept originated in government to maximize competition. The problem with this approach is that the issues are always in the details and production details can significantly impact architecture concepts and even needs.

Author Comments: In the past applied Research and Development (R&D) worked closely with company system architects and marketing to assess needs and what is possible. Today many company managers clearly state that their organizations do not engage in R&D. Instead the goal is to maximize revenue for the short term via constant cost reduction until the organization is barely able to function. Even lawsuit costs associated with bad designs are factored into the costs of doing business.

Author Comments: In government system development the needs and architecture concepts are viewed as a conflict of interest when the lucrative design, development, and production contracts are released. The concern is that the company developing the needs and architecture will bias the result towards their technologies and products. This has led to the divestiture of company divisions[39]. This leaves the Federally Funded Research and Development Centers (FFRDC) and a handful of small companies to try and understand the needs and develop the architecture concepts. Unfortunately they do not come close to previous organizations like Hughes Aircraft[40]. R&D, architecture, design, development, implementation production, and delivery need to be fully integrated in a single organization to maximize design breakthroughs with minimum overhead. In other settings there is usually a complete loss of important new designs and systems. Then there needs to be acknowledgement that there will be failure and one of the ways to deal with the failure is to have many such organizations working in a competitive industrial base.

Artifacts just like the major milestones are unique to each project. However there are general patterns that can be reviewed and used as guidance in identifying artifacts and their potential major milestone dates.

Table 18 Artifacts and Milestones

Artifacts	SNA	SRR	SDR	PDR	CDR	TRR	O&M
Plans							
Program / Project Plan	S	D	M	M	M	M	M
Systems Engineering	S	U	D	M	M		

---

[39] The Aerospace Corp was spun off from TRW in September 1959, United States Congress issued House Report 1121 which recommended that STL be converted into a non-profit institution. The-SI Organization was spun off from Lockheed Martin in 2010.

[40] Hughes Aircraft was a non-profit that engaged in both needs / conceptual architectures and follow on design development implementation production and delivery of new systems.

Table 18 Artifacts and Milestones

Artifacts	SNA	SRR	SDR	PDR	CDR	TRR	O&M
Plan							
Systems Engineering Management Plan	S	U	D	M	M		
System Test Plan				S	U	D	
System Test Procedures					S	D	
System Test Reports						S	D
Specifications	S	U	U	U	D		
Design Documents				S	U	D	
General System Analysis							
Needs	S	D	M	M	M	M	M
Stakeholder	S	D					
Architecture		S	D	M	M		
Functional		S	D	M			
Interface		S	U	U	D		
Maintenance		S	U	U	U	D	
Reliability Availability		S	D				
Fault Tree Analysis			S	U	D		
Failure Mode Effects			S	U	D		
Timing and Sizing	S	U	U	U	D		
Algorithms	S	U	U	U	D		
Training					S	U	D
Quality	S	U	U	U	U	U	D
Logistics		S	U	U	U	U	D
Support		S	U	U	U	U	D
Human Factors	S	U	U	U	D		
Specialty Analysis							
Engineering Disciplines	S	U	U	U	U	U	D
Project Specific	S	U	U	U	U	U	D
Note: S: Start, U: Update, D: Deliver, M: Maintain							

The New York District Design Submission Requirements Manual[41] offers standard procedures and instructions to accomplish required design, drawings, specifications, project definition narrative, design analyses, cost estimates, and related support tasks for Military (Army and Air Force, including Medical projects),

---

[41] Design Submission Requirements Manual, US Army Corps of Engineers New York District, NANP-1110-1-1, August 2009.

and support for other projects. The manual offers designers, both In-House (I-H) and Architect-Engineer (A-E) consultants, with a consistent logical approach to performing design and develop design related documents. The manual offers five phases A though E, suggesting milestones and information products associated with the expected phases.

Table 19 Milestones for Buildings

No.	A	B	C	D	E
1 NTP		X	X	X	X
2 Grade Site - Building Pad				X	X
3 Foundation	X	X	X	X	X
4 Underslab Utilities				X	X
5 Slab on Grade				X	X
6 Structural Frame	X	X	X	X	X
7 Roof Framing - Deck				X	X
8 Roofing		X	X	X	X
9 Exterior Walls and Windows			X	X	X
10 Building Dry-in	X	X	X	X	X
11 Interior Walls-Framing				X	X
12 Permanent Power				X	X
13 Wall Finish			X	X	X
14 Prime Paint				X	X
15 Mechanical/Electrical Rough-in		X	X	X	X
16 Plumbing				X	X
17 Mechanical/Electrical above Ceiling				X	X
18 Flooring (VTC/Ceramic)				X	X
19 Doors-Hardware				X	X
20 HVAC - Ductwork/Controls			X	X	X
21 Ceiling Finish				X	X
22 Finish Paint				X	X
23 Mechanical/Electrical Systems		X	X	X	X
24 Site Work - Utilities/Pavement				X	X
25 Carpet				X	X
26 QC System test - Debugging		X	X	X	X
27 QA System Test - Acceptance				X	X
28 CQC Inspection		X	X	X	X
29 HVAC Test and Balance			X	X	X
30 Landscape/Grassing				X	X
31 Pre-Final Inspection	X	X	X	X	X
32 Commissioning HVAC	X	X	X	X	X
33 Final Inspection/Acceptance BOD	X	X	X	X	X
Note: Design submittal phases: A Phase I Project Definition, B Phase II Concept, C Phase III Interim, D Phase IV Final, E Phase V Ready to Advertise					

NASA has a number of milestones that overlap the milestones suggested in MIL-STD-1521B. They also offer different program phases that overlap DOD phases[42].

Table 20 NASA Phases and DOD Acquisition Process

NASA Phases	DOD Acquisition Process
• Pre-Phase A - Find a suitable project • Phase A - Make sure the project is worthwhile • Phase B - Define the project • Phase C - Develop the system design • Phase D - Build, integrate, test and certify the system • Phase E - Prepare for operations • Phase F - Operate the system and dispose of it properly	• Concept Exploration and Definition • Demonstration and Validation • Engineering and Manufacturing Development • Production and Deployment • Operations and Support

Each organization attempts to develop a common set of milestones that makes sense for their activities. They also tend to think in terms of project or program phases.

Table 21 NASA Milestones and Phases

NASA Milestones	Phase
Mission Concept Review (MCR)	Pre-Phase A - Advanced Studies
Mission Definition Review (MDR)	Pre-Phase A - Advanced Studies
Non-Advocate Review Preliminary	Pre-Phase A- Advanced Studies
Program/Project Approval Review Preliminary	Pre-Phase A- Advanced Studies
Non Advocate Review	Phase B - Definition
Program/Project Approval Review	Phase B - Definition
System Requirements Review (SRR)	Phase B - Definition
System Definition Review (SDR)	Phase B - Definition
Preliminary Design Review (PDR)	Phase B - Definition
Critical Design Review (CDR)	Phase C - Design
Production Readiness Review (PRR)	Phase D - Development
Flight Readiness Review (FRR)	Phase D - Development
System Acceptance Review (SAR)	Phase D - Development
Operational Readiness Review (ORR)	Phase D - Development
System Integration Review (SIR)	Phase D - Development
Program Implementation Review (PIR)	Phase D - Development
Test Readiness Review (TRR)	Phase D - Development
Functional and Physical Configuration Audits	Phase D - Development
System Upgrade Reviews	Phase E - Operations

---

[42] NASA Systems Engineering Handbook, NASA/SP-2007-6105 Rev1, December 2007.

Table 21 NASA Milestones and Phases

NASA Milestones	Phase
System Operations Readiness reviews	Phase E - Operations
Post-Launch Assessment Review (PLAR)	-
Critical Events Readiness Review (CERR)	-
Post-Flight Assessment Review (PFAR)	-
Decommissioning Review (DR)	Phase E - Operations

1.5 System Design Terminology

Deciding on the terminology to use in a new systems design effort can be a significant activity if the organization is new to systems engineering. There are several sources that can be referenced and used by the team.

Table 22 Hierarchical System Terminology

Program Project	Management

System
    Segment
        Element
            Subsystem
                Assembly
                    Subassembly
                        Part
	Decomposition

The first sets of terms are associate with how the system is decomposed. These terms include the management structure and the system decomposition. That is because the system decomposition affects the management structure to some extent.

The issue is to not get fixated on the terms. Select and use them consistently throughout the activity. Changing terms will have significant impact because information products will become inconsistent and a tower of babble will cause the project to get lost.

The DOD acquisition phases follow the V-model where the early phases are associated with decomposition, definition, & design. The later phases are associated with integration, verification, & validation. On many projects and programs the milestones are defined and are associated with possible artifacts. These artifacts are usually summarized and they are typically a subset of MIL-STD-1521B[43].

---

[43] Technical Reviews And Audits Systems Equipments And Computer Software, MIL-STD-1521A June 1976, MIL-STD-1521B June 1995.

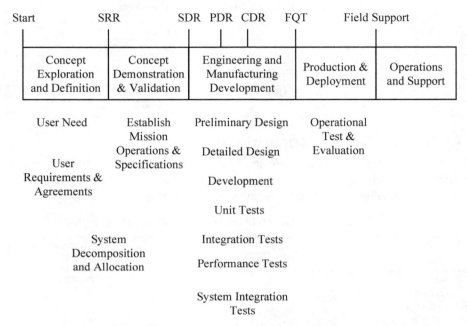

Figure 33 DOD Acquisition Phases Milestones and Activities

Table 23 Milestones and Possible Artifacts

System Requirements Review (SRR)	Functional Qualification Audit
Mission objectives / constraints	
System concept / architecture	<u>Functional Configuration Audit</u>
Draft functional baseline	System ready for production
Product process risk assessments	All development specifications
Draft specification tree	Functional configuration approved
Customer contractor understanding	Integration tests complete
	Qualification / certification complete
System Design Review (SDR)	
System specification	<u>Physical Configuration Audit</u>
Segment specifications	Approval of product specifications
Draft development specifications	Acceptance test
Functional baseline for products	As built agrees with design documents
Trade studies identified	Product baseline
	Certify operational readiness
Preliminary Design Review (PDR)	
Allocated baseline approval	**Field Support**
Requirements baseline	Conduct mission
Draft functional and physical interfaces	Training

Table 23 Milestones and Possible Artifacts

Methodology for verification of requirements	Maintenance Material management System disposal
Critical Design Review (CDR) Requirements satisfy functional baseline Requirements baseline and Specifications authenticated Requirements satisfied by design Agreed methodology for qualification Interface Control Documents approved	

1.6 Technical Director Role

The technical director role tends to exist in organizations engaged in complex systems engineering. The role is important to the success of the system design. The question arises, what are the good and bad attributes of a technical director?

Unlike the program or project manager whose primary focus is cost and schedule with task execution monitoring, the technical director is primarily focused on the technical aspects of the program or project. The technical director works closely with the project or program manager but they always ensure that the technical vision is not compromised. The following are some attributes of the technical director:

- Works closely with program or project management
- Does not compromise the technical vision and system solution
- Challenges the team to think outside the box
- If the technical director is not doing anything except coordinating leads there is a problem
- If the technical director is engaged in developing and maintaining cost and schedule data there is a serious problem
- If the technical director is asking for less than the team thinks is reasonable there is a problem
- If the technical director is asking to mature a solution that is less capable than an existing solution perhaps there is a desire for strong innovation
- The team may not have the same information as the technical director so the issue is to determine if that is the case or if the technical director individual is wrong for the technical director role

1.7 Systems and Design Key Points

➤ The medium modifies the solution:
- When an artist works the artists' vision is modified by the medium

- When engineers and systems engineers develop a solution the solution is modified by technology cost and schedule

➤ If engineers work their respective areas with no consideration to the rest of the system the risk is:
  - Each engineering area optimizes their solution from their point
  - Each area may compromise the solutions of the other engineering areas
  - With one or more engineering areas unknowingly compromised the system may not work

➤ Engineering is:
  - Application of scientific and mathematical principles to practical ends such as the design, manufacture, and operation of efficient and economical structures, machines, processes, and systems
  - Profession of applying scientific principles to the design, construction, and maintenance of engines, cars, machines, etc. (mechanical engineering), buildings, bridges, roads, etc. (civil engineering), electrical machines and communication systems (electrical engineering), chemical plant and machinery (chemical engineering), or aircraft (aeronautical engineering)
  - Practical application of science and mathematics, as in the design and construction of machines, vehicles, structures, roads, and systems
  - Application of science to practical uses such as the design of structures, machines, and systems. Engineering has many specialties such as civil engineering, chemical engineering, and mechanical engineering

➤ Design has different meanings depending on the audience or context: there are the artist's, engineer's, and philosopher's views

➤ Design from the artists' point of view is:
  - Sketch or drawing
  - Arrangement or pattern or features of an artistic or decorative work
  - An artistic or decorative creation

➤ Design from the engineers' point of view is:
  - Create, fashion, execute, or construct according to plan, devise, contrive
  - Form or conceive in the mind, invent
  - Plan out in mind, conceive or execute a plan, make artistically or skillfully
  - Have as a purpose, intend, plan

- Devise for a specific function or end
- Make a drawing, pattern, or sketch, lay out, draw the plans for
- Work out structure or form, by making a sketch, outline, pattern, or plans

➢ Design from the philosophers' point of view is: coherent pattern, purposeful pattern, opposite of chaos

➢ Art takes a medium like paint and canvas and transforms those fundamental building elements into a finished item, a final design

➢ Systems thinking is: the opposite of reductionism, views the system as a whole within the context of its environment

➢ Systems engineering:
- Concentrates on the design and application of the whole (system) as distinct from the parts, involves looking at a problem in its entirety
- Considers all facets and all variables and relates the social to the technical aspect

➢ In the visual arts design concepts are driven by: style/motiff, color schemes, textures, shapes, layout

➢ In systems engineering design concepts are driven by: functions, performance and technology

1.8 Exercises

1. What is art?
2. What is science?
3. What is engineering?
4. What is systems thinking?
5. What is systems engineering?
6. What is design?
7. What is systems engineering design?
8. Do you think you need to be an artist to engage in systems engineering design? If so why, if not why not?
9. Do you think you need to be an engineer to engage in systems engineering design? If so why, if not why not?
10. Do you think you need to be a systems thinker to engage in systems engineering design? If so why, if not why not?
11. Do you think you need a foundation in science to engage in systems engineering design? If so why, if not why not?

1.9 Additional Reading

1. A Theory of Human Motivation, A.H. Maslow, Psychological Review 50(4), 1943.
2. Applied Imagination: Principles and Procedures of Creative Problem Solving, A.F. Osborn, New York, NY: Charles Scribner's Son, Third Revised Edition 1963.
3. Art of Thought, Wallas, 1926.
4. Design Submission Requirements Manual, US Army Corps of Engineers New York District, NANP-1110-1-1, August 2009.
5. Educating, Gowin, D.B., Ithaca, N.Y., Cornell University Press. 1981.
6. Engineering Graphics, James S Rising, M. W. Almfeldt, P. S. DeJong, W. C. Brown Co; 4th edition (1970), ISBN 0-697-08601-1, 1970.
7. International Council on Systems Engineering (INCOSE) Systems Engineering Handbook 2011.
8. Managing The Development Of Large Software Systems, Winston W. Royce, Technical Papers of Western Electronic Show and Convention (WesCon), Los Angeles, USA, 1970.
9. Modern Control Systems, Richard C. Dorf, Addison-Wesley Publishing Company, 1967, 1974, Library of Congress CCN 67-15660, ISBN 0201016060.
10. NASA Systems Engineering Handbook, NASA/SP-2007-6105 Rev1, December 2007.
11. NASA Systems Engineering Handbook, SP-6105, June 1995.
12. National Airspace System Engineering Manual, Federal Aviation Administration, V 3.1, 2006.
13. Peopleware, DeMarco, Tom, Yourdon Press, 1987. Second edition, Dorset House Publishing Company, Inc, ISBN: 0932633439
14. Sandia Software Guidelines Volume 5; Tools, Techniques, and Methodologies; Sandia Report, SAND85–2348 l UC–32, Reprinted September 1992.
15. Sequential Thematic Organization of Publications (STOP), Hughes Aircraft Fullerton, 1963.
16. Systems Engineering for Intelligent Transportation Systems, Department of Transportation, Federal Highway Administration, Federal Transit Administration, January 2007.
17. Systems Engineering Fundamentals, Supplementary Text, Defense Acquisition University Press, January 2001.
18. Systems Engineering Management Guide, Defense Systems Management College, January 1990.
19. Technical Reviews And Audits Systems Equipments And Computer Software, MIL-STD-1521A June 1976, MIL-STD-1521B June 1995.
20. The Relationship of System Engineering to the Project Cycle, Kevin Forsberg and Harold Mooz, National Council On Systems Engineering (NCOSE) and American Society for Engineering Management (ASEM), 21–23 October 1991.

2 Needs Problem Market

The Needs Analysis changes with different organizations trying to satisfy the need. For example NASA uses phase A to provide the needs assessment. Companies that pursue projects using a business development organization to scout for opportunities engage in pre-proposal then proposal activities to address the need. Companies that offer products engage in significant market analysis. Technology organizations also may engage in market analysis but are focused more on the technology for its own sake, pushing it to new levels, thus satisfying their own need to pursue and break new ground.

Recently many have started to address the topic of needs. Terms such as needs assessment, statement of needs, and needs analysis have entered into the discussion when developing a new solution, system, design, architecture, etc. However there are older words that address the same space and it is worth considering them and the approaches and ideas they considered.

Problem solving is a very generic phrase that was used in the 1970's, 80's, and even 90's for identifying and addressing a problem. Many viewed the ability to solve problems as the most important skill someone could possess. Many engineering schools base their education concept around the ability of a student to solve a complex problem. Engineers are thus considered extremely valuable because of their powerful problem solving skills. How does problem solving work?

2.1 Problem Solving in Mathematics and Engineering

Problem solving has several steps in mathematics and engineering. It begins by stating the problem. This seems simple but that is not the case. There is enormous complexity in detecting the problem and then properly stating it for closure. The problem statement needs to be clear so that when a solution is offered it is obvious that the problem is solved. Further it needs to be the correct problem and not a different problem.

The next step is the identification of the given or known conditions. These are precisely stated. Although this seems like a simple task yet many fail to identify the relevant given conditions. Many times some known elements are missed while others are irrelevant and just add noise or distraction to the problem solving space.

Next come the assumptions. Many times the problem has unknowns and assumptions need to be made to address the unknowns. Again the trick is to find all the possible assumptions and pick the relevant assumptions.

Finally with the problem clearly stated with the givens and assumptions, different techniques, methods, practices can be applied to try and solve the problem.

2.2 Problem Solving in a Body of Knowledge

Within the problem space there is also the act of solving a problem in a body of knowledge and publishing a paper on the work. This can be part of a technical conference or as part of a product development. In this case a simple set of questions is used to frame the content of the paper. They are:

1. What problem is being potentially solved?
2. What are the current approaches to dealing with the problem?
3. What is wrong with the current approaches?
4. What are the alternatives to consider?
5. What is the proposed solution?
6. Why is the proposed solution better than the current approaches and the other possible alternative approaches?

So the techniques and methods, and practices used for problem solving are as varied as the entire body of knowledge we have at our disposal. They can be quantitative using complex mathematics and logic or qualitative using analogies and the soft sciences.

2.3 Filling a Market Void

Viewing the market and addressing a market void is paramount when starting a new company or developing a new product. The methods, techniques, and practices are to perform a market analysis and use elements such as:

- Surveys
- Focus groups
- Market research and testing

It becomes interesting when a new product, system, or solution, is offered for which there is no market. For example early introductions of the automobile, telephone, radio, television, and electricity fall into this category. A market needed to be created for each of these new technology solutions. These solutions anticipate a need rather than determine the need from existing stakeholders. So what tools, techniques, strategies can be used to create a market:

- Great marketing campaign, but what does that mean? Use the Veblen effect[44]; appeal to the ego and exclusivity of the less enlightened.
- Establish small example and point to the exceptional advantages. Niagara

---

[44] The Veblen effect is described in this text.

Falls provided AC electric power for the first time on a large scale[45]. This was used to show the benefits of AC electricity.

- Educate the stakeholders. This was a technique used to successfully introduce computers in the last century.
- Broadcast the new breakthrough design promising a new way far and wide.
- Use the Socratic method of discourse where questions and answers stimulate critical thinking and illuminate ideas. The goal is to lead to the obvious conclusions.

2.4 Fulfilling the Need

This now takes us back to needs, identifying the need, and satisfying the need. It is complex and buried within this is solving a perceived problem and filling a market void even if no one acknowledges the problem initially and a market void does not initially exist.

Identifying the need becomes easier if there is a sponsor that suspects there may be a void that must be addressed. For example there is sufficient data from stakeholders or other systems to suggest there is a need. To offer a more specific example, there may be consumers of automobiles and electric power who may want the energy sources to be more sustainable. So a need starts to emerge for cleaner personal transportation and energy production.

These are possible steps that can be taken to identify and bound the need. These steps are similar to and overlap requirement elicitation:

- Research
- Clear problem statement
- Understand the market
- Site surveys and visits of similar systems
- Understand the current approaches
- Interviews, questionnaires, user observations
- Workshops, working groups, prototyping
- Brainstorming, role playing, operational examples

2.5 Assessing Need Value

There may be a clearly defined need and there may be broad statements that suggest the size of the consumers wanting the need to be satisfied. However, without knowing the value of the need it is difficult to justify the costs associated with fulfilling the need. The value can be either financial or non-financial. For

---

[45] The Electrical World, A weekly Review of Current Progress in Electricity and Its Practical Applications, Volume 29, WJJC (The W.J. Johnston Company), Library of Princeton University, January 2 to June 26 1897.

example some value a day at the beach more than a day at the mountains.

Non financial value can be captured with the Measure of Effectiveness (MOE). The MOE is a critical measure used in the last century to evaluate systems and make major decisions associated with extremely large projects. It is a measure of goodness for each dollar spent. Measure of Effectiveness (MOE) = sum of tradeoff criteria / total cost. This will be discussed further in selecting architectures.

Financial value metrics falls under the broad area of economics. They are based on two important economic principles: (1) Fixed and Variable Costs, and (2) Supply Versus Demand. Examples of financial metrics are:

- Lowest Cost
- Highest Profit
- Greatest Return on Investment (ROI)
- Total Cost of Ownership (TCO)
- Internal Rate of Return (IRR)

- Economic Value Added (EVA)
- Real Option Value (ROV)
- Return on Assets (ROA)
- Return on Infrastructure Employed (ROIE)

Market value metrics falls under the broad area of market analysis. They are based on understanding the potential market size, competitors, and anticipated market saturation rate. This information is usually captured in a new business plan that has multiple topics but a key element is the understanding of the need value from a market perspective. These are some of the topics offered in a business plan:

- **Executive Summary**: market, products, strategy, management team, (owners, board members, external advisors), objectives, mission, keys to success, competitive edge
- **Company Summary**: ownership, history, locations and facilities
- **Products**: product descriptions (1, 2, n), industry impacts, competitive comparison, sales literature, sourcing, technology, future products
- **Market Analysis Summary**: market segmentation, target market segment strategy, (market needs, market trends, market growth), industry analysis, (industry participants, distribution patterns, competition and buying patterns, main competitors)
- **Strategy and Implementation Summary**: strategy pyramids, value propositions, competitive edge, marketing strategy, (positioning statement, pricing strategy, promotion strategy, distribution strategy, marketing programs), sales strategy, (accomplishments, sales forecast), strategic alliances, milestones
- **Management Summary**: organizational structure, management team, (owners, board members, external advisors), management team gaps, personnel plan
- **Financial Plan**: key tasks, important assumptions, key financial indicators,

break even analysis, projected profit and loss, projected cash flow, projected balance sheet, business ratios
- **Summary**: appendix product brochures

2.6 Examination of Previous Art

When developing a design, previous work and history must be investigated. Recreating the wheel or falling into traps that others have documented and are easily avoided is inexcusable. The previous work and history is approached methodically. It starts simple and grows in complexity as the search for information becomes more intense and complete.

- **Literature Search:** An analysis of previous work and history always starts with a literature search. In the past a literature search was limited to print and microfiche. Today computer-based searches yield electronic media. The literature search includes popular media, trade journals, conference proceedings, books, magazines, and websites with their own unique content. Although scholarly works need to reference high quality works, other information sources should not be discounted. For a large program usually someone collects relevant articles and makes them available to the team. Do not discount this activity especially when the team has concluded they completed the data gathering activity. There is always new data that should be considered.
- **Examination of Other Designs:** There may be existing designs that satisfy a portion of the need. These designs should be identified and analyzed for their strengths and weaknesses.
- **Examination of Patents:** The patent database offers descriptions of potential designs that may satisfy a portion of the need. These patent descriptions should be identified and analyzed for their strengths and weaknesses.
- **Industry and Technology Surveys:** At some point the broad literature search starts to focus on related industries, technologies, and products. Various design trends and relationships are captured and presented to the team. Vendors may be contacted but this is still a library research activity.
- **Vendor Search:** In complex systems with many element designs eventually key venders surface as possibilities for satisfying portions of the system design. The venders should be analyzed and presented to the team. In some cases, selected venders are invited to present their products and technologies.
- **Samples and Demonstration Requests:** After selected venders present their information, some can be invited to offer samples and demonstrations. These venders may become future subcontractors offering key elements in

the system.

- **Customer and Sponsor Visits:** Visiting the customer allows the systems design staff to see perspectives not possible in other setting. There tend to be experts and other valuable stakeholders that will suddenly appear at meetings only at the customer site. There are also resources such as access to documents, facilities, equipment, related work that a site tour usually surfaces and aids in understanding the needs and customer perspectives. The sponsor may or may not be collocated with the customer. Visiting the sponsor in their environment also provides insights not possible in other settings. Although not necessary, it is efficient to simultaneously visit the customer and sponsor on the same trip. This builds confidence in both stakeholders and allows the systems design team to expose the new visit findings to the customer and sponsor, sponsor hears about the customer visit or customer hears about the sponsor visit.

- **Site Surveys:** A site survey is used to gather physical and other information about and from a location. It can be a survey of vacant land to determine its ability to accept new, modified, or expanded structures. It can be a survey of an existing facility and its ability to accept a new, modified, or and expanded system design. The site survey results feed into the system design in the same way as any other stakeholder input. In many ways the results of the site survey may be the most important stakeholder input as reality is used to temper the idealistic system design visions. A site survey includes a visiting and host team. The visiting team gathers physical information such as space, heating, cooling, power, ingress, egress, storage, humidity, vibration, noise levels, lighting, and other environmental and physical characteristics. The host team gathers information ahead of time to minimize time spent in physical surveys and maximize time spent interviewing the host team. Talking to the host team about the unique needs and previous experience including maintenance and support issues will almost always surface key system design requirements. At the conclusion of a site survey a report is prepared that contains the data gathered and references to information products provided. The site survey report identifies the needs, goals, issues, and requirements surfaced. The new information is clearly noted. The site survey report is shared with the host team so that all information is accurately represented.

2.7 Research and Development Technology Innovation

Research technology and innovation are critical to great system designs. But what is research, how does it fit into technology, and how do we know if we are truly innovating? Research tends to fall into two categories, fundamental research and applied research. We normally expect research to lead to a new technology however that is not the case. Research can lead to new practices and processes. For example a short order cook in a restaurant can engage in research and eventually establish a whole new menu for an entirely new cuisine.

As we venture down the path of research, we start to realize there are different kinds of research. As we start to venture down the technology and innovation path we start to wonder how much of our design should be based on technology and innovation. This then takes us down the path of how much of our design should be based and or driven by research. The steps in conducting research are:

- Identify research problem
- Literature review
- State purpose of research
- Data collection
- Interpreting data
- Analysis of interpreted data
- Reporting and evaluation of research

2.7.1 Fundamental Research

Fundamental research or pure research is research that everyone acknowledges may not lead to immediate benefits other than increasing the body of knowledge in a particular area. Some suggest that it is performed out of curiosity, but that is not accurate because many activities are performed out of curiosity, but the curiosity may have immediate benefit in the form of machines, processes, tools, products, systems, organizations, etc. Fundamental research is associated with fundamental principals. It is not intended to result in immediate practical benefits. However, fundamental research does eventually play a role in activities that lead to immediate benefits, starting with applied research and ending with successful systems. Also the concept of body of knowledge does not just apply to fundamental research but it also applies to all other activities in establishing of designs, products, and systems.

Basic research tends to be performed in universities and non-profit organizations with a research charter. The funding sources can be from government, foundations, and corporations. In the past some very large technology driven companies were engaged in fundamental research. Today there are few fundamental research activities of note in corporations.

Why were companies engaged in fundamental research? That is an important question that needs to be understood but this text will not address this question. It is enough to acknowledge that there has been a change as of the writing of this text.

There is a split in why fundamental research should be performed. On the one hand some believe fundamental research should be performed for research sake. Taking the path of least resistance within the fundamental research arena. On the other hand some believe that fundamental research should be performed to solve an important problem[46].

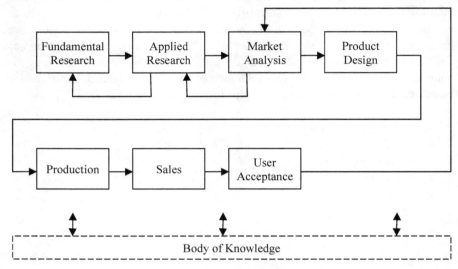

Figure 34 Impact of Research

This is similar to technology driven systems engineering where practitioners let technology evolve on its own taking its own path of least resistance and when someone decides, the technology is thrown into a real world operational setting, letting the human participants adapt it into their work[47]. This is a opposed to identifying the goals / mission / needs requirements and then attempting to develop a system with current, modified, or new technologies, machines, and processes. The reality is that complex systems require both approaches. The same is true for fundamental research. There is a need for both use inspired and basic fundamental research.

2.7.2 Applied Research

Many times' fundamental research leads to applied research. Applied research deals with solving practical problems. These problems may be the result of a market analysis or other system need analysis. It also may be the result of inspiration while engaged in or examining fundamental research. However the purpose is always to further some practical goal. This is in contrast to basic fundamental research, which is to discover new phenomena or new ideas of general interest. The funding sources can be from government, foundations, and corporations[48].

---

[46] Louis Pasteur is typically used as an example of Use-inspired basic research.

[47] Systems Practices as Common Sense, by Walter Sobkiw, CassBeth, 2011, ISBN 978-0983253082, the discussion is associated with Technology Versus Goal Driven Systems.

[48] Thomas Edison is typically used as an example of applied research.

Applied research also exists in companies where technology is a key component to their operations. The research might be associated directly with new products or with new internal processes and tools used in design, manufacturing, distributions, sales, and support. The need tends to surface from marketing, which identifies new opportunities or challenges from the competition. It also can originate from internal visionaries, however unless the organization is highly unusual[49], the visionaries must be the principals or owners of the organization.

Although the accepted body of knowledge suggests that organizations must engaged in research and development to ensure long term survival, many today chose to sacrifice a stable future for a very profitable near term result. The issue for why this turn of events has unfolded is fully documented even in popular media. The result is that the system designers need to be aware of their organizational settings as they develop system solutions. It may be possible that some practitioners just need to leave certain organizations prior to their demise. Otherwise they will find themselves developing very poor system engineering designs that no one will need, want, use, or trust.

2.7.3 Technology Life Cycle

The point of Research and Development is to surface new technologies that can be used in new and innovative designs. The Technology Life Cycle includes research and development and the product life phase. It can be in terms of time or other metrics such as financial metrics.

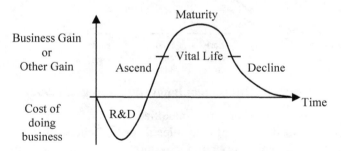

Figure 35 Technology Life Cycle

Some technologies have a long life with minor variations in technology gains made over long periods of time. Other technologies have a short life span with large variations in technology gains over short periods of time. Initially it is viewed as a relationship. As a better understanding surfaces it can include time. The goal is to apply financial metrics so that an investment decision can be made. From a historical perspective all the data can be surfaced and exact metrics can be offered. This historical perceptive of similar technologies and designs can be used to predict

---

[49] Hughes Aircraft, and many US technology driven companies in the 1960's and 1970's.

the possible results for new technologies and designs.

The research and development (R&D) phase costs money and takes time. This is investment and the cost of doing business however today many view it as a negative business gain. It is a time when risk of failure is high. During the ascending phase the R&D costs are recovered and the technology begins to gather strength. During the maturity phase the gain is high and stable. The market is starting to saturate at this phase. During the decline phase the market is fully saturated. There also may be a new technology that has surfaced to remove the remaining market, including those that would make replacement buys as the product wears out in the field.

Every existing system consists of different technologies. Every new system will consist of different technologies. Technologies have a life cycle that represents technology maturity.

In the beginning new technologies are complex, difficult to manage, and have few practitioners. In the end a technology is old overcome by other technologies. Some might assume that because of its age it is easy to manage. However, as many practitioners have moved on to newer technologies there are fewer practitioners making it difficult to manage and complex because of missing information.

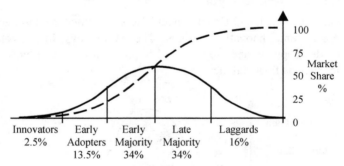

Figure 36 Diffusion of Innovations - Rogers (1962)

Technology adoption occurs in a modified S curve[50] as suggested by the logistics curve and the diffusion of innovation theory[51]. Rogers using more of a bell shape groups the technology curve by Innovators, Early Adopters, Early Majority, Late Majority, and Laggards. These adopters are associated with five stages of technological maturity starting with Bleeding Edge, Leading Edge, State-of the-Art, Dated, and Obsolete.

---

[50] Pierre François Verhulst (1845) studied the logistic curve in relation to population growth. The S-shaped curve of the initial stage of growth is approximately exponential, as saturation begins the growth slows, and at maturity growth stops.

[51] Technology not initially exponentially adopted, Textbook: Diffusion of Innovations, Everett Rogers, 1962.

Table 24 Technology Adopters and Maturity Levels

Adopters	Numbers	Maturity
1. Innovators	2.5%	Bleeding Edge
2. Early Adopters	13.5%	Leading Edge
3. Early Majority	34%	State of The Art
4. Late Majority	34%	Dated
5. Laggards	16%	Obsolete

Technologies and their applications are as varied as the needs that drive their development. When engaging in design it is important to maintain a list of the possible technologies, their life cycles, and maturity levels.

Table 25 Technologies and Applications

Maintenance	Computing	Healthcare	Sustainability
Training	Electronics	Transportation	Food
Test	Software	Logistics	Water
Production	Communications	Supply Chain	Clothing
Support	Biological	Algorithmic	Housing
Distribution	Chemical	Civil	Education
Materials	Pharmaceutical	Propulsion	Energy
Packaging	Human factors	Aerospace	

2.7.4 Innovation

Innovation is the result of nonlinear thinking. When you go into uncharted territory you typically learn something new, but not what you expected to learn. The uncharted territory is what forces the nonlinear thinking. So there is a need that current solutions are unable to satisfy. However, in many instances no one is able to detect the unique aspect of a need that leads to uncharted territory. For example why would anyone want to replace the horse and buggy when everyone knows the world functions perfectly well with the tried and true horse and buggy? So innovative designs are coupled to innovative views of the need.

Table 26 Innovative Team Characteristics

Conservative – Less Innovative	Progressive – More Innovative
• Very tightly related focused ideas	• Very loosely related unfocused ideas
• Remove connections to shrink scope	• New connections including external
• Refine the system	• Replace the system
• Incremental change	• Radical change
• Build on assumptions	• Challenge and create new assumptions
• Encourage continuity and stability	• Encourage radical shifts
• Risk averse wants to close	• Thrive on risk wants the challenge

Innovation involves increasing the system boundary or scope. It also includes pulling elements from outside the current accepted domain. This typically is associated with progressive high-risk teams. This is in contrast to low risk teams. In the non-innovative setting the context or system boundary keeps shrinking until everyone declares success. The problem with this approach is that all progress stops.

By definition state-of-the-art has few patterns and true innovation or beyond state-of-the-art has no patterns. Being willing to enter into a space where all the existing patterns are abandoned may lead to an innovation. The idea is one of punching through to a new level of thinking.

Example 3 Traceability to the Line of Code

In the late 1990's a process and tool was developed to trace software requirements to the line of code and output the requirements as log data during live testing[52]. This was done to support certification of mission critical systems. The original technology was developed for an E-commerce website to track how and why visitors arrive.

The first innovation was the development of tracking how and why visitors arrive. All existing tools were centered on the needs of a web hosting company not a web portal owner. A new punch through approach was needed to understand why and how people arrive at a web site. This forced the innovation that led to extremely flexible data mining concepts that were implemented in a final solution.

The second innovation led to the application and modification of this technology to address the needs to support certification of mission critical systems. The innovation was to support the new need of traceability to the line of code for certification and the second innovation was the use of serious data mining techniques developed for the E-commerce website.

The technology was quickly modified adapted and matured for a pilot program. When it was clear that the technology significantly benefited the pilot program it was successfully rolled out to other programs. This was accomplished within 12 months with little cost.

Each program had their own unique needs and even though a "product model" was used for this technology, the technology or product model was expanded to include new needs. For example on the pilot program the largest test generated a maximum of approximately 1000 log entries representing requirements allocated to the line of code. The second program had tests yielding in excess of 30,000 log entries. The third program had tests yielding in excess of 20 million log entries.

Obviously the technology needed to advance to address the correlation and visualization challenges of the new programs. Without this advancement the verification strategy would have failed with significant cost and schedule impacts.

The big picture was to create a mechanism that would transparently add

---

[52] Walt Sobkiw developed this, your Author.

traceability down to the line of code in software. However no one wanted to pay for technology using their budget. In this case there was a strong need to show this traceability to shorten the traditional certification cycle. So there was a desire to investigate the technology and try to make it work.

The details were in the implementation. They included using the new Internet technologies of a web server, browser, and PERL to parse and process the software text. They also include the details of the System Requirements Database and the interface to the mechanism that implemented the traceability to the line of code. The details also included modifications to the process such as code walk through to ensure the traceability was accurate and the test environment to allow for the automated output of the log data.

It was estimated that it took approximately 500 hours of computer execution time to mature the PERL implementation. This was in a time when 10 MIP personal computers just surfaced. Just one year earlier and this approach would have proved unfeasible because the 500-hour execution time would have converted to 5000 hours. Perhaps the 5000 hours could have been shortened with the addition of more computers and people however the program would have then rejected the idea and just done things the old way, even though it would have required significant time and resources.

Author Comment: Where does innovation really come from? Is it the slow incremental movement of research and development? Is it the slow incremental movement of the next design? Is it the slow test and evaluation in a lab while trying to develop a new device for an eventual patent? In 1964 a movie called The Golden Arrow[53] was released. Approximately 45 minutes into the movie 3 people in a tree are looking at a mirror showing a distant scene of action that looks remarkably similar to a modern Tablet Computer. Was the Tablet Computer design influenced by this fantasy movie?

Author Comment: One of the most important design team members are the innovators and creative people who can punch through to new levels of thinking. If there are no innovative creative voices then you will fail or at most develop a marginally successful design. Many managers with no background in systems design or experience only in low technology established settings view innovators as a distraction. They will try to remove them and believe they have successfully managed a team to closure and removed risk.

2.8 Technology Infusion

The last century is filled with examples of Research and Development leading to

---

[53] The Golden Arrow, released 1964, Distribution: Metro-Goldwyn-Mayer, Production: Titanus.

new technologies infused into existing and new systems. As of the writing of this text smart phone technology is new and App developers are teaming with savvy state-of-the-art companies and organizations to infuse new App technologies into their existing and new systems. This same scenario unfolded when the Internet technologies surfaced. Smart system developers and users embedded these technologies as they were initially pushed by the technologists and then eventually pulled[54] by all stakeholders everywhere.

From a needs point of view this suggests that new technology specialists search the world to find where their technologies can make a difference and improve a system. This means that eventually the technologist should understand and then affect system needs before the traditional system users, developers, and other stakeholders detect the need. This is beyond random vision and suggests that organizations understand the role of Research and Development, technology, and how these elements result in new systems that make a difference and result in overall positive progress.

Sometimes designs are started with known technology shortfalls, or with areas where new technology will result in substantial design improvement. Technology development can be done in parallel with the design evolution and inserted late in the design process. However a parallel lower technology approach that is not dependent on the development of new technology should be used as a backup to minimize risk of the total design which consists of many different technologies.

Existing designs can be updated and improved by inserting new technologies. However the technology insertion into an existing design must be effectively managed. Ideally the original design team should address planned updates or insertion of new technology into the design. In some instances this may impact the choice of the architecture and design details such that future technology insertion is more easily facilitated. This may take on the form of modularization and easily managed interfaces so that subsystems, assemblies, and parts can be replaced with newer better technology alternatives. A design that allows for future technology insertion has many advantages but fundamentally may delay obsolescence and reduce maintenance costs. This can be forced on the design team by ensuring the integrated logistics support plans and other related artifacts, such as a Technology Insertion Plan or the Systems Engineering Management Plan, challenge the design team to maximize technology and insertion. The plans and artifacts should address the strategy for future technology insertion activities.

Example 4 Needs and Technology Development

---

[54] Technology push pull is discussed in Systems Practices as Common Sense, by Walter Sobkiw, CassBeth, 2011, ISBN 978-0983253082. New technologies may need to be pushed into a community until it is understood and then the community wants and or demands the new technology.

The Early Bird, Intelsat I, was world's first communication satellite. NASA launched the satellite built by Hughes Aircraft Corporation[55] on April 6, 1965 at 6:48pm EST from Complex 17a at Cape Kennedy, Florida. Early Bird was built for the Communications Satellite Corporation and weighed about 85 pounds after being placed in a synchronous orbit of 22,300 miles above the Earth. It was positioned over the Atlantic to provide 240 two-way telephone channels or 2-way television between Europe and North America. The outer surface of Early Bird was covered with 6,000 silicon-coated solar cells, which absorbed the sun's rays to provide power to the satellite for its intricate transmitting and receiving equipment.

Figure 37 Early Bird - First Communications Satellite[56]

Who had the vision to surface and satisfy this need with what many would consider magic? How is it that some organizations were pushing technological boundaries at breathtaking speed, and why?

Example 5 Needs and Technology Development Becomes Common

Intelsat IV in an anechoic (sound absorbing) chamber. Built by Hughes Aircraft it stood over 17 feet tall with a capacity of about 6,000 voice grade circuits or 13 television channels. Intelsat was an international organization of 65 nations that was established August 20, 1964 out of the growing demand for channels of communication and greatly expanded the commercial communications network. The Intelsat IV was placed in a synchronous orbit over the Atlantic.

---

[55] Hughes Aircraft Company was a major American defense contractor founded in 1932 by Howard Hughes in Culver City, California. In 1953 it was donated to the non-profit Howard Hughes Medical Institute.

[56] Photo: NASA. Engineers checkout Early Bird-Communication Satellite.

Figure 38 Intelsat IV Communication satellite[57]

Two beautiful girls standing next to this massive machine. A machine that would bring their worlds together and elevate their understanding and consciousness of the world to such levels that some would have considered it impossible just a few short years ago. Who had the vision to surface and satisfy this need with what many would consider magic? This was now becoming ingrained in society. Technological leaders in the sole business of pushing technologies to make a better world. How does this compare with the need to come up with a scheme to make money?

2.9 Needs and Wants

Needs and wants are a very important concept. Needs suggests minimum solutions, even below being utilitarian. Wants suggests excess and waste such as when the Veblen effect is not understood and is used to offer useless items or services rather than introducing new innovations. There is a balance between needs and wants. Understanding that balance is part of a discovery process while engaged in design. A suggested guiding principle is that:

- Useful products, services, and systems are offered that satisfy the needs and wants of stakeholders so that life is always improved in some way

---

[57] Photo: NASA. Intelsat IV in an Anechoic chamber

This is an important concept because the users may not know what will lead to a better state of affairs. Users tend to only view the world from their immediate perspectives. They do not engage in developing what if scenarios and they do not have views outside their immediate responsibilities. This is where the technologists step in and offer alternative views of a better future.

2.10 Stakeholders

When addressing the need the stakeholders must be identified and understood. The term stakeholder is relatively new and comes from the project management world[58]. The idea is that project success is based on the acceptability of all that have a vested interest in the project. The traditional systems engineering viewpoint was to consider all those who will interact with the system. This is a subtle but important distinction. For example what is the role of a company president in the operation of an infrastructure system like Air Traffic Control. Yet the roles of passengers, air traffic controllers, pilots, maintainers, and system managers are apparent. The old terms were system users, maintainers, and operational managers.

So the dilemma is to make sure that at the start of a project the stakeholders in the system are identified and separated. There are stakeholders that may have the ability to kill a project but they will never interact with the system. The system engineering design team should not get lost in the noise of project management issues and instead must focus on identifying the true stakeholders in the system. One way to do this is to identify all the system external interfaces. Most individuals normally identify people interacting with a system as an external interface. As the system evolves, it becomes apparent that many of these people interacting with the system are a part of the system and they get moved back into the system boundary to become internal interfaces interacting with a machine subsystem or other people.

The following is a generic list of stakeholders. It can be used to stimulate discussion and identify stakeholders for the system being developed. Each system is unique and it is critical that the system stakeholders be identified.

Table 27 Generic List of Stakeholders

• Customers	• Policy Makers
• Competitors	• Operators
• Markets	• Users
• Sponsors	• Maintainers
• Visionaries	• Administrators
• Prototypes	• Regulators
• Previous Systems	• Producers

---

[58] Strategic Management: A stakeholder approach, Freeman, R. Edward, Pitman Publishing, 1984, ISBN 0273019139.

Table 27 Generic List of Stakeholders

• Interfacing Systems	• Providers
• Investors	• System Opponents

Once the stakeholders are identified, the needs for each stakeholder are understood and clearly stated. The needs are then converted to key requirements. This is the start of the top-level requirements for the system.

One way to begin the process of identifying the stakeholders is to list the high-level system requirements and associate them with a stakeholder. As the stakeholder list starts to unfold, other stakeholders start to surface. The requirements of the new stakeholders are then identified. This is a chicken and egg sequence and is not complete until the analysts exhaust their list of stakeholders and their requirements. Then their needs can start to be tabulated. In many instances the requirements and needs will overlap.

Many times some stakeholders have divergent needs and resulting requirements. For example health insurance companies have the primary requirements of increasing earnings and profits while the policyholders have the primary requirements for good health and long life. One need is for earnings and profits the other need is for good health and long life. These are divergent needs and resulting requirements. Some will attempt to argue that maximizing earnings and profits in a health insurance company will result in maximum health and long life to the customers, but there is no analysis that can show this linkage.

Sometimes the needs and requirements match between stakeholders. At other times the needs and requirements are complementary. Yet at other times the needs and requirements are conflicting. When there are conflicting needs and requirements, choices must be made, however if the conflicting needs and requirements are reasonable they may be carried forward as the system is studied and an architecture concept is produced. During this process it may be possible to find a solution that addresses the divergent stakeholders. However, the system designers must not be delusional. If a stakeholder must be removed from the system or modified in such a way that the divergence is not present, then that must be the solution that is offered otherwise the system design will be broken.

Author Comment: Is figuring out how to make money off a situation the same as satisfying a need? Recently technology has been applied to traffic lights to determine when people illegally drive through a light. This same technology can be used to control the switching of traffic lights to prevent an accident. For example holding the light yellow until traffic can safely stop and holding the other lights red until the dangerous situation can pass in a few seconds. Instead these systems just offer a citation when there is a violation and in some instances the lights have been tuned to maximize revenue by shortening the yellow light state. In these instances sudden stops result in rear end collisions[59]. So there is the need for a municipality to maximize revenue via traffic violations and there is a need to protect citizens. Currently the need to protect citizens has been ignored by grossly misusing technology and chasing a false if not dangerous and unsafe need.

The stakeholders and their needs must be identified and clearly communicated. This can be done using a set of tables, presentation slides, or via text with supporting graphics in a document. It should include the following key items:

- Stakeholder category by specific clear name
- Brief description of stakeholder job, role, activities
- Number in that stakeholder category
- Specific needs of the stakeholder category
- Key requirements of the stakeholder category
- Key issues associated with the stakeholder category
- Conflicts with other stakeholders

In a systems organization the legitimate needs of the customer outweighs the needs of the company. In an industry leading systems engineering organization the legitimate needs of the stakeholders outweigh the needs of the sponsor. These are very difficult situations when an organization becomes stressed.

Example 6 Air Traffic Controller Needs

- **Name:** Air Traffic Controllers
- **Role:** Responsible for the safe separation of aircraft in controlled airspace
- **Number:** 10,000
- **Needs:** System stability, clear presentation of information, proper human factors to minimize stress and sources of error
- **Key Requirements:** System does not fail, system does not make mistakes, System does not freeze, system is never disrupted by maintenance
- **Key Issues:** Existing automation level is insufficient to handle future traffic loads, previous new system introductions severely impacted air traffic controllers – develop proper transition strategy
- **Stakeholder Conflicts:** Maintenance needs occasional access to system, controllers can not be distracted by maintenance activities

2.11 Needs Process

The following process table is offered as a starting point and an example. It is a

---

[59] A search of the Internet of the following phrase "red light cameras cause accidents" resulted in 170,000 returns, September 20, 2013.

guideline that can be used for the needs problem market portion of the systems engineering design activity.

Table 28 Process Table – Needs Problem Market

Needs Problem Market	
• Identify the needs problem and market • Identify the stakeholders and their unique needs • Identify the potential shortfalls and areas for innovation and new technology	
Input	**Output**
• Start with nothing • Vague need notion	• System Needs Analysis (SNA) • Report Proposal • System Specification
Tools	**General Information Products**
• Office Automation: Word Processing, Spreadsheet, Presentation, Email	• Plan Documents • Analysis Documents • Business Plan
Activities	**Artifacts**
Needs assessment Market analysis Research and development Technology infusion injection Establish library Previous work Existing work Similar work Innovations for progress	Clear need statement Clear need assessment Market assessments R&D assessments Stakeholder assessments Technology assessments Sustainability impacts Ethical impacts Key need based requirements
Additional Information	**Deliverables**
• NASA Feasible Concept	• Report

2.12 Needs Problem Market Socratic Discourse

The following are suggestions of questions to ask as the Needs analysis unfolds. They can be used as a guideline to expand upon the questions that should be asked for each unique project.

- What is the need?
- Why is this a need?
- Are there similar needs?
- Has this need been addressed?
- How has this need been addressed in the past?
- Why are the current solutions not addressing the need?

2.13 Needs Problem Market Key Points

➤ System design begins as early as needs identification and analysis because
  • There may be design limitations
  • An effective process has feedback loops that go to any previous activity

➤ System design continues during implementation and production to
  • Ensure the design is not compromised
  • Requirements are met
  • Architecture is preserved

➤ Technology limitations drive design

➤ New designs may need to drive new technologies to satisfy new or old needs

➤ A failed design is where we did nothing new

➤ Identifying the system need is similar to identifying a market for a commercial application

➤ Needs analysis includes identifying current approaches for addressing the need

➤ Needs may not be fully addressed in the past because of existing system limitations

➤ Satisfying new needs typically requires new design elements to be part of the solution

➤ When identifying the needs
  • Asking indirect questions reveals stakeholder information, when talking about other things
  • Listen actively because the information may be between the lines
  • Get to know stakeholders as people, the more you know them outside their immediate system need the better you'll know their true needs
  • Speak stakeholder language, stay away from industry jargon and, use the words stakeholders use

➤ Design concepts can come from a few descriptive words during needs analysis such as elegant, affordable, friendly, dynamic

2.14 Exercises

1. What are the approaches to identifying a system need?
2. What are the approaches to identifying a market void?
3. Is there a difference between identifying needs & identifying market voids?
4. What are the approaches to identifying current solutions?
5. What are the approaches to identifying new design elements?
6. How do you know if you identified the correct need and or market void?
7. How do you know if you identified the full set of current solutions?
8. How do you know if you identified new design elements?

2.15 Additional Reading

1. Designing And Developing Maintainable Products And Systems, DOD Handbook, MIL-HDBK-470A August 1997, MIL-HDBK-471 June 1995.
2. Diffusion of Innovations, Everett Rogers, 1962.
3. Improving R&D Productivity: A Study Program and Its Applications, Robert M Ranftl, National Conference on Productivity and Effectiveness in Educational Research and Development, December 1977.
4. Improving R&D Productivity: A Study Program and Its Applications, Robert M Ranftl, National Conference on Productivity and Effectiveness in Educational Research and Development, December 1977.
5. NASA Systems Engineering Handbook, NASA/SP-2007-6105 Rev1, December 2007.
6. R&D Productivity Second Edition; Hughes Aircraft, June 1978, AD Number A075387, Ranftl, R.M., Carver City, CA: Hughes Aircraft Co., Second Edition, 1978, OCLC Number: 4224641 or 16945892. ASIN: B000716B96.
7. Strategic Management: A stakeholder approach, Freeman, R. Edward, Pitman Publishing, 1984, ISBN 0273019139.
8. Systems Practices as Common Sense, by Walter Sobkiw, CassBeth, 2011, ISBN 978-0983253082.
9. The Electrical World, A weekly Review of Current Progress in Electricity and Its Practical Applications, Volume 29, WJJC (The W.J. Johnston Company), Library of Princeton University, January 2 to June 26 1897.
10. The Golden Arrow, released 1964, Distribution: Metro-Goldwyn-Mayer, Production: Titanus.

3 System Architecture Design

This section is an introduction to the next sections to follow that will address system design. It should be referenced and returned to as each of the discussions on system design and technology are offered.

Architecture design is an extremely important element of the systems engineering design effort. It is the starting point of trying to address a need, maturing that starting point and taking it to a level of maturity where a design is available for implementation and production.

In the past when we thought of architecture many thought in terms of buildings. Today with the rise of computer based systems, many also think in terms of computing and software when architecture is mentioned. However architecture is much broader and can even include what we think of as abstract structures such as websites, companies, organizations, and even food offered on a restaurant menu.

There are several organizations that offer a definition of architecture. They tend to come from the computer and software perspectives. These definitions are broad and it is easy to apply them to non-computer and or software systems: The following items are associated with the term Architecture:

- Structure of levels and / or branches that partition a system into its constituent parts or components (DERA[60])
- Design and interconnection of the main components of a hardware / software system (DSMC[61])
- Organizational structure of a system or component. (IEEE-STD-610.12[62])
- How functions are grouped together and interact with each other (NASA MDP92[63])
- A logical or physical representation of a product, which depicts its structure, but, provides few or no implementation details (IEEE P1220[64])

---

[60] The Defence Evaluation and Research Agency (DERA). Part of UK Ministry of Defence until July 2, 2001. At the time it was the United Kingdom's largest science and technology organization.

[61] Defense Systems Management College (DSMC) provides the United States Department of Defense acquisition, technology & logistics training.

[62] IEEE 610.12 Standard Glossary of Software Engineering Terminology, 1990.

[63] Definition appears in the International Council On Systems Engineering (INCOSE) Systems Engineering (SE) Terms Glossary, 1998 and used NASA MDP92 as the source, NASA Metrics Data Program (MDP) 92.

[64] IEEE-P1220 Standard For System Engineering - A Commercial Standard For

- The organizational structure of a system or component. (IEEE 610.12)

The following is a definition of Architectural Design:

- Process of defining a collection of hardware and software components and their interfaces to establish the framework for the development of a computer system. (IEEE 610.12)

So what is architecture? Architecture is that initial abstract description that suggests how a need might be addressed. It is devoid of details that eventually are the design, implementation, and production. Architecture is a generic approach for satisfying a need.

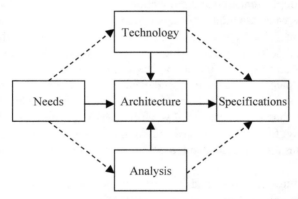

Figure 39 Systems Engineering Design and Architecture

The architecture has impacts across the stakeholders, interfacing systems, and the community where the architecture resides.

Example 7 New Restaurant Architecture

Selecting food combinations on a menu represents an architecture, which impacts the architecture of a restaurant building, business[65], and organization of the people who work in the restaurant. For example should the focus be Italian, Japanese, Indian, Ukrainian, Polish, American, or other food choices. Continuing, should the choices be high end with beautiful presentation and associated pricing. If the concept of a New Jersey diner is selected then the meal choices are almost endless. This impacts the architecture of the kitchen and even location of the diner. For example the diner needs to be within a reasonable distance of the food

---

Improving Competitiveness, 1994.

[65] If the food choices and or concept are new then perhaps a franchise empire is a possible business model.

wholesalers capable of providing the diverse types and qualities of food.

Example 8 Post World War II Housing Architecture

Prior to World War II many people were living in one-room flats with shared bathrooms and no kitchen facilities. After World War II people decided they had different needs and went about to build new cities. They overcame the ignorant social and political challenges and went to work. Some of these new cities are wonderful places to live and include diverse housing for all, schools, municipal facilities, parks, libraries, shopping, industrial parks, varied forms of transportation, houses of worship and many other things most people take for granted. Other new cities were poorly planned, especially in the last 2 decades of the last century. There is no shopping, industry, or even effective transportation. These cities had no plans, no system visions, and no common sense.

Author Comment: Recently there has been regression and many have once again settled for one-room flats with shared bathrooms and no kitchen facilities. Perhaps they view their needs as very small or perhaps their needs are being ignored. This is unfortunately at the risk of losing a stable happy future for all. Perhaps ignorant social and political challenges resurface with each new generation.

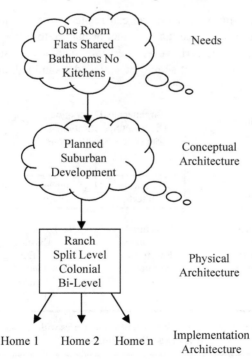

Figure 40 Needs Conceptual Physical Implementation Architecture

So why did people accept the idea of stand-alone houses like ranchers, split levels, colonials, bi-levels, etc? Why did this need surface? They rejected row houses and large common living area buildings in existing cities. Further it was a complex need because to support this new vision new infrastructure was needed in the form of roads, dependable personal transportation, power, water, sewage, communications, hospitals, schools, parks, houses of worship, etc.

What was buried in this new vision and implementation concept was the idea of open space and green areas. The open space allowed people to have privacy and not hear their neighbors' music, arguments, discussions, or other activities. Also their space became private, they could play the radio or later the stereo and not disturb the neighbors. Also the children were able to play in safe areas in the back or front yard with no fear of being hit by an automobile in the old cities. This was a growing concern as the automobile was entering the city landscape. There were also issues of finding parking for the new family automobile. The narrow streets were the only alternatives and they could not hold all the automobiles of the residents. This more peaceful lifestyle in the new cities came at a price. People could no longer walk to work, school, shops, hospitals, houses of worship, etc. So the automobile was a displacement technology that impacted all aspects of life.

Because we are non-linear thinkers we can relate to the previous architecture design discussion. We also can use it as a model or pattern to move forward in new architecture design challenges. However there are details and subtleties buried within the previous discussion that should be surfaced, examined, and explained in terms of architecture design practices.

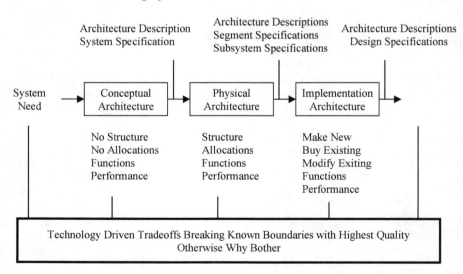

Figure 41 Architecture Design Big Picture

One possible system architecture design process is to acknowledge that there are 3 stages of system architecture design:

- Conceptual Architecture Design
- Physical Architecture Design
- Implementation Architecture Design

Each stage results in artifacts. Each stage represents a different abstraction level. However each stage is subjected to an extremely important test – is the design technology driven with new boundaries of performance and quality. As the abstraction level goes from less detail to more detail we move closer to implementation. As we proceed to integrate the system we test it at different levels. This provides an indication of how the performance and quality boundaries have been challenged at each abstraction level.

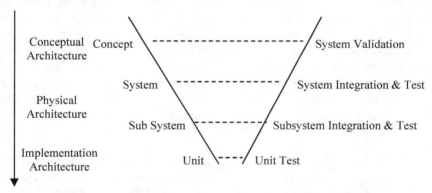

Figure 42 V-Diagram Systems Decomposition and Abstraction Levels

All systems exist in some physical location. They can exist on land, in the air, in outer space, on the water, under the water, or any combination. Complex systems may exist in many different types of locations with their implied environmental conditions. These complex systems have different system segments. So a system segment suggests some location type. A system segment also can suggest different locations in the same location type, such as land, but the individual segments have different sub-needs that result in different functionality, performance, and perhaps architecture, design, and implementation. For example a large air traffic control system can be thought of as having the following land based segments:

- Tower Segment
- Terminal Segment
- Enroute Segment
- Research and Development Segment

- Support and Upgrade Segment
- Simulation Training Segment

As the system architecture design proceeds from trying to satisfy the need to offering an implementation architecture design the segments decompose into subsystems. The subsystems can be based on people or machines. If they are based on machines then different machine types are considered as typically embodied in an engineering discipline such as civil, mechanical, chemical, electrical engineering. In each of these subsystems, the considerations should be vendor independent. The goal being that ideal generic subsystems are identified and understood. Eventually the subsystem design and implementation details need to be addressed.

One of the first issues is to determine how the system should be divided into subsystems. Then the focus changes and subsystems become systems. Partitioning stops when subsystems are simple enough to be holistically managed. Within this conceptual framework is the idea of having simple interfaces between the subsystems. If the interfaces are complex the system may not integrate or may not even function because of unknowns that are part of the interface complexities. However simplifying the interfaces may introduce complexity into one or more subsystems. It also may make a subsystem technologically impossible to implement.

At the highest levels the considerations are make, buy, modify and then technology. The technology can be from bleeding edge to obsolete.

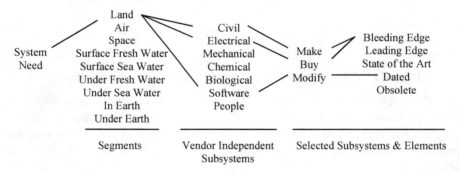

Figure 43 System Architecture Design Considerations

Author Comment: There is a value system associated with design. This value system is a major theme in this text. The suggested value system is:

- If you have not pushed the technology envelope then you have failed
- If you have not pushed the technology, functional, performance, and quality envelopes then you have done nothing except waste precious resources

Example 9 Business Oriented Website Architecture

A business-oriented website is a great experience to architect and eventually design and implement because within it is every aspect of a modern business. It also allows someone to quickly grasp the architecture design mystery because it quickly can be moved from abstract architecture to design, implementation, and production (going live in this case). It includes areas such as legal, marketing, sales, customer support, supply chain management, and even research and development collaborations and findings. Going through the architecture design process of an effective website is the same as going through the architecture and design process as a new business. For example what is the market, who are the stakeholders, what are the products and or services, what is the distribution method, how is knowledge captured and measured, what are the organizational departments groups sections, and what is the personnel organizational structure.

3.1 Process

This process table is a high-level table that results in lower level process tables.

System Architecture Design	
• Develop the system architecture design	
Input	**Output**
• System Needs Analysis (SNA)	• See lower level process
• Needs artifacts	descriptions
Tools	**General Information Products**
• Office Automation: Word Processing, Spreadsheet, Presentation, Email	• Plan Documents
	• Analysis Documents
	• Business Plan
Activities	**Artifacts**
Conceptual architecture design Physical architecture design Implementation architecture design	See lower level process descriptions
Additional Information	**Deliverables**
• See lower level process descriptions	• See lower level process descriptions

3.2 Some Key Points

➢ System architecture design is the starting point of
  • Trying to address a need
  • Maturing that starting point

- Taking it to a level of maturity where a design is available for implementation and production

➤ Architecture is that initial abstract description that
  - Suggests how a need might be addressed
  - Is devoid of details that are the design, implementation, production

➤ Architecture
  - Considers needs
  - Considers technology
  - Considers various analysis
  - Offers information for the system specifications

➤ Architecture is a generic approach for satisfying a need

➤ Architecture impacts
  - Stakeholders
  - Interfacing systems
  - Community where the architecture resides

➤ System architecture design has 3 stages:
  - Conceptual Architecture Design
  - Physical Architecture Design
  - Implementation Architecture Design

➤ System architecture stages have artifacts at different abstraction level

➤ As architecture abstraction levels goes from less detail to more detail we move closer to implementation

➤ Each architecture stage is subjected to a test asking fundamental questions
  - Is the design technology driven
  - Are there new boundaries[66] of performance
  - Are there new boundaries of quality

➤ A system segment suggests location and segments have subsystems

➤ Subsystems can be based on people or machines

---

[66] Boundary is used instead of level because is suggestions that it is hard to break through a boundary and achieve a new level. Level suggests that there is no significant challenge.

➤ When a system is decomposed into subsystems interfaces should be simplified

➤ Simplifying subsystem interfaces may
  • Introduced complexity into one or more subsystems
  • May result in a subsystem that is technologically impossible to implement

➤ System segments exist in different environments and include
  • Air
  • Land
  • Space
  • Water

➤ Vendor independent subsystems consider many elements, some of which are engineering disciplines
  • Civil
  • Electrical
  • Chemical
  • Biological
  • Software
  • People

➤ Subsystems and lower level elements are subjected to 3 key decisions
  • Make
  • Buy
  • Modify

➤ Subsystems and their elements have technology levels that can be
  • Bleeding edge
  • Leading edge
  • State-of-the-art
  • Dated
  • Obsolete

3.3 Exercises

1. What do you think is system architecture design?
2. Do you think an architecture description is needed before specifications are developed?
3. Do you think there is more to architecture than needs, technology, and analysis?

3.4 Additional Reading

1. NASA Systems Engineering Handbook, NASA/SP-2007-6105 Rev1, December 2007.
2. NASA Systems Engineering Handbook, NASA-SP-6105, NASA-SP-610S, June 1995.
3. Sustainable Development Possible with Creative System Engineering, Walter Sobkiw, 2008, ISBN 0615216307.

4 Conceptual Architecture Design

What is a conceptual architecture and how is conceptual architecture design performed? Defining and describing a conceptual architecture is relatively easy. The challenge is to showing how conceptual architecture design is performed. The following are some dictionary definitions[67]:

- **Concept**: an abstract or generic idea generalized from particular instances
- **Architecture**: a unifying or coherent form

There are several organizations that offer a definition of conceptual or concept elements. They tend to come from the computer and software perspectives. These definitions are broad and it is easy to apply them to non-computer and or software systems: The following items are associated with the term concept or conceptual[68]:

- A concept description sheet is for relating gross level designs to the functions, requirements, and constraints that the design is to meet (AFM)
- The concept phase is the initial phase of a software development project, in which user needs are described and evaluated through documentation (IEEE-STD-1012[69])
- The concept phase is the period of time in the software development cycle during which the user needs are described and evaluated (IEEE-STD-1002[70])
- The concept phase is the initial phase of a software development project, in which the user needs are described and evaluated (IEEE 610.12[71])
- The conceptual (concept) phase is identification and exploration of alternative solutions or solution concepts to satisfy a validated need (MIL-STD-785B[72])

---

[67] Webster's New World Dictionary, 1982, Simon & Schuster, ISBN 0-671-41816-5 (edged) or ISBN 0-671-41816-3 (indexed)

[68] The following definitions appear in the International Council On Systems Engineering (INCOSE) Systems Engineering (SE) Terms Glossary, 1998.

[69] IEEE-STD-1012 IEEE Standard for Software Verification and Validation Plans, 1986.

[70] IEEE-STD-1002 IEEE Standard Taxonomy for Software Engineering Standards, 1987.

[71] IEEE 610.12 Standard Glossary of Software Engineering Terminology, 1990.

[72] Reliability Program For System and Equipment, Military Standard, MIL-STD-785B, 15 September 1980.

- Conceptual design is synthesis. (AFM)
- Conceptual model is a requirements model of the system / software system to be developed, its internal components, and the behavior of both the system and its environment
- The conceptual phase is the initial period when the technical, military, and economic bases for acquisition programs are established through comprehensive studies and experimental hardware development and evaluation (AFSCP 800-7)

The conceptual architecture for our purpose is an idea with some philosophy behind it that has form and structure, which attempts to satisfy a need. It is very generic in nature devoid of details that would suggest dependence on an existing product or product element. This is very difficult to express and difficult to understand when presented, but that is the challenge. The reality is the conceptual architecture surfaces as the team does engage in architecture representations that include existing products. They are typically used as analogies to express the conceptual architecture elements during discussions of various conceptual architecture alternatives.

Example 10 Changing Personal Computer Architecture

As of the writing of this text the architecture concept of computing is changing. The personal computer (PC) where all applications and data are processed and stored on a physical device owned and controlled by the user is being threatened. Concepts of batch computing are re-emerging and are being referred to as cloud computing. Cloud computing has the advantage of sticking a meter on it and forcing the user to pay for services normally performed on the PC. Even though the PC has up front costs for the purchase of application software, there was the option of open source software from the free software stakeholders. These are the same stakeholders that pushed the early PC revolution and stopped batch computing services. Also in the PC model there is no charge for storing and accessing your data. In this setting the architecture concept arguments are not being viewed or discussed in this way. Instead they are being discussed from the perspective of monopolies trying to take control of a segment of society. These are some of the arguments:

Argument 1: Initially all vehicles were trucks because the US was an agrarian nation and that's what was needed on the farm. As vehicles were used in urban centers, cars became more popular. Now perhaps one out of every 25 to 30 vehicles is a truck[73]. PCs will be like trucks. They will be present, offer significant value, but only certain people will use them to satisfy their needs.

---

[73] Argument was being made circa 2010.

This view suggests a highly fragmented market where different devices satisfy different niches. Tablets with cloud computing replace traditional PCs, but for many users, they satisfy the need. If the US became agrarian again there would be a shift away from cars to trucks. Perhaps we have seen the rise of the sport utility vehicle to match the needs of those in the suburbs.

What should not be lost is that vehicles like computers started as cars and PCs using the Veblin effect, where the wealthy used and worked with cars and PCs as toys and status symbols. The toy and status symbol is still present in the personal vehicle. What also should be noted is that the car was matured in a setting of play.

Play is an important lesson known by innovators and technologist who naturally push boundaries. This is unknown by non-innovators and non-technologists. The play environment is essential to progress. Without someone playing no progress is made. This setting of play is anathema to managers and non-research institutions.

Argument 2: The PC will continue to shift in form factor. There may be a reason why they call them trucks, but PCs are not going to be trucks. They will continue to offer a variety of things people want to do with information[74]. This approach takes the benefits of a tablet and the benefits of a PC, and it's able to support both of those environments. There is the portability of a tablet and the richness of the PC. Tablet only users can't type or create documents. This approach provides them with the Tablet benefits without giving up what they expect in a PC.

Argument 1 offers a view of the market that is highly fragmented where different devices satisfy different niches. Tablets can never fully replace traditional PCs, but for many users, they are enough. In contrast, Argument 2 suggests a single unified device, one that combines the benefits of a tablet (portability) with the benefits of a traditional PC (content creation, power). Users might not be able to edit Excel documents on a Tablet, or type a paper in Word, but how many people really want to do that on their Tablet? A 10-inch screen is not ideal for work, regardless of the device power. Although it is too early to determine which argument will win, it appears that as of 2013 Argument 1 appears to be winning from a market perspective. Demand for traditional PCs has fallen, suggesting there is a market that does not need the power of the PC.

The conceptual architecture is occasionally referred to as a functional architecture. This suggests functional analysis be performed to capture a full understanding of the system, which is not possible in the early stages of satisfying a need with some conceptual solution. Instead as the system concepts are considered various levels of functional decomposition unfold. The full set of functionality is not known and understood until the physical architecture is described. In many ways the conceptual architecture design exploration supports the functional

---

[74] Argument was being made circa 2013.

decomposition of the system. Also the conceptual architecture design is a single high level picture representing the solution to the need. In many instances this may not be depicted with functionality. Instead it may be depicted with shapes that represent known patterns or new patterns and structure.

The conceptual architecture development starts when someone draws the first picture representing how a need is fully or partially satisfied. It may actually be a picture of the physical architecture or even include elements of the implementation, but it does not matter. It is the start of the conceptual architecture and it eventually will be transformed into an effective conceptual architecture showing how a need is satisfied without showing the limitations of significant physical structure and allocations or implementation details. This is a difficult journey for many especially if they are vendor-oriented with previous problem solving associated with internal products or existing external vendor products.

Key Issues:
- Too Many Steps

Key Issues:
- Too Big

Key Issues:
- Small Garage

Figure 44 Architecture Concepts

When developing the conceptual architecture the team immerses themselves in the need. As part of this process they identify the key issues and if available the key requirements. To identify the key requirements and issues many times a picture is needed for illustration. These pictures from various team members when taken together start to form one or more architecture concept pictures.

As one or more architecture concepts start to emerge the team needs to start to consider the system boundary, top level functions and top level operational scenarios. This fundamental system analysis will continue as the system design moves from concept to physical and finally to implementation.

Table 29 Conceptual Architecture Initial Analysis

Stakeholders
System Boundary
Top Level Functions
Top Level Operational Scenarios
Top Level Requirements

It is at the concept architecture phase that the detailed analysis should be identified. This analysis tends to be specific to the system type however there are additional generic analysis elements to consider. The analysis not only includes the target system but also the infrastructure that needs to be established to perform the next level system design activities.

Table 30 Conceptual Architecture Future Analysis Possibilities

Tools	Reliability	Growth
Processes	Safety	Technology Insertion
Organizational Structure	Security	Performance
Maintenance	Algorithms	Interoperability
Training	Human Factors	Sustainability
Support	Technology Assessment	Environment
Logistics		Production

The conceptual architecture evolves as the problem solution space is examined. The result is a high level picture, key requirements, key functions, key issues, and a plan for moving forward in terms of future analysis. There may be artifacts that surface during the conceptual architecture design representing the next steps of physical and implementation architecture designs. These artifacts need to be preserved and moved forward when the time comes to address these topics.

Conceptual design is one of the most difficult designs to surface. That is because we are all familiar with existing designs that have form function performance characteristics and other elements that are found in existing products and systems by existing vendors. So when given a need we naturally gravitate to an existing product or products and vendors. We may also realize that some solutions are more state-of-the-art and or better than other solutions, so we move in the state-of-the-art direction. However a conceptual design is devoid of the details of products or venders. It is product and vender independent. It is also devoid of significant structure details. There is only sufficient structure to show how the need is satisfied.

With some foundation of what a conceptual architecture is supposed to offer, the work needs to be performed. Three possible approaches for surfacing the conceptual architecture are suggested:

- Generalize existing products and designs
- Consider only technology
- Consider only functions and performance
- Any combination of the above plus ad hoc approaches

4.1 Existing Products and Designs Generalizations Driven

One approach to surface a conceptual architecture is to postulate a detailed solution with structure, products, and vendors and then start to remove the details. Begin by making the design vendor independent then product independent then remove all but the most essential structure. This can be the first approach to a conceptual architecture. This pattern then can be used to spur discussion and identify other potential conceptual architectures. This is a non-technology initiated conceptual architecture design approach. This does not mean that technology is not addressed and becomes the driver, it just means the starting point is not technology.

Table 31 Conceptual Design by Generalizations of Existing Designs

Vendors	Concept A	Concept B	Concept C
Subsystem 1 of n			
Vendor Product 1	X		X
Vendor Product 2	X	X	
Vendor Product 3			X
General Product a	X		X
General Product b			X
General Product c		X	
General Product d	X	X	
General Product e		X	

4.2 Technology Driven

An alternative to surfacing the conceptual architecture design is to think in terms of technologies to satisfy the need. The technologies in this case are usually new but they also can be proven or old technologies. As the technologies are applied to the need a conceptual architecture with minimal structures surfaces. This structure is a representation of the technologies and their interactions.

Table 32 Conceptual Design by Technology Choices

Technologies	Concept A	Concept B	Concept C
Subsystem 1 of n			
Technology 1.1	X		
Technology 1.2		X	
Technology 1.3			X

Table 32 Conceptual Design by Technology Choices

Technologies	Concept A	Concept B	Concept C
Technology 1.4			
Subsystem 2 of n			
Technology 2.1	X		
Technology 2.2			X
Technology 2.3		X	

Sometimes it is difficult to separate technology from product and or a vendor. A classic example is the Xerox machine. It was a product, company, and technology that was used to represent the ability to copy paper. This function is an essential element in some systems.

4.3 Function Performance Driven

This brings us to the next approach to surfacing a conceptual architecture design, satisfying the need by identifying and understanding the functions and performance. This approach translates into a functional block diagram at the highest level. When the diagram is annotated and augmented with technology, minimal structure and key performance a conceptual architecture design approach surfaces.

Table 33 Conceptual Design by Functional Performance Choices

Function Choices	Concept A	Concept B	Concept C
Function F1	X	X	X
Function F2	X	X	
Function F3	X	X	X
Function F4	X	X	X
Function F5			
Function F6			
Function F7	X		X
Function F8		X	X
Function F9		X	X
Performance P1	X		
Performance P2	X	X	
Performance P3		X	
Performance P4			X
Performance P5	X	X	X

4.4 All Possibilities Driven

When developing the conceptual architecture all the approaches just mentioned are used plus ad hoc approaches from the team. The issue is to ensure that there are alternative architecture design approaches and that these approaches are analyzed using systems engineering and other practices. Some key points to consider when engaged in conceptual architecture design are:

- Clear simple clever idea on which everything is based
- May happen after the physical or implementation architecture surfaces
- Diagram is extremely simplistic and clear
- When there are no specifications you create your own
- Satisfies specifications if they are present
- When developing concept use keywords, draw pictures based on keywords
- When engaged in conceptual design find the key issues and problems and offer design theories, then merge concept with design

Author Comment: In the last century there was an interesting idea that surfaced and became reality. The idea was based on the current condition that most machines were special purpose and what would or could happen if a general-purpose machine could be developed. A machine that once given a few simple instructions could perform multiple functions, in multiple domains, satisfying multiple needs. That general-purpose machine is the computer.

4.5 Analysis to Consider

As previously stated, during the concept architecture design the development process and analysis should be considered. The process and analysis is specific to the need and the conceptual system being considered, however there are generic analysis elements that apply to most system design activities[75]. The analysis not only considers the system but also the organization that will engage in the design project or program. This is a long list.

Table 34 Generic Systems Analysis to Consider for Design

Maintenance	Reliability	Growth
Training	Safety	Technology Assessment
Logistics	Security	Technology Insertion
Interoperability	Algorithms	Performance
Sustainability	Human factors	Environment
Tools	Project or Program Structure	Production
Processes	Skill Levels	Ethics

However there are a few fundamental practices to consider for all designs to get the activity going and understand what additional analysis may be needed. The

---

[75] The detailed approaches for performing these and other systems engineering analysis are described in Systems Practices as Common Sense, by Walter Sobkiw, CassBeth, 2011, ISBN 978-0983253082. The focus of this text is design; analysis is only described as needed to facilitate the design discussion.

fundamental practices are:

- Eliciting Gathering Requirements
- Finding the System Boundary
- Finding the System Functions
- Finding the System Operations

Notice that these practices use eliciting and finding as key action verbs. This suggests a discover process. A discovery process suggests learning. Learning suggests staffs who are constantly open to learning. This is the essence of high technology and it is a major difference from everything that followed prior to this new approach to design that led to massive progress in the last century.

4.5.1 Eliciting Gathering Requirements

Eliciting and gathering requirements is the practice of surfacing requirements while interacting with stakeholders and performing system analysis. Many narrow eliciting requirements to just users, customers, maintainers, managers, and other stakeholders. However they only provide a limited view of the possible requirements. In many instances this view is bounded by their own experiences and limited exposure to the challenge.

So part of the effort is to build a team of stakeholders that is able to learn and evolve as the system is being conceived. These stakeholders are frequently called Subject Matter Experts (SME). They are different from the other team members because they must maintain the ultimate vision of the system mission and its peculiarities. As the technologists run down their particular paths the SME must understand the ramifications of these paths and provide appropriate checks and balances. The elicitation practice includes:

- Interviews
- Questionnaires
- User Observations
- Workshops
- Working Groups
- Brainstorming

- Operational Examples
- Role Playing
- Prototyping
- Site Surveys
- Previous Systems
- Similar Systems

The information is extracted from the SMEs but the entire team participates. There is a two-way exchange between the SMEs and the rest of the team.

The non-SME portion of the team focuses on their respective disciplines and offers requirements based on their research and studies. The introspective research and studies include:

- Site surveys, previous systems, similar systems
- Operational and functional analysis
- Maintenance training and support analysis
- Various performance analysis such as timing, sizing, capacity, thruput, load, power, cooling, heating, structural, electro-magnetic interference, environment, etc analysis
- Reliability, maintainability, safety, human factors analysis
- Specialized algorithms analysis
- Manufacturing, production, transport, installation, shutdown, decommissioning, disposal analysis
- Transition and interoperability analysis
- Environmental impact analysis
- Sustainability analysis including cost shifting
- Life cycle cost analysis
- Architecture alternatives and selection
- Models, simulations, mockups, prototypes analysis

Science and engineering are based on connections. A literature search is performed before new science is offered. Current solutions are understood before new engineering approaches are proposed. These simple ideas also apply to surfacing potential requirements. So the team also looks to external sources and performs research and studies from an external perspective to surface requirements:

- Study the past and understand historical connections
- Literature searches
- Industry surveys
- Vendor searches, requests for information
- Technology searches, forecasting, and prediction
- Marketing surveys
- Emerging technologies tracking
- Emerging products tracking

All these analysis and study efforts result in multiple requirements. They need to be vetted by the stakeholders and moved into the baseline as appropriate.

Although the list of requirement elicitation and gathering suggestions is long, do not discount simple reading of related documents[76] and interacting with the team members. This is a very low cost approach but can result in significant understanding of the system and its requirements.

Many times people need to take on different roles. This is especially true for

---

[76] Do not discount the information offered on the Internet.

small teams. The technologists need to read literature describing the needs of the stakeholders and act on their behalf when they are not physically part of the team. At the same time others may need to enter a specialist role that is new for them and they need to learn by reading literature so that they can act on behalf of the missing specialist. This is how true systems practitioners are born. They are forced by necessity to take on these other roles so that an effective system solution can be offered when the team is deficient or broken.

Author Comment: As the years click by and an organization practices this broad approach to requirement elicitation and gathering, the organization starts to change to conform to the activity. For example subject matter experts tend to group together. Senior staff with new members tends to group together and look outside the organization being less introspective. New members that previously were part of the less introspective activities are pulled into the introspective group and eventually they themselves become senior staff. So there are three groups that hone their craft and interact with each other to elicit and gather requirements.

Table 35 Requirements Analysis Team

• **Subject Matter Experts (SME):** Familiar with the same or similar systems, designs, and technologies. Many equate these individuals with systems operators but they also can be high technology staff such as engineers that just work the same and similar systems, designs, and technologies
• **Non subject Matter Experts (Non SME):** Familiar with new systems, designs, and technologies. These tend to be high technology staff such as engineers. There can be SME staff that find themselves in research and development settings where they transition to Non SME perspectives.
• **Internal Perspective:** Tend to perform traditional systems engineering analysis. Also tend to be established SME members. They are typically mid career and have not yet reached senior staff levels. Although there can be extremely senior staff members in this role.
• **External Perspective:** Tend to look outside the current system boundary. These are typically Non SME and senior staff who were previously SME oriented but then were expanded to realize a broader perspective.
• **Role Players:** These are SME and Non SME members who realize a stakeholder perspective is missing from the team and are willingly step up to fill that role.

As the discussions unfold and requirements surface there is a constant culling activity where some requirements are accepted and others are rejected. The process should have the mechanisms to preserve this body of work. Some requirements become goals and others get moved to the dream category.

Author Comment: Goals are tomorrow's requirements. Dreams are next week's requirements. When we stop making goals and loose our dreams we stop progress. The challenge is to constantly challenge ourselves and every so often greatness happens when least expected. So always keep track of the Requirements, Goals, and Dreams. You now have the technology with System Requirements Databases (SRDB). Write specifications to house your requirements and figure out how to make your dreams come true.

4.5.2 System Boundary

The system boundary can be shown with a context diagram[77]. Draw a square or a circle on a piece of paper. Put the name of the system in the circle. Label the inputs and outputs of your system. Explain why the system boundary is the system boundary. If you are given a system boundary, a context diagram, convince yourselves the system boundary is valid. If it is not the correct system boundary, then fix it. Always include the system boundary and its rationale with all discussions and presentations of the system architecture. It is the highest level view of a system.

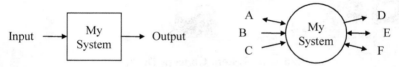

Figure 45 Generic Context Diagram

Your system is shown surrounded by external systems that interface to your system. These systems are not part of your system, but they interact with your system via its external interfaces. The external systems can impact your system, and your system does impact the external systems. They play a major role in establishing the requirements for your system. Systems further removed are those in your system's context that can impact your system but cannot be impacted by your system. These systems in your system's context are responsible for some of your system's requirements.

Your context diagram changes significantly during the early stages of a project as participants attempt to bound the system. At some point stability is achieved. That stability is based on various arguments. Those arguments must be captured and presented each time the context diagram is shown and the system boundary presented. At some point near the implementation phase someone eventually starts to think about a marketing flyer for the system. The context diagram always appears in some form in a good marketing flyer. Just as project participants needed to

---

[77] The system boundary is more fully discussed in Systems Practices as Common Sense, by Walter Sobkiw, CassBeth, 2011, ISBN 978-0983253082.

understand the boundary of the system, so do the clients who will buy, use, and maintain the system. So the context diagram never goes away.

The system boundary also can be shown with a concept diagram. The system concept diagram contains pictorials, or icons, of the system and its interfaces. A simple picture readily recognizable by the team can represent each interface.

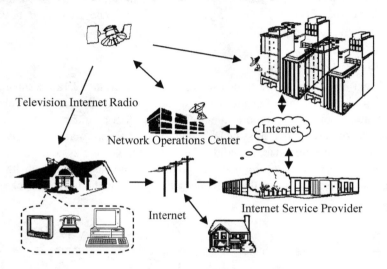

Television Internet Radio

Network Operations Center

Internet

Internet

Internet Service Provider

Figure 46 System Concept Diagram

One suggestion is to draw a system concept diagram by hand and scan the image. As the concept matures and is accepted someone within the organization will eventually clean up the picture. Another suggestion is to find a similar image in a library and modify it to support your needs. However, you may find yourself compromising on your vision, as your try to modify the picture and the modification is difficult and not exactly in line with your original vision. Do not compromise. Your vision is key and must be captured for all to see and understand.

In many ways this simple issue of being able to create a free form concept diagram, an artists rendering, is at the heart of many engineering issues today. Since so much has been created in the past 50 years, reuse has become common practice. However, as these systems have aged and become stressed new visions and concepts are needed to fill the void. This means someone somewhere must create the first picture.

Author Comment: Are you working with artists that are trying to understand the vision? If not why not?

4.5.3 Functions

Why is a functional analysis view of a system so important? That is an interesting question today because too many have started to ignore functional analysis and allocation in favor of what they consider to be more modern techniques not realizing what they lose without a functional view of the system. A functional view of a system allows stakeholders to understand the system at different abstraction levels.

For example, assume a software intensive system is in place with dozens of processors and hundreds of software components, some of which were newly developed while others are commercial products. If there is no functional view a simple question such as how can we split the system into 2 parts and have them optionally interface so that we can support 3 different missions (A, B, A+B) is difficult if not impossible to effectively and quickly answer.

Unless there is a functional view with decomposition, allocation to processors, and mapping to implementation, the view created will be useless. No one will be able to relate to the vast numbers of software products allocated to a single processor. However they will be able to relate to the 7 +/- 2 functions allocated to that processor[78]. Further, those engaged in details can examine the functional decomposition and map the functions to the software components and or products as needed.

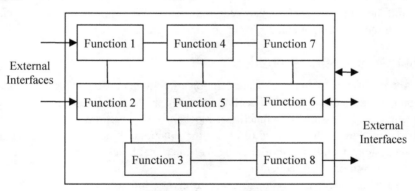

Figure 47 Functional Block Diagram

Quickly understanding the system at different abstraction levels is not only important when the system is operational and eventual upgrades are needed, it is also critically important during development. Getting lost in the details with an inability to traverse up and down the abstraction levels is one of the reasons why

---

[78] George A. Miller published a landmark journal article entitled "The Magical Number Seven, Plus or Minus Two, 1950. Chunking, modularization, and this important work is discussed in "Systems Practices as Common Sense", Walter Sobkiw, 2011, ISBN 978-0983253082.

systems' engineering exists. So lets look at a quick description of the how to perform this analysis[79].

Begin the functional analysis by looking at the system context diagram and listing the system functions. As part of the process it is natural to surface functions at different levels. This is not unlike developing an outline for a composition paper in grade school. Use a single sheet of paper to list the functions. The ideas will flow, be nonlinear, and be on different levels. If a system concept diagram exists, look at it and continue to identify functions on the same sheet of paper.

Take the paper and start grouping the functions. At some point you start to slow down in the function identification rate. Stop after approximately one hour. Group the lists into 7 plus or minus 2 functions and draw your Level 1 functional block diagram. Try to identify connections between your functions. Label connections where you can at this point in the analysis and leave the others unlabeled.

Depending on the depth of the analysis needed, you can stop at this point. The analysis will have errors, which will surface, but this is all you may need at this time. To continue to refine the analysis you need to move to a more formal method called Functional Decomposition. This method has roots in set theory and logic.

Once you have a set of functions, start to identify key functional and performance requirements. These functional and performance requirements should be list oriented and clearly grouped by the functions. From this list, find and list key system functional and performance requirements. These requirements are associated with your context diagram and system concept diagram.

4.5.4 Operational Scenarios

An operational scenario is a description of how a portion of the system will accomplish a function while interacting with a user. It can be described as a list of sequential steps or shown as functional blocks using interconnecting lines flowing in one direction. It should trace to or use the functional block diagrams developed for the system. Ideally a pictorial using the functional block diagrams described by text and summarized by sequential steps.

It some instances it may make sense to create operational sequence diagrams. These diagrams are similar to functional block diagrams but capture the system from an operational point of view. In this case the operational sequence diagrams augment the functional block diagrams and both should be consistent with each other. Initial inconsistencies are a good sign suggesting the analysis is worth the effort. The inconstancies must however be addressed.

Various performance parameters can be allocated to each element in the operational scenario elements just like in functional block diagrams. These performance numbers are typically timing, but they can be failure rates, reliability,

---

[79] A full description is offered in Systems Practices as Common Sense, by Walter Sobkiw, CassBeth, 2011, ISBN 978-0983253082.

error introductions, noise, frequency response loss, power loss, energy loss, death rate, cure rate, lines of code, processing load, cost of operations or any performance number needing to be allocated for some important insight into the system.

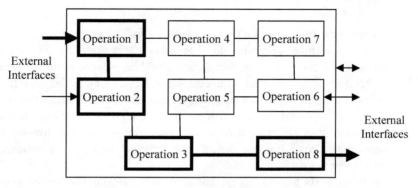

Figure 48 Operational Scenario

The Operational Threads conceptually are like the operational sequence diagrams except they do not show the context of other functions, which are not stimulated. Threads tend to be associated with a human initiating an activity with a system. Identifying the system threads from a user point of view essentially groups many functions together to accomplish a desired result[80].

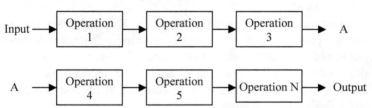

Figure 49 Operational Thread Diagram

4.5.5 Life Cycle Cost Considerations

Many, who engage in design, constantly track costs without capturing the full set of costs. The full set of costs is the Life Cycle Costs (LCC). The following is a starting point for considering the **LCC = R+D+P+O+M+S+I+E** Where:

R = Research   M = Maintenance
D = Development   S = Shut Down & Disposal
P = Production   I = Infrastructure
O = Operation   E = Environment & Waste

---

[80] A full description is offered in Systems Practices as Common Sense, by Walter Sobkiw, CassBeth, 2011, ISBN 978-0983253082.

From a design point of view the LCC can be viewed from the following perspectives:

- **Up front costs versus back end costs:** A system can have large up front costs that increase reliability to such a level that there are no back end maintenance costs. Also front-end costs could be reduced at the expense of backend disposal. In some instances disposal even may be impossible. For example the pipes used in a steam engine can use material where they never need to be replaced but the up front cost are high. Alternatively low cost pipe material can be used with very low up front costs but extremely high maintenance costs because the massive structure needs to be removed to replace the pipes annually.
- **Up front costs versus design costs:** In this case up front costs may be reduced at the expense of the design costs. For example a technology may be almost ready for movement into design but there is no desire to take on that risk and so and older technology is selected with a much higher design cost. For example when mainframe computing was entrenched and mini computers were entering the space, up front costs to mature the mini computers could have been used to offset the design costs for many less complex needs.
- **Production costs versus all other costs:** This is most easy to relate to because production is always used as an example in design. A design can be optimized to reduce production costs. However, just as in the other discussions of LCC other cost areas may increase or even become unreasonable. For example moving commercial product production to off shore facilities may require a nation state army to protect those facilities.

4.6 Putting it Together

The concept architecture evolves as the problem solution space is examined. The result is a high level picture, key requirements, key functions, key issues, and a plan for moving forward in terms of future analysis. There may be artifacts representing the next step of physical and implementation architecture designs. These artifacts must be preserved and moved forward when the time comes to address these topics.

The key requirements and issues along with how the team addresses these items are the essence of the solution. So it is important to have some understanding of what the term key really means and how to find the key items.

Author Comment: Hughes Aircraft was and is to this date the only systems engineering organization whose process was based on the concept of key items. There was an attempt to capture this in the Systems Engineering Capability

Maturity Model[81]. It was erroneously captured; again most attempts to document a process fail. These authors failed to acknowledge that Hughes Aircraft was a non-profit and as such had many practices outside the limited cost schedule view to make major decisions and develop designs. Thus few understand the meaning of key requirements, issues, functions, etc and how it was used at Hughes Aircraft. It is one of the elements that separated them from the pack and why they were so successful. Trying to capture this ingredient and allow someone to cook in the same successful way is challenging. I make a humble attempt.

Identifying and tracking the key requirements and issues may mean the difference between success and failure. Not all requirements and issues are the same. Some are make or break situations. Key requirements are drivers of the system solutions. They can be technology, performance, cost, schedule, production, maintenance, logistics, support, and other drivers. These drivers may exist because the state of the art is being pushed in an area or previous knowledge shows these requirements and issues are make or break items.

Everyone should know the key requirements. They should never be hidden. It is possible that some requirements and issues are so significant that management will try to hide them, but then no one will be able to use the magic of their abilities to tackle and address these key requirements. This is a typical of an organization that is driven by cost and schedule rather than service and success[82]. In the end the key requirements and issues don't go away, they always remain, but the successful teams address and effectively satisfy each of the key requirements and know how the key issues are closed. It is the essence of the solution.

Key requirements and issues come in layers. There are key requirements and issues at the highest level and are parts of the architecture dialog. There are key requirements and issues at the subsystem levels. There are key requirements and issues at the component levels. There are key requirements and issues at the abstract levels like maintenance, training, support, and other areas that do not make up the physical solution but are part of the system solution.

So key requirements and issues are very important. In many ways they are the kickoff of the activity. Everyone tries to find them then everyone wraps around them until they are one with the key requirements and issues.

Visualize a world where it is difficult to write lots of text, draw detailed pictures, and distribute these information products. Suddenly the concept of "key" starts to make sense. If "key" is now a concept, then what are the criteria for determining if something is key or not key? Does the criteria change with different challenges? In the end the team does the vetting to determine what is key and the vetting process

---

[81] A Systems Engineering Capability Maturity, Version 1.1, SECMM-95-01, CMU/SEI-95-MM-003, November 1995.

[82] The reward system in an organization can offer bonuses, promotions, etc based on short term earnings or long term success. These needs may not always converge.

then becomes important. For example, to enable and encourage full and proper vetting, transparency in a non-hostile setting is key, no pun intended.

Example 11 First Airborne Computer to Control Aircraft Flight

The following example is offered to try and suggest what some of the key items were in the design of the first computer based autopilot.

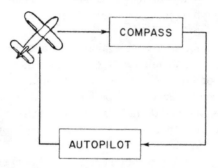

Figure 50 DigiTac Basic Heading Control Loop

The Basic Heading Control Loop was the original name for this figure. It is a representation of a conceptual architecture design trying to satisfy the need of having an aircraft be guided by machine. The image shows that an autopilot would use compass information to direct the aircraft in its flight.

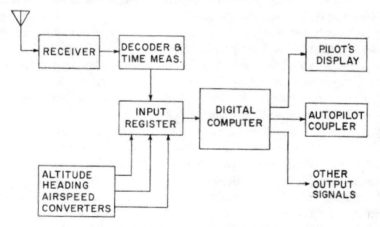

Figure 51 DigiTac Airborne Digital System

In the Airborne Digital System figure we start to see the next level understanding of the Basic Heading Control Loop. We see functions, interfaces at a very high level, and a deeper understanding of the conceptual architecture. There is also a suggestion of the physical architecture, which includes the subsystems shown as rectangles and squares with descriptive names.

Figure 52 DigiTac Computer

The DigiTac Computer is a photograph that clearly illustrates the Physical Architecture Packaging of one subsystem in the system, the computer. We see interface connectors on what appears to be the front of the computer. We also see ventilation openings suggesting significant heat.

Figure 53 DigiTac Input Output Equipment

The DigiTac Input Output equipment is a photograph that clearly illustrates the Physical Architecture Packaging of one subsystem in the system, the input output subsystem. We also start to see some of the materials used. It is based on vacuum tube technology. This has many implications, which translate into heat, weight, power, and size characteristics. It also drives the selection of all other components such as resistors, capacitors, transformers, inductors, and even wiring. We also see an interesting maintenance concept where there is modularity and modules are able to slide out of the cabinet for instrumentation, measurement, adjustment, and replacement or servicing. The tubes themselves can be replaced as needed.

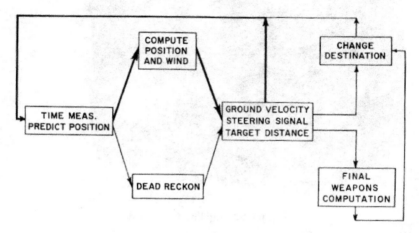

Figure 54 DigiTac Navigation Problem

The Navigation Problem graphic is addressing the key processing of the system. It is addressing a question surfaced by the Concept Architecture Design approach. There are details, which show that the system is more than an autopilot steering an aircraft. It also includes the need of supporting the weapons delivery.

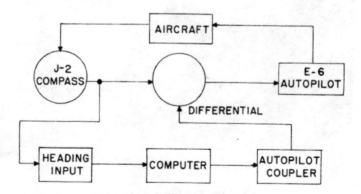

Figure 55 DigiTac Autopilot Control

The Autopilot Control shows that there is an interface between the computer and the aircraft controls. It also shows an interface to the compass. This is still an element of understanding the conceptual architecture, but there are suggestions for the physical architecture design.

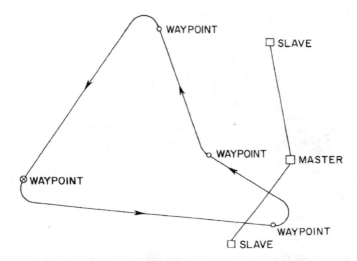

Figure 56 DigiTac Typical Programmed Course

The Typical Programmed Course is an example of an Operational Scenario. This scenario is used to test the conceptual, physical, and eventually the final implementation architecture. As the system understanding unfolds questions centered on this scenario are asked and the design appropriately matured.

Figure 57 DigiTac Magnetic Drum Memory

The Magnetic Drum Memory is a major component that is part of the computer. Today this major component may have been a commercial off the shelf item, but like the computer itself Magnetic Drum Memory in 1954 was probably a new development. It probably needed technology development to function in the severe environment of an airplane. This includes vibration, temperature, and pressure changes. It also may include severe G-Forces that may be encountered in combat situations.

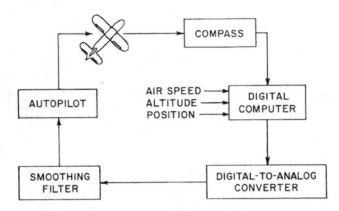

Figure 58 DigiTac Control Loop Including Navigation Computer

The Control Loop Including Navigation Computer graphic is an expanded view of the Conceptual Architecture. There is also a suggestion of a physical architecture that includes a digital computer rather than an analog computer. This surfaces the introduction of a digital to analog converter with appropriate smoothing to prevent control oscillations. It focuses on the key functions that allow the system to satisfy its needs, but it uses a new digital computer.

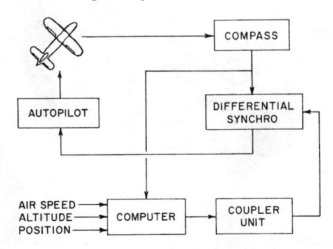

Figure 59 DigiTac Heading Control

The Heading Control graphic is an expanded view of the Conceptual Architecture and shows key elements of the Physical Architecture design. It is an alternative to the previous approach suggested in the Control Loop Including

Navigation Computer graphic. In the first approach the computer-processing load is very high because it constantly provides position information to the aircraft. In this approach the computer processing only provides correction information to the Differential Synchro. The Differential Synchro is responsible for providing the constant position control information to the aircraft. So these two graphics represent two different physical architecture alternatives with significantly different effects on the performance requirements placed on the computer.

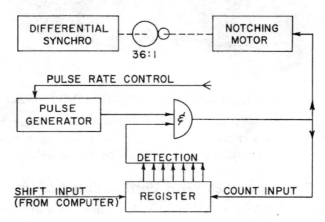

Figure 60 DigiTac Coupler Block Diagram

The Coupler Block Diagram is addressing a key issue associated with the Physical Architecture Design. It shows how the computer will interface to the Differential Synchro.

Figure 61 DigiTac Register and Control Chassis

The DigiTac Register and Control Chassis is a photograph that clearly illustrates the Physical Architecture Packaging of one subsystem in the system. This subsystem interfaces the computer to the Differential Synchro. A key issue of complexity of this new device is illustrated.

Figure 62 DigiTac Differential Synchro Drive Assembly

The DigiTac Differential Synchro Drive Assembly is a photograph that clearly illustrates the Physical Architecture Packaging of one subsystem in the system. This subsystem controls the aircraft and receives computer course updates.

4.7 Early Conceptual Design Verification and Validation

Before formal verification and validation starts there are early verification and validation activities that are used to further refine the design. This is centered on the process of selecting the conceptual architecture design and includes formal and informal studies, analysis, and models.

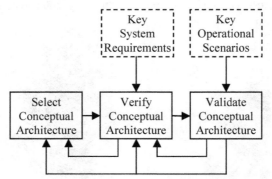

Figure 63 Early Conceptual Architecture Verification and Validation

The team points to the information products supporting the final decision and conceptual design approach. At the highest level the key requirements are used to verify the conceptual architecture design and the operational concepts are used to validate the conceptual architecture design. Many times the essence of the operational concepts may be captured in one or more models with various scenarios.

4.8 Conceptual Design Process

There is usually a great deal written about architecture design synthesis. In this case we begin with a definition, a brief description of the process, then an example.

Definition of Synthesis: 1. The putting together of parts or elements so as to form a whole 2. A whole formed in this way 3. The formation of a complex compound by combining two or more simpler compounds, elements, or radicals[83].

Synthesis is about aggregation, putting things together, the opposite of decomposition. It is a reverse decomposition[84]. However it is done in an environment of analysis. The analysis includes models, alternative architectures for comparison, technology assessment, failure analysis, etc - many of the systems engineering practices. This analysis is embodied in tradeoff criteria and quality attributes. Synthesis is tightly coupled to the architecture design selection process.

Synthesis starts with aggregating a conceptual architecture, then the physical architecture, then the subsystem architectures, then the assembly architectures, and then the component architectures. Do not get fixated on the definition of terms. The concept is to aggregate at different levels from top to bottom. Our model is conceptual, physical, and implementation design abstraction levels.

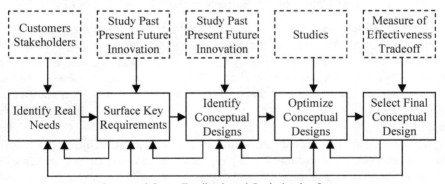

Inner and Outer Feedback and Optimization Loops

Figure 64 Conceptual Architecture Design Process

The conceptual architecture design follows a model that can be shown as a process. The model includes needs, requirements, alternatives, respect for all stakeholders, key understanding of the past, anticipations of the future and studies.

---

[83] Webster's New World Dictionary, 1982, Simon & Schuster, ISBN 0-671-41816-5 (edged) or ISBN 0-671-41816-3 (indexed)

[84] Reverse decomposition: take the known and generalize until the implementation details are removed.

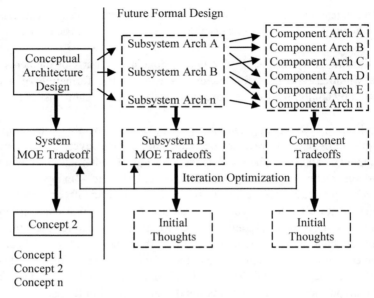

Figure 65 Conceptual Architecture Design Abstraction Levels

As there is movement down the decomposition tree the lower abstraction level architecture designs may impact the upper level architecture designs. As there is movement down the architecture design tree there is more reliance on existing components that are commercially available. Depending on the solution some of the components, assemblies, subsystems, and systems may not offer sufficient performance even at the state-of-the-art level and so new technologies may need to be developed.

So how is this really done, this thing called conceptual architecture design? When that question is asked many will jump into a process description. Others will fixate on one, two, or a few analysis techniques. All these views are incomplete and when new teams are formed and they are given a vetted process description along with descriptions of how to execute some of the analysis, they fail unless there are designers in the team who have done design in the past.

The designer experience can come at any time in the life of the designer. It does not magically happen to someone after they have completed a formal education as an adult. For example the designs from an individual can be simple designs developed by someone at the young age of 10 or more complex designs developed as professionals in an industry. Designers rely on previous works that are designs. Sometimes others develop the designs and the new designers study these previous bodies of work while at other times the previous designs are works developed by the designer that forms their experience base. Designers may surface as they support other aspects of the project. For example they may be engaged in one of the analysis practices or they may be apprentices assigned to existing designers.

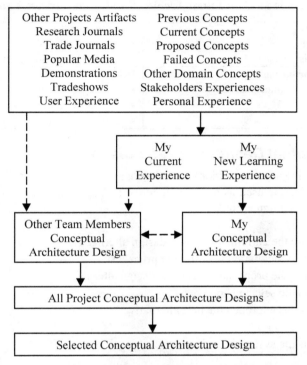

Figure 66 Conceptual Architecture Design Sources

The following process table is offered as a starting point and an example. It is a guideline that can be used for the conceptual architecture design portion of the systems engineering design activity.

Table 36 Conceptual Architecture Design Process Table

Conceptual Architecture Design	
• Develop the conceptual architecture design	
Input	**Output**
• System Needs Analysis (SNA) • Needs artifacts	• System Conceptual Architecture (SCA)
Tools	**General Information Products**
• Office Automation: Word Processing, Spreadsheet, Presentation, Email	• Plan Documents • Analysis Documents • Business Plan
Activities	**Artifacts**
Stakeholders analysis System boundary Top level functions	Tradeoff analysis Conceptual architecture description Key needs requirements

Table 36 Conceptual Architecture Design Process Table

Top level operations	Key conceptual architecture Reqs
Key requirements	System specification
Tradeoff analysis	Key need based requirements
Additional Information	**Deliverables**
• Conceptual Architecture Design	• Analysis Documents
	• Models, Prototypes
	• Specifications

4.9 Conceptual Design Socratic Discourse

The following are suggestions of questions to ask as the conceptual design unfolds. They can be used as a guideline to expand upon the questions that should be asked for each unique project.

- What are the current conceptual design alternatives
- What is wrong with the current approaches
- What are the proposed conceptual design alternatives
- What is the selected approach
- Why is this approach the best alternative

- What is the system boundary

- What are the key requirements
- What are the key functions
- What are the key performance elements
- What are the key issues
- What is the next step

- What are the expected analysis
- What are the proposed development methodologies
- What is the selected development methodologies and why
- What are the expected artifacts
- What are the expected milestones

4.10 Conceptual Design Key Points

➢ If you have not pushed the technology envelope then you have failed

➢ If you have not pushed the technology, functional, performance, and quality envelopes then you have done nothing except waste precious resources

➤ The conceptual design or architecture is captured in the functional baseline information products

➤ A conceptual architecture
- Can be represented with functions
- Should include a set of key requirements
- Should include a set of key issues
- Should be represented with a picture

➤ The conceptual architecture
- Does not include allocations to segments, subsystems, or components
- Shows how it might address a need
- Can be differentiated from other conceptual architectures

➤ A design concept can be the same as a conceptual architecture if the design is associated with function and performance

➤ Examples of design concepts typically not associated with architecture concepts
- A painting
- An automobile body style
- A piece of clothing

➤ The best design solutions start with a great design concept

➤ The best design solutions start with a great conceptual architecture

➤ A design concept or architecture concept
- Has the underlying logic, thinking, and reasoning
- A plan for solving the design problem
- Will lead to choices
- Becomes the framework for all your design decisions

➤ Architecture and design concepts are
- Represented with words
- Represented with pictures
- Involve both right and left brain activities

➤ Key requirements are discriminators that can be driven by
- Technology
- Cost and Schedule

➤ An architecture or design concept comes from
  • Defining the problem
  • Identifying the need
  • Research into the current state of affairs

➤ In a commercial setting surfacing the architecture or design concept involves knowing / understanding the
  • Brand if it applies
  • Customers or potential market
  • Any existing requirements
  • Objective
  • Budget and schedule

➤ When researching the industry especially in commercial settings it is important to know and understand
  • What is consistent across existing solutions in the industry
  • What part of the market is being under served, what are the needs
  • What are the key selling points, what are the new discriminators
  • What resonates with the market, what do the stakeholders expect
  • What interests does the market have in common, do the stakeholders have common interests

➤ The conceptual design or architecture is captured as the functional baseline

4.11 Exercises

1. Do you find it hard to identify and work with a conceptual architecture? If so why, if not why not?
2. Identify 3 conceptual architectures describe them using descriptive text, identify 5-10 key requirements for each of the architectures, identify the conceptual architecture design discriminators.
3. What approaches can be used to identify functions that satisfy a system need?
4. When addressing a system need should a conceptual architecture design always be developed?
5. Do you think a conceptual architecture design only can be represented with functions? If so why, if not why not?
6. How do you come up with concepts for a new design? Do you have a specific process you go through or do you wait for inspiration to find you?

4.12 Additional Reading

1. A Logical Approach to Requirements Analysis, Dr. Peter Crosby Scott, A Dissertation in Systems, Presented to the Faculties of the University of Pennsylvania in Partial Fulfillment of the Requirements for the Degree of Doctor of Philosophy, 1993.

2. A Systems Engineering Capability Maturity, Version 1.1, SECMM-95-01, CMU/SEI-95-MM-003, November 1995.

3. NASA Systems Engineering Handbook, NASA/SP-2007-6105 Rev1, December 2007.

4. National Airspace System Engineering Manual, Federal Aviation Administration, V 3.1, 2006.

5. Reliability Program For System and Equipment, Military Standard, MIL-STD-785B, 15 September 1980.

6. Systems Engineering for Intelligent Transportation Systems, Department of Transportation, Federal Highway Administration, Federal Transit Administration, January 2007.

7. Systems Engineering Fundamentals, Supplementary Text, Defense Acquisition University Press, January 2001.

8. Systems Engineering Management Guide, Defense Systems Management College, January 1990.

9. Systems Practices as Common Sense, by Walter Sobkiw, CassBeth, 2011, ISBN 978-0983253082.

10. Technology Readiness Assessment (TRA) Deskbook, DOD, May 2005, July 2009.

11. Webster's New World Dictionary, 1982, Simon & Schuster, ISBN 0-671-41816-5 (edged) or ISBN 0-671-41816-3 (indexed).

5 Technology and Great Designs

There is a tension between user versus technology driven systems. When we respond to users we typically respond to a market or a sponsor. However what if the users are stuck in the present and unable to imagine a different future? This is where technology driven systems can make a difference. Technology driven business is about pushing the technology so that the market and users will beat down your doors for the system or product. This means the design is great. Great designs:

- Push technology limits
- Push quality limits

These elements when pushed to their limits without compromising other design elements including reasonable cost form the foundation for all future designs.

So how does one approach technology in a new design? The first step is to understand what is currently available in terms of new technologies. The information products come from different areas and include:

- **Fundamental Research:** Typically performed in universities and unique organizations engaged in fundamental research. The information is usually found in scholarly works and government sponsored research reports.
- **Applied Research:** Typically performed in companies and many times funded by government. This is usually found in R&D journals and reports from companies, government lab, and Federally Funded Research and Development Centers (FFRDC)[85].
- **Trade Journals:** Commercial publications where organizations advertise and write about their latest offerings and investigations.
- **Technical Societies:** Peers publish their latest works[86]. In some cases these are associated with new technologies and their applications.
- **Popular media**: Companies prepare sophisticated marketing campaigns in

---

[85] Federally Funded Research and Development Centers (FFRDC) engage in research for the United States Government. The FFRDC is administered by universities and non-profit corporations using U.S. Code of Federal Regulations, Title 48, Part 35, Section 35.017. There are 39 FFRDC(s) sponsored by the U.S. government.

[86] International Council on Systems Engineering (INCOSE), Institute of Electrical and Electronics Engineers (IEEE), American Institute of Aeronautics and Astronautics (AIAA), American Radio Relay League (ARRL), etc.

anticipation of rolling out of new technologies. This is also a venue for all stakeholders outside the specialists to learn, understand, and comment on major new technologies and systems.

- **US Patent Office:** Database that includes new technology disclosures. The individual inventors and assigned companies are willing to place this information in the public domain.
- **Non Disclosure Agreement:** Between companies allows the exchange of proprietary information on their new technologies.

The next step is to then start to produce outstanding design concepts with outstanding quality. The designs might be great because they address one or more of these elements:

- Key Requirements breakthroughs are achieved
- Key Issues are closed with new breakthroughs
- Key Discriminators are now breakthroughs
- Key Quality elements are now breakthroughs
- Key Technologies are now breakthroughs

The question should be asked at the highest design level: Why is this design better than all previous, current, and proposed deigns. This needs to be clearly communicated on paper so everyone can see and agree with the statement. This can be accomplished by listing the best and worst designs in a table. If this design is truly new, what is the list of similar designs and why can't they be used. There also should be discussion to determine if elements of existing designs can be used or drawn upon to develop this new breakthrough design.

5.1 Quality Attributes

Quality is about doing everything well. The implication is that function and performance is pushed to the limits in a balanced reasonable solution. At the highest levels when we think of quality we tend to have a view of what we consider to be high quality.

• Makes life easier	• Non disruptive	• Reasonable costs
• Easy to use	• Seamlessly	• Accessible by all
• Never breaks	integrates	

From a more detailed point of view, quality attributes are sometimes referred to as the "ilities". They are non-functional and are very similar to tradeoff criteria when selecting architecture alternatives. They are:

- Accessibility, Autonomy, Accountability, Credibility
- Accuracy, Precision, Correctness, Integrity
- Adaptability, Customizability, Composability, Configurability, Tailorability
- Availability, Dependability, Reliability, Durability
- Deployability, Distributability, Discoverability
- Efficiency, Effectiveness, Affordability
- Elegance, Simplicity, Demonstrability
- Failure Transparency, Fault Tolerance, Resilience, Recoverability, Orthogonality, Degradability
- Fidelity, Responsiveness, Seamlessness
- Growth, Flexibility, Modifiability, Scalability, Upgradability, Evolvability, Extensibility
- Interchangeability, Compatibility, Reusability, Interoperability, Ubiquity
- Maintainability, Modularity, Installability, Serviceability, Debugability
- Manageability, Operability, Learnability, Administrability, Auditability, Understandability, Usability
- Mobility, Portability
- Predictability, Repeatability, Reproducibility, Determinability
- Relevance, Timeliness
- Robustness, Stability, Survivability, Safety, Securability
- Self Sufficiency, Internal Sustainability, External Sustainability
- Standards Compliance, Testability, Provability, Traceability

Example 12 Quality Attribute of Minimizing Overhead

One of the more important Quality Attributes that many overlook is minimizing system overhead. If the overhead approaches 35% the system reaches a thrashing level and is unable to perform useful work. This observation was made when multitasking multiprocessing computers were introduced. An operating system that identifies tasks to be preformed and allocates available resources is unable to perform as the system utilization approaches 65%. If we look at a machine we always try to improve efficiency. When we look at organizations we also try to improve efficiency. In the case of an organization this can be accomplished via new tools, new technologies and new processes. Few are willing to consider management as an overhead and will instead focus on the people who actually perform the work. Also few will focus on the concept that an entire organization might not be needed. For example the healthcare insurance industry in the US presents enormous overhead to the healthcare function[87].

---

[87] To address this issue the US Affordable Health Care Act was introduced and led to a government shutdown in 2013.

Quality cannot be inspected or tested into a product or system. Quality is designed and built into the system or product to minimize defects. The ideal goal is to have zero defects at the end of design and implementation. Evidence of high quality includes:

- Small tolerances and extreme accuracy such as narrow compartment lid seams, perfect spacing between adjoining areas, straight lines, no burs or surfaces that can cut
- Sensitivity to maintainability such as color coded or stripped wires, hoses, pipes, modularity, ease of access
- Human machine interface (HMI) that is easy to use, complete, consistent, properly uses colors, text size, field of view, controls, alerts, indicators, tactile feedback
- Ergonomics that uses proper sizes, weights, reach, and adjustments
- Ability to not only handle design peak load but above design peak load with no loss of function, performance, or damage to system
- Excellent finishes and coatings with uniform application, no drips, thin areas, blotches, changes in reflection, immune to scratching and rub off
- Ability to do everything well without degradation, attention to ALL the details no matter how far hidden from users

Some designs are inherently more prone towards higher quality. For example some approaches have fewer parts, interfaces, and process steps. Elegantly simple designs and low complexity lead to inherently higher quality approaches. When a tradeoff is performed, use the quality-criterion as a tradeoff criterion and consider the past history and the design complexity when rating the approach.

In many ways adopting the systems approach for the project will significantly enhance the quality. Many elements associated with quality are normal systems design practices:

- Understand past quality problems - history is critical
- Do Impact of Failure analysis (IOF)[88] early, regularly update - start simple then expand into Failure Mode Effects Analysis (FMEA)
- Quality function deployment (QFD)[89] - design the right system
- Use multi-functional teamwork - basic to systems engineering
- Begin with the concept or architecture - start as early as possible

---

[88] Described in Systems Practices as Common Sense, by Walter Sobkiw, CassBeth, 2011, ISBN 978-0983253082.

[89] System engineering is about capturing the stakeholder needs so that the correct system can be developed. QFD and capturing the voice of the customer is a restatement of basic System Engineering.

- Simplify the design - less interface, parts, complexity
- Use high quality parts - pay me now pay me later
- Design with fewest parts - less things to break
- Use highest quality automated tools - intuitively obvious
- Raise and resolve issues early - so others learn from you
- Identify critical dimensions, tolerances, and precision parts
- Reuse proven designs - learn from others
- Document thoroughly and completely - no finger pointing or blame games
- When designing always address quality - make statements

Whenever a defect is detected as much information about the defect should be gathered and documented. This should include an initial assessment of the defect[90].

Table 37 Priorities Used For Classifying Defects

Priority	Applies if a problem could
1 Grave	a. Prevent accomplishment of an operational or mission essential capability b. Jeopardize safety, security, or other requirement designated critical c. Result in loss of life or health
2 Catastrophic	a. Adversely affect the accomplishment of an operational or mission essential capability and no work-around solution is known b. Adversely affect technical, cost, or schedule risks to the project or to life cycle support of the system, and no work-around solution is known
3 Critical	a. Adversely affect the accomplishment of an operational or mission essential capability but a work-around solution is known b. Adversely affect technical, cost, or schedule risks to the project or to life cycle support of the system, but a work-around solution is known
4 Marginal	a. Result in user operator inconvenience or annoyance but does not affect a required operational or mission essential capability b. Result in inconvenience or annoyance for development or support personnel, but does not prevent the accomplishment of those responsibilities
5 Negligible	Any other effect

Author Comment: There is a severe quality downward spiral that easily surfaces with defect tracking. The danger is that the team finds defects and fixes them in isolation. There is no desire to spot trends or worse no desire to fix a collection of defects even if the defects are located in the same area. In these settings it is not uncommon to see teams touch a single element such as a software file dozens of times rather than touch it once and fix all the defects at once. The excuses are usually cost and schedule. Meanwhile most of the cost is in the touching

---

[90] MIL-STD-498 Appendix C Category And Priority Classifications For Problem Reporting. There is an overlap with the FMEA categories found in MIL-STD-1629A.

of the element not in the individual fixes. An approach to recover from this downward quality spiral is to create a single defect whose sole purpose is to improve quality and let the personnel work in a level of effort mode to increase the quality. There are dozens, hundreds, or even thousands of elements that can not be micro-managed, but a focused team could address. This is easy for software and problematic when physical elements are involved.

So what can designers do to understand the quality level in their designs and push to new levels? The answer is to offer an effective information product that summarizes the analysis of the quality attributes in the design space. This can be accomplished with a quality attributes tradeoff table.

Table 38 Quality Attributes Design Alternatives Tradeoff Summary

Quality Attributes	Current Design	Design 1	Design 2	Design n	Dream Design
Makes life easier	1	4	2	3	5
Easy to use	1	2	3	4	5
Never breaks	1	3	2	4	5
Non disruptive	1	2	3	4	5
Seamlessly integrates	1	2	3	4	5
Reasonable costs	1	2	3	4	5
Accessible by all	1	2	3	4	5
Total[91]	7	18	21	27	35

The current design is the state of the design space as it exists in the industry. It is the best that the industry has to offer. It is the baseline. The dream design is what those engaged in the industry would consider outstanding, a true breakthrough in the industry. The other design approaches fall between these two extremes. The ratings can use different methodologies. These include rank, ratings 1-10, ratings 1-4, or other ratings systems[92].

In a system the design can be for a part, assembly, subsystem, element, segment, or system. It can be a roll up of the individual decomposed items in the system or product. It also can be an independent assessment of the system or product regardless of the individual roll up results.

5.2 Technology Versus Goal Driven System Design

There are three approaches to system design. These approaches are based on either being technology driven, mission goal driven, or both. No approach is right or wrong but it is important to know that new technology is a key element in all the

---

[91] This tradeoff used the ranking approach; they are lined up from worst to best.

[92] Analytic Hierarchy Process (AHP) offers suggestions for determining pair wise comparisons. The rating scale choices are also discussed in the tradeoff sections of this text.

design approaches.

The first design approach is to identify the goals / mission / needs requirements and then attempt to design a system with current, modified, or new technologies, machines, and processes. Examples of this might be the goal of sending a person to Mars before the end of decade. Even if the goal is less challenging than going to Mars the design may force the development of one or more technologies so that it can separate itself from all previous designs.

The second design approach is to let the technology evolve on its own taking its own path of least resistance and when someone decides, throw it into a real world operational setting, letting the human participants make it work in their operational settings. An example of this might be the Internet[93]. All of the sudden the Internet technology appeared and everyone embraced or rejected it. Those that embraced the Internet technologies have new systems that have transformed their worlds. This is a scenario where the newest technologies are identified for possible inclusion in a new design.

The third design approach is a combination of being both technology driven and goal driven. This is for extremely complex system designs where it is important to not rule out any possible avenues. An example of this might be a new air traffic control system where there is a need to increase capacity, that is a reasonable goal, and it may translate into developing one or more new technologies. At the same time there are existing new technologies that can be studied and tested to determine if they can result in increased system capacity. So coming from the requirement driven approach and technology driven approach the most effective system design might emerge. Also technology is a key element in both approaches.

5.3 Patents and Intellectual Property

The following description is offered to provide insight into innovation and the documenting of a new invention as viewed from the patent process. This can be used as a framework for engaging in technology, innovation, and documenting the systems engineering designs. It is also a guide for those who may pursue intellectual property protection[94]. There are general rules in the United States to determine if there is an invention eligible for a patent. The rules fall into 4 broad categories:

- **Statutory Class:** Is the invention in a statutory class? Is it a machine, article, process, composition, or a new use of one or more of these items? Many

---

[93] High Performance Computing and Communications Act of 1991 (HPCA) Public Law 102-194, the Gore Bill. It helped fund the University of Illinois National Center for Supercomputing Applications where programmers developed the Mosaic Web browser.

[94] This information was extracted from the United States Patent and Trademark office circa 1998. It is only offered as a guideline and for specific rules and regulations the latest information should be accessed from the appropriate authorities.

software and system patents are granted as part of a process description. Mathematics and algorithms can not be patented, but if they are described in terms of a process, a patent can be granted.

- **Usefulness:** Is it useful? The patent should provide some utility. This criterion is rarely used to reject a patent application. Examples of rejection would be perpetual motion machines. This category is used to reject other types of inventions such as those associated with nuclear weapons.
- **Novelty:** Does it have novelty? Is there a new physical feature, new combinations of old features, or new use of an old feature (different application of prior art)?
- **Not Obvious:** Is it not obvious? Does the novelty provide new and unexpected results? This is where many engineers, especially software engineers assume that an idea will fail to be patented. The patent office however, follows a set of rules to determine this characteristic and what is obvious to the inventor may not be treated as obvious to the patent office.

Some of the criteria used to determine if an invention is not obvious. This is one of the approaches to encourage innovation in a system design activity. The non-obvious criteria include:

1. Succeeds where others fail
2. Successfully solves a problem never before recognized
3. Successfully solves problem previously thought or found to be unsolvable
4. Attained commercial success
5. Classified in small class where small advance in prior art has great weight
6. Omits an element in a prior art without loss of capability
7. Contains modification not suggested in the prior art
8. Provides advantage which never before was appreciated
9. Provides operative result previously prevailed by failure
10. Implements an ancient idea, but never implemented idea
11. Solves long-felt, long-existing, and unsolved need
12. Contrary to the teachings of prior art

A major criterion used to determine if an invention is not obvious is to determine if the invention is based on new combinations of prior art. This is one of the approaches to encourage innovation in a system design activity. The combinations of prior art include:

1. The combination is not expressly suggested or implied by the prior art
2. The prior art references could not be combined physically
3. The references would not show the invention even if physically combined
4. The prior art references would not operate if combined

5. Three or more references are combined to show invention
6. The references teach that they should not be combined
7. Awkward, separate, or involved steps required to combine the references
8. References from different technical fields are combined to form invention
9. Synergism, results are greater than the sum of the results of the references

5.3.1 What is a Patent

A patent for an invention is a grant of a property right by the United States Government to the inventor (or his heirs or assignees), acting through the Patent and Trademark Office. The term of the patent is 17 years from the date the patent is granted, subject to the payment of maintenance fees.

The right conferred by the patent grant extends throughout the United States and its territories and possessions. The right conferred by the patent grant is, in the language of the statute and of the grant itself, the right to exclude others from making, using, or selling the invention. What is granted is not the rights to make, use, or sell, but the right to exclude others from making, using, or selling the invention.

Some persons occasionally confuse patents, copyrights, and trademarks. Although there may be some resemblance in the rights of these three kinds of intellectual property, they are different and serve different purposes.

5.3.2 Copyrights and Trademarks

A copyright protects the writings of an author against copying. Literary, dramatic, musical and artistic works are included in the protection of the copyright law, which in some cases also confers performing and recording rights. The copyright goes to the form of expression rather than to the subject matter of the writing. A description of a machine could be copyrighted as a writing, but this would only prevent others from copying the description; it would not prevent others from writing a description of their own or from making and using the machine.

A trademark relates to any word, name, symbol or device that is used in trade with goods to indicate the source or origin of the goods and to distinguish them from the goods of others. Trademark rights may be used to prevent others from using a confusingly similar mark but not to prevent others from making the same goods or from selling them under a non-confusing mark. Similar rights may be acquired in marks used in the sale or advertising of services (service marks). Trademarks and service marks that are used in interstate or foreign commerce may be registered in the Patent and Trademark Office.

5.3.3 What Can Be Patented

The patent law specifies the general field of subject matter that can be patented and the conditions under which a patent may be obtained.

In the language of the statute, any person who invents or discovers any new and useful process, machine, manufacture, or composition of matter, or any new and useful improvements thereof, may obtain a patent, subject to the conditions and requirements of the law. By the word process is meant a process or method, and new processes, primarily industrial or technical processes, may be patented. The term machine used in the statute needs no explanation. The term manufacture refers to articles that are made, and includes all manufactured articles. The term composition of matter relates to chemical compositions and may include mixtures of ingredients as well as new chemical compounds. These classes of subject matter taken together include practically everything that is made and the processes for making the products.

The Atomic Energy Act of 1954 excludes the patenting of inventions useful solely in the use of special nuclear material or atomic energy for atomic weapons.

The patent law specifies that the subject matter must be useful. The term useful refers to the condition that the subject matter has a useful purpose and also includes operativeness, that is, a machine which will not operate to perform the intended purpose would not be called useful, and therefore would not be granted a patent.

Interpretations of the statute by the courts have defined the limits of the field of subject matter that can be patented; thus it has been held that methods of doing business and printed matter cannot be patented.

In the case of mixtures of ingredients, such as medicines, a patent cannot be granted unless there is more to the mixture than the effect of its components. (So called patent medicines are ordinarily not patented; the phrase patent medicine in this connection does not have the meaning that the medicine is patented.) A patent cannot be obtained upon a mere idea or suggestion. The patent is granted upon the new machine, manufacture, etc., and not upon the idea or suggestion of the new machine. A complete description of the actual machine or other subject matter for which a patent is sought is required.

5.3.4 Novelty And Conditions For Obtaining A Patent

In order for an invention to be grated a patent it must be new as defined in the patent law, which provides that an invention cannot be patented if:

- The invention was known or used by others in this country, or patented or described in a printed publication in this or a foreign country, before the invention thereof by the applicant for patent, or
- The invention was patented or described in a printed publication in this or a foreign country or in public use or on sale in this country more than one year prior to the application for patent in the United States

If the invention has been described in a printed publication anywhere in the world, or if it has been in public use or on sale in this country before the date that the applicant made his invention, a patent cannot be obtained. If the invention has been described in a printed publication anywhere, or has been in public use or on sale in this country more than one year before the date on which an application for patent is filed in this country, a valid patent cannot be obtained. In this connection it is immaterial when the invention was made, or whether the printed publication or public use was by the inventor himself or by someone else. If the inventor describes the invention in a printed publication or uses the invention publicly, or places it on sale, the inventor must apply for a patent before one year has gone by, otherwise any right to a patent will be lost.

Even if the subject matter to be patented is not exactly shown by the prior art, and involves one or more differences over the most nearly similar thing already known, a patent may still be refused if the differences are obvious. The subject matter to be patented must be sufficiently different from what has been used or described before that it may be said to be not obvious to a person having ordinary skill in the area of technology related to the invention. For example, the substitutions of one material for another, or changes in size, are ordinarily not eligible for a patent.

Author Comment: By the time I started my career most high technology companies had started to abandon the patent route. It was recognized that time to market was key and that the time to complete a patent would render the new invention obsolete. Recently there has been resurgence in patents however some of the items being granted patents are absurd and really not defendable if there was serious challenges from organizations with significant resources. Patents made sense when invention was rare and progress was slow, not in our new technology invention based world. However the words used in this process are useful for designers to understand the fundamental elements of innovative designs. There is also a challenge in this new century associated with the concept of ownership and who really owns what in these settings.

5.3.5 General Information

- **WHAT IS A PATENT:** A patent is a grant of a property right by the Government to the inventor to exclude others from making, using or selling the invention. Patents are granted for a term of 17 years, (14 years for design patents) which may be extended only by a special act of Congress (except for certain pharmaceutical patents). After expiration of the term, the patentee loses rights to the invention.
- **WHEN TO OBTAIN A PATENT:** A valid patent may not be obtained if the invention was in public use or on sale in this country for more than one year prior to the filing of your patent application. Your own use and sale of the invention for more than a year before your application is filed will bar

your right to a patent just as effectively as though this use and sale had been done by someone else.

- **WHO MAY OBTAIN A PATENT:** Patents are granted only to the true inventor. Methods of doing business and printed matter cannot be patented. A patent cannot be obtained on a mere idea or suggestion.
- **TYPES OF PATENTS:** The patent law provides for the granting of patents in three major categories:
  - **Utility Patents** are granted to anyone who invents or discovers any new and useful process, machine, manufacture, or compositions of matter, or any new and useful improvement thereof. 'Process' means a process or method; new industrial or technical processes may be patented. 'Manufacture' refers to articles, which are made. 'Composition of matter' relates to chemical compositions and may include mixtures of ingredients as well as new chemical compounds.
  - **Design Patents** are granted to any person who has invented a new, original and ornamental design for an article of manufacture. The appearance of the article is protected.
  - **Plant Patents** are granted to any person who has invented or discovered and asexually reproduced any distinct and new variety of plant, including cultivated sports, mutants, hybrids, and newly found seedlings, other than a tuber-propagated plant or a plant found in an uncultivated state.
- **OWNERSHIP AND SALE OF PATENT RIGHTS:** The inventor may sell all or part of his interest in the patent application or patent to anyone by a properly worded assignment. The application must be filed in the U.S. Patent and Trademark Office as the invention of the true inventor, however, and not as the invention of the person who has purchased the invention from the inventor.
- **PATENT PENDING:** The terms patent pending and patent applied for are used by a manufacturer or seller of an article to inform the public that an application for a patent on that article is on file. The law imposes a fee on those who use these terms falsely.
- **PATENT PROTECTION IN FOREIGN COUNTRIES:** The United States patent protects your invention only in this country. Normally a license must be obtained from the Commissioner of Patents and Trademarks before you can file for a patent in another country, unless the filing in another country occurs more than six months after the filing in this country, in which case no license is necessary.

5.3.6 Who May Apply For A Patent

According to the law, only the inventor may apply for a patent, with certain exceptions. If a person who is not the inventor should apply for a patent, the patent, if it were obtained, would be invalid. The person applying in such a case who falsely states that he / she is the inventor also would be subject to criminal penalties. If the inventor is dead, the legal representatives, administrator, or executor of the estate may make the application. If the inventor is insane, a guardian may make the application for patent. If an inventor refuses to apply for a patent or cannot be found, a joint inventor or a person having a proprietary interest in the invention may apply on behalf of the missing inventor.

If two or more persons make an invention jointly, they apply for a patent as joint inventors. A person who makes a financial contribution is not a joint inventor and cannot be joined in the application as an inventor. It is possible to correct an innocent mistake in erroneously omitting an inventor or in erroneously naming a person as an inventor.

Officers and employees of the Patent and Trademark Office are prohibited by law from applying for a patent or acquiring, directly or indirectly, except by inheritance or bequest, any patent or any right or interest in any patent.

5.3.7 Application For Patent

An application for a patent is made to the Commissioner of Patents and Trademarks and includes:

- Written document which includes a specification (description and claims)
- Drawing in those cases where a drawing is necessary
- An oath or declaration
- Filing fee

The specification and oath or declaration must be legibly written or printed in permanent ink on one side of the paper. The Office prefers typewriting on letter or legal size paper, 8 to 8-1/2 by 10-1/2 to 13 inches, (20.3 to 21.6 by 26.7 to 33.0 cm) 1-1/2 or double-spaced with margins of 1 inch (2.54 cm) on the left-hand side and at the top. If the papers filed are not correctly, legibly, and clearly written, the Patent and Trademark Office may require typewritten or printed papers.

The application for patent is not forwarded for examination until all its required parts, complying with the rules relating thereto, are received. If the papers and parts are incomplete, or so defective that they cannot be accepted as a complete application for examination, the applicant will be notified about the deficiencies and be given a time period in which to remedy them.

5.3.8 Specification Description And Claims

The specification must include a written description of the invention and of the manner and process of making and using it. It is required to be in such full, clear, concise, and exact terms as to enable any person skilled in the technological area to which the invention pertains, or with which it is most nearly connected, to make and use the same.

Author Comment: This is a good read for new designers and organizations that think they do not need specifications. It is also a good guideline to follow when writing specifications and other design information products such as analysis and design documents. The information products can be physical paper, electronic, using traditional written formats and new formats possible with the Internet technologies. For example a web portal can house all the documents describing a design with appropriate hyperlinks. I prefer rocks to house the information to ensure longevity. Digital formats expire about very 5 years, acid free paper can last a few hundred years, and rocks last a long time. You see the issue.

The specification must set forth the precise invention for which a patent is solicited, in such manner as to distinguish it from other inventions and from what is old. It must describe completely a specific embodiment of the process, machine, manufacture, composition of matter or improvement invented, and must explain the mode of operation or principle whenever applicable. The best mode contemplated by the inventor for carrying out his invention must be set forth.

In the case of an improvement, the specification must particularly point out the part or parts of the process, machine, manufacture, or composition of matter to which the improvement relates. The description should be confined to the specific improvement and to such parts as necessarily cooperate with it or as may be necessary to a complete understanding or description of it.

The title of the invention, which should be as short and specific as possible, should appear as a heading on the first page of the specification, if it does not otherwise appear at the beginning of the application.

A brief abstract of the technical disclosure in the specification must be set forth in a separate page immediately following the claims in a separate paragraph under the heading Abstract of the Disclosure.

A brief summary of the invention indicating its nature and substance, which may include a statement of the object of the invention, commensurate with the invention as claimed and any object recited, should precede the detailed description. Such summary should be that of the invention as claimed.

When there are drawings, there shall be a brief description of the several views of the drawings, and the detailed description of the invention must refer to the different views by specifying the numbers of the figures, and to the different parts by use of reference numerals.

The specification must conclude with one or more claims particularly pointing out and distinctly claiming the subject matter that the applicant regards as the invention.

The claims are brief descriptions of the subject matter of the invention, eliminating unnecessary details and reciting all essential features necessary to distinguish the invention from what is old. The claims are the operative part of the patent. Novelty and patentability are judged by the claims. When a patent is granted questions of the courts on the basis of the claims judge infringements.

When more than one claim is presented, the claims may be placed in dependent form in which a claim may refer back to and further restrict one or more preceding claims.

A claim in multiple dependent form must contain a reference, in the alternative only, to more than one claim previously set forth and then specify a further limitation of the subject matter claimed. A multiple dependent claim must not serve as a basis for any other multiple dependent claims. A multiple dependent claim must be construed to incorporate by reference all the limitations of the particular claim in relation to which it is being considered.

The claim or claims must conform to the invention as set forth in the remainder of the specification. The terms and phrases used in the claims must find clear support or antecedent basis in the description so that the meaning of the terms in the claims may be ascertainable by reference to the description. The following order of arrangement should be observed in framing the specification:

1. Title of the invention
2. Cross-references to related applications, if any
3. Brief summary of the invention
4. Brief description of several views of the drawing, if there are drawings
5. Detailed Description
6. Claim or claims
7. Abstract of the disclosure

5.3.9 Drawing

The applicant for a patent will be required by law to furnish a drawing of the invention whenever the nature of the case requires a drawing to understand the invention. However, the Commissioner may require a drawing where the nature of the subject matter admits of it; this drawing must be filed with the application. This includes practically all inventions except compositions of matter or processes, but a drawing also may be useful in the case of many processes.

Author Comment: All designs must have one or more drawings representing different aspects of the design. The drawings must be consistent with the text descriptions of the design. Any inconsistencies are a sign that the design has serious flaws and should not be implemented. The drawings can be physical paper, electronic, using traditional formats and new formats possible with the Internet technologies. For example a web portal can house all the drawings describing a design with appropriate hyperlinks. I prefer rocks to house the drawings to ensure longevity. Digital formats expire about very 5 years, acid free paper can last a few hundred years, and rocks last a long time. You see the issue.

The drawing must show every feature of the invention specified in the claims and is required by the Office rules to be in a particular form. The Office specifies the size of the sheet on which the drawing is made, the type of paper, the margins, and other details relating to the making of the drawing. The reason for specifying the standards in detail is that the drawings are printed and published in a uniform style when the patent issues, and the drawings must also be such that they can be readily understood by persons using the patent descriptions.

No names or other identification will be permitted within the sight of the drawing, and applicants are expected to use the space above and between the hole locations to identify each sheet of drawings. This identification may consist of the attorney's name and docket number or the inventor's name and case number and may include the sheet number and the total number of sheets filed (for example, sheet 2 of 4). The following rule, reproduced from title 37 of the Code of Federal Regulations, relates to the standards for drawings:

(a) **Paper and ink.** Drawings must be made upon paper, which is flexible, strong, white, smooth, non-shiny and durable. India ink, or its equivalent in quality, is preferred for pen drawings to secure perfectly black solid lines. The use of white pigment to cover lines is not normally acceptable.

(b) **Size of sheet and margins.** The size of the sheets on which drawings are made may either be exactly 8 by 14 inches (21.6 by 35.6 cm.) or exactly 21.0 by 29.7 cm. (DIN size A4). All drawing sheets in a particular application must be the same size. One of the shorter sides of the sheet is regarded as its top.

 1. On 8 1/2 by 14 inch drawing sheets, the drawings must include a top margin of 2 inches (5.1 cm) and bottom and side margins of 1/4 inch (6.4 mm) from the edges, thereby leaving a sight precisely 8 by 11-3/4 inches (20.3 by 29.8 cm). Margin borderlines are not permitted. All work must be included within the sight. The sheets may be provided with two 1/4 inch (6.4 mm) diameter holes having their center lines spaced 11/16 inch (17.5 mm) below the top edge and 2-3/4 inches (7.0 cm) apart, said holes being equally spaced from the respective side edges.

 2. On 21.0 by 29.7 cm drawing sheets, the drawing must include a top margin of at least 2.5 cm, a left side margin of 2.5 cm, a right side margin of 1.5 cm, and a bottom margin of 1.0 cm. Margin border lines are not permitted. All work must be contained within a sight size not to exceed 17 by 26.2 cm.

(c) **Character of lines.** All drawings must be made with drafting instruments or by a process that will give them satisfactory reproduction characteristics. Every line and letter must be durable, black, sufficiently dense and dark, uniformly thick and well defined; the weight of all lines and letters must be heavy enough to permit adequate reproduction. This direction applies to all lines however fine, to shading, and to lines representing cut surfaces in sectional views. All lines must be clean, sharp, and solid. Fine or crowded lines should be avoided. Solid black should not be used for sectional or surface shading. Freehand work should be avoided wherever it is possible to do so.

(d) **Hatching and shading.** (1) Hatching should be made by oblique parallel lines spaced sufficiently apart to enable the lines to be distinguished without difficulty. (2) Heavy lines on the shade side of objects should preferably be used except where they tend to thicken the work and obscure reference characters. The light should come from the upper left-hand corner at an angle of 450 degrees. Surface delineations should preferably be shown by proper shading, which should be open.

(e) **Scale.** The drawing scale must be large enough to show the mechanism without crowding when the drawing is reduced in size to two-thirds in reproduction. Views of portions of the mechanism on a larger scale should be used when necessary to show details clearly. Two or more sheets should be used if needed, but the number of sheets should not be more than is necessary.

(f) **Reference characters.** The different views should be consecutively numbered figures. Reference numerals (and letters, but numerals are preferred) must be plain, legible and carefully formed, and not be encircled. They should, if possible, measure at least one-eighth of an inch (3.2 mm) in height so that they may bear reduction to one twenty-fourth of an inch (1.1 mm); and they may be slightly larger when there is sufficient room. They should not be so placed in the close and complex parts of the drawing as to interfere with a thorough comprehension of the same, and therefore should rarely cross or mingle with the lines. When necessarily grouped around a certain part, they should be placed at a little distance, at the closest point where there is available space, and connected by lines with the parts to which they refer. They should not be placed upon hatched or shaded surfaces but when necessary, a blank space may be left in the hatching or shading where the character occurs so that it shall appear perfectly distinct and separate from the work. The same part of an invention appearing in more than one view of the drawing must always be designated by the same character, and the same character must never be used to designate different parts. Reference signs not mentioned in the description shall not appear in the drawing, and vice versa.

(g) **Symbols, legends.** Graphical drawing symbols and other labeled representations may be used for conventional elements when appropriate, subject to approval by the Office. The elements for which such symbols and labeled representations are used must be adequately identified in the specification. While descriptive matter on drawings is not permitted, suitable legends may be used, or may be required in proper cases, as in diagrammatic views and flow sheets or to show materials or where labeled representations are employed to illustrate conventional elements. Arrows may be required, in proper cases, to show direction of movement. The lettering should be as large as, or larger than, the reference characters.

(h) **Views.** The drawing views must contain as many figures as needed to show the invention; the figures should be consecutively numbered if possible in the order in which they appear. The figures may be plain, elevation, section, or perspective views, and detail views of portions of elements, on a larger scale if necessary, also may be used. Exploded views, with the separated parts of the same figure embraced by a bracket, to show the relationship or order of assembly of various parts, are permissible. When necessary, a view of a large machine or device in its entirety may be broken and extended over several sheets, if there is no loss in facility of understanding the view. Where figures on two or more sheets form in effect a single complete figure, the figures on the several sheets should be so arranged that the complete figure can be understood by laying the drawing sheets adjacent to one another. The arrangement should be such that no part of any of the figures appearing on the various sheets is concealed and that the complete figure can be understood even though spaces will occur in the complete figure because of the margins on the drawing sheets. The plane upon which a sectional view is taken should be indicated on the general view by a broken line, the ends of which should be designated by numerals corresponding to the figure number of the sectional view and have arrows applied to indicate the direction in which the view is taken. A moved position may be shown by a broken line superimposed upon a suitable figure if this can be done without crowding; otherwise a separate figure must be used for this purpose. Modified forms of construction can only be shown in separate figures. Views should not be connected by projection lines nor should center lines be used.

(i) **Arrangement of views.** All views on the same sheet should stand in the same direction and, if possible, stand so that they can be read with the sheet held in an upright position. If views longer than the width of the sheet are necessary for the clearest illustration of the invention, the sheet may be turned on its side so that the top of the sheet with the appropriate top margin is on the right-hand side. One figure must not be placed upon another or within the outline of another.

(j) **Figure for Official Gazette.** The drawing should, as far as possible, be so planned that one of the views will be suitable for publication in the Official Gazette as the illustration of the invention.

(k) **Extraneous matter.** Identifying indicia (such as the attorney's docket number, inventor's name, number of sheets, etc.) not to exceed 2-3/4 inches (7.0 cm) in width may be placed in a centered location between the side edges within three-fourths inch (19.1 mm) of the top edge. Authorized security markings may be placed on the drawings provided they are outside the illustrations and are removed when the material is declassified. Other extraneous matter will not be permitted upon the face of a drawing.

(1) **Transmission of drawings.** Drawings transmitted to the Office should be sent flat, protected by a sheet of heavy binder's board, or may be rolled for transmission in a suitable mailing tube; but must never be folded. If received creased or mutilated, new drawings will be required. (See 1.152 for design drawing, 1.165 for plant drawings, and 1.174 for reissue drawings.)

The requirements relating to drawings are strictly enforced, but a drawing not complying with all of the regulations may be accepted for purpose of examination, and correction or a new drawing will be required later.

5.3.10 Models, Exhibits, Specimens

Models are not required in most patent applications since the description of the invention in the specification and the drawings must be sufficiently full and complete and capable of being understood to disclose the invention without the aid of a model. A model will not be admitted unless specifically requested by the examiner. A working model, or other physical exhibit, may be required. For example a working model may be requested in the case of applications for patent for inventions that may not work such as alleged perpetual motion devices.

When the invention relates to a composition of matter, the applicant may be required to furnish specimens of the composition, or of its ingredients or intermediates, for inspection or experiment. If the invention is a microbiological invention, a deposit of the microorganism involved is required.

5.4 Formal Technology Assessment

Technology assessment has always been a part of systems engineering design. However it was more of an ad hoc process closely related to research and development cultures rather than development or production process oriented cultures. That process started to be formalized by NASA in 1974[95]. Some organizations included the activity as part of feasibility analysis and studies[96]. Many

---

[95] NASA researcher, Stan Sadin, conceived the first scale in 1974. It had seven levels, which were not formally. In the 1990s NASA adopted a scale with nine levels which gained widespread acceptance across industry: Technology Readiness Levels Demystified, NASA, August 2010.

[96] Feasibility Analysis is a result of technology assessments and trade studies to justify system design approach. From Systems Engineering Fundamentals, Supplementary Text, Defense Acquisition University Press, January 2001.

project problems and failures have been attributed to poor requirements. However history keeps repeating itself and there is evidence to suggest that in some of these cases there is a lack of understanding the maturity of the technologies for a successful project[97]. Understanding the maturity of the key technologies and identifying the needed technological advancement will help projects to understand their challenges and avoid technology surprises.

Technology assessment consists of performing a Technology Maturity Assessment (TMA) and an Advancement Degree of Difficulty Assessment (AD2).

Technology assessment should start very early in the concept design phase, continue as part of the architecture design development and selection, and proceed during design and implementation. The initial TMA is a baseline maturity of the systems technologies. It allows for monitoring progress as the system unfolds.

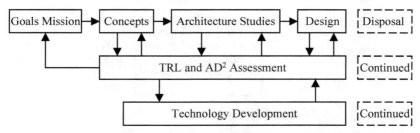

Figure 67 System Life Cycle and Technology Development

Some suggest that the final TMA be performed as part of the preliminary design review. However, key technologies associated with implementation, verification, validation, maintenance, training, installation, switch on, decommissioning, and disposal may need to be understood throughout the systems life. For example disposal may have significant sustainability needs and the technologies may need to be tracked and matured as the system ages but before its disposal and abandonment.

There is a two-way relationship between technology assessment and other system engineering design practices. As a practice design offers a straw man[98] for technology assessment, the assessment offers its findings, which then alters the straw man design approach. This relationship is especially important in the concept and architecture stages. A poor foundation will only lead to serious problems as a system design unfolds.

---

[97] NASA Appendix G Technology Assessment, NASA Systems Engineering Handbook, NASA/SP-2007-6105 Rev1, National Aeronautics and Space Administration NASA Headquarters Washington, D.C. 20546, December 2007.

[98] Straw man is an approach intended to stir debate and discussion to surface disadvantages so that a stronger approach can surface. As an approach becomes more mature and difficult to knock down it is a given name suggesting more mass and strength such as stone-man and iron-man.

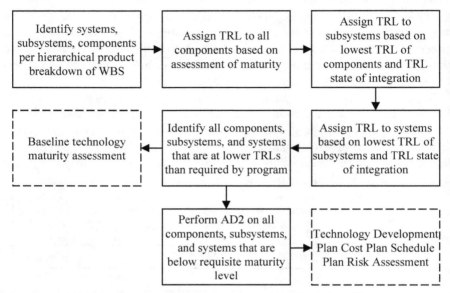

Figure 68 Technology Assessment Process[99]

The technology assessment needs to be done against something tangible and traceable to the project. The problem is that at the early concept stage a system block diagram, architecture, or product break down may be unavailable. A suggestion is to try to list the technologies along side the context diagram or concept diagram. Eventually the technology assessment should be organized by systems, subsystems, and components, which should be traceable to the work break down structure, so that reporting is in a form that facilitates the project cost and schedule tracking mechanisms including Earned Value Management System (EVMS).

Although technology assessment is performed through out the life cycle it is extremely important when considering alternative system architecture designs. Many times architecture design selection is based on the underlying technologies.

Technology assessment is used to determine the need to develop or inject technological advances into a system design. The first step is to determine the current technological maturity of the system design in terms of technology Readiness Levels (TRL). The second is to determine the difficulty with moving a technology from one TRL to the next level using an Advancement Degree of Difficulty Assessment (AD2).

TRL is a gage that measures the state of the art of a technology. There are different TRL scales associated with different organizations. There is overlap between the different scales and some translation may be needed as part of

---

[99] NASA/SP-2007-6105 Rev1, NASA Systems Engineering Handbook, December 2007.

establishing the TRL scale for an organization. The following is a list of different organizations offering TRL scales:

- National Aeronautics and Space Administration (NASA)
- Department of Defense (DOD)
- North Atlantic Treaty Organization (NATO)
- European Space Agency (ESA)
- Federal Aviation Administration (FAA)

Table 39 Technology Readiness Levels - NASA[100]

NASA TRL	Description
1. Basic principles observed and reported.	Lowest level of technology readiness. Scientific research begins to be translated into applied research and development. Examples might include paper studies of a technology's basic properties.
2. Technology concept and / or application formulated.	Invention begins. Once basic principles are observed, practical applications can be invented. The application is speculative, and there is no proof or detailed analysis to support the assumption. Examples are still limited to paper studies.
3. Analytical and experimental critical function and / or characteristic **proof of concept**.	At this step in the maturation process, active research and development (R&D) is initiated. This must include both analytical studies to set the technology into an appropriate context and laboratory-based studies to physically validate that the analytical predictions are correct. These studies and experiments should constitute "proof-of-concept" validation of the applications / concepts formulated at TRL 2.
4. Component and / or **breadboard** validation in **laboratory environment**.	Following successful "proof-of-concept" work, basic technological elements must be integrated to establish that the pieces will work together to achieve concept-enabling levels of performance for a component and / or breadboard. This validation is devised to support the concept that was formulated earlier and also should be consistent with the requirements of potential system applications. The validation is relatively "low-fidelity" compared to the eventual system: it could be composed of ad hoc discrete components in a laboratory.
5. Component and / or **breadboard** validation in **relevant environment**.	At this level, the fidelity of the component and / or breadboard being tested has to increase significantly. The basic technological elements must be integrated with reasonably realistic supporting elements so that the

---

[100] Generic TRL descriptions found in NPR 7123.1, NASA Systems Engineering Processes and Requirements, Table G-19.

Table 39 Technology Readiness Levels - NASA[100]

NASA TRL	Description
	total applications (component-level, subsystem-level, or system-level) can be tested in a "simulated" or somewhat realistic environment.
6. System / subsystem model or **prototype** demonstration in an operation environment.	A major step in the level of fidelity of the technology demonstration follows the completion of TRL 5. At TRL 6, a representative model or prototype system or system, which would go well beyond ad hoc, "patch-cord," or discrete component level breadboarding, would be tested in a relevant environment. At this level, if the only relevant environment is the environment of space, then the model or prototype must be demonstrated in space.
7. System **prototype** demonstration in an operational environment.	Prototype near or at planned operational system. TRL 7 is a significant step beyond TRL 6, requiring an actual system prototype demonstration in a space environment. The prototype should be near or at the scale of the planned operational system, and the demonstration must take place in space. Examples include testing the prototype in a test bed.
8. Actual system competed and "flight qualified" through test and demonstration.	Technology has been proven to work in its final form and under expected conditions. In almost all cases, this level is the end of true system development for most technology elements. This might include integration of new technology into an existing system.
9. Actual system flight proven through successful mission operations	Actual application of the technology in its final form and under mission conditions, such as those encountered in operational test and evaluation. In almost all cases, this is the end of the last "bug fixing" aspects of true system development. This TRL does not include planned product improvement of ongoing or reusable systems.

Although the TRL descriptions appear to be straightforward it is important to define the terms. Moving the domain from Space to a different domain such as Air Traffic Control will add even more confusion further necessitating clear definitions. Without these definitions trying to assign levels even in the Space domain is a challenge. Many will think they can define a breadboard, but not everyone will have the same definition and the alternative definitions may be appropriate. This is a classic communications and perception problem that surfaces when a team starts to work on any problem. A relevant environment in one application may be irrelevant to another. Many of these terms cross engineering fields and had, at one time, very specific meanings to a particular field. The following TRL related definitions and terminology come from NASA[101] and can be used as a starting point:

- **Proof of Concept (TRL 3)**: Analytical and experimental demonstration of hardware / software concepts that may or may not be incorporated into subsequent development and / or operational units.
- **Breadboard Laboratory (TRL 4)**: A low fidelity unit that demonstrates function only, without respect to form or fit in the case of hardware, or platform in the case of software. It often uses commercial and / or ad hoc components and is not intended to provide definitive information regarding operational performance.
- **Breadboard Relevant Environment (TRL 5 - 6)**: Sometimes called a Brassboard, a medium fidelity functional unit that typically tries to make use of as much operational hardware / software as possible and begins to address scaling issues associated with the operational system. It does not have the engineering pedigree in all aspects, but is structured to be able to operate in simulated operational environments in order to assess performance of critical functions.
- **Prototype Unit (TRL 6 - 7)**: The prototype unit demonstrates form, fit, and function at a scale deemed to be representative of the final product operating in its operational environment. A subscale test article provides fidelity sufficient to permit validation of analytical models capable of predicting the behavior of full-scale systems in an operational environment.
- **Engineering Unit (TRL 6 - 8)**: A high fidelity unit that demonstrates critical aspects of the engineering processes involved in the development of the operational unit. Engineering test units are intended to closely resemble the final product (hardware / software) to the maximum extent possible and are built and tested so as to establish confidence that the design will function in the expected environments. In some cases, the engineering unit will become the final product, assuming proper traceability has been exercised over the components and hardware handling.
- **Mission Configuration (TRL 9)**: Final architecture / system design of the product that will be used in the operational environment. If the product is a subsystem / component, then it is embedded in the actual system in the actual configuration used in operation.
- **Laboratory Environment (TRL 1 - 4)**: An environment that does not address in any manner the environment to be encountered by the system, subsystem, or component (hardware or software) during its intended

---

[101] Lists hardware and software TRLs and offers a description of the terminology: Appendix J. Technology Readiness Levels (TRLs), NPR 7120.8, NASA Procedural Requirements, NASA Research and Technology Program and Project Management Requirements, February 05, 2008.

operation. Tests in a laboratory environment are solely for the purpose of demonstrating the underlying principles of technical performance (functions), without respect to the impact of environment.

- **Relevant Environment (nominally TRL 5)**: Not all systems, subsystems, and / or components need to be operated in the operational environment in order to satisfactorily address performance margin requirements. Consequently, the relevant environment is the specific subset of the operational environment that is required to demonstrate critical "at risk" aspects of the final product performance in an operational environment. It is an environment that focuses specifically on "stressing" the technology advance in question.

- **Operational Environment (TRL 6 - 9)**: The environment in which the final product will be operated. In the case of space flight hardware / software, it is space. In the case of ground-based or airborne systems that are not directed toward space flight, it will be the environments defined by the scope of operations. For software, the environment will be defined by the operational platform.

Past experience is needed to make judgment calls on the actual TRL. Even with clear definitions, deciding if a prototype is really a prototype or an engineering breadboard can be challenging. Describing elements in terms of form, fit, and function based on design intent and subsequent performance helps in assessing the TRL.

A team should perform the TRL assessment. Team members can be systems engineers, other engineers, users, and other stakeholders. They do not have to be discipline experts but they must understand the current state of the art technology. Some feel the team should be well balanced and experienced. I feel the team should include young engineers, mathematicians, or scientists who will challenge the status quo. This will obviously require an open non-threatening environment. The questions, especially the obvious questions will stimulate learning and offer different perspectives.

There will be significant discussion when attempting to assign TRL numbers to the various system elements. Sometimes it helps to view the TRL elements from a different perspective. For example a series of questions that frame the TRL can be developed with the accepted set of definitions and terms.

Table 40 Assigning TRL Strategy

NASA TRL Assessment Questions		TRL
1. Has an identical unit been successfully operated / launched in identical configuration / environment?	If Yes	9
If NO then		
2. Has an identical unit in a different configuration / system architecture	If	5

Table 40 Assigning TRL Strategy

NASA TRL Assessment Questions		TRL
been successfully operated in space or the target environment or launched? If so, then this initially drops to TRL 5 until differences are evaluated.	Yes	
If NO then		
3. Has an identical unit been flight qualified but not yet operated in space or the target environment or launched?	If Yes	8
If NO then		
4. Has a prototype unit (or one similar enough to be considered a prototype) been successfully operated in space or the target environment or launched?	If Yes	7
If NO then		
5. Has a prototype unit (or one similar enough to be considered a prototype) been demonstrated in a relevant environment?	If Yes	6
If NO then		
6. Has a breadboard unit been demonstrated in a relevant environment?	If Yes	5
If NO then		
7. Has a breadboard unit been demonstrated in a laboratory environment?	If Yes	4
If NO then		
8. Has analytical and experimental proof-of-concept been demonstrated?	If Yes	3
If NO then		
9. Has concept or application been formulated?	If Yes	2
If NO then		
10. Have basic principles been observed and reported?	If Yes	1
If NO then		
Rethink position regarding this technology.		

Question number two refers to reuse from heritage or previous systems. Apparently, from NASA's point of view, using a proven technology in a new environment or architecture is considered risky and the TRL rating drops significantly. Additional testing is needed for the new use or new environment. If the new environment is sufficiently close to the old environment or the new architecture is sufficiently close to the old architecture then the resulting evaluation could be a TRL 6 or 7, but it is no longer at a TRL 9 rating.

To summarize the TRL assessment findings, a matrix is developed which lists the systems, subsystems, and components and then associates TRL findings with each of the items in the list. The columns identify the categories that are used to determine the TRL ratings. The columns are grouped into the maturity of the units, the environment the units have been operating in, and an assessment of the form fit and function.

The TRL ratings are rolled up in the hierarchy of the list. The TRL of a subsystem is driven by the lowest TRL rating of its components. The TRL of a system is driven by the lowest TRL rating of its subsystems. So the TRL of the system is determined by the lowest TRL present in the system even if it is a single element in a subsystem. Multiple elements at low TRL ratings are addressed in the AD2 process.

TRL Assessment Summary															
	Demonstration Units						Environment				Unit Description				
R Red = Below TRL 3 **Y** Yellow = TRL 3,4 & 5 **G** Green = TRL 6 and above **W** White = Unknown **X** Exists	Concept	Breadboard	Brassboard	Developmental Model	Prototype	Operation Qualified	Laboratory Environment	Relevant Environment	Operational Environment	Live Operations	Form	Fit	Function	Appropriate Scale	Overall TRL
1.0 System															
1.1 Common Console															R
1.1.1 FDDI Interface															
1.1.2 Sector Processor															
1.1.3 Display Processor				X					X		X	X	X	X	G
1.1.4 Display Monitor															
1.1.5 Touch Entry															
1.1.6 Voice Recognition							X				X	X			Y
1.1.7 Voice Synthesis		X													R
1.1.8 Sector Software															
1.1.9 Display Software															
1.1.10 Composite Console															
1.1.11 VSCS Panel	X														R
1.1.12 Overhead Maps															
1.2 Display Record Playback															
1.3 Radar Gateway															
1.4 Communications Gateway															
1.5 Mass Storage Device															
1.6 AERA Processors															

Figure 69 TRL Assessment Summary

Integration affects the TRL of every system, subsystem, and component. All of the elements can be at a higher TRL, but if they have never been integrated as a unit, the TRL will be lower for the unit. How much lower depends on the complexity of the integration.

Applying this process at the system level and then proceeding to lower levels of subsystem and component identifies those elements that require development and sets the stage for the subsequent phase, determining the AD2 levels.

The DOD TRL descriptions and ratings are very similar to the NASA TRL descriptions and ratings. The process used to determine the TRL rating is the same as described for the NASA TRL assessment[102].

Table 41 Technology Readiness Levels - DOD

DOD TRL	Description
1. Basic principles observed and reported	Lowest level of technology readiness. Scientific research begins to be translated into applied research and development. Examples might include paper studies of a technology's basic properties.
2. Technology concept and/or application formulated	Invention begins. Once basic principles are observed, practical applications can be invented. Applications are speculative and there may be no proof or detailed analysis to support the assumptions. Examples are limited to analytic studies.
3. Analytical and experimental critical function and/or characteristic proof of concept	Active research and development is initiated. This includes analytical studies and laboratory studies to physically validate analytical predictions of separate elements of the technology. Examples include components that are not yet integrated or representative.
4. Component and/or breadboard validation in laboratory environment	Basic technological components are integrated to establish that they will work together. This is relatively "low fidelity" compared to the eventual system. Examples include integration of "ad hoc" hardware in the laboratory.
5. Component and/or breadboard validation in relevant environment	Fidelity of breadboard technology increases significantly. The basic technological components are integrated with reasonably realistic supporting elements so it can be tested in a simulated environment. Examples include "high fidelity" laboratory integration of components.
6. System/subsystem model or prototype demonstration in a relevant environment	Representative model or prototype system, which is well beyond that of TRL 5, is tested in a relevant environment. Represents a major step up in a technology's demonstrated readiness. Examples include testing a prototype in a high-fidelity laboratory environment or in simulated operational environment.
7. System prototype demonstration in an operational environment	Prototype near, or at, planned operational system. Represents a major step up from TRL 6, requiring demonstration of an actual system prototype in an operational environment such as an aircraft, vehicle, or space. Examples include testing the prototype in a test

---

[102] Technology Readiness Assessment (TRA) Deskbook, Department Of Defense, May 2005, July 2009. Systems Engineering Fundamentals, Supplementary Text, Defense Acquisition University Press, January 2001. Defense Acquisition Guidebook, Defense Acquisition University, August 2010.

Table 41 Technology Readiness Levels - DOD

DOD TRL	Description
	bed aircraft.
8. Actual system completed and 'flight qualified' through test and demonstration	Technology has been proven to work in its final form and under expected conditions. In almost all cases, this TRL represents the end of true system development. Examples include developmental test and evaluation of the system in its intended weapon system to determine if it meets design specifications.
9. Actual system 'flight proven' through successful mission operations	Actual application of the technology in its final form and under mission conditions, such as those encountered in operational test and evaluation. Examples include using the system under operational mission conditions.

The North Atlantic Treaty Organization (NATO) TRL descriptions and ratings are very similar to the NASA TRL descriptions and ratings except that there is a new level added for basic research. So there is a conscious distinction between basic and applied research. Applied research is worthy of a TRL rating while basic research, although acknowledged, has no TRL value (i.e. the TRL is 0).

Table 42 Technology Readiness Levels - NATO[103]

NATO TRL	Description
0. Basic Research with future Military Capability in mind	Systematic study directed toward greater knowledge or understanding of the fundamental aspects of phenomena and /or observable facts with only a general notion of military applications or military products in mind. Many levels of scientific activity are included here but share the attribute that the technology readiness is not yet achieved.
1. Basic Principles Observed and Reported in context of a Military Capability Shortfall	Lowest level of technology readiness. Scientific research begins to be evaluated for military applications. Examples of Research and Technology (R&T) outputs might include paper studies of a technologys basic properties and potential for specific utility.
2. Technology Concept and / or Application Formulated	Invention begins. Once basic principles are observed, practical applications can be postulated. The application is speculative and there is no proof or detailed analysis to support the assumptions. Example R&T outputs are still mostly paper studies.
3. Analytical and Experimental Critical Function and/or	Analytical studies and laboratory/field studies to physically validate analytical predictions of separate

---

[103] Website, http://www.nurc.nato.int/research/trl.htm, Year 2010.

Table 42 Technology Readiness Levels - NATO[103]

NATO TRL	Description
Characteristic Proof of Concept	elements of the technology are undertaken. Example R&T outputs include software or hardware components that are not yet integrated or representative of final capability or system.
4. Component and/or Breadboard Validation in Laboratory / Field (e.g. ocean) Environment	Basic technology components are integrated. This is relatively low fidelity compared to the eventual system. Examples of R&T results include integration and testing of ad hoc hardware in a laboratory/field setting. Often the last stage for R&T (funded) activity.
5. Component and/or Breadboard Validation in a Relevant (operating) Environment	Fidelity of sub-system representation increases significantly. The basic technological components are integrated with realistic supporting elements so that the technology can be tested in a simulated operational environment. Examples include high fidelity laboratory/field integration of components. Rarely an R&T (funded) activity if it is a hardware system of any magnitude or system complexity.
6. System / Subsystem Model or Prototype Demonstration in a Realistic (operating) Environment or Context	Representative model or prototype system, which is well beyond the representation tested for TRL 5, is tested in a more realistic operational environment. Represents a major step up in a technologys demonstrated readiness. Examples include testing a prototype in a high fidelity laboratory/field environment or in simulated operational environment. Rarely an R&T (funded) activity if it is a hardware system of any magnitude or of significant system complexity.
7. System Prototype Demonstration in an Operational Environment or Context (e.g. exercise)	Prototype near or at planned operational system level. Represents a major step up from TRL 6, requiring the demonstration of an actual system prototype in an operational environment, such as in a relevant platform or in a system-of-systems. Information to allow supportability assessments is obtained. Examples include extensive testing of a prototype in a test bed vehicle or use in a military exercise. Not R&T funded although R&T experts may well be involved.
8. Actual System Completed and Qualified through Test and Demonstration	Technology has been proven to work in its final form and under expected conditions. In almost all cases, this TRL represents the end of Demonstration. Examples include test and evaluation of the system in its intended weapon system to determine if it meets design specifications, including those relating to supportability. Not R&T funded although R&T experts may well be involved.

Table 42 Technology Readiness Levels - NATO[103]

NATO TRL	Description
9. Actual System Operationally Proven through Successful Mission Operations	Application of the technology in its final form and under mission conditions, such as those encountered in operational test and evaluation and reliability trials. Examples include using the final system under operational mission conditions.

The European Space Agency (ESA) TRL descriptions and ratings are very similar to the NASA TRL descriptions and ratings. Instruments and spacecraft sub-systems are classified according to a TRL on a scale of 1 to 9. Levels 1 to 4 relate to creative, innovative technologies before or during mission assessment phase. Levels 5 to 9 relate to existing technologies and to missions in definition phase. If the TRL is too low then a mission risks being jeopardized by delays or cost over-runs.

Table 43 Technology Readiness Levels - ESA

ESA TRL	Level description
1	Basic principles observed and reported
2	Technology concept and/or application formulated
3	Analytical & experimental critical function and/or characteristic proof-of-concept
4	Component and/or breadboard validation in laboratory environment
5	Component and/or breadboard validation in relevant environment
6	System/subsystem model or prototype demonstration in a relevant environment (ground or space)
7	System prototype demonstration in a space environment
8	Actual system completed and "Flight qualified" through test and demonstration (ground or space)
9	Actual system "Flight proven" through successful mission operations

The FAA[104] has taken a slightly different path for the TRL ratings. The first observation is that there are fewer levels. The second is that they have been closely tied to their process, in this case it is associated with human factors. Also there is a concept that to move from one level to another, research products must meet a number of exit criteria.

---

[104] This table and text following this table comes from DOT/FAA/AR-03/43, FAA/NASA Human Factors for Evolving Environments: Human Factors Attributes and Technology Readiness Levels, Human Factors Research and Engineering Division, FAA, April 2003.

Table 44 Technology Readiness Levels - FAA

FAA TRL Description	Exit Criteria
1. Basic Principles Observed / Reported	Initial concept description is provided and is consistent with top-level Concept of Operations; benefits, risks, and research issues are identified.
2. Technology Concept and/or Application Formulated	Research management plan is delivered and FAA Research Management plan is delivered if applicable. Single year benefits assessment showing performance and economic benefits, preliminary safety risk assessment, and preliminary human factors assessment and research plan must be completed.
3. Analytical / Experimental Critical Function or Characteristic Proof-of-Concept	Initial Feasibility report is submitted showing capability is feasible from technical, benefits, safety, and human factors perspectives. Initial analytic or experimental quantification of technical performance metrics shows improvement over baseline.
4. Component and / or Integrated Components Tested in a Laboratory Environment	Research demonstrates capability is feasible from safety, human factors, and development perspectives, and expected benefits outweigh costs based upon human-in-the-loop testing with representative potential users. A FAA baseline Concept of Use for the capability is developed.
5. Components and / or Subsystems Verified in a Relevant Environment	Pre-development prototype is developed and evaluated in a high fidelity environment. This could involve a full mission simulation in a laboratory or a demonstration or test in a field setting. Specifications and design documentation are updated based upon lessons learned in testing. An updated report documents capability feasibility from safety, human factors, and development perspectives and summarizes what has been learned to date. R&D organization continues research on as-built prototype while FAA begins acquisition program baseline definition.
6. System Demonstrated / Validated in a Relevant Environment	Field evaluations demonstrate technical functionality of prototypes, benefits, and resolution of human factors issues. FAA and research organization review capability to determine its readiness to transfer to development organization. An acquisition strategy is required and a development contractor is engaged.

TRL 1: Basic Principles Observed / Reported is the stage at which an Air Traffic Management (ATM) concept is initially identified and described. The appropriate development group analyzes a deficiency or need in the National Airspace System (NAS) for which the capability may be a solution. During this TRL phase, the following should occur: development of an initial operational

concept, completion of a trade/risk/benefit analysis, and identification of research issues. A key concern during this stage is the viability of the operational concept.

The Free Flight Research Program Plan notes that the research organization proceeds relatively independently and coordinates research activities with the FAA during TRLs 1-3 via the Interagency Air Traffic Management Integrated Product Team (IAIPT)[105].

TRL 2: Technology Concept and / or Application Formulated is the stage at which a detailed research plan is developed that provides a definition of the technical solution to the deficiency and identifies critical feasibility issues. The plan describes activities, schedule, likely facilities, and resources required to address research issues in tool development. Human factors research issues including human effectiveness are also identified in this research plan as well as resources necessary to resolve these human factors issues.

TRL 3: Analytical / Experimental Critical Function or Characteristic Proof-of-Concept is the stage during which a conceptual prototype of the tool is developed with initial requirements defined. Initial laboratory evaluations may include part-task computer-human interface (CHI) evaluations, preliminary procedures development, functionality testing, and performance evaluations. The proof-of-concept conceptual design should consider the relationships of roles and responsibilities with the conceptual design and architecture.

To successfully exit from this TRL, initial research should show the tool to be feasible from technical, benefits, safety, and human factors perspectives based on research to date. Also, initial quantification of technical performance metrics should reflect an improvement over the baseline, or if improvement cannot be demonstrated, the cause is understood and improvement is expected at some point.

TRL 4: Component and/or Integrated Components Tested in a Laboratory is the stage during which a research prototype is developed and evaluated by representative potential users. Evaluations may consist of medium-fidelity human-system interface evaluations, procedures evaluation, human performance evaluations, functionality testing, and performance evaluations. The laboratory real time simulation environment is at a higher fidelity level than at TRL 3 using standalone or integrated components. The research organization and the FAA participate in the laboratory and, if appropriate, site evaluations such as a shadow mode or back room test at a field site with user teams. Exiting from this TRL requires development and baselining of an initial FAA Concept of Use for the capability. The cost/benefit analysis is updated, as appropriate.

---

[105] In September 1995, FAA and NASA formed the IAIPT to plan and conduct integrated research related to air-based and ground-based Air Traffic Control (ATC) and Air Traffic Management (ATM) decision support tools and procedures. FAA, NASA, and research partners selected a model of Technology Readiness Levels (TRL) for coordinating various activities, roles, and expectations.

When TRL 4 evaluations are complete, the research team generates an updated feasibility report describing technical progress, life-cycle cost/benefits indicated, current safety and human factors status, and issues that might require a "return to the drawing board." The updated feasibility report is intended as an executive summary of what the team has learned to date and should be more reflective of the operational environment in which the capability is expected to operate.

Formal acquisition involvement begins at TRL 4 as design and architecture requirements are refined. Assessments of procedures along with roles and responsibilities become more robust relative to the range of conditions afforded in the laboratory environment.

TRL 5: Components / Subsystems Verified in a Relevant Environment is the stage during which a pre-development prototype of the tool is developed and evaluated. The evaluation environment should be at a high fidelity such as can be achieved through a full-mission simulation platform or through demonstration in the field with an integrated architecture for representative normal and off-normal traffic conditions. Based upon lessons learned, specifications and design documentation are updated during this TRL.

Also during this TRL, the FAA focuses on activities to prepare for acquisition. The FAA acquisition office forms user teams to address user inputs, specifications, maintenance concepts, concept of use issues, and human factors concerns. FAA will begin to develop contractual documentation such as statements of work and contract data requirements lists.

The research organization will continue on the as-built prototype system while the FAA begins its acquisition program baseline definition. It is FAA policy that research prototype development and evaluation should adhere to the same fundamental paradigm as a full-scale system acquisition that includes early user involvement. The FAA uses prototyping activities in this vein to assist in assessing alternative solutions to an identified mission need.

TRL 6: System Demonstrated / Validated in a Relevant Environment is the stage at which an operational demonstration of the pre-production prototype system is conducted in a FAA field facility if deemed feasible and necessary. Field evaluations may include a substantial demonstration of the prototype's functionality, and could involve a daily use version of the pre-development operational software application. Comprehensive human factors assessment for the prototype capability should be completed to exit TRL 6. The research organization focuses on completing the technology transfer and cost/benefits activities based on data obtained during the field test. Final system engineering documents are produced including system specifications, interface requirements, and design descriptions. It is critical that when operational demonstrations and field evaluations are conducted they involve FAA operational personnel.

During TRL 6, the final high fidelity, integrated system demonstration of the transfer prototype is accomplished, using a large variety of traffic nominal and off-nominal conditions. Documents produced at earlier TRLs will be finalized for formal transfer to the FAA.

Table 45 TRL Human Factors Considerations - FAA[106]

TRL	Pipeline Output	HF Component
1. Basic Principles Observed / Reported	ATM concept initially developed and described	Initial identification of human factors issues
2. Technology Concept and / or Application Formulated	Detailed research plan developed	Preliminary human factors assessment and research plan: - Prioritize human factors research issues - Identify the activities, schedule, and resources required to resolve identified human factors issues
3. Analytical / Experimental Critical Function or Characteristic Proof-of-Concept	Conceptual prototype of tool developed and evaluated; initial feasibility report developed	Address human factors issues identified in TRL 2
4. Component or Integrated Components Tested in a Laboratory Environment	Research prototype developed and evaluated; initial FAA Operational Concept of Use developed and baselined	Assess human factors issues associated with the concept to show how they have been resolved; document human factors research; update human factors plan
5. Components / Subsystems Verified in a Relevant Environment	Pre-development prototype of tool developed and evaluated	Resolve human factors issues from the TRL 4 update
6. System Demonstrated / Validated in a Relevant Environment	Operational demonstration of the pre-production prototype system	Collect human factors data to show that all issues have been addressed and that operations are practicable in nominal and off-nominal conditions

Once there is a TRL assessment the next step is to determine how to move the TRL to the next levels. The Advancement Degree of Difficulty Assessment (AD2) has been suggested[107].

Initial AD2 provides information needed to develop preliminary cost and schedule plans and offer preliminary risk assessments. Detailed AD2 provides information to build a technology development plan in a process that identifies alternative paths, fallback positions, and performance de-scope options. Once an

---

[106] DOT/FAA/AR-03/43, FAA/NASA Human Factors for Evolving Environments: Human Factors Attributes and Technology Readiness Levels, Human Factors Research and Engineering Division, FAA, 2003.

[107] NASA/SP-2007-6105 Rev1, NASA Systems Engineering Handbook, December 2007.

effort is established, the AD2 information is also used to prepare milestones and metrics for subsequent Earned Value Management (EVM) for the project or program.

AD2 is a very tricky subject. On the one hand there is the desire to create a scale and somehow equate that scale to time, cost and risk. On the other hand we know that some technologies can move from TRL 1 to TRL 9 very quickly. The following is an example of a technology that moved from Level 1 to Level 9 in the span of 12 months with little cost.

Example 13 Traceability to the Line of Code

In the late 1990's a process and tool was developed to trace software requirements to the line of code and output the requirements as log data during live testing[108]. This was done to support certification of mission critical systems. The original technology was developed for an E-commerce website to track how and why visitors arrive.

The technology was quickly modified adapted and matured for a pilot program. When it was clear that the technology significantly benefited the pilot program it was successfully rolled out to other programs. This was accomplished within 12 months with little cost.

Each program had their own unique needs and even though a "product model" was used for this technology, the technology or product model was expanded to include new needs. For example on the pilot program the largest test generated a maximum of approximately 1000 log entries representing requirements allocated to the line of code. The second program had tests yielding in excess of 30,000 log entries. The third program had tests yielding in excess of 20 million log entries.

Obviously the technology needed to advance to address the correlation and visualization challenges of the new programs. Without this advancement the verification strategy would have failed with significant cost and schedule impacts.

The big picture was to create a mechanism that would transparently add traceability down to the line of code in software. However no one wants to pay for technology using their budget. In this case there was a strong need to show this traceability to shorten the traditional certification cycle. So there was a desire to investigate the technology and try to make it work.

The details were in the implementation. They included using the new Internet technologies of a web server, browser, and PERL to parse and process the software text. They also include the details of the System Requirements Database and the interface to the mechanism that implemented the traceability to the line of code. The details also included modifications to the process such as code walk through to ensure the traceability was accurate and the test environment to allow for the automated output of the log data.

---

[108] Walt Sobkiw developed this, your Author.

It was estimated that it took approximately 500 hours of computer execution time to mature the PERL implementation. This was in a time when 10 MIP personal computers just surfaced. Just one year earlier and this approach would have proved unfeasible because the 500-hour execution time would have converted to 5000 hours. Perhaps the 5000 hours could have been shortened with the addition of more computers and people however the program would have then rejected the idea and just done things the old way, even though it would have required significant time and resources. So there are many lessons in this example:

- No technology before its time. Some technology's take long times to mature others are very fast.
- Shifting from one domain or application may be less risky than some might suggest.
- It is important to constantly consider new technologies and not be afraid of the initial low TRL rating.
- New technologies work only when the details are addressed but it is important to watch the key gates and decide to cut the losses if the technology gets stuck and is unable to mature.

The AD2 descriptions and rating are the inverse of the TRL ratings. They can be stated as generic tasks that must be performed to move from the current TRL to the next TRL. Obviously the resulting technology plan will contain the details specific to the technology. Each of the AD2 ratings can be given a number and an arbitrary development risk can be applied to each AD2 level.

We see that different organizations have slightly different TRL ratings. In this text the AD2 ratings are numbered 1 - 9 to track to the corresponding TRL ratings. Other approaches may use a reverse AD2 rating scale or a shortened AD2 scale[109].

The AD2 ratings are the inverse of the TRL ratings that are eventually adopted by the organization. In other words if a TRL item addresses a deficiency the AD2 item describes the generic activity to address the deficiency.

Some organizations have more TRL ratings and others have less. What matters is that each organization adopts a standard scale and tries to adhere to the scale so that meaningful comparisons can be made as the portfolio increases. If the scale changes then a translation map should be offered until the transition to the new scales are completed and the organization has internalized the new scales.

There are general maturing activities that are associated with each AD2 level[110].

---

[109] John C. Mankins proposed 5 degrees of difficulty in a White Paper Research & Development Degree Of Difficulty (R&D3) March 10, 1998, Advanced Projects Office, Office of Space Flight NASA Headquarters.

[110] Based on white paper Systematic Assessment of the Program / Project Impacts of Technological Advancement and Insertion, James W. Bilbro George C. Marshall Space

The idea is that you perform these activities to move to the next AD2 level. These activities translate into a potential risk level.

The risk associated with an AD2 item and its activity is arbitrary until the organization develops a significant history at which time a non-linear distribution might be assigned to the AD2 ratings. In this text the risk is uniformly applied across the AD2 items with a jump at AD2 rating 4.

Table 46 AD2 Level and General Maturing Activities

AD2 Level and General Maturing Activities	Status	Risk
1. Requires new development outside of any existing experience base. No viable approaches exist that can be pursued with any degree of confidence. Basic research in key areas needed before feasible approaches can be defined.	Chaos RED	90%+
2. Requires new development where similarity to existing experience base can be defined only in the broadest sense. Multiple development routes must be pursued.	Unknown Unknowns RED	80%
3. Requires new development but similarity to existing experience is sufficient to warrant comparison in only a subset of critical areas. Multiple development routes must be pursued.	Unknown Unknowns RED	70%
4. Requires new development but similarity to existing experience is sufficient to warrant comparison on only a subset of critical areas. Dual development approaches should be pursued in order to achieve a moderate degree of confidence for success. (desired performance can be achieved in subsequent block upgrades with high degree of confidence.	Unknown Unknowns RED	60% normally 50%
5. Requires new development but similarity to existing experience is sufficient to warrant comparison in all critical areas. Dual development approaches should be pursued to provide a high degree of confidence for success.	Known Unknowns Yellow	40%
6. Requires new development but similarity to existing experience is sufficient to warrant comparison across the board. A single development approach can be taken with a high degree of confidence for success.	Well Understood GREEN	30%
7. Requires new development well within the experience base. A single development approach is adequate.	Well Understood GREEN	20%
8. Exists but requires major modifications. A single development approach is adequate.	Well Understood GREEN	10%
9. Exists with no or only minor modifications being required.	Well	00%

Flight Center, December 2006, with acknowledgements: Dale Thomas, Jack Stocky, Dave Harris, Jay Dryer, Bill Nolte, James Cannon, Uwe Hueter, Mike May, Joel Best, Steve Newton, Richard Stutts, Wendel Coberg, Pravin Aggarwal, Endwell Daso, and Steve Pearson.

Table 46 AD2 Level and General Maturing Activities

AD2 Level and General Maturing Activities	Status	Risk
A single development approach is adequate.	Understood GREEN	

5.5 Technology Maturity and Adoption

Every existing system consists of different technologies. Every new system will consist of different technologies. Technologies have a life cycle that represents Technology Maturity (TM). Knowing TM levels in a design is important.

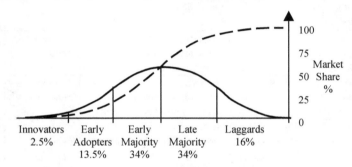

Figure 70 Diffusion of Innovations - Rogers (1962)

In the beginning new technologies are complex, difficult to manage, and have few practitioners. In the end a technology is old overcome by other technologies. Some might assume that because of its age it is easy to manage. However, as many practitioners have moved on to newer technologies there are fewer practitioners making it difficult to manage and complex because of missing information.

Technology adoption occurs in a modified S curve[111] as suggested by the logistics curve and the diffusion of innovation theory[112]. Rogers using more of a bell shape groups the technology curve by Innovators, Early Adopters, Early Majority, Late Majority, and Laggards. These adopters are associated with five stages of TM starting with Bleeding Edge, Leading Edge, State-of-the-Art, Dated, and Obsolete.

Table 47 Technology Adopters and Maturity Levels

Adopters	Numbers	Maturity
1. Innovators	2.5%	Bleeding Edge

---

[111] Pierre François Verhulst (1845) studied the logistic curve in relation to population growth. The S-shaped curve of the initial stage of growth is approximately exponential, as saturation begins the growth slows, and at maturity growth stops.

[112] Technology not initially exponentially adopted, Textbook: Diffusion of Innovations, Everett Rogers, 1962.

Table 47 Technology Adopters and Maturity Levels

Adopters	Numbers	Maturity
2. Early Adopters	13.5%	Leading Edge
3. Early Majority	34%	State of The Art
4. Late Majority	34%	Dated
5. Laggards	16%	Obsolete

5.6 Technology Assessment and Sustainability

There is a huge caution that needs to be addressed with technology assessment. Organizations will try to minimize risk and in the process no new technology will be introduced or considered. In this case it is thought that the competition will remove these organizations as the technology maturity and adoption rates follow their normal course. However what happens if the adoption rate drops across the board in an industry or a nation state?

In many ways organizations have an obligation to push the technology envelopes, just in case there are competitors, but more importantly for a sustainable company, industry, world. So what is a reasonable distribution of TRLs within an organization and how do they relate to different project types?

Just because the TRL is very low it does not mean that the organization is engaged in a healthy research and development activity. The organization might actually be attempting to adopt technologies that other organizations and industries may have abandoned because of obsolescence. One way to prevent this false view of technology is to link the technology maturity level to the TRL. If the TRL reasonably tracks the maturity then the activity is reasonable. There is nothing worse than working with dead technology.

Table 48 Project Types and TRL

Project Types	TRL	Maturity
Basic Research	0 or 1	1
Applied Research	2 or 3	1
Advanced Research	4 or 5	1
Advanced Technology Demonstration	6 or 7	1 or 2
Development Program	8 or 9	1, 2, or 3

5.7 Technology Prediction

Systems are in development and used for several years even if the initial capability might be offered in 6 months. These systems use technologies that are moving. Some are in their infancy, some are maturing, others are being overcome and becoming obsolete. The issue is to understand the maturity of these technologies and make reasonable predictions of where various technologies will be with the initial system delivery, its mid life operations, and its final stages of operations. This requires developing strong relationships[113] with the technology leaders to gain visibility into where they think they will be in 1, 3, 5, and 10 years.

Fundamentally technology is driven by societies needs. Knowing and respecting this relationship is important to technology prediction. So a basic approach to trying to predict technology is to examine existing designs and find the points of pressure where the community is trying to make improvements and then use forecasting by analogy, growth curves, trend curves, and extrapolation. History is also an element that can be used to determine what happened in the past when a new technology surfaced.

For example when audio surfaced in the last century designers were always trying to push the performance in terms of improving the frequency response, reducing noise, and increasing power. This led to the development of new components. Triode tubes led to Tetrodes and Pentodes and Beam Power tubes, then transistors replaced tubes meanwhile transformer coupling was replaced by resistor capacitor coupling and then direct coupling between amplifier stages. So the technology prediction for someone engaged in amplifier design circa 1930 might speculate what the new performance levels might be and when those performance levels might arise. The same argument can be made for miniaturization and how that might impact computing.

These are near term predictions that are based on a community already engaged in a push in a particular direction. In many ways this is what happens in a healthy industry where there are many players each trying to offer the next better product. This scenario unfolded in electronics for:

- Radios
- Televisions
- Stereos
- Tape recorders
- Computers
- Cell Phones
- Smart Phones

Displacement technologies are unexpected. For example the Internet was a displacement technology for many industries. It was developed in one narrow area but then found use in many new areas. Predicting displacement technologies is problematic because they are unanticipated in an industry or across industries.

The tools for technology prediction are not unique. They are general tools used in other systems engineering activities. Although there are quantitative elements to some of the tools the final result is always a qualitative analysis. The tools are:

- **Quantitative Trend Forecasting:** This approach uses data that is placed into different graphs for extrapolation and curve fitting. Some may take the time to perform complex statistical analysis, but the bottom line is the past

---

[113] Non disclosure agreements enable communications between entities.

will rarely predict the future.

- **Qualitative Trend Forecasting:** This approach uses history, analogies, monitoring of activities, and scenarios. When scenarios are considered there are usually three cases: best, nominal, and worst case scenarios.

Author Comment: Today many engaged in education are asking where online learning or E-Learning is going and if this is the demise of the teacher. Many do not realize that simulation and training systems were important elements of the high technology systems using computers, communications, and mechanical platforms. One analogy that can be used is the Semi Automatic Ground Environment (SAGE) and Air Traffic Control (ATC) systems. Initially these systems extended the senses. Then they organized vast amounts of information. The final steps were massive automation starting with simple manual tasks and then attempts at automating the cognitive functions of the humans in the loop.

In the 1980s there was an attempt to add the cognitive decision making processes of the air traffic controller. During that time expert systems and then neural networks were postulated to move the human from an active participant in the control loop to an observer and system manager, as the system would make the decisions. It did not happen. It took from 1945 to 1975 to come to the point where someone might suggest replacing the human in the loop.

Let us now examine online-based education. It is still not on par with the sophistication of the simulation and training systems that became available in the 1960s for the air defense and air traffic control communities. It is big and ubiquitous but not as sophisticated. So it is basically at the 1945 or 1960 level depending on your perspectives. Being able to add the simulation and training capability present in air defense and air traffic control to online learning systems is a few years down the timeline. Then being able to add cognitive processing associated with replacing the teacher is decades away. So one would have to make a strong argument of why the technology would grow fast in online education to replace the teacher in the next few years rather than the next few decades.

Perhaps I am too pessimistic. This should then cause someone to propose a more optimistic scenario in the technology prediction analysis if this were a real setting of an organization engaged in technology prediction using timelines, analogies, and scenarios.

Table 49 Technology Assessment Timeline Analogies

Year	Air Defense	Air Traffic Control	Simulation & Training	E-Learning
1930	communications for extended senses			
1940	RADAR for extended senses	communications for extended		

Table 49 Technology Assessment Timeline Analogies

Year	Air Defense	Air Traffic Control	Simulation & Training	E-Learning
		senses		
1950	computer for organized data System: SAGE	RADAR for extended senses	SAGE used this in air defense computer used for Navy simulator trainer	
1960	SAGE was used as the example for ATC and the Internet.	computer for organized data ATCRBS ATC adopts technology from SAGE	computer & communications for remote learning PLATO	
1970		software for manual automation aids NAS Stage A	computer & communications for alternative instruction paths learning driven by student progress CBI CBT	
1980		expert systems & and neural networks for cognitive processing AERA This level of automation never made it into the system Automation technology plateau	computers, communication, actuators, projectors, software high fidelity simulation and training	
1990	SAGE used as example for Internet, it had full worldwide connectivity in 1950's. Packet	Introduction of GPS for oceanic and navigation Automation technology still	Software, voice recognition & synthesis for pilot free controller training	At extended senses stage

Table 49 Technology Assessment Timeline Analogies

Year	Air Defense	Air Traffic Control	Simulation & Training	E-Learning
	switching was invented in SAGE setting.	plateau		
2000		GPS matured Automation technology still plateau		Automaton aids being added not at level of CBI or real time simulation and training
2010				When will
2020				teachers be
2030				replaced?
2040	AERA: Automated Enroute Air Traffic Control[114] ATCRBS: Air Traffic Control Radar Beacon System CBI: Computer Based Instruction CBT: Computer Based Training GPS: Global Positioning System NAS: National Air Space System PLATO: Programmed Logic for Automatic Teaching Operations RADAR: **Ra**dio **D**etection **A**nd **R**anging SAGE: Semi Automatic Ground Environment[115]			This suggests cognitive processing ATC took 40 years to make a serious attempt at this and they eventually abandoned attempt

Author Comment: The PLATO system pioneered online forums and message boards, email, chat rooms, instant messaging, remote screen sharing, and multi player games, leading to the emergence of what was perhaps the world's first online community. This was two decades before the World Wide Web.

Control Data Corporation dedicated its corporate resources to take PLATO to the business and other communities. Many corporations at the time were engaged in training to support the new complex technology driven systems they were developing. At that time some of the best programmers in the world came from Burroughs Corporation and Control Data Corporation. There was a connection

---

[114] WarGames, movie, writers: Lawrence Lasker, Walter F. Parkes, Walon Green, 1983. Film is about a fully automated defense system that decides to play the ultimate game as the humans try to stop it before its too late.

[115] Colossus: The Forbin Project, movie, writers: James Bridges (screenplay), D.F. Jones (novel), 1970. Film is about a fully automated defense and social monitoring system that starts making its own decisions as the humans try to stop it.

between using these new technologies for training to help staff develop even newer and better technologies outside the training and education areas.

Figure 71 SAGE Computer 1957

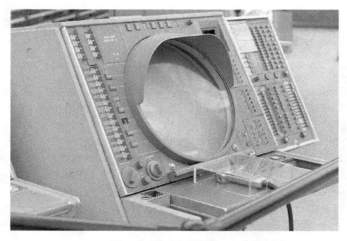

Figure 72 SAGE Console 1957

Figure 73 Navy Simulation and Training System circa 1960

Figure 74 ATC Simulation and Training Consoles 1980

5.8 Technology Selection

At some point the alternative technologies and their selections need to be offered at the conceptual, physical and implementation design stages. As part of this selection there are visualization approaches. The most obvious is to offer ad hoc presentation slides, next is a storyboard, then there are ad hoc outline based text and graphic based documents. An alternative is to use a Morphological Matrix as part of an analysis.

Table 50 Air Traffic Control Technology Morphological Matrix

	Function	1	2	3	4	5	6
A	Display	Mono-chrome stroke	Color stroke	Projection	2Kx2K Raster CRT	Plas-ma	LCD
B	Computer	main-frame	mini	super mini	Micro-processor		
C	Console	metal	composite	desktop			
D	Communication	copper parallel	copper serial	copper CDMA (Ethernet)	fiber CDMA (Ethernet)	token ring fiber bus	
E	Software Language	assembly	JOVIAL	FORTRAN	C/C++	Ada	
F	Operating System	none	single user single processing	single user multi processing	multi processing multi user UNIX		
G	Maintenance	offline manuals	online manuals	message board	expert system		
H	Automation Level	extend senses	organized data	automated manual activities	automated decision making		

The left column shows the functions at the conceptual stage, subsystems at the physical stage, and products or designs at the implementation stage of the design. The row represents possible technologies for the function, subsystem or implementation. The columns are the possible technologies to consider. These technologies can also represent designs that are at a certain level of technology maturity. For example a Liquid Crystal Display (LCD) display is a higher technology choice than a monochrome stroke display.

When we pick the columns for each function we have a design choice based on a certain level of technology. The results for the Air Traffic Control Technology Morphological Matrix are the following possible but not necessarily delivered designs across the years:

Table 51 Air Traffic Control Technology Morphological Analysis

1950	A1	B1	C1	D1	E1	F1	G1	H1	
1960	A1	B1	C1	D1	E1	F1	G1	H2	
1970	A1	B1	C1	D1	E1	F4	G1	H3	
1980	A2 A3	B3	C2	D5	E5	F4	G2	H3 H4	Peak, H4 rejected
1990	A4	B4	C3	D5	E5	F4	G3	H3	Going backwards
2000	A4	B4	C3	D5	E4	F2 F4	G3	H3	E5 rejected F4 rejected
2010	A4	B4	C3	D5	E4	F2 F4	G3	H3	

In the case of the reel to reel tape recorder we see that there are choices that appear to be more aligned with design approaches. However when the design approach is new many will refer to it as a new technology. For example solenoid control was not new but its application in a consumer audio product was considered a major new technology that protected many tapes from rewind and fast forward catastrophes.

Table 52 Reel to Reel Tape Recorder Technology Morphological Matrix

		1	2	3
A	Transport	belt wheel single motor	direct drive 3 motor	
B	Control	mechanical	solenoid	
C	Heads	pressure pad	non glass ferrite	glass ferrite
D	Amplifiers	tube	transistors	integrated circuit
E	Chassis	direct wire	bus card based	
F	Chassis Packaging	separate units	single integrated unit	
G	Recording Bias Control	none	speed controlled	user and speed controlled
H	Equalization	none	speed controlled	user and speed controlled
I	Noise Reduction	none	Dolby	DbX
J	Exterior Packaging	metal	wood grain exterior wood	vinyl exterior plastic
K	VU meters	analog	analog with peak light	digital
L	Controls	rotary analog	slide analog	digital
M	Capstan drive	dc mechanical switch governor with fly wheel	fly wheel ac synchronous	dynamic speed control using audio control

The technology of the reel to reel tape recorder moved very quickly and peaked in early 1980[116]. There was not much more that could be done to the designs as they reached audio perfection. The reel to reel tape recorder technology transitioned into consumer video recorder products[117]. The video recorder would not have been possible with the technology push to have perfect audio recording as found in the reel to reel tape recorder. The video recorder changed television viewing and displaced film cameras for home video recording[118].

Table 53 Reel to Reel Tape Recorder Technology Morphological Analysis

		1960-1965	**1966-1975**	**1975-1980**
A	Transport	1	1	2
B	Control	1	1	2
C	Heads	1	2	3
D	Amplifiers	1	2	3
E	Chassis	1	1	2
F	Chassis Packaging	1	2	2
G	Recording Bias Control	1	2	3
H	Equalization	1	2	3
I	Noise Reduction	1	2	3
J	Exterior Packaging	1	2	2 or 3
K	VU meters	1	2	3
L	Controls	1	2	3
M	Capstan drive	3 for studio 1 for others	3 for studio 2 for others	3 for studio 2 for others

5.9 Function and Performance Allocation

At some point functional requirements and performance budgets need to be allocated to the various system elements. These allocations need to be based on sound analysis. It makes no sense to allocate a budget such as weight to an element if that allocation exceeds the known available products or worse the technologies for that element, and that portion of the weight budget can be easily accommodated by another element.

So technology impact is a key issue that needs to be considered when

---

[116] This is a true credit to Japan. They pushed all consumer electronics to perfection.

[117] Connections, TV Series, 1978, The series explores the various paths of how technological change happens and the social effects of these changes on Western society.

[118] I am a firm believer that the reason the Berlin Wall fell is because of video recorders taping soldiers in their tanks and shouts crying out from the crowds that they would send the tapes of their actions to their parents. This is not said in jest. I have an Aunt who was run over and killed by a Soviet tank in the 1960's. This was before the ubiquitous consumer videocassette recorder and player (VCR).

decomposing and allocating function and performance. This means that someone must always be cognizant of the technology impacts throughout the system engineering effort especially during the architecture development phases. Architecture that is based on an imbalance of technology maturity or worse needlessly uses excessive technology immaturity must be avoided.

5.10 Misuse of Technology

Misuse of technology is an interesting topic. There are different dimensions that should be known to the stakeholders. Most will focus on the simple philosophical case of technology being used for good or bad activities. If it is used for bad activities then it is a misuse of technology. However there are other dimensions to misuse of technology. The following are other perspectives on technology misuse. At what point is technology in a system being misused?

- The technology adds no value to a system
- The technology actually hurts the system but the stakeholders are unaware of the damage
- The technology hurts the system, the stakeholders are aware of the damage, but are powerless to stop using it

- The technology is prematurely abandoned
- The technology is stopped because of status quo
- The technology is viewed as a commodity

- The technology only appeals to the ego
- The technology is poorly understood
- The technology is not sustainable

At what point does misuse of technology translate into deviant design practices? Systems thinking should prevent deviant design practices and misuse of technology. Some deviant design practices and misuse of technology are:

- Wasting peoples time by forcing useless actions especially for ulterior motives
- Fooling or deceiving people into taking undesired actions especially when the user is harmed
- Manipulating biological systems to mask poor system performance while doing harm to the biological system
- Manipulating biological systems to mask poor system performance even though there is no harm
- Consciously reducing performance even though the technology supports

much higher levels of performance at no additional cost
- Reducing performance to allow large quantity but undesired low quality content when performance can match technology with a reasonable quantity level of high quality content
- Ignoring scientific knowledge and previous experience especially as related to human factors
- Using technology to compromise inalienable rights

When we look at a system from a functional or requirements point of view we see that there are root functions and requirements. From the roots other elements are identified via decomposition until we reach a natural limit where no more decomposition is possible. These are the leaves or primitives. We also see that there are core functions and requirements. Without this core, the system does not exist.

So if inalienable[119] rights is a core root requirement where does the decomposition lead? The most famous first level decomposition is "life, liberty, and the pursuit of happiness" from the United States Declaration of Independence. Are there other decompositions from the key requirement of technology not compromising inalienable right? The following is a possible list:

- Technology that does not violate peoples inalienable rights to privacy. This is interesting because inalienable or natural rights are not dependent on cultural or government laws, customs, or beliefs.
- Technology that does not knowingly harm people. Knowingly harm is based on some human in some setting knowing the technology can cause harm to the uninformed or misinformed.
- Technology that does not place a significant burden on a people or society. This is where people become slaves to the technology regardless of benefit. It is most egregious if the benefit is small or nonexistent.

5.11 Technology Infusion

At one time technology infusion was not a difficult political task. It was accepted that technology was good and more technology would lead to more good. It was also thought that technology was precious and difficult to mature and apply where needed. However, in the last two decades of the previous century some have come to think that technology is a commodity to be enabled and disabled when it makes financial sense. The reality is technology can and has been lost and that form of thinking will lead to an unsustainable world. Our world relies on technology for growth and stability. Technology is very precious.

Technology either can be pushed into an organization or pulled by an

---

[119] Inalienable rights are self evident and universal.

organization. So technology has a characteristic associated with user acceptably.

If the originators of the mission concept, the system stakeholders, identify the technology as needed, then it is pull.

If technologists surface a technology that is a potential solution to a system or enables an entirely new concept then it is push.

Once system stakeholders accept it, it becomes pull. It remains pull until it is either successfully integrated into the mission architecture or rejected as not applicable or unsuccessful. So the trick is to convert technology acceptance into a pull activity. This is the source inspiration for great designs. They are designs that people need or want that push technology and quality to new boundaries.

Table 54 Technology Infusion TRL and TM impacts

Conceptual Designs	Initial TRL	Initial TM	Final TRL	Final TM	Make	Buy	Modify
Concept 1	-	-	-	-	-	-	-
Subsystem A	8	Obsolete	9	Dated			X
Subsystem B	9	Obsolete	Same	Same		X	
Concept 2	-	-	-	-	-	-	-
Subsystem A	1	Bleeding Edge	9	Same	X		X
Subsystem B	6	Bleeding Edge	9	Same	X		

During the conceptual design we discussed the approaches for surfacing the design alternatives. They are:

- Design by generalizations of existing designs
- Design by technology choices
- Design by functional performance choices

The following tables are modifications of the design approaches tables offered during the conceptual architecture design discussion once technology is factored into the picture.

Table 55 Design by Generalizations of Existing Designs and Technology

Vendors	TRL	TM	Concept A	Concept B	Concept C
Subsystem 1 of n					
Vendor Product 1	8	Dated	X		
Vendor Product 2	8	Dated	X		
Vendor Product 3	9	Bleeding Edge			X
General Product a	8	Obsolete			X
General Product b	8	State-of-Art			X

Table 55 Design by Generalizations of Existing Designs and Technology

Vendors	TRL	TM	Concept A	Concept B	Concept C
General Product c	8	State-of-Art		X	
General Product d	9	State-of-Art		X	
General Product e	9	State-of-Art		X	

Table 56 Design by Technology Choices and Technology

Technologies	TRL	TM	Concept A	Concept B	Concept C
Subsystem 1 of n					
Technology 1.1	9	Bleeding Edge	X		
Technology 1.2	5	Obsolete		X	
Technology 1.3	5	Obsolete			X
Technology 1.4	7	Dated			
Subsystem 2 of n					
Technology 2.1	7	Date	X		
Technology 2.2	5	State-of-Art			X
Technology 2.3	4	Leading Edge		X	

Table 57 Design by Functional Performance Choices and Technology

Function Choices	TRL	TM	Concept A	Concept B	Concept C
Function F1	8	Bleeding Edge	X	X	X
Function F2	7	Obsolete	X	X	
Function F3	7	Obsolete	X	X	X
Function F4	9	Dated	X	X	X
Function F5	9	Unknown			
Function F6	7	Dated			
Function F7	8	State-of-Art	X		X
Function F8	7	Leading Edge		X	X
Function F9	7	State-of-Art		X	X
Performance P1	6	Leading Edge	X		
Performance P2	6	Bleeding Edge	X	X	
Performance P3	7	Dated		X	
Performance P4	8	State-of-Art			X
Performance P5	7	Leading Edge	X	X	X

5.12 Organization Longevity and Research & Development

Organizations need to have some level of research and development to feed the pipeline so that in later year's systems can be fielded. Just because innovators arrive, it does not mean that there always will be early adopters. The solution could be abandoned by another approach or overcome by other technologies. There could be a failure at each stage of the maturity curve where a solution is displaced. The maturity curve in many ways represents only the most successful solutions, products, or systems. It is an idealized representation. A solution can even fail at the Innovators stage.

Table 58 Research and Development Success Scenarios

Adopters	No	Maturity	Scenarios			
1. Innovators	2.5%	Bleeding Edge	S	S	S	S
2. Early Adopters	13.5%	Leading Edge	F	S	S	S
3. Early Majority	34%	State of The Art	-	F	S	S
4. Late Majority	34%	Dated	-	-	F	S
5. Laggards	16%	Obsolete	-	-	-	F
		Total Market Reached	2.5%	16%	50%	84%

An organization can be evaluated for technology maturity. The technology maturity evaluation consists of the process, tools, and product for each product, product line, or system. This information can be used to visualize the remaining market and compare it with assessments from marketing staff. At some point a product, product line, or system needs technology infusion for it to become viable from a business point of view.

Table 59 Organizational Technology Maturity Assessment

Business	Product	Process	Tool	Product	Remaining Market
Area 1	product 1	Leading	Dated	Bleeding	100%
	product 2	Bleeding	Leading	Leading	84%
	product n	Obsolete	Obsolete	Obsolete	16%
Area 2	product 1	Dated	Obsolete	State of Art	50%
	product 2	Bleeding	Leading	Dated	16%

A product, product line, or system can be evaluated for Technology Readiness Levels (TRL) to support market expansion goals. The TRL evaluation consists of determining the TRL of each product for different domains such as air, land, sea, space or military, industrial, commercial. This can be used to determine the level of difficulty of moving to a new customer base.

For example a product may be considered obsolete with one customer base but state of the art for another customer base. For example a product that is obsolete for a Space based system may be considered state-of-the-art for a commercial application. Alternatively a commercial product may be considered state-of-the-art but leading edge for a military based system. The trick is to determine how to commercialize a Space based product or to military harden a commercial product.

When assessing a product for application in a new domain there are always key requirements that need to be addressed. For example sea applications need to protect against salt fog. Space applications need to protect against radiation. Air applications need to protect against vibration. Land applications need to protect against mud and rain. Air traffic control needs to be very fault tolerant, while military and industrial applications may be fault tolerant. Removing fault tolerance is easier than building in new levels of fault tolerance.

Table 60 Organizational Technology Readiness Levels Assessment

Domain	Prod 1	Prod n	Domain	Prod 1	Prod n
Space	5	9	Military	9	8-5
Sea	9	8-5	Air Traffic Control	9-5	9
Air	8-5	8-5	Industrial	8-5	9-5
Land	8-5	8-5	Commercial	8-5	8-5

5.13 Technology Discussion

The following discussion is associated with fuel cell technology. The technology alternatives are identified, described, and then there is a small tradeoff comparison analysis[120]. These technologies can be viewed as design alternatives. This raises the question of what is the difference between technology and design? Design exists when a technology is applied to satisfy a need.

Example 14 Fuel Cell Technologies and Designs

Fuel cells are classified by the kind of electrolyte they use. The electrolyte determines the chemical reactions, catalysts, operational temperature range, and fuel required. The resulting characteristics drive the applications the potential applications. There are several fuel cell technologies currently under development, each with its own advantages, limitations, and potential applications.

- Polymer Electrolyte Membrane (PEM) Fuel Cells
- Direct Methanol Fuel Cells
- Alkaline Fuel Cells
- Phosphoric Acid Fuel Cells
- Molten Carbonate Fuel Cells
- Solid Oxide Fuel Cells
- Regenerative Fuel Cells
- Comparison of Fuel Cell Technologies

---

[120] US Department of Energy, Energy Efficiency and Renewable Energy, February 2011, http://www.hydrogenandfuelcells.energy.gov accessed October 2013.

The intent of the following discussion is not to dive deep into fuel cell technologies[121] but to offer an example of the technology discussion that could be part of a design effort. This discussion is only a guideline.

PEM Fuel Cells

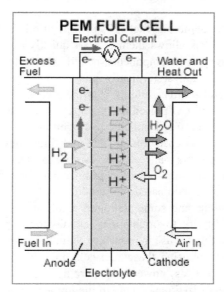

Figure 75 Polymer Electrolyte / Proton Exchange Membrane Fuel Cell

The Polymer Electrolyte Membrane (PEM) also called Proton Exchange Membrane fuel cell consists of a polymer electrolyte membrane sandwiched between an anode (negatively charged electrode) and a cathode (positively charged electrode). The processes that take place in the fuel cell are:

1. Hydrogen fuel is channeled through field flow plates to the anode on one side of the fuel cell, while oxygen from the air is channeled to the cathode on the other side of the cell.
2. At the anode, a platinum catalyst causes the hydrogen to split into positive hydrogen ions (protons) and negatively charged electrons.
3. The Polymer Electrolyte Membrane (PEM) allows only the positively charged ions to pass through it to the cathode. The negatively charged electrons must travel along an external circuit to the cathode, creating an electrical current.
4. At the cathode, the electrons and positively charged hydrogen ions combine

---

[121] Energy Efficiency and Renewable Energy, U.S. Department of Energy, February 2011.

with oxygen to form water, which flows out of the cell.

PEM fuel cells use a solid polymer as an electrolyte and porous carbon electrodes containing a platinum catalyst. They need only hydrogen, oxygen from the air, and water to operate and do not require corrosive fluids like some fuel cells. They are typically fueled with pure hydrogen supplied from storage tanks or on-board reformers.

Polymer electrolyte membrane fuel cells operate at relatively low temperatures, around 80°C (176°F). This allows them to start quickly (less warm-up time) and results in less wear on system components, resulting in better durability. However, it needs a noble-metal catalyst (typically platinum) to be used to separate the hydrogen's electrons and protons, adding to system cost. The platinum catalyst is also extremely sensitive to CO poisoning, making it necessary to use an additional reactor to reduce CO in the fuel gas if the hydrogen is derived from an alcohol or hydrocarbon fuel. This adds cost. Researchers and future developers are exploring platinum / ruthenium catalysts that are more resistant to CO.

PEM fuel cells deliver high-power density and offer the advantages of low weight and volume once compared with other fuel cells. They are used for transportation applications and some stationary applications. Because of their fast startup time, low sensitivity to orientation, and favorable power-to-weight ratio, PEM fuel cells are suitable for use in passenger vehicles, such as cars and buses.

A significant issue for using these fuel cells in vehicles is hydrogen storage. Most fuel cell vehicles (FCVs) powered by pure hydrogen store the hydrogen as a compressed gas in pressurized tanks. Due to the low-energy density of hydrogen, it is difficult to store enough hydrogen on-board to allow vehicles to travel the same distance as gasoline-powered vehicles before refueling, typically 300 to 400 miles. Higher-density liquid fuels, such as methanol, ethanol, natural gas, liquefied petroleum gas, and gasoline, can be used for fuel, but the vehicles must have an on-board fuel processor to reform the methanol to hydrogen. This increases costs and maintenance. The reformer also releases carbon dioxide (a greenhouse gas), though less than that emitted from current gasoline-powered engines.

Direct Methanol Fuel Cells

Most fuel cells are powered by hydrogen, which can be fed directly or can be generated within the fuel cell system by reforming hydrogen-rich fuels such as methanol, ethanol, and hydrocarbon fuels. Direct methanol fuel cells (DMFCs) are powered by pure methanol, which is mixed with steam and fed directly to the fuel cell anode.

Direct methanol fuel cells do not have many of the fuel storage problems typical of some fuel cells because methanol has a higher energy density than hydrogen but less than gasoline or diesel fuel. Methanol is also easier to transport and supply to the public using our current infrastructure because it is a liquid, like gasoline.

Direct methanol fuel cell technology is relatively new compared with pure hydrogen fuel cells, and DMFC research and development is roughly 3 to 4 years behind that for other fuel cell types.

Alkaline Fuel Cells

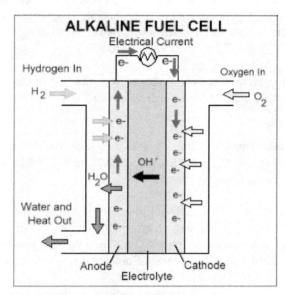

Figure 76 Alkaline Fuel Cell

An Alkaline Fuel Cell (AFC) consists of an alkaline electrolyte, typically potassium hydroxide (KOH), sandwiched between an anode (negatively charged electrode) and a cathode (positively charged electrode). The processes that take place in the fuel cell are:

1. Hydrogen fuel is channeled through field flow plates to the anode on one side of the fuel cell, while oxygen from the air is channeled to the cathode on the other side of the cell.
2. At the anode, a platinum catalyst causes the hydrogen to split into positive hydrogen ions (protons) and negatively charged electrons.
3. The positively charged hydrogen ions react with hydroxyl (OH-) ions in the electrolyte to form water.
4. The negatively charged electrons cannot flow through the electrolyte to reach the positively charged cathode, so they must flow through an external circuit, forming an electrical current.
5. At the cathode, the electrons combine with oxygen and water to form the hydroxyl ions that move across the electrolyte toward the anode to continue the

process.

AFCs were one of the first fuel cell technologies developed, and they were the first used widely in the U.S. space program to produce electrical energy and water on-board spacecrafts. The fuel cells use a solution of potassium hydroxide in water as the electrolyte and can use a variety of non-precious metals as a catalyst at the anode and cathode. High-temperature AFCs operate at temperatures between 100°C and 250°C (212°F and 482°F). However, newer AFC designs operate at lower temperatures of roughly 23°C to 70°C (74°F to 158°F).

AFCs' high performance is a direct result of the rate of the chemical reactions taking place in the cell. They have demonstrated efficiencies near 60% in space applications.

Author Comment: Note that a system or subsystem design needs to select a fuel cell technology. At the same time the individual fuel cell is undergoing design, trying to push the performance envelopes.

The disadvantage of this fuel cell technology is that it is easily poisoned by carbon dioxide (CO_2). Even the small amount of CO_2 in the air can affect the cell's operation, making it necessary to purify both the hydrogen and oxygen used in the cell. This purification process is costly. Susceptibility to poisoning also affects the cell's lifetime. This affects the life cycle costs.

Cost is less of a factor for remote locations, such as space or under the sea. However, to effectively compete in most mainstream commercial markets, these fuel cells need to be more cost-effective. AFC stacks have been shown to maintain sufficiently stable operation for more than 8,000 operating hours. To be economically viable in large-scale utility applications, these fuel cells need to reach operating times exceeding 40,000 hours, something that has not yet been achieved due to material durability issues. This obstacle is possibly the most significant in commercializing this fuel cell technology.

Phosphoric Acid Fuel Cells

A Phosphoric Acid Fuel Cell (PAFC) uses liquid phosphoric acid electrolyte sandwiched between an anode (negatively charged electrode) and a cathode (positively charged electrode). The processes that take place in the fuel cell are:

1. Hydrogen fuel is channeled through field flow plates to the anode on one side of the fuel cell, while oxygen from the air is channeled to the cathode on the other side of the cell.
2. At the anode, a platinum catalyst causes the hydrogen to split into positive

hydrogen ions (protons) and negatively charged electrons.

3. The phosphoric acid electrolyte allows only the positively charged ions to pass through it to the cathode. The negatively charged electrons must travel along an external circuit to the cathode, creating an electrical current.

4. At the cathode, the electrons and positively charged hydrogen ions combine with oxygen to form water, which flows out of the cell.

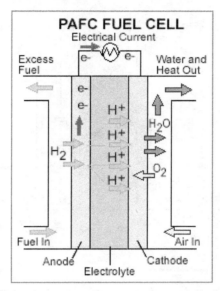

Figure 77 Phosphoric Acid Fuel Cell

Phosphoric acid fuel cells use liquid phosphoric acid as an electrolyte and porous carbon electrodes containing a platinum catalyst. The acid is contained in a Teflon-bonded silicon carbide matrix.

The PAFC is considered the first generation of modern fuel cells. It is one of the most mature cell types and the first to be used commercially. This type of fuel cell is typically used for stationary power generation, but some PAFCs have been used to power large vehicles such as city buses.

PAFCs are more tolerant of impurities in fossil fuels that have been reformed into hydrogen than PEM cells, which are easily poisoned by carbon monoxide because carbon monoxide binds to the platinum catalyst at the anode, decreasing the fuel cell's efficiency. They are 85% efficient when used for the co-generation of electricity and heat but less efficient at generating electricity alone (37%–42%). This is only slightly more efficient than combustion-based power plants, which typically operate at 33% to 35% efficiency. PAFCs power output per unit of weight and size is less other fuel cells, so they take up more space and weight. As a result, these fuel cells are typically large and heavy. Like PEM fuel cells, PAFCs require an expensive platinum catalyst, which raises the cost of the fuel cell. PAFCs are expensive.

Molten Carbonate Fuel Cells

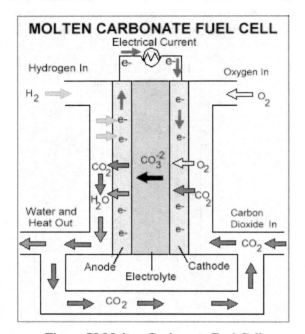

Figure 78 Molten Carbonate Fuel Cells

A Molten Carbonate Fuel Cell (MCFC) consists of an electrolyte, typically a molten carbonate salt mixture suspended in a ceramic matrix, sandwiched between an anode (negatively charged electrode) and a cathode (positively charged electrode). The processes that take place in the fuel cell are:

1. Hydrogen fuel is channeled through field flow plates to the anode on one side of the fuel cell, while oxygen from the air, carbon dioxide, and electricity (electrons from the fuel cell circuit) are channeled to the cathode on the other side of the cell.
2. At the cathode, the oxygen, carbon dioxide, and electrons react to form positively charged oxygen ions and negatively charged carbonate ions.
3. The carbonate ions move through the electrolyte to the anode.
4. At the anode, a catalyst causes the hydrogen to combine with the carbonate ions, forming water and carbon dioxide and releasing electrons.
5. The electrolyte does not allow the electrons to pass through it to the cathode, forcing them to flow through an external circuit to the cathode. This flow of electrons forms an electrical current.

6. The carbon dioxide formed at the anode is often recycled back to the cathode.

MCFCs are currently being targeted for natural gas and coal-based power plants for electrical utility, industrial, and military applications. MCFCs are high-temperature fuel cells that use an electrolyte composed of a molten carbonate salt mixture suspended in a porous, chemically inert ceramic lithium aluminum oxide (LiAlO2) matrix. Because they operate at extremely high temperatures of 650°C (roughly 1,200°F) and above, non-precious metals can be used as catalysts at the anode and cathode, reducing costs.

Improved efficiency is another reason MCFCs offer significant cost reductions over phosphoric acid fuel cells (PAFCs). Molten carbonate fuel cells, when coupled with a turbine, can reach efficiencies approaching 65%, considerably higher than the 37% to 42% efficiencies of a phosphoric acid fuel cell plant. When the waste heat is captured and used, overall fuel efficiencies can be as high as 85%.

Unlike alkaline, phosphoric acid, and polymer electrolyte membrane fuel cells, MCFCs do not require an external reformer to convert more energy-dense fuels to hydrogen. Because of the MCFCs high operational temperatures, these fuels are converted to hydrogen within the fuel cell itself by a process called internal reforming, which also reduces cost.

Molten carbonate fuel cells are not prone to carbon monoxide or carbon dioxide poisoning, they can even use carbon oxides as fuel, making them more attractive for fueling with gases made from coal. Because they are more resistant to impurities than other fuel cell types, some suggest they could be capable of internal reforming of coal. This is assuming they can be made resistant to impurities such as sulfur and particulate that result from converting coal into hydrogen. Coal is a dirtier fossil fuel source than many others.

The primary disadvantage of current MCFC technology is durability. The high temperatures at which these cells operate and the corrosive electrolyte used accelerate component breakdown and corrosion, decreasing cell life. Investigators are exploring corrosion-resistant materials for components as well as fuel cell designs that increase cell life without decreasing performance.

Solid Oxide Fuel Cells

A Solid Oxide Fuel Cell (SOFC) consists of a non-porous metal oxide electrolyte (typically zirconium oxide) sandwiched between an anode (negatively charged electrode) and a cathode (positively charged electrode). The processes that take place in the fuel cell:

1. Hydrogen fuel is channeled through field flow plates to the anode on one side of fuel cell, while oxygen from the air is channeled to the cathode on the other side of the cell.

2. At the cathode, a catalyst causes electrons from the electrical circuit to combine with oxygen to create negatively charged oxygen ions.
3. The negatively charged oxygen ions flow through the electrolyte to the anode.
4. At the anode, the catalyst causes the hydrogen to react with the oxygen ions forming water and free electrons.
5. The negatively charged electrons cannot flow through the electrolyte to reach the positively charged cathode, so they must flow through an external circuit, forming an electrical current. 6. At the cathode, the electrons combine with oxygen to create negatively charged oxygen ions, and the process repeats.

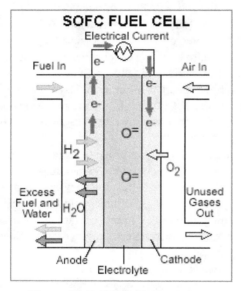

Figure 79 Solid Oxide Fuel Cells

SOFCs use a hard, non-porous ceramic compound as the electrolyte. Because the electrolyte is a solid, the cells do not have to be constructed in the plate-like configuration typical of other fuel cell types. SOFCs are expected to be 50% to 60% efficient at converting fuel to electricity. In applications designed to capture and use the system's waste heat (co-generation), overall fuel use efficiencies could top 80% to 85%.

Solid oxide fuel cells operate at very high temperatures, near 1,000°C (1,830°F). High-temperature operation removes the need for precious-metal catalyst, reducing cost. It also allows SOFCs to reform fuels internally, which enables the use of a variety of fuels and reduces the cost associated with adding a reformer to the system.

SOFCs are also the most sulfur-resistant fuel cell type; they can tolerate several orders of magnitude more of sulfur than other cell types. In addition, they are not poisoned by carbon monoxide (CO), which can even be used as fuel. This property allows SOFCs to use gases made from coal.

The high-temperature operation disadvantages are slow startup and significant thermal shielding to retain heat and protect personnel. This may be acceptable for utility applications but not for transportation and small portable applications. The high operating temperatures also place stringent durability requirements on materials. The development of low-cost materials with high durability at cell operating temperatures is the key technical challenge facing this technology.

Investigators are currently exploring the potential for developing lower-temperature SOFCs operating at or below 800°C that have fewer durability problems and cost less. Lower-temperature SOFCs produce less electrical power, however, and stack materials that will function in this lower temperature range have not been identified.

Regenerative Fuel Cells

Regenerative fuel cells produce electricity from hydrogen and oxygen and generate heat and water as byproducts, just like other fuel cells. However, regenerative fuel cell systems also can use electricity from solar power or some other source to divide the excess water into oxygen and hydrogen fuel. This process is called electrolysis. This is a comparatively young fuel cell technology being developed by NASA and others.

Fuel Cell Technologies Summary

The following tables summarize the fuel cell technologies. These are some but not all of the considerations. This analysis could be coupled with a list of vendors and delivered systems using the technologies. A time line would also provide further insight into the technologies including their maturity curves.

Table 61 Fuel Cell Technologies Construction and Applications

Fuel Cell Type	Common Electrolyte	Applications
Polymer Electrolyte Membrane (PEM)	Perfluoro sulfonic acid	Backup power Portable power Distributed generation Transpiration Specialty vehicles
Direct Methanol Fuel Cells (DMFC)	Unknown	Unknown
Alkaline (AFC)	Aqueous solution of potassium hydroxide soaked in a matrix	Military Space

Table 61 Fuel Cell Technologies Construction and Applications

Fuel Cell Type	Common Electrolyte	Applications
Phosphoric Acid (PAFC)	Phosphoric acid soaked in a matrix	Distributed generation
Molten Carbonate (MCFC)	Solution of lithium, sodium, and/ or potassium carbonates, soaked in a matrix	Electric utility Distributed generation
Solid Oxide (SOFC)	Yttria stabilized zirconia	Auxiliary power Electric utility Distributed generation
Regenerative Fuel Cells	Unknown	Unknown

Table 62 Fuel Cell Technologies Characteristics

Fuel Cell Type	Operating Temperature	Typical Stack Size	Efficiency
Polymer Electrolyte Membrane (PEM)	50-100°C 122-212° typically 80°C	< 1kW–100kW	60% transportation 35% stationary
Direct Methanol Fuel Cells (DMFC)	Unknown	Unknown	Unknown
Alkaline (AFC)	90-100°C 194-212°F	10–100 kW	60%
Phosphoric Acid (PAFC)	150-200°C 302-392°F	400 kW 100 kW module	40%
Molten Carbonate (MCFC)	600-700°C 1112-1292°F	300 kW-3 MW 300 kW module	45-50%
Solid Oxide (SOFC)	700-1000°C 1202-1832°F	1 kW–2 MW	60%
Regenerative Fuel Cells	Unknown	Unknown	Unknown

Table 63 Fuel Cell Technologies Advantages Disadvantages

Fuel Cell Type	Advantages	Disadvantages
Polymer Electrolyte Membrane (PEM)	Solid electrolyte reduces corrosion & electrolyte management problems Low temperature Quick start-up	Expensive catalysts Sensitive to fuel impurities Low temperature waste heat
Direct Methanol Fuel Cells (DMFC)	Unknown	Unknown

Table 63 Fuel Cell Technologies Advantages Disadvantages

Fuel Cell Type	Advantages	Disadvantages
Alkaline (AFC)	Cathode reaction faster in alkaline electrolyte, leads to high performance Low cost components	Sensitive to CO_2 in fuel and air Electrolyte management
Phosphoric Acid (PAFC)	Higher temperature enables CHP Increased tolerance to fuel impurities	Pt catalyst Long start up time Low current and power
Molten Carbonate (MCFC)	High efficiency Fuel flexibility Can use a variety of catalysts Suitable for CHP	High temperature corrosion and breakdown of cell components Long start up time Low power density
Solid Oxide (SOFC)	High efficiency Fuel flexibility Can use a variety of catalysts Solid electrolyte Suitable for CHP & CHHP Hybrid/GT cycle	High temperature corrosion and breakdown of cell components High temperature operation requires long start up time and limits
Regenerative Fuel Cells	Unknown	Unknown

5.14 Technology and Great Designs Process

A process table is not appropriate. Instead the following text is offered.

Author Comments: Technology, The Internet, and Organizations circa 1997.

I have been watching this interchange for a while and I really wanted to stay out of this discussion, but my funny bone has been hit...

A long time ago in a far away place there was an engineer who loved machines and building them, ever since the age of 9 or so. As this engineer worked with his creations, it was always obvious what the next step should be to make progress, and progress is after all what it was about.

Well, eventually this engineer got a formal education and went to work for a great and wondrous company in yet another far off place. This company could do anything, and they had a track record to prove it. However this great and wondrous company approached machines and their creations in a different way. They had people that included economists, bureaucrats, politicians, scientists, managers, and yes even a few from the land of Hollywood. Their approach was to try to understand the need of the customer. What was the customer really trying to accomplish, study the history, study the current state of affairs, and postulate a possible future mode of customer being. Understand the requirements, clearly state the requirements, and then begin to identify what the machine should look like. Determine if the machine could be made of existing machines and technology, or if new machines and maybe even technologies need to be created that would fill the perceived void of the customer in the future.

A great and wondrous machine was created, on paper, and the engineer thought, wow, so this is really how machines are created. Alas, however, no one understood the machine. The money kept flowing, but the machine was never instantiated with the customer. Lots of people worked many years attempting to understand the machine, discussing the machine, but never passing the machine to the customer. Great loss and remorse followed for those who watched and pondered why.

Alas, this engineer now a bit older began to recall his previous view of machines, how machines grow and take on a life of their own. And he thought about what really happened at this great and wondrous company and began to realize that the great machine he helped to create really would not change the drudgery of the customer. In fact little if any automation leaps occurred that could really transform the customers' state of being into something better.

And so the engineer quietly wrote a paper describing these thoughts and quietly submitted it to a conference for publication in that customers' world. It ended with the great question:

-- Should you try to study a customers need and invent machines to satisfy that need or should you let those literate in machines and their technologies, grow their machines in a way that only makes logical sense to them, those babbling techies. Further more, when those same techies say "throw my creations into a controlled operation" it would happen. The operation would then proceed to learn and study this machine, a machine so different that no one could anticipate its enormous ramifications on changing everything that the users would do in their operation. --

Alas the engineer knew that these were extremely powerful ideas, and great sums of money had already been expended (billions) and so he submitted this paper to the conference after the closing date. Its interesting to see that this customer has adopted many of the ideas suggested in the paper. It remains to be seen if this customer will finally get relief in the future from the enormously complicated operation that is present a decade and a half later. The engineer is quietly watching and hoping for the best along with some of his buddies.

OK, so here we are. Someone dropped this incredible machine in our laps and they didn't give us an instruction manual. The way I see it, we have 4 alternatives. Lets say you could go back a few thousand years and drop off a "wheel" with tribes around the planet. Don't let yourself be seen, just dump a wheel in a field near a tribes camp. After a brief period of time I would speculate that you would start to see a pattern.

1.   The first group of tribes might notice something strange in the field or they

might not. In any case they would ignore it and go about their caveman way of life. Yes there are brain dead companies out there, I know first hand...

2. The second group of tribes would be terrified of this thing and order everyone to stay away from it. In fact the elders would probably put anyone to death if they approached it. Curiously only young cave people would approach this wheel thing and attempt to play with it, shortly followed by an elder witch-hunt. Needless to say the tribe would eventually die off due to lack of young cave people.

3. The third group would have the priests take over the wheel. They would use it to move their offerings around in their caves and sacrifice anyone who would attempt to use the wheel. Eventually these tribes would only consist of priests, and since priests don't do anything, they would starve to death and the tribe would vanish.

4. The forth group would have wagons, wheel barrows, and hang wheels on walls and around their necks, just for the heck of it. Now that they have leisure time, thanks to the wheel, they would approach the tribes in the first group and say hey, this is a wheel.

There you have it; this is my response to this Internet thing (circa 1997). As far as the other system thing at the start of this description, I / we are still waiting.

Author Comment: Hughes Aircraft produced great technology. Everyone in the world recognized they produced outstanding high technology systems. They had a culture that was unique and that culture eventually transferred to the new people as they entered that culture. That culture was based on a formula:

1. **Symbol:** Howard Hughes mystique and values of breaking the boundaries, doing it with outstanding quality, don't tell anybody what you are doing, non conflict of interest compensation, no stock holding, no shared equity everyone working for non profit medical foundation.

2. **Cold War:** Unlimited funds.

3. **Private Ownership:** It was a cocoon, technology first, profits second, no quarterly stockbrokers to answer to and disrupt operations.

4. **Recruit Superb Talent:** Recruited from Universities especially those on the Ph.D. tracks or orientation and pay them more than others would pay.

5. **Unique Management Style:** Modeled after Bell Labs, key word is labs, invent, ask people to do things that have never done before, have people be unbounded, just go for it, find experts across company, family sharing. Provide extremely stable work environment[122] and pay more than anyone else in the industry pays.

---

[122] Hughes never had a layoff.

These attributes made the company extremely successful and prized by the world in its time. It is difficult to find these attributes in most companies. The statement "We are a technology driven company" was a common statement made in meetings as tough challenges were being discussed and decisions to pursue or not pursue projects were being made. One of the decision tools was the Opportunity Lost decision analysis where the driving factor was the opportunity to develop new and challenging technologies.

5.15 Technology and Great Design Key Points

➤ A technology survey is conducted if the goal is to develop a technology driven design

➤ Technology surveys need non-disclosure agreements and perhaps long term business relationships

➤ The fundamentals of a great design are
  - New levels of performance are achieved
  - New levels of functionality are achieved
  - New levels of quality are achieved

➤ Technology readiness level assessment should be performed for
  - Conceptual design or architecture
  - Physical design or architectures
  - Implementation design or architecture

➤ Technology maturity assessment should be performed for
  - Conceptual design or architecture
  - Physical design or architectures
  - Implementation design or architecture

➤ Technology driven conceptual designs or architectures based on immature technologies must include plans for and apply resources to mature the technologies prior to the establishment of the physical architecture

➤ If an immature technology is not ready for an implementation architecture
  - The fall back position may be an older technology driven implementation
  - The system function needing the new technology can be pushed to future versions rather than delaying delivery of the system
  - The system can be put on hold until the technology is ready for implementation

➤ Quality
- Can not be inspected into the system
- Needs to be designed into the system

➤ Having high quality in one part or more parts of the system and low quality in one or more parts of the system is
- A low quality system
- A symptom of severe design imbalances

➤ The technology and quality goals for all new designs should be high technology high quality

5.16 Exercises

1. What are the fundamentals of great systems and why?
2. Describe the technology issues associated with 3 conceptual architectures, and identify the 3-5 key technologies in each of the architectures.
3. Do you think new systems should always push the functional envelope in one or more areas? If so why, if not why not?
4. Do you think new systems should always push the performance envelope in one or more areas? If so why, if not why not?
5. Do you think new systems should always push the quality envelope in one or more areas? If so why, if not why not?
6. What was the formula that made Hughes Aircraft a premiere system engineering design organization?
7. What is the relationship between quality and new system designs?

5.17 Additional Reading

1. Colossus: The Forbin Project, movie, writers: James Bridges (screenplay), D.F. Jones (novel), 1970. Film is about a fully automated defense and social monitoring system that starts making its own decisions as the humans try to stop it.
2. Connections, TV Series, 1978, The series explores the various paths of how technological change happens and the social effects of these changes on Western society.
3. Defense Acquisition Guidebook, Defense Acquisition University, August 2010.
4. Diffusion of Innovations, Everett Rogers, 1962.
5. Energy Efficiency and Renewable Energy, U.S. Department of Energy, February 2011.
6. Human Factors for Evolving Environments: Human Factors Attributes and Technology Readiness Levels, DOT/FAA/AR-03/43, FAA/NASA Human

Factors Research and Engineering Division, FAA, 2003.

7. Managing a Technology Development Program, James W. Bilbro & Robert L. Sackheim, Office of the Director George C. Marshall Space Flight Center, augments NASA Procedures and Guidelines, NPG 7120.5, NASA Program and Project Management Processes and Requirements.

8. NASA Procedural Requirements NASA Systems Engineering Processes and Requirements w/Change 1 (11/04/09), NPR 7123.1A, March 26, 2007.

9. NASA Research and Technology Program and Project Management Requirements, NASA Procedural Requirements, NPR 7120.8, February 05, 2008.

10. NASA Systems Engineering Handbook, NASA/SP-2007-6105 Rev1, December 2007.

11. Research & Development Degree Of Difficulty (R&D3) A White Paper, John C. Mankins, Advanced Projects Office of Space Flight NASA Headquarters, March 10, 1998.

12. Systems Engineering Fundamentals, Supplementary Text, Defense Acquisition University Press, January 2001.

13. Systems Practices as Common Sense, by Walter Sobkiw, CassBeth, 2011, ISBN 978-0983253082.

14. Technology Readiness Assessment (TRA) Deskbook, DOD, May 2005, July 2009.

15. Technology Readiness Levels A White Paper, John C. Mankins, Advanced Concepts Office, Office of Space Access and Technology, April 6, 1995, NASA.

16. WarGames, movie, writers: Lawrence Lasker, Walter F. Parkes, Walon Green, 1983. Film is about a fully automated defense system that decides to play the ultimate game as the humans try to stop it before its too late.

17. White Paper, Systematic Assessment of the Program / Project Impacts of Technological Advancement and Insertion, James W. Bilbro George C. Marshall Space Flight Center, December 2006, with acknowledgements: Dale Thomas, Jack Stocky, Dave Harris, Jay Dryer, Bill Nolte, James Cannon, Uwe Hueter, Mike May, Joel Best, Steve Newton, Richard Stutts, Wendel Coberg, Pravin Aggarwal, Endwell Daso, and Steve Pearson.

6 Physical Architecture Design

A physical architecture design begins with a collection of artifacts including top level needs, functions, operational scenarios, requirements, architecture design concepts and evolves into a physical architecture design that is vendor and product independent. The need is revisited and updated. The functions are fully identified, decomposed and allocated to structural entities. The requirements are also fully identified, decomposed and allocated to the same structural entities as the functions. This suggests that there is also a clear consistent mapping of requirements to functions. It is at this time that the internal interfaces start to surface as various structures and their interconnections are considered. The structures, their names, their connectivity, the topology or layout of the structures, structure sizes then fall into different physical architecture alternatives.

A fundamental question is why should functions be introduced with the physical entities and requirements? The answer is that the team starts to address various issues and questions while discovering the physical architecture design. A functional view allows for a consistent dialog between the stakeholders. So the next question is what is a function?

Functions are noun verb phrases. However we instinctively name many functions using a single word. That is because we have context that translates the single word into a noun verb phrase. This is especially true in an industry area. If you are in the business, you can immediately relate to a single word as the accepted noun verb phrase and all its underlying implications. However not every stakeholder may be in the business and they may have completely different interpretations of a single word name for a function. This is the fundamental reason why function names should be paired with a noun verb phrase and explained via descriptive text and requirements.

Many times the functions seem obvious and so there is a resistance to take the time to discuss and understand the obvious functions. However as the functions are allocated to different structures with different characteristics and performance, the obvious then usually becomes a serious topic of discussion and analysis between stakeholders.

Author Comment: A common function in air defense and air traffic control is range scale. Even though this is a noun verb phrase its operation is different than what most outside the community would expect. It is a display function. When the operator selects a range scale the display zooms in or zooms out on a particular area. For example they may select a 5 or 300 mile view on the display. Most outside the community expect this to be similar to an optical zoom in / out where the screen objects change size. However that is not the case. In this community all the screen objects remain the same size and no information is added or deleted except for what is now in the new geographic range view that the system is tracking. So the only thing that happens is the display surface represents a 5 or 300 mile view in this case.

Offset is a single word version of a display function that also has massive requirements in this community. When an offset is selected the display center changes instantaneously and no information is added or deleted except for what forms the new view.

An important aspect is performance and presentation. When a different range scale or offset is selected the response time is instantaneous (sub second). Also there is no appearance of display build up where some objects appear before other objects. Display anomalies, flashing, or other artifacts are not permitted.

The range scale and offset functions had enormous impacts on the design of the display subsystem. In the past these two functions translated to a design approach of using ping / pong memory in the hardware implementation of the display hardware. As one memory is displaying the current situation, another memory is being populated with the new display setting. Once the population is complete a switch to the other memory then offers the active display information. So the actual display information switches, or will ping / pong between the two separate display-memories. Vendors who did not have ping / pong display memories with the resulting performance were not viable for air defense or air traffic control console design solutions.

So where do we begin with the physical architecture design? The act of taking the system functions and allocating them to a physical structure is physical architecture design. The various structure alternatives lead to different interfaces and performance characteristics. Optimizing the physical architecture design is accomplished by formal and informal trade studies. The steps are actually simple but executing the steps and ensuring the result is effective is not so simple. The following is a sample of possible steps to follow:

- Draw a physical architecture design block diagram
- Allocate functions to the block diagram elements
- Identify the interfaces
- Perform analysis to determine the performance of the physical architecture design shown in the block diagrams
- Repeat this process for 3 to 5 physical architecture design alternatives
- Perform a physical architecture design tradeoff analysis using the Measure of Effectiveness (MOE) approach
- Document the physical architecture design trade study

- Document the selected physical architecture design
- Using all the analysis capture all the requirements in the specifications
- Stay vendor and product independent

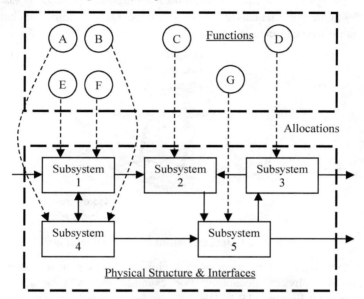

Figure 80 Physical Architecture Design Allocations

Just like with the conceptual architecture design we all have patterns that we naturally gravitate towards and we will incorporate them into the physical architecture design. Allow that to happen and capture the result. Then proceed to remove vendor and product dependencies. In some cases that may not be possible, there may be only one vendor and or product. For example when developing an air traffic control system the government only may provide the air traffic controllers in the system. In other cases a state-of-the-art solution may be available from only one vendor and that solution may be a critical part of the system.

6.1 Allocations

Allocations are multi dimensional and address various aspects of the design view. We can start the allocation process from any perspective. Once the functions are allocated to possible physical entities, analysis can be performed to test the effectiveness of the allocation. The analysis can include availability, maintenance, performance, safety, etc[123]. The following is a list of possible allocation targets:

---

[123] The idea of allocating the DFD functions to physical entities based on various analyses was part of Hughes Aircraft circa 1982.

- **System**: This is the highest level of the system and an allocation to this level suggests that the process, function, and resulting requirements apply to all the system elements. For example a maintenance philosophy that dictates electronic user manuals are to be developed. Other examples include safety, fault tolerance, security, etc.

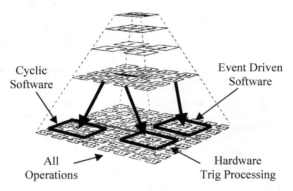

Cyclic Software

Event Driven Software

All Operations

Hardware Trig Processing

Figure 81 Decomposition[124] and Allocations

- **Segment**: A system segment is a physical location in a system that has multiple physical locations. For example the ATC system has four segments: Enroute, TRACON, Tower, and Support segments. At one time there were 23 Enroute facilities, 234 TRACONS and 400 Towers[125]. Other examples are ground, space, surface sea, under sea, and under ground segments typically found in very large defense systems. The segments will share common subsystems and lower level functions and their implementations.

- **Subsystem**: A subsystem is a physical entity that executes the processes or functions. In computer automation it is a computer with software that supports the functions. Subsystems can decompose into subsystems.

- **Hardware Configuration Item**: A Hardware Configuration Item (HWCI) is a hardware element that supports a function. For example an amplifier supports the functions of bass, treble, and loudness control. An HWCI also can be a computer, display, keyboard, mouse, cell phone, etc that are absent any software or firmware.

- **Software Configuration Item**: A Software Configuration Item (SWCI) is a software package that supports a group of functions. Examples include operating systems like UNIX, Windows, servers like Apache, applications

---

[124] Basic pyramid showing decomposition is from functional analysis section in Systems Engineering Management Guide, Defense Systems Management College, January 1990.

[125] These are approximate numbers circa 1982.

like client web browser, applications that support functions like word processing, drawing, spreadsheets, etc.

- **Operations**: Operations are processes or functions performed by humans. Prior to computer automation, people in large organizational entities performed many processes or functions. Today people tend to be in maintenance roles and augment automation implemented on computer based systems. When systems are studied, automation tends to be the first approach to making a system better. However, not all system problems can be solved with technology. The system solutions might come from the social political economic sciences. For example, replacing teachers with a computer screen may not yield an effective educational system.

- **Operating System User**: In a Multi User Operating System like UNIX, a process or group of processes can be allocated to users. For example in the ATC the RADAR data processing function can be allocated to each air traffic controller as a UNIX user account. If something should cause a failure for one user that failure would be isolated to that user, it will not propagate. An example is an overrun condition or divide by zero, which would cause processing to get stuck in an endless loop.

- **Operating System Task**: In a Multi Tasking Operating System like UNIX a process or group of processes can be allocated to a task. For example in the ATC the RADAR data processing function can be allocated to several tasks based on region of airspace. If something should cause a failure for a part of the airspace that failure would be isolated to that task, it will not propagate. An example is an overrun condition or divide by zero, which would cause processing to get stuck in an endless loop. UNIX can take advantage of its Multi Tasking and Multi User capabilities and use both mechanisms to minimize failure propagation.

- **Directory**: The software that implements the processes or functions can be grouped into various file system computer directories. This grouping affects maintainability of the system.

- **Source File**: The software that implements the processes or functions can be grouped into various source code files. This grouping affects maintainability of the system.

- **Class**: The software that implements the processes or functions can be grouped into a class. The class then can be instantiated to support the system. For example the ATC RDP class can be instantiated for each air traffic controller. This is similar to the isolation achieved in UNIX. This grouping affects maintainability and performance of the system.

- **Process or Function Characteristics**: Processes or functions tend to behave in certain ways. As a staring point there are event driven, cyclic, real time, extremely important such that the function is always available, complex, simple, new, old and proven, etc. Categorizing the functions adds more understanding of the system and helps in the decomposition and allocation to an physical architecture design solution.

A hierarchy tree can be used to show the system functions and the hierarchy. The tree then can be annotated to show allocation to a physical structure.

When capturing abstraction levels the functional allocation can begin at the highest levels such as a machine or human. Functions allocated to machines then can be allocated to different machines. Functions allocated to different humans can be allocated to different roles they have in the system.

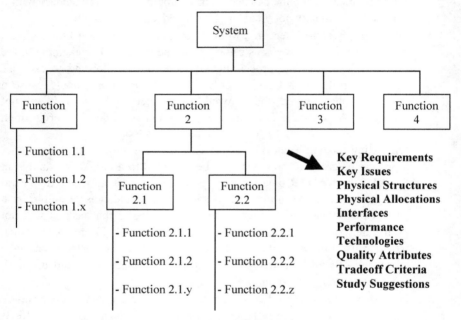

Figure 82 Functional Decomposition Tree

A function allocation table can capture the evolution of the physical architecture. As the table evolves the detailed structures soon overcome the broader structures. The allocation table also can capture different attributes of the physical architecture. For example version numbers associated with hardware and software can be associated with each function, its subsystem, and lower level abstractions in the subsystem. It has the ability to capture significant detail, different abstraction levels, and different views.

Table 64 Function Allocation Table

Functions	Automation	Subsystem	Vendor
Function 1	Machine	Computer	RCA
Function 2	Human	User	Government

Table 64 Function Allocation Table

Functions	Automation	Subsystem	Vendor
Function 3	Machine	Radar	Hughes
Function 4	Machine	Engine	Ford
Function 5	Human	Maintainer	Contractor
Function 6	Human	Customer	Citizens

A functional physical matrix can be used to show the allocation of functions to physical elements in the system. The physical elements can be shown in a decomposition tree format and the functions annotated on the physical tree. The hierarchy tree and function allocation tables do not show the system internal interfaces or the topology of the system.

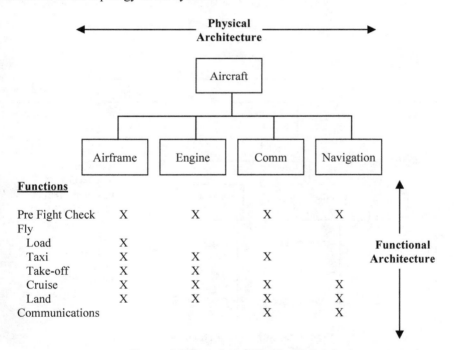

Figure 83 Functional Physical Matrix

The internal and external interfaces can be represented using an interface table. The table lists the interfaces by name the connecting elements and any characteristics that are considered important. However the interface table still lacks information needed for the physical architecture depiction. This information is the topology, flow, and or openness of the interface. The interface table is most effective when capturing the detailed design details as part of the implementation architecture.

Table 65 Computer Based Interface Table

Interface	#	Rate	Media	Protocol	Subsystems
RS-422	10	56K	RS-422	HDLC	A to J
Video 1	2	18Gb/s	Digital	HDMI	A
Video 2	4	NA	Analog	Composite	B
Satellite	1	1Mb/s	Satellite	TCP/IP	C
Research LAN	2	100Gb/s	Fiber	Token Ring TCP/IP	All

Eventually the segments, subsystems, assemblies and other physical elements of the system surface. A subsystem decomposition tree can show the relationship between these various elements. The tree can be augmented with text to provide a full description of the system in a view that shows decomposition and hierarchy.

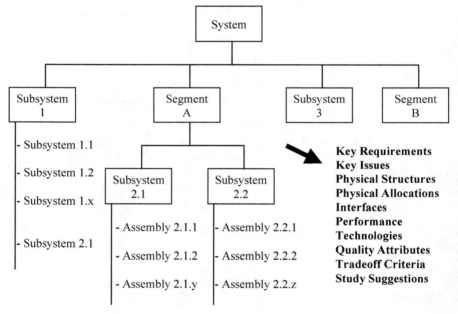

Figure 84 Subsystem Decomposition Tree

Example 15 Dwelling Physical Architecture

There are many functions that can be associated with a dwelling. As we attempt to allocate the dwelling functions we immediately jump to known patterns form our personal experience. In the case of a dwelling we might jump to and have concepts and physical views of the following types of dwellings: hut, apartment, farm, and a suburban house.

However what if we are looking for a different pattern? For example is a house supporting a young family the same in terms of physical design as a retired couple or a young single adult? What if the dwelling is on a ship or in space?

Recently with the introduction of the computer and multimedia we can use the same functions that translate into a physical space to translate into services provided by a computer in a smart house. So there is a function that a physical space supports with a certain level of performance and then there are automation functions that can be applied to the physical space to help further improve the quality of life or the dwelling performance.

Table 66 Dwelling Physical Allocations

Function	Hut	Apartment	Farm	Suburban House
Personal hygiene	-	Room 3	Out house	Bathrooms
Sleeping	Room 1	Room 2	Room 2	Bedrooms
Cooking	Room 1	Room 1	Room 1	Kitchen
Dressing	Room 1	Room 2	Room 2	Bedrooms
Recreation	-	Room 1	Room 1	Rec Rooms
Reading	-	Room 1	Room 1	Office
Formal eating	Room 1	Room 1	Room 1	Dining Room
Formal guest meeting	Room 1	Room 1	Room 1	Living Room
Informal eating	Room 1	Room 1	Room 1	Kitchen
Paying bills	-	Room 1	Room 1	Office
Working	-	Room 1	Barn	Office
House maintenance	-	-	Barn	Garage, Basement
Storage	Room 1	Room 2	Barn	Garage, Basement, Attic
Automobile parking	-	-	Barn	Garage
Automobile maintenance	-	-	Barn	Garage
Lighting	-	All Rooms	All Rooms	All Rooms
Power	-	All Rooms	All Rooms	All Rooms
Communications	-	Room 1	Room 1, 2	All Rooms
Heating	-	All Rooms	All Rooms	All Rooms
Cooling	-	All Rooms	-	All Rooms
Power generation	-	-	Barn	Yard
Water	-	Room 3	Room 3	Kitchen, Bathrooms, Laundry Room
Sewage	-	Room 1, 3	Room 1, 3	Bathrooms

Although the hierarchy tree, function allocation table, interface table, and functional physical matrix are very effective, they usually are insufficient to capture the physical architecture. At some point a drawing is needed to show the physical structure and interfaces. A floor plan and artist rendering of the house exterior are an example of showing the physical architecture design of a house. A block diagram showing allocated functions and interface information is an example of showing an automation system.

6.2 Coupling and Cohesion

A strategy is needed when decomposing and grouping functions. Typically the strategy is based on the concept of coupling and cohesion. Coupling and cohesion are conceptual measures of how tightly connected two things are in a system.

Depending on what you are trying to accomplish you might want tight coupling or lose coupling. Coupling implies that you have control over the connectivity. In other words you have control on the level of coupling between functions.

Cohesion implies that you have no control on the degree of connectivity between functions. High cohesion suggests that the functions naturally need to be grouped together and if you separate them, the system performance will degrade.

Functions with high cohesion are associated with robustness, reliability, reusability, and understandability while low cohesion is associated with undesirable traits such as being difficult to maintain, difficult to test, difficult to reuse, and difficult to understand. However this is from the point of view of the functions that are grouped. From the functions that are not part of the same group, you are looking for low coupling or cohesion.

For example from a failure point of view low coupling is the desired attribute. The goal is to slowdown or stop fault propagation in the system. This also applies when considering security and how security breaches may propagate through the system. The functions may naturally display high cohesion but you must break that cohesion (binding) with low coupling to stop the propagation of an undesirable event or element in the system.

From a performance point of view, such as response time, high coupling is the desired attribute. However the functions in this group may actually exhibit low cohesion, but you need to somehow tightly couple them to maximize performance. Also, there may be a tradeoff that needs to happen between response time and failure propagation or security.

1. **Functional Cohesion**: Functions are grouped because they all contribute to a single well-defined activity. For example the RF front end, mixer / oscillator, and demodulator form the FM receiver function.
2. **Temporal Cohesion**: Functions are grouped because they conceptually or actually perform at similar times.
3. **Logical Cohesion**: Functions are grouped because they logically do the same thing but they are different by nature. For example grouping all radio

functions together in an amplifier receiver even though they are AM or FM or Short Wave, etc.

4. **Procedural Cohesion**: Functions are grouped because they always follow a certain sequence of operation. For example a login function takes the user name and compares it with the password.
5. **Sequential Cohesion**: Functions are grouped because the output from one function is the input to another function. For example the FM receiver always has an RF front end to amplify the incoming signal, passes the signal to the mixer / oscillator to extract the appropriate channel, then passes the signal to the demodulator to extract the audio.

6.3 Modular Design

Modularization was a big trend in the 1970s and it transformed many designs from television sets to major infrastructure systems. Yourdons' famous structured system analysis from the 1970s was based on this finding[126]. The concept behind modular design is to identify fundamental building blocks and then develop a design based on those building blocks. These building blocks may or may not exist in the industrial base. However once the building blocks are part of a successful design they quickly become standard items available in the industrial base.

Modular design using physical items is easy to visualize today because so many standard components are available. However in the case of software, modular software is still a challenge and software designers on projects tend to reject this very important design concept. The result is usually unstable software code with many unnecessary performance and functional compromises.

Table 67 Advantages of Modular Design

• Failure propagation can be minimized
• Safety, security and other critical boundaries are easily established
• Modules can be easily replaced in maintenance
• Total structure is more comprehensible
• Growth and technology insertion are easier
• Many different configurations of the system are possible
• Vendor lock-in is minimized because of standardization
• Changes in one part of system minimize impacts to other parts of the system
• Work can be divided and passed to those without the full system view

There are advantages and disadvantages to modular design. This suggests the need and the evolving solution must be understood so that modularity can be applied effectively in the system design. For example only a portion of system

---

[126] Tom De Marco applied decomposition to software in 1978 in his book Structured Analysis and System Specification, ISBN 0917072073

design may use modularity.

Table 68 Disadvantages of Using Existing Modules

• Interface costs may be high for certain interfacing modules
• Modules with unwanted functions need additional analysis and test
• Module assembly or integration may not be possible without changes
• Modules may be sub-optimized because they need to be universal
• Modules may be sub-optimized because they need to use standard interfaces
• Less variation in products because of overuse of the same modules
• Total system design performance may be lowered
• Total system design quality may be lowered
• Loss of team creativity and innovations as catalog engineering takes over

Some of the disadvantages of modular design do not apply if the team is developing the first modules in existence. In this case the disadvantage is associated with taking the time to develop universal modules that can be easily mixed and matches in the design and then perhaps used in future designs. In this design scenario the design team is leading the industry and breaking new ground suggesting a great design is about to surface.

6.4 Performance

Performance can be identified for one or more functions, however the performance may exceed the state-of-the-art for the subsystem or subsystems that will support the functions. Yet the desired performance may be critical to the system. New designs push performance in one or more areas. The challenge is to identify these areas and apply resources so that the design can become a reality.

Finding the quantitative measures of a design is not a simple task. Pioneers in previous centuries showed us how to extract and analyze performance numbers for electrical circuits and mechanical structures. Today we have a plethora of legacy systems and knowing the key performance numbers is critical so that various alternatives can be understood, compared, and form the foundation for new designs.

Example 16 Performance and Quality

Performance is a requirement for a design being developed. It is a metric that should be measured and tracked for an existing design. For new or modified designs, existing designs should be studied and their performance should be extracted and applied to the new design vision. The following are some examples of design performance measures:

1. **Amplifier**: Power output in watts, distortion in %, noise in dB, frequency

response in Hz, total harmonic distortion in %, inter modulation distortion in %, and dynamic range in dB are the performance measures for an amplifier. As the amplifier evolved over time new performance measures were added. For example, power output was a primary performance measure. Then people realized that power output was useless if the distortion was high. And so the performance metrics continued to evolve until an amplifier could be fully characterized and compared with different implementations.

2. **Radio**: The radio has an amplifier subsystem and a receiver subsystem. Sensitivity in microvolts, selectivity in dB, noise in dB, and stereo (channel) separation in dB quantify the receiver performance. The functionality of a radio went from AM to AM FM to AM FM stereo. Each of those functional elements has performance characteristics that matter.

3. **Tape Recorder**: The tape recorder has an amplifier subsystem and a mechanical subsystem. The mechanical subsystem performance is quantified with the steadiness of the speed as music is recorded and played back. This is referred to as flutter and wow both identified in terms of percent. High quality studio recorders would measure speed on the fly and adjust as needed to minimize the flutter and wow. This was accomplished by using an extra audio track that would record at a fixed frequency. Upon playback the frequency would be read and adjusted as needed. That is the level of detail applied to something simple like the flutter and wow performance number.

4. **Color Televisions**: Screen size, brightness, contrast, detail, color purity, color depth, stability, linearity, resolution, apparent resolution, and convergence stability are some of the performance numbers for a television video subsystem. Linearity is interesting and is based on drawing a circle and moving it across the screen. All TVs that try to fit the image in the useable screen area have terrible linearity if the original content does not match the aspect ratio of the TV screen. Apparent resolution is even more interesting. If projection TV with continuous phosphor Red Green Blue CRTs is compared to non-continuous displays such as LCD, Plasma, or 3 gun CRT, the resolution will appear to be greater on the projection TV. This appearance can even be measure as the continuous phosphor CRT paints a line or dot on the screen. Then there is the perception of resolution. The human eye sees and the mind perceives things at 120 (peripheral vision), 60 (typical), and 1 to 6 (when focused) degrees. If the screen changes format from the 3 X 4 X 5 triangle and the image is distorted or shrinks, the ability to discern human facial elements, such as the eye, falls dramatically.

5. **Car**: Acceleration usually 0-60 in x seconds, breaking distance in feet, efficiency in miles per gallon, wheel base inches, trunk space in cubic feet, passenger compartment in number of passengers head room leg room,

engine power in horsepower, turning radius in feet.

6. **MP3 Player**: Number of songs in terms of memory in gigabytes, quantization distortion[127] in dB (no one currently offers this performance), bit sample rate are the performance characteristics associated with MP3 players. Notice the traditional audio performance characteristics are missing. The primary reason is based on the quantization distortion, which is based on the number of bits used to capture a single value in the digital to analog converter. The quantization distortion is so high that capturing the other metrics would be a severe embarrassment. The lay person has detected something is not right and there have been movements back into analog audio. However this is probably more of an anomaly. Music has actually changed to hide the issues associated with digitization and the audience has come to accept the "computer metallic sound" from these devices.

7. **Flat Screen Televisions**: Screen size, resolution, screen update, and power consumption and the performance characteristics associated with new flat screen TVs. Sometimes consumers are given performance numbers that do not capture the system performance properly. For example the human eye can discern movement at a 30 Hz rate yet modern TV manufacturers advertise screen refresh rates well beyond that number. What is really hidden is the performance number for being able to update the entire screen with new content using a decaying brightness level that matches the eye. The entire screen cannot be updated fast enough with new content using a continuous decaying brightness level as in a CRT, so key information is not offered and a performance number is inflated that makes no sense.

8. **House**: Number of bedrooms, bath rooms, the presence of a living room, recreation room, office, laundry room, kitchen eat in area, basement. The sizes of the rooms, the size of the land, land improvements such as swimming pool, fence, and patio area. Level of maintenance free construction materials and techniques while preserving aesthetics.

So searching for performance in a design is not a marketing activity. It is an engineering activity that never must be compromised. Without meaningful performance measures, designs will never evolve and get better. In some cases the design may not even work or cause damage.

What are the performance characteristics associated with your house, community, and heath care system? If you are a homeowner you probably are able to quickly surface the performance characteristics of your house and community that most will understand. If you built your house and you were involved in the details you will surface performance characteristics of your house and community that most people will find foreign. It will not be common knowledge until you

---

[127] Discrete Time Systems, James A. Cadzow, Prentice Hall, 1973, ISBN 0132159961.

describe them in some setting.

All designs start relatively small and evolve. The focus changes and things that were once impossible are added to the design as the decades unfold. In the beginning the story of the automobile was about speed, then durability, then suspension, aesthetics in form versus function arguments, safety like lights and brakes, comfort like windows, then wipers, heat, air conditioning, radio, FM radio, stereo, power windows, power seats, cruise control, and now GPS. In many ways this is like a pyramid model. You start with a base and build upon each layer until a pinnacle of perfection is reached in terms of function, performance, quality, and aesthetics.

Author Comment: It is always sad when progress is lost and things go back in terms of function or performance. In many ways the digital revolution is an example of this scenario as high quality analog solutions were abandoned for the flexibility or quantity of digital. In some areas like healthcare these resets may be intolerable. Buried within the concept of performance is quality. A high quality solution is a solution that does everything exceptionally well.

6.5 Subsystems

It is sometimes difficult to separate the subsystem view from functional analysis. Don't try to separate the functional analysis from the subsystems. You are human and a non-linear thinker. Don't fight your natural tendencies. Non linear thinking is good but you should keep track of your work. That means you need to separate the functional and subsystem information products into two groups when you are ready to present the functional findings.

Example 4: Healthcare systems exist around the world. They have functions, which are grouped into subsystems and the performance can be measured. There is performance data in the form of metrics gathered for various health care systems from around the world. But how do you start to represent these health care systems from a functional point of view? Is there a generic functional block diagram that can represent all of the healthcare systems? Is the performance driven by the implementation of these generic healthcare functions? Are there systems that have more functionality than other systems? Is more functionality associated with a more capable healthcare system? Are the connections between functions different for different healthcare systems?

Many times the functions are known but the interfaces between the functions are vague or unknown. This should not prevent the development of a functional block diagram. In some instances it even may be prudent to show the key functions without the interfaces so that the discussion can begin. During the physical architecture design one would expect this analysis to be complete, but that is in the ideal setting. The reality is that the physical architecture design may need to be started to coax out the interfaces.

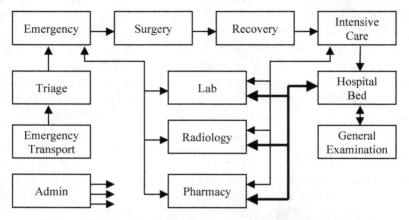

Figure 85 Functional Block Diagram - Health Care View 1

Figure 86 Functional Block Diagram - Health Care View 2

As a first step in identifying the functions it is easy to move to the subsystem level. It is also easy to start identifying the stakeholders. The same word or word phrase can easily be interpreted as a stakeholder, function or subsystem. That is why clear supporting text is important when presenting any analysis.

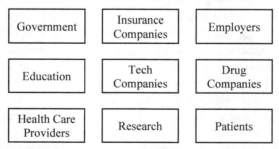

Figure 87 Functional Block Diagram - Health Care View 3

There is always a danger of using vague words or phrases. This is usually because there is an inability to commit. Commitment is very important. The team cannot delay commitment and move to the next level. It is like building a house on sand. A poor foundation will lead to collapse.

Example 17 Abstraction Level Needed for Current View

Sometimes when we start to identify the system functions we plunge a level or two down, but then we have enough information to abstract the level 1 functions. However when we look at the functions they are extremely generic and might apply to other systems. For example if we look at electric power generation, a view develops that includes extraction, distribution, refining, use, and waste. The focus shifts to the fuel that powers the system. The power generation and its applications fall into a "use" block.

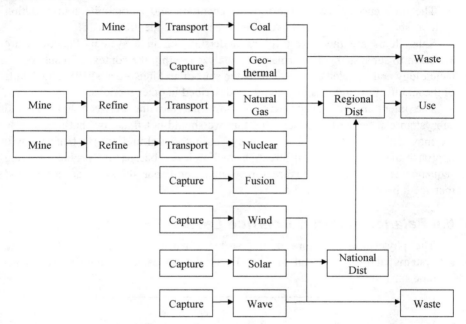

Figure 88 Electric Power Generation – Automobile Detailed View

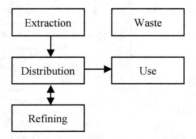

Figure 89 Electric Power Generation - Automobile Broad View

This same view can apply to a system of personal transportation, the automobile. The automobile system can be reduced to its source of fuel. Not only can the functional block diagram be similar between power generation and automobile transportation, but also the high-level sequence diagram can be similar.

Figure 90 Electric Power Generation / Automobile Sequence View

The differences between the power generation and automobile transportation systems start to surface when lower level functions are identified.

Subsystems are the next level of understanding in a system. Functions are allocated to subsystems. Performance is analyzed within the context of a subsystem technology and its selected size. This is the start of architecture analysis. The details of the architecture and its subsystems are described in other sections.

The intent in this section was to show that the line between function and subsystem can be hard to control and that we should not fixate on that line or else we may get stuck. The goal is to always push forward and realize that you will approach the problem from different abstraction levels because the problem solving sequence is not linear. You are forced into non-linear thinking, accept it, and manage it by keeping all the data.

6.6 Balance and Performance Levels

The physical architecture design surfaces when functions are allocated to subsystems and or physical spaces. Functions allocated to physical elements become subsystems.

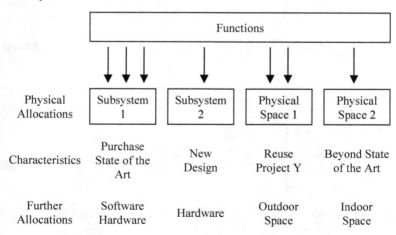

Figure 91 Functions Allocated to Physical Elements Become Subsystems

The allocations affect the subsystem interfaces and the subsystem performance needs. This drives the choice of subsystem technologies, physical space characteristics, and detailed design choices. This also drives system performance.

Functional allocation and the design choices will affect the architecture balance. Architecture balance suggests that all subsystems and or physical spaces in the architecture are matched from a performance view. If there is a subsystem that limits the maximum performance of other subsystems, then it should be examined for improvement. This may mean a different design for the deficient subsystem.

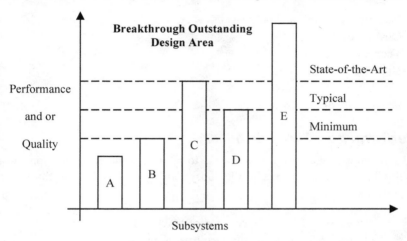

Figure 92 Unbalanced Architecture

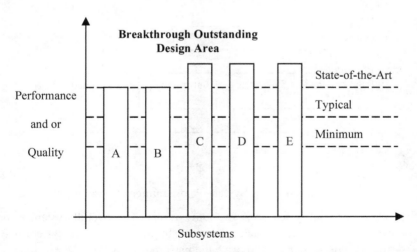

Figure 93 Balanced Outstanding Physical Architecture Design

From a processing point of view this is a processing bottleneck and is called an architecture bottleneck. The physical architecture design should minimize the architecture bottlenecks. Similar arguments can be made for other characteristics of the design. For example one subsystem should not be pushed to a beyond state of the art condition by other subsystems because of a poor functional or detailed design allocation. For example on a system that is weight constrained a subsystem should not be given a severe weight budget because of the convenience of other subsystems or worse because of predatory management or business practices. The following are some of the items to consider when examining architecture balance:

- Performance levels and bottlenecks
- Quality levels
- Technology levels
- Number of new designs
- Number of interfaces
- Complexity of interfaces

6.7 Performance Allocatio n

At some point in the design there needs to be a performance allocation to the subsystems in the design. Typically the subsystems will contribute to the loss of overall performance.

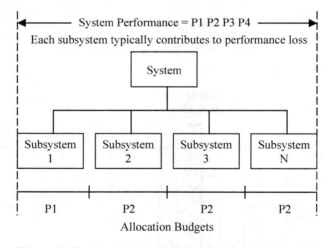

Figure 94 End to End System Performance Degradation

For example each subsystem may introduce errors. The overall system error would be the sum of errors from each subsystem. In other cases a subsystem may act as the weakest link in a chain and drive the performance down of the system to its individual performance level. For example connecting a low performance loud speaker to a high performance sound system will not make the speaker sound better. Instead all the benefits of the high quality sound system are lost and the overall quality is a provided by the loud speaker.

The search for the key performance parameters in a design is part of the system engineering and design process. Examples of similar designs in the same and other domains should be investigated. Usually a design is trying to push the envelope of existing designs so this hunt for the key performance measures should not be as difficult as some might suggest.

Table 69 Possible Performance Measures

Response Time	Heat	Humidity
Frequency Response	Contrast	Pressure
Noise	Color Depth	Shock
Distortion	Resolution	Vibration
Errors	Reliability	RF Radiation
Linearity	Availability	Acceleration
Weight	Maintenance Time	Stopping Distance
Power	Temperature	Driving Distance

6.8 Critical Functions

Not all functions are the same, some are more critical than other functions. Critical functions are treated differently in the process and the design. Usually the critical functions require a significantly more rigorous and methodical process and the design needs to be more robust and immune to unexpected external elements. The following is a partial list of critical functions:

- Safety
- Security
- Performance Intensive
- Reliability Challenged
- Other

The first step in the process usually centers on the system functions and identifying the critical functions. That is why a functional view of the system is so important. The next step then focuses on the critical requirements associated with the critical functions. This is usually tracked in the Systems Requirements Database (SRDB) using attributes associated with both the functions and requirements:

- Safety critical functions
- Security critical functions
- Performance Intensive critical functions
- Reliability Challenged critical functions
- Other critical functions

- Safety critical requirements
- Security critical requirements
- Performance Intensive critical requirements
- Reliability Challenged critical requirements
- Other critical requirements

Bypassing either the critical functional or requirement view leads to problems later on during the analysis. The analysis includes criteria for determining why a function and its associated requirements are critical, the approach for dealing with the criticality, its level of risk, and any mitigation strategies for residual risk associated with the critical functions and their requirements.

6.8.1 Safety Critical Functions and Requirements

The safety critical functions and requirements discussion will include more detail than the other critical function and requirement sections. It should be used as a guide when addressing the other areas. As you read the following content try to visualize how other critical functions and requirements might be addressed.

Safety critical functions are those that can lead to a mishap in the system. Not all functions are safety critical. This is an important concept because precious resources need to be applied to the safety critical functions and not wasted in other areas. Also it needs to be known that additional resources are applied to these functions. These functions also translate into requirements, both of which are allocated to physical elements in the physical architecture design.

Early in the design process the system view is primarily functional with few key requirements. As the system design evolves the key requirements are expanded and include all the requirements. However, the design should capture an understanding of the safety elements early in the design process. They then can be effectively mitigated at each level of the system rather than addressed as a crisis at the end of the system design when all decisions have been made and mitigation may not be possible or practical. The result is accepting a risk that must be signed off at the executive levels. This is also a potential ethical dilemma because a system might have been made safer.

Table 70 Safety Critical Function Allocation Table View[128]

Functions	Safety Critical
Function Name 1	Yes
Function Name 2	Yes (because of lower level)
Function Name 2.1	No
Function Name 2.2	**Yes**
Function Name 2.n	No
Function Name 3	No
Function Name x	No

As the information about the design expands it needs to be correlated and made consistent. When the requirement details become available and they are entered into

---

[128] This approach can be used for any critical functions in the system.

the System Requirements Database (SRDB), the safety critical functional analysis is captured and placed in the SRDB as attributes associated with each requirement.

Table 71 Safety Critical Requirement Allocation Table View[129]

PUI	Requirements	Functions	Safety Critical
1	Req Text	Function Name 3 **Function Name 2**	Yes (because of function 2, suggest decomposing this requirement into safety and non safety critical requirements)
2	Req Text	Function Name 1	Yes
3	Req Text	Function Name 1	Yes
4	Req Text	Function Name 3	No
X	Req Text	Function Name 3	No

The first step is to identify the unsafe conditions that can lead to a mishap. The mishap can be as serious as loss of life to something that is just an injury that causes pain but has no physical artifacts. The mishaps can be associated with unsafe:

- Toxic material
- Electromagnetic radiation
- Physical elements
- Manual or automated decisions that cause others harm

Mishaps are the result of system hazards. They are hazards until they are mitigated by the system design, then they are no longer hazards. The following is a list of possible hazards:

- **Light Hazards (Eyes)**: Mixing blue with other colors causes the eyes to constantly refocus thus potentially leading to myopia. Poor contrast ratio such as using gray letters on black buttons leads to eyestrain. Poor ambient light for documents or machine markings leads to eyestrain. Loss of night vision due to on coming bright lights or non-use of red lights in cabin instrumentation. Small letters forcing eye strain. Small objects with close placement forcing excessive crossing of eyes.
- **Noise Hazards (Ears)**: Excessive noise for short periods of time or low level noise for long periods of time leading to hearing loss. Quick air pressure changes that may burst eardrums. Talking over loud ambient noise leading to strained vocal cords.
- **Physical Hazards (Body)**: Sharp edges that can cut. Poor placement causing frequent bumps and bruising. Excessive physical weight, shock (traumatic movement), or vibration that can pull muscles, damage tendons,

---

[129] This approach can be used for any critical functions in the system.

or break bones. Repeated motion causing damaged tendons. Loud vocalizations for long periods of time.

- **Environmental Hazards (Body)**: Excessive heat or cold. Exposure to high voltage or radiation. Poor, polluted, or poisoned air. Dangerous substances or poisons ingested or absorbed by the skin. All of these can seriously damage the body.
- **Cognitive Processing Hazards (Brain or Mind)**: Shift changes that do not follow natural circadian cycles. Frequent shift changes with no time to transition internal body clock. Long periods of work without rest. Long periods before sleep cycles. Visual, sound, and or tactile sensory overload. Light and noise hazards, which result in unnecessary cognitive processing to detect images. Trying to detect garbled speech in high noise static settings. Trying to detect objects in high noise low contrast light settings. All of these lead to impair thinking, judgement, and cognitive abilities.
- **Physical and Emotional Stress Hazards**: Can lead to temporary or permanent physical or cognitive impairment. Sources can be poor machine, social, and economic systems. For example constant reorganization and workforce churn in a company or industry is a significant stress source with future indirect health care costs not paid by the offending system.

Some hazards are more serious than other hazards and so they need to be understood and assessed in some consistent manner. When a hazard results in a mishap there are different impacts or levels of severity.

Table 72 Hazard Severity Levels

LVL	Severity	Description 1[130]	Description 2[131]
1	Catastrophic	Death or system loss.	Could result in death, permanent total disability, loss exceeding $1M[132], or irreversible severe environmental damage that violates law or regulation.
2	Critical	Severe injury, occupational illness, major system or environmental damage.	Could result in permanent partial disability, injuries or occupational illness that may result in hospitalization of at least three personnel, loss exceeding $200K but less than $1M, or reversible environmental damage causing a violation of law or

---

[130] Software System Safety Handbook, Joint Services Computer Resources Management Group, US Navy, US Army, And US Air Force, December 1999.

[131] Practice For System Safety, Department of Defense Standard, MIL-STD-882D, 10 February 2000.

[132] The monetary value keeps changing with inflation and is reflected in the standards documents updates through the years.

Table 72 Hazard Severity Levels

LVL	Severity	Description 1[130]	Description 2[131]
			regulation.
3	Marginal	Minor injury, occupational illness, minor system or environmental damage.	Could result in injury or occupational illness resulting in one or more lost work days, loss exceeding $10K but less than $200K, or can mitigate environmental damage without violation of law or regulation where restoration activities can be accomplished.
4	Negligible	Less than minor injury, illness, system damage or environmental damage.	Could result in injury or illness not resulting in a lost workday, loss exceeding $2K but less than $10K, or minimal environmental damage not violating law or regulation.

Once the hazards are identified they are assigned a severity level. Some hazards may have multiple mishaps with different severity levels. The hazards and mishap ratings are maintained in a hazard assessment table.

Table 73 Hazard Assessment Table

Hazard	Mishap	Severity
Hazards 1	Mishap 1.1	1 Catastrophic
Hazards 1	Mishap 1.2	3 Marginal
Hazards 2	Mishap 2	2 Critical

Analysis can be performed in the hazard or mishap domain. For this discussion the hazard domain is elected. Different hazards and mishaps have different probabilities of occurring. These probabilities are described in terms of potential occurrences per unit of time, events, population, items, or activities. The ideal approach is to assign a quantitative hazard probability but that may be impossible, especially if all hazards are consistently treated. A qualitative approach based on history of similar systems is offered. There are suggested hazard mishap probability levels that can be used for the analysis.

Table 74 Hazard Probability Levels

LVL	Description	Prob.	Comments
A	Frequent	1 in 100	Likely to occur often in the life of an item. Continuously experienced. Will constantly occur.
B	Probable	1 in 1000	Will occur several times in the life of an item. Will occur frequently. Will occur.
C	Occasional	1 in 10,000	Likely to occur some time in the life of an item. Will occur several times. Likely to occur.
D	Remote	1 in	Unlikely but can reasonably be expected to occur.

Table 74 Hazard Probability Levels

LVL	Description	Prob.	Comments
		100,000	Unlikely to occur.
E	Improbable	1 in 1,000,000	Very unlikely to occur, but possible. Assume it will not occur.

Risk assessment is performed using the hazard severity and its probability. A risk assessment matrix is used to assign a Hazard Risk Index (HRI). The values in the risk assessment matrix are arbitrary but follow a logical pattern.

Table 75 Risk Assignment Matrix

Probability	Catastrophic		Critical		Marginal		Negligible	
Frequent	1	**very high**	3	**very high**	7	high	13	medium
Probable	2	**very high**	5	**very high**	9	high	16	medium
Occasional	4	**very high**	6	high	11	medium	18	low
Remote	8	high	10	medium	14	medium	19	low
Improbable	12	medium	15	medium	17	medium	20	low

Finding the intersection of the severity and probability yields an HRI number. The lower the HRI the greater the hazard risks. The HRI numbers are assigned to levels, which require different action.

Table 76 HRI Hazard Risk and Acceptance Levels

HRI	Hazard Risk	Hazard Risk Acceptance
1 to 5	Very high	Unacceptable risk. If not reduced, needs acquisition executive approval.
6 to 9	High	Unacceptable risk. If not reduced, needs program executive.
10 to 17	Medium	If not reduced, needs program manager approval.
18 to 20	Low	As directed by program policy.

So each hazard is listed in a table. The hazard has its associated mishaps. In many cases there is only one mishap per hazard. Severity and probability are assigned. This then results in an HRI and the HRI yields an overall risk and actions to be taken.

The safety analysis is an iterative process where hazard risk is identified then reduced for all hazards until there are no hazards or hazard risks. However at the end of the system design there will be residual risk. These are hazard risks not lowered or eliminated. These remaining hazards need to be clearly re-stated to all impacted stakeholders and incorporated into documents, training, refresher courses, and warning labels.

There are different formal and informal analysis techniques that can be used to support the safety design of the system. They are:

- **List of Possible Hazards Analysis:** Lists possible hazards in the system.
- **Safety Requirements Hazard Analysis:** Identifies new requirements associated with making the system safe.
- **Fault Tree Analysis:** Identifies unsafe events and shows how the system might trigger those unsafe events.
- **Failure Mode Effects Analysis:** Reviews FMEA reports and tags safety-related issues.
- **Impact of Failure Analysis:** Identifies at the highest level how failures might impact safety.
- **Safety Requirements Verification:** This is a different but parallel path to testing. These tests verify that safety requirements are satisfied. The level of rigor may be substantially higher than in normal tests. Also the tests may move into black box or what is sometimes called structural testing. This suggests standalone safety requirements be tracked in their own verification cross-reference matrix (VCRM).
- **System Hazard Analysis:** The system hazard analysis focuses on the system functions and interfaces. Its focus is to provide a level of safety risk for the overall system. It does this by assessing the safety risk of the system building blocks.
- **Subsystem Hazard Analysis:** The subsystem hazard analysis is like the system hazard analysis. It examines the subsystem functions and interfaces to provide a level of safety risk associated with the subsystem. This information feeds the system level hazard analysis.

There are various safety mitigation approaches. They each have their levels of effectiveness. The approaches for developing the safest system starting with the most effective and ending with the least effective are:

- **Inherently Safe**: Use design selection to make the architecture, design, and implementation inherently safe by eliminating the hazard. If the hazard cannot be removed try to make the mishap of minimal consequence via an inherently safe approach exclusive of safety mechanisms.
- **Use Safety Devices**: If hazards cannot be eliminated or their risk not reduced through design selection use fixed, automatic, or other protective design features or devices. Consider fault tolerances and make provisions for periodic safety checks of the safety devices.
- **Warning Devices**: When Inherent Safety or Safety Devices are not possible, use devices to detect an unsafe condition and produce an adequate alarm signal to alert personnel of the hazard. The signals are designed to minimize incorrect personnel reaction. Standards when present are

followed. Use a warning device for each Safety Device just in case it fails.

- **Procedures and Training**: When Inherent Safety, Safety Devices, or Warning Devices are not possible, use procedures and training to mitigate the risk. Procedures and training can include personal protective equipment, checklists, and two or more people checking each other's actions in a fault tolerant process. Certification or personnel proficiency training is used for safety-critical tasks and activities. For Level 1 and 2 hazards using just warning, caution, or other forms of write advisories is unacceptable. They can be used but the hazard remains and appropriate approvals are needed as part of the hazard risk acceptance rules. Use procedures and training as a backup mechanism for other mitigation approaches just in case they fail.

The safety elements in the physical architecture design are a combination of safety mitigation approaches. The safest architecture uses inherent safety as the strongest mitigation approach for all hazards. Strong architectures use the next highest-level mitigation approach followed by the lower levels as backups. The weakest use a mitigation approach with no lower level backup. For example no procedures or training is offered.

Table 77 Safety Mitigation Architectures

Mitigation	1	2	3	4	5	6	7	8
Inherently Safe	X							
Safety Device		X	X	X				
Warning Device		X	X		X	X		
Procedures and Training		X			X		X	

Arch 1: Most Safe and Arch 8: Least Safe

Failsafe is acknowledging that if there is any unexpected failure, the system fails in a safe manner. Many times this means a graceful degradation or loss of functions so that the system can continue to operate but at a significantly reduced performance and or functional level otherwise the loss of the system might lead to an unsafe condition.

Most safety issues are traceable to human error. It is the job of the automation system or manual process to protect the humans from themselves by making sure they do not make errors. The following is a list of practices that attempt to mitigate safety hazards. They are safe practices that can be applied to the design:

- Minimize potential of human error via automation, process, training, and other techniques
- Unobstructed clear safety labels such as for high voltage, heat, pressure, radiation exposure
- Rounded corners of shelves, tabletops, chairs, controls

- Proper use of ambient light
- Proper use of color in displays
- Sufficient size for display text and symbols
- Sufficient size for physical label lettering and symbols
- Sufficient display size to allow for proper distance to prevent crossed eyes
- Normal reach and field of view not exceeded
- Weight of objects less than 10 pounds
- Size of objects well within typical arm length

Author comment: If an airplane falls from the sky normally the airplane is blamed for the failure rather than the pilot (e.g. wing falls off). If an airplane crashes on the ground with no evidence of failure in the sky the pilot is blamed rather than faulting the system. The reality is that automated pilot control surfaced over 60 years ago. To blame a pilot for a system failure that should protect the pilot against human error is no longer appropriate unless criminal activity can be identified where the pilot wants the aircraft to crash.

6.8.2 Security Critical Functions and Requirements

The strategy for dealing with security critical functions is similar to the strategy used to deal with all critical functions. The first steps are to tag the security critical functions and the security critical requirements in the SRDB using well-understood and accepted criteria. Then there are different formal and informal analysis techniques that can be used to support the security design of the system[133].

- **List of Possible Security Failures Analysis:** Lists possible security failures in the system.
- **Security Requirements Analysis:** Identifies new requirements associated with making the system secure.
- **Fault Tree Analysis:** Identifies security failure events and shows how the system might trigger those security failure events.
- **Failure Mode Effects Analysis:** Reviews FMEA reports and tags security-related issues.
- **Impact of Failure Analysis:** Identifies at the highest level how failures might impact security.
- **Security Requirements Verification:** This is a different but parallel path to testing. These tests verify that security critical requirements are satisfied. The level of rigor is substantially higher than in normal tests. Also the tests move into black box or what is sometimes called structural testing. This

---

[133] These analysis techniques are described in detail in the text *Systems Practices as Common Sense*, by Walter Sobkiw, CassBeth, 2011, ISBN 978-0983253082.

suggests standalone security requirements be tracked in their own verification cross-reference matrix (VCRM). In the most secure systems there is a standalone set of security critical specifications that are usually in a need to know setting.

There are security techniques and mechanisms that can be used to assess and protect physical and or information items. The initial physical and information security elements to consider are:

- **Threat Assessment**: Identify the things that must be protected or secured and rate their importance or value.
- **Security Perimeter**: Establish security perimeters or boundaries and place the most important or valuable items in the inner most security boundaries.
- **Penetration Analysis**: Identify the threats, determine the changes of each threat associated with an item penetrating the boundary. Once the boundary is penetrated determine the impact (loss of life, physical harm, significant financial harm, etc)

As the security analysis and architecture are further refined additional security techniques and mechanisms need to be considered. Those that tend to be associated more with information security are need to know, authentication, and non-repudiation. Other security elements to consider are security abuse, simplicity, logging auditing, overhead impacts. There is a difference between the safety and security threat assessment levels. However the concept is the same.

Table 78 Security Threat Assessment Levels

Level	Threat Assessment	Description
1	Grave	Loss of life or Physical Harm
2	Financially Catastrophic	Financially destroys an organization or and individual, no chance of recovery
3	Financially Devastating	Financial losses causing reorganization or change in life style
4	Financially Serious	Financial losses leading to setbacks in plans, investments, or savings / profits
5	Financially Insignificant	No impact on organization or individual

Table 79 Penetration Analysis Criteria

Level	Penetration Result	Minimum
1	Grave	Three backup security mechanisms fail.
2	Financially Catastrophic	Two backup security mechanisms fail.

Table 79 Penetration Analysis Criteria

Level	Penetration Result	Minimum
3	Financially Devastating	Multiple security mechanisms fail.
4	Financially Serious	Security mechanism failed.
5	Financially Insignificant	No security mechanisms triggered.

Inherent in security is simplicity. It is like fault tolerance. The simpler the mechanisms the more secure. The less people have to do the more secure. When establishing a security boundary simplicity also translates to smaller size. That is why a reasonable threat assessment needs to be performed. If everything in the system is tagged at the same high threat level then there is a high probability that nothing will be secure as the system struggles with traditional system load and capacity issues. So simplicity also translates to making sure the things that need protecting are protected and not surrounded by less critical system elements that burden the security-processing core.

Security always translates to system overhead. The overhead results in reduced response time and more processing needs. This translates to cost. If the system is subjected to excessive security processing because of a poor threat assessment, security effectiveness will decrease.

Safety does not have this luxury of controlling the security critical boundary. Security can and should minimize its functionality, performance, and complexity.

Fail secure acknowledges that if there is any unexpected system failure, the system fails in a secure state. A secure state is achieved if no security compromise is possible. For example a broken access control mechanism should fail such that access is prevented under all but the most extreme trusted conditions.

A security monitor is a passive mechanism that searches for insecure patterns. A camera in a bank or department store coupled to some form of processing to detect insecure patterns is an example. A separate computer program that scans all inputs, outputs, and process start-ups shutdowns is another example of a security monitor. This is generally referred to as virus detection software. A monitor may or may not take action if a security issue is detected. For example a security monitor may detect three unsuccessful account login attempts and lock the account requiring the user to be re-established in the system. Re-establishing the account is accomplished with a more secure mechanism.

Example 18 Appropriate Inappropriate Security Monitoring

A security monitor takes resources away from the system. It becomes less and less effective as more elements are monitored more often. If everything is monitored, it is not a very effective approach to security. A count of the incorrect number of logins mechanism (three tries and account is locked) is an effective security monitor. It is also better than forcing users to have long obscure passwords that they will just write down. Alternatively scanning every piece of data entering a computer is not an effective security monitor as evidenced by the constant release of virus scanning software and patterns. In fact this approach always results in some number of users being compromised before the new security (virus) detection pattern and or software is released. A good analogy is that you cannot monitor every blade of grass and then tell each blade of grass which direction it should grow. It eventually becomes silly and futile.

As in all architecture approaches, the best security architecture is the simplest least complex approach. As complexity increases so does the possibility of failure. Complexity can be measured by the number of functions, interfaces, and items subjected to security. Complexity also can be measured by the number of people in the loop. They are in the loop because of flexibility that does not lend itself well to automation. The problem is that people make mistakes especially under stressful repetitive conditions. As with all architectures there is a bag of tricks[134] and lessons learned that should be considered:

- **Changing computer passwords too frequently**. Forcing the use of very obscure passwords. Too many passwords. These will lower security as people violate policy and write them down. A better approach might be to lock the account after three unsuccessful login attempts.
- **Applying the same tight security screening measures equally** to all threat elements even those that are obviously very low security threat levels. This wastes precious resources that can be applied to the real potential threats.
- **Not logging security related events**. Not reviewing the logs. Not using automation techniques to review the logs.
- **Ignoring audit findings**. Not modifying or improving the system when there are security breaches.

Security abuse is an interesting concept. Everyone is familiar with the concept of people given special privileges in the name of security and then abusing these privileges. History is full of horrific events in this regard. Electronic security abuse is new. The following is a sampling of recent security abuses:

- Blocking access to legitimate websites because of security software filters thus infringing or breaking restraint of free trade laws in the U.S.
- Forcing users to frequently change or have obscure passwords rather than unsuccessful login account activity detection and block.
- Allowing computer operating systems that are inherently insecure to

---

[134] This is a slang term describing the body of knowledge used to solve a problem

proliferate through an infrastructure.

- Forcing automated downloads and installation without user knowledge or understanding.
- In large systems there is a simple concept of freezing a proven stable baseline. Serious damage is done with moving baselines and unstable releases.

Author Comment: Today many are concerned about Internet security. Some might suggest that a technology could be developed to ensure privacy. However, there always will be those who will break the technology and compromise privacy. Today the model is to use commercial companies to provide email, web hosting and other computing and communications services. Regardless of contracts and agreements, companies can and do go out of business. When that happens, security and privacy become academic. A few hundred years ago our ancestors also engaged in communications and they had the same issues of security and privacy. Trade secrets between business associates could be compromised and private information between people could be used for blackmail. One of the approaches was to write into the US constitution a Post Office[135] mechanism and make it a crime to tamper with the mail. In this modern age of electronic communications should the Post Office be offering Internet web hosting and email services? Some solutions to problems are not technology. This was a massive revelation to me when I started working on the Air Traffic Control automation problem as a young engineer. This shook me to my core because I believed all problems could be solved with technology. These words came from the non-technologists in the community like economists and administrators. I now understand and accept this concept. Not all problems can be solved with technology.

6.8.3 Performance Critical Functions and Requirements

All systems have functions and performance. Performance is stated in quantitative terms and can be measured. The performance is associated with a function and how the function is implemented. Many times the function is implemented with technology, which then bounds the upper and lower limits of the resulting performance.

Performance is analyzed[136] within the context of a subsystem technology and its selected size. Performance numbers are typically timing, but they can be failure

---

including developing an effective design.

[135] United States Constitution, Section 8 Clause 7: To establish Post Offices and post Roads; The Constitution was adopted by a convention of the States on September 17, 1787 in Philadelphia, Pennsylvania.

[136] These analysis techniques are described in detail in the text Systems Practices as Common Sense, by Walter Sobkiw, CassBeth, 2011, ISBN 978-0983253082.

rates, reliability, error introductions, noise, frequency response loss, power loss, energy loss, death rate, cure rate, lines of code, processing load, cost of operations or any performance number needing to be allocated for some important insight into the system.

A system must have a certain level of function and performance and the level of function and performance will be at a cost. The cost may be excessive because the system may be inefficient. But implementation efficiency should not be tied to function level and performance. Poor efficiency can be the result of excessive system overhead or poor technology, which a good system functional and performance analysis should surface. For complex systems with limited or no competition there is no relationship between functional performance and maximizing financial results.

Performance can be identified for one or more functions, however the performance may exceed the state-of-the-art for the subsystem or subsystems that will support the functions. Yet the desired performance may be critical to the system. For example a serious automobile accident on a highway may block traffic for miles. Yet people are critically injured. The introduction of a helicopter into the health care system seems like common sense today but it was a major breakthrough for the previous generation. Only 50 years ago there was no solution. It was beyond the state-of-the-art.

New systems push the state-of-the-art in one or more areas. The challenge is to identify these areas and apply resources so that the system can become a reality.

Finding the quantitative measures of a system is not a simple task. Pioneers in previous centuries showed us how to extract and analyze performance numbers for electrical circuits and mechanical structures. Today we have a plethora of legacy systems and knowing the key performance numbers is critical so that various alternatives can be understood, compared, and form the foundation for new systems.

All systems start relatively small and evolve. The focus changes and things that were once impossible are added to the system as the decades unfold. In the beginning the story of the automobile was about speed, then durability, then suspension, aesthetics in form versus function arguments, safety like lights and brakes, comfort like windows, then wipers, heat, air conditioning, radio, FM radio, stereo, power windows, power seats, cruise control, and now GPS. In many ways this is like a pyramid model. You start with a base and build upon each layer until a pinnacle of perfection is reached both in terms of function and performance.

Author Comment: Again, it is always sad when progress is lost and things go back in terms of function or performance. Buried in the concept of performance is quality. A high quality solution is a solution that does everything exceptionally well.

The strategy for dealing with performance critical functions is similar to the strategy used to deal with all critical functions. The first steps are to tag the performance critical functions and the performance critical requirements in the SRDB using well-understood and accepted criteria. Performance is a function of the design approaches. The performance should be tracked for each design approach even if they all meet the accepted performance expectations. The reason for this is to always try to push the envelope of performance and quality.

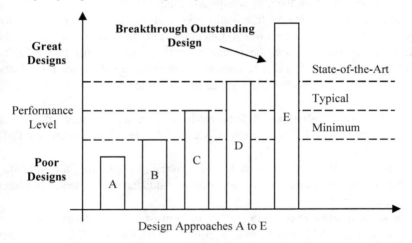

Figure 95 Breakthrough Outstanding Design Performance

At some point functional requirements and performance budgets need to be allocated to the various system elements. These allocations need to be based on sound analysis. It makes no sense to allocate a budget such as weight to an element if that allocation exceeds the known available products or worse the technologies for that element, and that portion of the weight budget can be easily accommodated by another element.

So technology impact is a key issue that needs to be considered when decomposing and allocating function and performance. This means that someone must always be cognizant of the technology impacts throughout the system engineering effort especially during the physical architecture design. A physical architecture design based on an imbalance of technology maturity or worse needlessly excessive technology immaturity must be avoided

6.8.4 Reliability Critical Functions and Requirements

Many systems have elements where reliability is extremely important or because of the nature of the functions and or performance the components may be inherently more unreliable. Today we tend to equate new components with higher reliability than old components. However that was not always the case.

Future systems may need to deal with these older scenarios again as new components are developed, new structures are offered, and new environments are in new systems. For example this may include using devices and or systems in certain environmental conditions they may not have been designed to withstand. There may be a design choice to use commercial smart phones and tablet computers on ships out at sea with salt fog or airplanes with high frequency vibration and pressure changes. These environmental conditions will degrade the reliability of traditionally high reliability components, devices, subsystems, and systems.

The strategy for dealing with reliability critical functions is similar to the strategy used to deal with all critical functions. The first steps are to tag the reliability critical functions and the reliability critical requirements in the SRDB using well-understood and accepted criteria. Then there are different formal and informal analysis techniques that can be used to support the design of the system[137].

- **Reliability Prediction:** Reliability is a measure of how quickly a component will fail and provide Mean Time Between Failure (MTBF) estimates.
- **Reliability Block Diagrams:** Part of reliability prediction, the reliability block diagrams depict the system from a redundancy and non-redundancy point of view.
- **Maintainability Prediction:** Offers the lowest replaceable unit definition and the expected Mean Time to Repair (MTTR), the MTTR includes many time elements that eventually lead to a repair.
- **Availability Prediction:** Considers the MTBF and MTTR to identify the probability that the system is operational in the expected operational time interval. This can be applied to the whole system or portions of the system such as an emergency mode of operation. This is typically the reason identifying reliability critical functions and requirements.
- **Reliability Growth:** Sometimes the only way to achieve high reliability and availability is through a reliability growth program.
- **Failure Reporting Analysis and Corrective Action System (FRACAS):** A FRACAS is used to increase reliability and safety. Security may use a parallel system to maintain a need to know separation.

6.8.5 Other Critical Functions and Requirements

Many systems have their own unique critical functions and requirements. The stakeholders are a source for many of these functions and requirements. The following are examples of other critical functions and requirements:

- **Fault Tolerance:** Fault tolerance is a critical function with critical requirements. All the details must be addressed and converted to lock tight

---

[137] These analysis techniques are described in detail in the text *Systems Practices as Common Sense*, by Walter Sobkiw, CassBeth, 2011, ISBN 978-0983253082.

requirements. The fault tolerant function and the mechanism that implements that function are very critical.

- **System Stability:** The system can not freeze or crash ever, there are functions at the infrastructure level that fall into this category.
- **System Integrity:** The system can not lose data or damage data, functions that handle data fall into this category.
- **Emergency Mode:** When there is a catastrophic event the system is able to transition to an emergency mode of operation and support a minimal set of emergency functions and performance levels.
- **System Critical Responses:** Some system functions can not make a mistake otherwise there are catastrophic results, these are functional that tend to offer decisions and control sensitive life dependent machinery.

The resulting requirements to satisfy these critical functions may translate into different technology levels during implementation. As the technology level increases and moves into and beyond state-of-the-art the resulting implementation becomes more unproved. Unproven designs may have more risk of negative emergence.

6.9 Interfaces

When designing the physical architecture minimizing the number and complexity of the interfaces will minimize the complexity of the system. However this may come at a cost where one or more subsystems have increased complexity. This complexity may push the subsystem to a beyond state-of-the-art status. Thus there are tradeoffs. There are also issues associated with maintainability and future growth that may impact the interface choices.

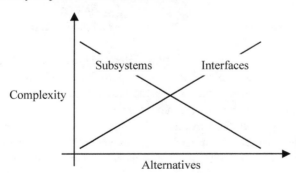

Figure 96 Complexity Interfaces Versus Subsystems

There are two broad categories of system interfaces to consider. They are internal and external interfaces. Today when we think of interfaces we jump to computer and communications devices. However the way a living room connects to a dining room in a floor plan is also an example of an interface where depending on the floor plan layout the space will have different characteristics. For example one approach is to have a great room that includes both the living room and dining room functions. The delineation can be nothing more than the placement of lighting fixtures. Alternatively the living room and dining room can be interfaced via a hallway. Yet in another instance the living room and dining room can interface via an entrance foyer.

Example 19 Interface Translation Box or Gateway

There are times when there is a desire to interface two computer-based systems together. For example there is a new system replacing an old system and the old system has a backup that the stakeholders would like to preserve until the new system is proven to be stable with its new backup mechanisms. The question is what is the best approach to implement the interface between the new system and the old backup system. One approach is to make the needed changes in the old backup system. Another approach is to add temporary elements to existing parts of the new system. A third approach is to add a translation box or gateway between the systems and not make any changes to the new system or old backup system. Each of these approaches has advantages and disadvantages that need to be surfaced and understood.

There are four broad interface types that should be considered when structuring a system. The interfaces exist within the system linking the various subsystems. These are internal interfaces. There are also interfaces to other systems, these are external interfaces. The interface types are:

- Person to person
- Machine to machine
- Person to machine
- Machine to person

A system may use any combination of these interface types. Their characteristics are driven by the media and protocol used in the interface mechanism. Many will assume that a person to person interface is the slowest, however a simple voice communication from one person to the next person may be the fastest and most effective interface approach. For example there is no faster or more effective interface to provide an alert than a screaming passenger in an automobile with a distracted driver as brake lights are quickly approaching the front of the vehicle.

Table 80 Automation Interfaces to Consider

1 Physical Interface
1.1 Mechanical Requirements: Envelope, attachment, obscuration, alignment
1.2 Master Tooling
1.3 Mass Properties: Weight, moment-of-inertia, center-of-gravity location, axis

Table 80 Automation Interfaces to Consider

2 Electronic Interface
2.1 Command Signals: Format, rates, identification
2.2 Data signals: Radio frequency characteristics, format, rate
2.3 Telemetry Signals: Format, clock, identification, recording

3 Electrical Interface
3.1 Electrical Power: Type, voltage, power profile, protection
3.2 Interface Pin Assignments
3.3 Electromagnetic Compatibility

4 Hydraulic Pneumatic Interface: Type, flow rate, temperature, pressure

5 Software
5.1 Data: Inputs, outputs, rates, accuracy
5.2 Messages: Format, content, storage
5.3 Protocols: Enable, processing, validation, error detection, recovery

6 Hardware Software Interfaces
6.1 Interface: Diagrams, standards, and conventions
6.2 Timing and Sequencing: Control and logic, relationships, data transfers, input sensing

7 Environmental
7.1 Structural: Vibration, shock, acoustic, loads, dynamic mode shapes
7.2 Thermal: Temperature range, heating rates, heat transfer surfaces
7.3 Magnetic: Flux density, rate-of-change
7.4 Radiation: Type, flux density, total dose
7.5 Ambient: Pressure, temperature, containment
7.6 Air Conditioning: Temperature, flow rates

8 Human Interface
8.1 Voice Phraseology
8.2 Display
8.3 Tactile
8.4 Audio

9 Safety

10 Operational Limitations

6.10 Allocation Complexity

As the system functions are understood and grouped the system structure starts to surface. This will lead to different segments, elements, subsystems, assemblies, subassemblies, and parts. All of these system hierarchies may be needed, however if there are artificial hierarchies the system will have unnecessary overhead during operations and cost more to develop, produce, and maintain.

Table 81 Factors Associated with Complexity

Complexity Metrics (numbers of)	
• Hierarchies	• Segments
• External Interfaces	• Subsystems
• Internal Interfaces	• Assemblies
• Engineering Disciplines	• Parts
• Installation Locations	• Existing Technologies
• Location Types	• New Technologies
• Users	• Modified Designs
• Elements	• New Designs

The measure of complexity is qualitative unless there is historical data in the organization. Many suggest that complexity is non-linear and increases exponentially, so there is always a desire to minimize complexity. Another consideration in system complexity is the number of engineering disciplines needed to design the system. As the number of design disciplines increase so does the design complexity. There are many factors that can be tracked and used to gauge system complexity.

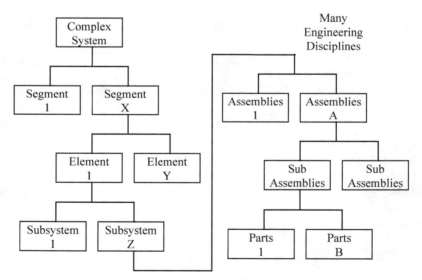

Figure 97 Complex System Design Hierarchy

The allocation decisions that lead to different system hierarchies can be shown with a tree diagram or a system hierarchy. It is structure and interface independent yet shows the system complexity and shows how information products might be organized. It is engineering discipline independent and allows most stakeholders to have a view of the system that will allow them to contribute to the design solution.

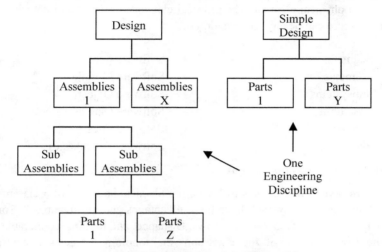

Figure 98 Simple Design Hierarchies

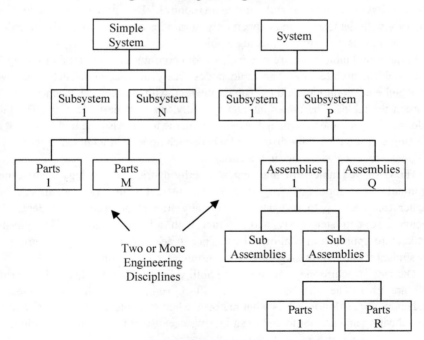

Figure 99 Less Complex System Design Hierarchies

6.11 Physical Structure

The design takes on a physical structure when the functions and performance are allocated to a physical element. The physical element is named and described. The physical structure can be any combination of:

- Segments
- Elements
- Subsystems
- Assemblies
- Subassemblies
- Parts

- Software Items
- Software Modules
- Software Objects
- Software Classes
- Software Files
- Software Executables

Example 20 Classroom Layout

There are several alternatives to layout the physical structure of a classroom in an education setting. They each have their advantages and disadvantages. Some of the more typical physical layouts are: rows, U shaped, and multiple roundtable

In the row structure of the classroom the topology suggests a centralized physical architecture. The teacher is the central node performing the processing associated with a lecture and classroom control. The student interactions are primarily with the teacher and happen only in rare instances when heads are willing to turn and focus on a student making a point.

In the round table structure of the classroom configuration the topology suggests a hierarchical architecture. The table nodes freely interact with each other with unencumbered communications. Tables interact with the central teacher walking between the tables. The tables interact typically via a single table node. The table node may be appointed or change depending on the topic. Also the table may not act as a single unit but be fully distributed where each node or student can interact with any other student and teacher in the classroom.

The U shaped table structure suggests a fully distributed topology using a mesh communications topology. Any student can interact with any student. Also the teacher can walk up to and interact with any student or group of students. The teacher also can step away and interact with all the students. This physical architecture approach also allows the teacher to see any work being performed by any student while minimizing movement through the classroom.

The row structure may minimize the ability for students to cheat when written tests are give. The victims are to the left or right of the cheating student. A fundamental question to ask is what happens when students are asked to rise above petty cheating and are not forced to sit in rows because of the threat of cheating.

Example 21 House Floor Plan

Today many new houses in the US are characterized in terms of an open or closed floor plan. The open floor plan is more of a modern trend and is made possible by truss roof structures that reduce the need for load bearing inner walls.

An open floor plan has the advantage of visually offering a large space. The interfaces between areas in the open space are simple. The interfaces to other spaces are also simple and tend to avoid hallways. The disadvantage of this architecture is that it does not attenuate sound. The sound travels freely through the space.

A closed floor plan uses separate rooms connected by one or more hallways. Many times these spaces have doorways that can be closed. This architecture offers visual privacy and also sound privacy.

One approach to have the advantage of the closed and open architecture floor plan is to combine an open space with other open spaces and a closed space. For example the center of the floor plan can be open while the left side can be partially closed and the right side can be fully closed. An example would be to have a master bedroom and it's associated spaces such as dressing and bathroom on the right as a closed space. On the left can be multiple bedrooms that open and flow to a bathroom and playroom space. This allows the adults to have full privacy and silence while allowing the children to have privacy when sleeping yet an open space when at play.

Certain functions have certain characteristics[138]. These characteristics are important because they will form the basis of allocation to the physical architecture design. The following is a list of words and word phrases to consider when characterizing functions:

Table 82 Function Types

Safety Critical	Highly Parallel	Offline
Security Critical	Extremely Important	Manually Intensive
Processing Intensive	Less Important	Cognitively Intensive
Data Intensive	System Level	Rarely Executed
Event Driven	Communications	Continuously Executed
Cyclic	Display Intensive	Aesthetically Sensitive
Random	Human Interaction	Aesthetically Neutral
Storage Intensive	Backbone	Correlation Intensive
Communications Intensive	Function Overhead	Fusion Intensive
Data Transport	Mission	Signal Processing
Data Translation	Maintenance	Vision Intensive
Data Transformation	Support	Sound Intensive
Transcendental (Trigonometric)	Delivery and Installation	Motion Intensive
Floating Point	Training	Decision Function
Algorithmically Intensive	Diagnostic Self Test	Cognitive Processing
Highly Linear	Online	

[138] MIL-STD-490 is an excellent source for function types. It is partially included in modified form as an appendix to this text.

This list is not exhaustive but it should help in identifying the function types in a system. The function types need to be clearly understood and grouped, allocated, and applied in the physical architecture design. For example highly parallel functions are ideal candidates for distributed processing. Aesthetically sensitive functions may trigger the need to add artists or industrial designers to the team who can impact the design.

There are broad physical structures that can be considered when performing the allocations. These structures give rise to an architecture typology and result in different interface characteristics.

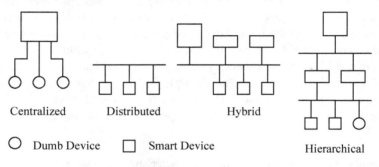

Figure 100 Architecture Types

Although the descriptions of architecture types and topologies is strongly related to computing and communications they strongly apply to systems where organizations of people and their activities are the heart of the system. Understanding these organizational structures will help when considering architecture alternatives for:

- Personal Transportation
- Electric Power
- Health Care

- Education
- Food Production
- Waste Management

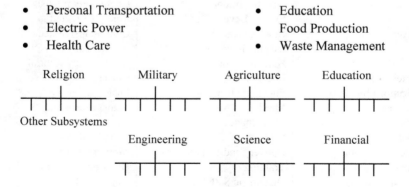

Figure 101 Centralized Architectures

The first questions are associated with the extremes of centralized or distributed structure. If distributed how distributed. What happens in the event of failure? What happens when the system needs to grow? How can technology be inserted? What are the maintenance ramifications? What system has the greatest longevity?

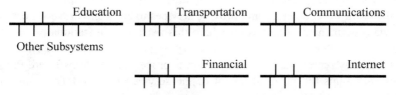

Figure 102 Distributed Architectures

Different subsystems have functionality that can be broadly characterized as processing, storage, distribution, or any combination. These subsystems then fall into some topology. For example a distribution subsystem can be the hub of a star topology or the central node of a top down centralized topology. A distribution subsystem also can take on the role of storage.

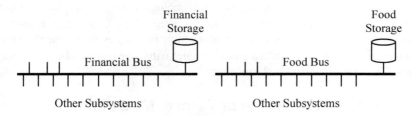

Figure 103 Distribution and Storage Architectures

Example 22 Schools Architecture Topology

Many towns in New Jersey, such as Cherry Hill, that empathize education have a distinct school architecture concept. Elementary schools are at the neighborhood level. This allows the children to walk to school or be bussed for very short distances in their neighborhoods. So there are large numbers of elementary schools. Middle schools are fewer in number and children are bussed form multiple neighborhoods, but walking is still a possibility. The high schools are usually one or two. Also the neighborhoods tend to be concentrated around the schools. Commercial and industrial areas do not break the neighborhoods apart, again allowing children easier access to the schools. So the school architecture interacts with the community architecture and is driven by zoning laws and master plans. In the last two decades of the last century many communities were created with no master plans or architecture concepts. Children in these communities travel long distances across commercial and industrial areas to regional schools and the concept of community is lost.

6.11.1 Organizational Topology

Topology is the interconnection of various elements providing functional services. The topology can be physical or functional. For example someone can physically work in New Jersey and provide services to someone in New York. This can be via a permanent organization where this person organizationally reports to the New York office. Or it can be temporary as part of a contract on a project. Logical topology represents how information is processed and transferred. Physical topology represents the physical layout of the service providers. There are broad processing topology categories:

- Point to Point or Line or Point to Multi Point
- Star or Centralized Topology
- Bus
- Ring

- Mesh
- Fully Connected
- Tree

Do not confuse these organizational topologies with computer network topologies. The computer network topologies were born from these processing topologies and their study. Also, these processing topologies do not apply to just computers. They can apply to machines, people, nature or any combination in our systems. They are organizational in nature.

6.11.2 Point to Point or Line or Point to Multi Point

The Point to Point Topology is the simplest topology. It is a permanent link between two endpoints. If multiple point to point nodes are linked in a chain, that is a line topology. There is no limit to the size of the chain. If one node is a central node that links to multiple nodes where the other nodes do not interact, that is a point to multi point topology. It is a classic example of a central architecture where one large node interacts with other less capable nodes. The central node has a majority of the functionality.

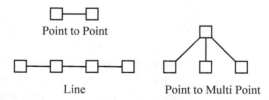

Point to Point

Line   Point to Multi Point

Figure 104 Point to Point / Line / Multi Point Topology

Its advantage is the simplicity of the connection, which minimizes possible loss or corruption of data. It is also easiest to secure the link in this topology. There is only one simple element to consider. There is minimal overhead because there is no need to consider the needs of other nodes on the same connection. So channel conflict is non existent.

Its disadvantage is that if data or information needs to move from one node to a far node it needs to pass through other nodes that perform a data transport. In some cases the data needs to be stored before it is forwarded. This is a store and forward function.

6.11.3 Star or Centralized Topology

The Star Topology uses a central resource to link to all other resources in a hub or spoke arrangement. All communications is through a hub processor. The hub is allocated functions such as processor scheduling, data fusion from the nodes, status monitoring management and other functions associated with two or more nodes. The nodes are allocated functions that minimize inter node communications. This is an example of a smart centralized architecture where the nodes have a significant amount of processing capability.

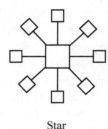

Star

Figure 105 Star / Centralized Topology

The disadvantage of this topology is that the hub is a single point of failure. It is also a potential processing bottleneck. Growth is also limited if the hub cannot be expanded to accommodate more data or more centralized functions.

The advantage of this topology is that failure propagation is minimized if a node fails. The other nodes continue providing services in the presence of failed nodes.

6.11.4 Bus Topology

A Bus Topology is a distributed topology. It links all the processing nodes via a common communications mechanism. This allows any processing node to communicate with any other processing node. It also allows for broadcast so that one node can make its findings simultaneously available to all other nodes.

Bus

Figure 106 Bus Topology

However a bus needs rules so that the participants do not simultaneous access it for their needs. A bus is basically a backbone. The rules start with some form of control where something identifies that the bus is about to be used by a node. There are multiple approaches to implementing a bus control mechanism but they fall into the following broad categories:

- **Interrupt:** In the interrupt approach a node raises an interrupt signal and this tells the other nodes to be silent until the interrupt is released. Since not all resources on the bus have the same urgency to deliver or receive data, a priority can be used on the interrupt mechanism. So if a higher priority interrupt is raised, the lower priority interrupt and transfer can stop, and release the bus to the higher priority interrupt. This allows for a significantly faster response time for high priority needs.

- **Master:** In the master approach there is a node on the bus that randomly solicits the other nodes for data. There can be variants where multiple masters using an interrupt mechanism allow one master to take control of the bus and solicit its selected nodes or resources.

- **Polling:** The polling approach is similar to the master approach except the solicitation for data is periodic rather than random.

- **Round Robin:** The round robin is an approach where each node is given a time slot to take control of the bus. The data is passed during that time slot or until the transfer is complete, depending on the round robin approach.

- **Collision Detection:** In the collision detection[139] approach each node listens to the bus. If it is silent and a node needs to access the bus, it just accesses the bus. It then listens to determine if the data is damaged. If two or more nodes access the bus at the same time the listening nodes detect their own respective damaged data. They then wait a random amount of time and try to access the bus with an new transmit of data. The collisions are rare when few nodes are present and there is little traffic.

Even though these ideas were used on internal computer buses, the interrupt, master, polling, and round robin techniques apply to people and organizations. Even Collision Detection a conceptual form of interrupt used in external computer communications applies and its analog is a shouting match among a group of people in a heated meeting.

The function allocations to the nodes could be anything but one of the goals should be to minimize traffic on the bus. Usually there is a tradeoff between a heavily used node (while the others are under used) and high bus traffic. The trick is to balance the architecture such that the nodes and bus are effectively used from a timing-and-sizing point of view. This is difficult because there is a temptation to

---

[139] Ethernet became a very popular personal computer communications mechanism in the late 1990's. Its performance was managed with the use of network switches that limited the number of nodes and thus collisions.

size all the nodes to be the same size. This has advantages from a maintainability and operations point of view. Making all the nodes the same is easier if the data can be sliced and allocated to the processors that then use all the same functions to process the different data sets. For example computer nodes process data[140] while healthcare facilities process different patients. The patients are analogous to data.

The advantage of a bus is that there is no single point of failure. Some might argue that the bus could be physically damaged or a node could fail in some way to prevent the bus from properly working. In most instances there are solutions for these failure cases including using redundant busses. The bus is excellent for broadcast messages. If the bus is implemented with a round robin or polling mechanism it exhibits many of the advantages of a token ring topology.

The disadvantage of this approach is that a standard must be developed and followed by all the nodes. If a node does not follow the standard, there is the potential for the node to seriously degrade the performance of the bus. As more nodes are added the bus traffic increases. At some point no more nodes can be added without the system failing to function properly. A bus is also limited by distance, depending on its implementation. As the distance increases the signal is susceptible to noise and timing delays which may lead to data errors. The bus is worst for point to point messages between nodes. If the bus is implemented with a collision detection mechanism, the collisions become excessive after approximately 30 nodes and performance significantly degrades. If the bus is implemented using an interrupt mechanism there is the risk that a node will hog the bus and prevent other nodes from accessing the bus. If the bus is implemented with a master mechanism, it then has a single point of failure.

6.11.5 Ring Topology

A Ring Topology is a distributed topology. It connects each node to exactly two other nodes. Data travels from node to node; each node is a repeater station where the signal is corrected before being sent to an adjacent node. The failure of a single node will stop the flow of information unless the ring can send data in both directions (clockwise and counter clockwise). From a processing point of view the ring brings order to the management of the individual processors. A token arrives at a node and the node gets the opportunity to provide data on the ring. If there is no data to be offered by the node, then the token is immediately passed to the next node. This is a very deterministic mechanism.

There are many advantages to the token ring. Its roots can be found in the round robin concept of internal computer buses. Since control is not random but based on the deterministic passing of the token, data integrity is very high. It cannot be lost because of random events. Its performance is also very predictable and stable. Every node on the ring is always given the opportunity to offer its data; other nodes cannot

---

[140] Computer processors transport, translate, and transform the data.

lock out nodes. Its structure allows for very high utilization rate. Basically the ring utilization can approach 100% without loss of data. No other topology offers that performance characteristic. There is no central controlling authority that can fail. The control is fully distributed to each node. When exceeding 30 nodes the token ring exhibits superior performance relative to collision detection buses.

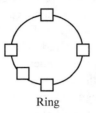

Ring

Figure 107 Ring Topology

The disadvantages are associated with the stopping of the token and the relative position of the nodes. If the token stops, there is the possibility the topology can fragment into two rings unless there is a backup mechanism such as reversing tokens and or redundant rings. Moving and adding nodes can affect response time relative to other nodes. For example if two cooperating nodes are adjacent the response time is minimal. If the cooperating nodes are at opposite ends of the ring the response time is maximized.

6.11.6 Mesh Topology - Fully or Partially Connected

A Mesh Topology is a distributed topology. It connects every node to every other node. In a mesh all nodes can simultaneous transmit to one or more other nodes. Most view this as point to point connections from every node to every node or multi point to multi point connections. However, this is just like a bus except that a bus has only one node transmitting at any given instant. From an implementation point of view this is difficult to imagine without time division or frequency division multiplexing and moving the time to infinitely small or the number of frequencies to infinity. From a practical point of view a bus can behave like a mesh if the bus transfer rates and delays are insignificant in the system timing budgets.

If the mesh is viewed as a multi point to multi point connection scheme then the number of physical connections is:

$$\text{Connections} = N*(N-1)/2$$

A mesh topology is self-healing. If one node breaks down or a connection goes bad the network can still operate. The network is very reliable because there are multiple paths to a node. Some can relate to the mesh topology in a wireless network setting.

In a partially connected mesh only some of the nodes are connected to other nodes. This allows for redundant paths in the event of failure while minimizing the connection complexity.

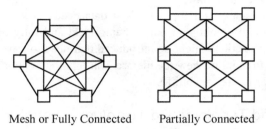

Mesh or Fully Connected   Partially Connected

Figure 108 Mesh Topology - Fully Partially Connected

The advantage of the mesh is the ability to continue to operate in the presence of multiple failures. It is the most survivable topology. There is no routing, so there is no place where data is only being transported and subjected to delay, possible corruption, or loss. The connection is direct from the source node to the destination node.

The disadvantages of the mesh are complexity associated with the connections. This translates to very complex physical connectivity, which becomes impossible with a large number of nodes. It needs a mechanism to route traffic to other nodes. Although every node is connected to every node and there is no forwarding as in the case of the Internet, something needs to decide which node should receive the data.

6.11.7 Tree or Hierarchical Topology

A Tree or Hierarchical Topology is a distributed topology. It must have a minimum of three levels since two levels is a Star or Centralized topology. The hierarchy can be implemented with point to point connections or a bus. Two levels of buses represent a two level hierarchy.

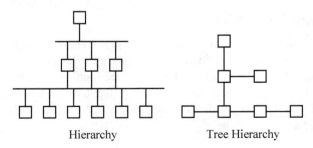

Hierarchy   Tree Hierarchy

Figure 109 Tree or Hierarchical Topology

The advantage of this topology is isolation of traffic and processing to selected levels. This isolation allows for performance optimization, security isolation, and less fault propagation. It is also advantageous from a maintenance point of view. If online maintenance is not possible, then only selected levels or tree branches are affected during the down time.

The disadvantage of this topology is if data needs to traverse across different levels. The topology might start out as being ideal and fully optimized but as the system evolves, functions might be introduced that need to traverse different levels. So from a growth point of view the hierarchical topology might start to break down and not allow for future capabilities.

6.11.8 Hybrid Topology and Topology Control

A hybrid topology is a combination of two or more topologies. Most infrastructure systems are a hybrid topology. This is not because of a conscious effort to structure the system in a certain way. Instead the systems evolve and through trial and error the systems are optimized to their levels of capability. The dilemma is what to do when an existing system that evolved over 50 years reaches its limit. So all of the sudden system practitioners today may be faced with creating systems that use multiple topologies.

Buried within all the topologies is the idea of connectivity and control. The issue of control is significant. Being able to statically assign functions and data to different nodes in a topology is a challenging task. The modeling effort is significant.

Creating a mechanism that dynamically assigns functions and data to available resources is difficult if that mechanism is centralized. It is extremely difficult if the assignment mechanism itself is distributed and tries to take full advantage of a distributed topology. The concept of a fully distributed operating system that has full view of the whole system and simultaneously lives in all nodes so that one or more node failures will not lead to a failure of the distributed operating system is a significant challenge.

6.11.9 Interface Topology

The system interfaces are driven by the physical structure of the design. The interfaces can be expressed in terms of topology. The goal is to have the most effective interface topology. This is an interface topology that matches the natural topology of the architecture. However it is possible to have an interface topology that does not match the architecture topology and thus reduces the performance of the total design.

Author Comment: Modern computer network designs are a good example where the network topology needlessly complicates the actual physical architecture. There are large numbers of switches, routers, and gateways that are usually placed in the name of security. These are management nightmares and sources of constant system failure after maintenance activities are performed.

6.12 Reverse Engineering a System

Reverse engineering an existing system is one approach to engage in new system design. The strengths and weaknesses of the design under study are surfaced. Also the technology becomes well understood and can be compared with the new technologies associated with the new design. The reverse engineering can be performed on pervious generation designs, existing designs, and similar designs in other application areas and industries.

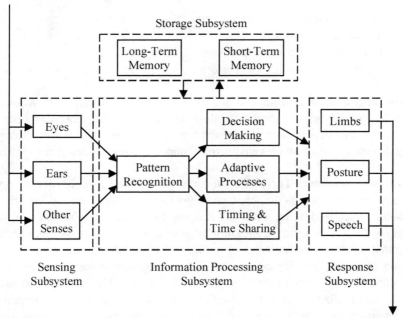

Figure 110 Human Information Processing System[141]

Understanding a system at the implementation level may require special equipment that is expensive and complex to use. It also may lead to the destruction of critical components. Understanding a system from a conceptual level is difficult without having the needs explicitly stated. The need may be a speculation, but it cannot be easily determined without investigation. Also there may be no information products such as analysis, architecture descriptions, specifications,

---

[141] Designing And Developing Maintainable Products And Systems, DOD Handbook, MIL-HDBK-470A August 1997, MIL-HDBK-470 June 1995, MIL-HDBK-471 June 1995.

design documents, etc to help in understanding the system at the conceptual level.

When we attempt to reverse engineer a system we usually start at the physical architecture design. This is an abstraction level that we usually are able to address with least resistance. We carefully disassemble the design and speculate on the function of each level of disassembly. We then reassemble the design to gain further insights into the design. The goal is to ensure that there is no damage and the design will work once re-assembled.

This reverse engineering process is similar to troubleshooting a system in the absence of maintenance manuals or during the early design test phases. This is a problem solving skill where the practitioner:

- Identifies the high level subsystems
- Speculates on behavior
- Correlates behavior to a function
- Deduces functionality and performance of subsystems

The process of observation and deduction requires significant time. Knowledge of similar systems helps to shorten the time. This is one of the reasons why previous maintainers can be excellent design team members. Seeing and troubleshooting many diverse designs provides a powerful foundation for developing new designs.

Author Comment: There is a fundamental question associated with reverse engineering – does it require more technology to reverse engineer a design than the technology used to develop a design? Reverse engineering an electron tube would be impossible without significant knowledge of electricity. Reverse engineering an integrated circuit is an exercise in visualization of very small structures. This requires serious technology beyond the simple integrated circuit. However gaining the initial idea for playing with electrons to create a valve (i.e. electron tube) is useful. Also realizing that miniaturization is a worthy goal to pursue because the end results are seen and appreciated. I raise this discussion because those who are technologically illiterate believe that reverse engineering allows someone less capable to duplicate a technology. That is incorrect. It requires more technology to understand something than to develop it using sound scientific and engineering practices. This elevates testing to a whole new level especially when it is part of a Research Development Test and Evaluation activity.

6.13 Identifying Physical Design Alternatives

If the need will be satisfied using some form of automation there are some basic approaches to identifying the physical architecture design alternatives. These same techniques also can be modified and applied to identify architecture design alternatives with little or no automation. The discussion begins with automated systems.

The first approach is to think only in terms of manual activities using no technology or automation. Instead people in an organizational structure perform the work. The team needs to identify the type of work activities performed and how they interrelate. They then identify organizational boundaries and name the organizations so that the activities are suggested by the organizational names. This also starts to identify the interfaces.

The second approach is to examine the manual activities in the first approach and determine what can be automated reasonably using existing technologies and known products or solutions. This will modify the organizational structure and resulting interfaces.

The third approach is to examine the manual and automated elements of the second approach and think in terms of state-of-the-art technologies and products or solutions. Also think in terms of modifying these state-of-the-art approaches to fit the need in this state-of-the-art physical architecture. Again the structure and interfaces will change.

The reality is that the team needs to strive to arrive at the 3d approach. However the team may not have the knowledge to arrive at the 3d approach without significant saturation and understanding of the problem solution space. Also if the team does operate in the state-of-the-art space, it is still prudent to develop the manual and reasonably automated physical architectures so that the structure and interface alternatives are fully understood. With this background it is possible to offer alternative physical architecture designs for selection and tradeoff. These alternatives have different performance characteristics associated with the individual physical elements and the interfaces. For example some alternatives may have heavily loaded interfaces. Some may have heavily loaded processing blocks. Some may have single points of failure or significant impacts in the presence of failure. Some alternatives may be more maintainable or producible than other alternatives.

If the need will be satisfied using more of a static structure (e.g. house, bridge, office building, industrial park) with limited functional processing a similar approach can be used to surface the physical architecture. The discussion shifts to identifying physical alternatives where automation is not the driving factor.

Although the first approach of identifying people in an organizational structure that performs some work is not applicable it is possible that different groups of people can interact with the physical structure in different ways. Capturing that interaction is the first approach.

The second approach for a static structure is similar to the automation intensive system. Identify existing technologies, products, or solutions to support the physical architecture. We are not picking them we are just surveying the available space. This will modify the physical structure.

The third approach for a static structure is also similar to the automation intensive system. Think in terms of state-of-the-art technologies and products or solutions. Again the structure will change. This should surface alternatives for tradeoff and selection. Also the knowledge gained in getting to this point will allow for an effective tradeoff of the solution.

6.14 Technology and Allocation Selections

The physical architecture design is dominated by technology and allocation selections. The technologies change the allocation alternatives. The allocations change the technology alternatives. The allocation alternatives change the interfaces. This is a multi dimensional problem that involves qualitative and qualitative information.

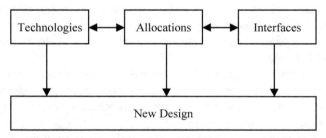

Figure 111 Technologies Allocations and Interfaces

This suggests that the staff is fluent in the pervious design alternatives and technologies before they start the new design process. However that is a false view and leads to significant problems including poor new designs. The new design is new, and so the team needs to be a mixture of insiders and outsiders. What is key is that the organization needs to be a learning organization so that the team can quickly learn the current state-of-the-art and its limitations.

Example 23 Technology and Allocation Selection Ship Propulsion

Today many are focused on computers, communications, and software. However there are still significant challenges outside these areas. The following example will describe different ship engine propulsion systems. They use different technologies and allocation alternatives. The technologies are gas turbines, diesel engines, electric motors, generators, and fixed or variable pitch propellers. The interfaces are accomplished via different gearbox and clutch assemblies.

The need is to provide ship propulsion while maximizing fuel efficiency, minimizing weight and space. The impact of failure is a significant driver because losing propulsion power at sea is a very bad situation. Diesel engines should operate at a certain RPM in order to maximize efficiency. This introduces the need for gear reduction boxes and or variable pitch propellers. Variable pitch propellers are less reliable than fixed pitch propellers and may not even be able to support certain load conditions.

Combined diesel and diesel (CODAD)

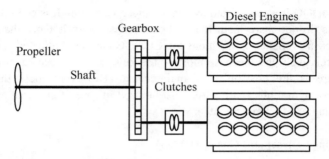

Figure 112 Combined Diesel and Diesel CODAD

Combined diesel and diesel (CODAD) uses two diesel engines to power a single propeller shaft. A gearbox and clutches enable either of the engines or both of them together to drive the shaft. This is one of the simplest designs. The CODAD is a distributed architecture design. It is distributed because the diesel engines share load. The gearbox is a single point of failure suggesting that there should be spares on the ship. If both diesel engines fail there is the possibility to cannibalize one diesel engine for parts to get the other diesel engine up and running, even if in a degraded mode. For a twin propeller ship the configuration can be duplicated.

Combined Diesel or Gas (CODOG)

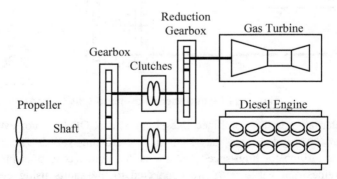

Figure 113 Combined Diesel or Gas CODOG

The Combined Diesel or Gas (CODOG) uses two different engine technologies. They are a gas turbine and a diesel engine. While engaged in normal cruising speed the diesel engine is the primary power source. When engaged in high-speed operations the gas turbine is activated and the diesel engine is deactivated. So there is only one power source engaged at any given time. In the CODOG there is a single shaft and propeller. If twin propellers are desired the configuration can be duplicated.

The CODOG is a centralized hybrid architecture design. It is centralized because the engines do not share load. It is hybrid because there is more than one engine type. For twin propeller applications the CODOG can be duplicated. The impact of failure is relatively low because most of the key parts are located in the ship hull where there is the possibility of maintenance. However unless there are two CODOG configurations spare parts must be used in case of an event as opposed to cannibalizing one to make the other run.

Combined Diesel and Gas (CODAG)

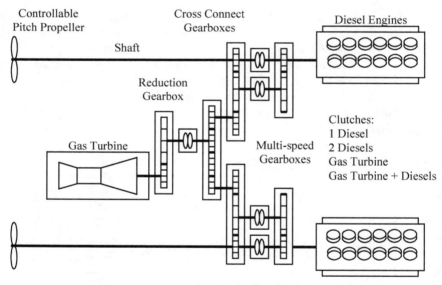

Figure 114 Combined Diesel and Gas CODAG

An alternative is the Combined Diesel and Gas (CODAG). For every propeller shaft there is one dedicated diesel engine for cruising speed. There is also one geared gas turbine for high-speed operations that connects to both propellers. The diesel engines and gas turbine are connected to the shafts using gearboxes and clutches. Although the CODOG uses simpler gearing compared to CODAG it needs more powerful (or more) gas turbines for the same maximum power output than the CODAG. The CODAG fuel consumption at high speed is less than the CODOG; the CODAG is more efficient than the CODOG. The CODAG maximum speed is considerably faster than their cruise speed.

Typically the output power when switching from the diesel engines to the diesel plus turbine engine combined is too large for controllable pitch propellers. So special multi-speed gearboxes are needed to limit the diesel rotations without changing the gear ratios of their transmissions. This is in contrast to CODOG designs, which couple the diesels to the shaft using a simple fixed ratio gearbox and disengages when the turbine is switched on.

In simple CODAG designs the gear ratio for the diesel engine is changed from two diesels only to two diesels plus turbine mode. Some designs have three different gear ratios: one each for a single diesel, the second for a double diesel, and the third when the gas turbine is engaged.

The power output per square foot is higher for a gas turbine than a diesel, however it is less fuel-efficient. Thus the CODAG has a smaller footprint than a diesel only power plant with the same maximal power output. The CODAG uses smaller diesel engines and the gas turbine and gearbox use little additional space. It has the high fuel efficiency of diesel engines when cruising, allowing greater range and lower fuel costs than with gas turbine alone. However a heavy and complex gearing subsystem is needed.

The CODAG is a distributed hybrid architecture design. It is distributed because the diesel and gas turbine engines share load. It is hybrid because there is more than one engine type. The impact of failure is relatively low because most of the key parts are located in the ship hull where there is the possibility of maintenance. This configuration uses one less gas turbine than the CODOG, if the CODOG is duplicated to offer twin propellers.

Combined Diesel-Electric and Gas (CODLAG)

Combined Diesel-Electric and Gas (CODLAG) is similar to the combined diesel and gas propulsion system except the engines are used to power generators and the generators power electric motors that drive the propellers. There is a variant called the Combined Diesel-Electric or Gas (CODLOG). The CODLOG doesn't allow the simultaneous use of both the gas turbine and electric motors. This is similar to the CODOG structure.

The CODLAG uses electric motors that are connected to the propeller shafts. Diesel generators power the electric motors[142]. For higher speeds, a gas turbine powers the shafts via a cross-connecting gearbox; for cruise speed, the drive train of the turbine is disengaged with clutches.

Since the diesel engines spin at an optimum RPM when used for electric power generation, efficiency significantly increases thus reducing fuel costs. Electric

---

[142] This technology was developed and used on trains. The diesel train locomotive is driven by electric motors from electric power provided by diesel generators.

motors work efficiently over a wide range of RPM and can be connected directly to the propeller shaft. There are multiple advantages to this design:

- Speed changes are continuous rather than stepped as when driven by gearboxes with a fixed number of selectable gear ratios
- Gearboxes that combine the mechanical output of gas turbine and diesel-electric engines are simpler
- Diesel generators can be acoustically de-coupled from the hull of the ship, making it less noisy

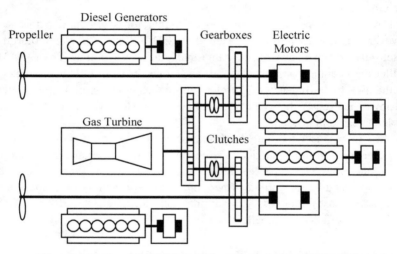

Figure 115 Combined Diesel Electric and Gas CODLAG

The CODLAG is a distributed hybrid architecture design. It is distributed because the diesel and gas turbine engines share load. It is hybrid because there is more than one engine type. The impact of failure is relatively low because most of the key parts are located in the ship hull where there is the possibility of maintenance. The architecture has the advantage of graceful degradation if multiple small diesel generators are used in a distributed configuration. The CODLOG variant is a centralized hybrid architecture design because only the gas turbine or electric motors can power the propellers.

Integrated Electric Propulsion (IEP)

Integrated Electric Propulsion (IEP) or Integrated Full Electric Propulsion (IFEP) is a design that uses diesel engines and gas turbines to generate electricity for electric motors. There is no mechanical transmission to the propellers. As soon as the mechanical linkages are disconnected from the power sources, diesel and or gas turbine, the electric motors can be moved from inside the hull to outside the hull. This is an Azimuth Thruster.

The IEP is a distributed hybrid architecture design. It is distributed because the diesel and gas turbine engines share load. It is hybrid because there is more than one engine type. The gearboxes are no longer present in this architecture. This significantly reduces the impact of failure.

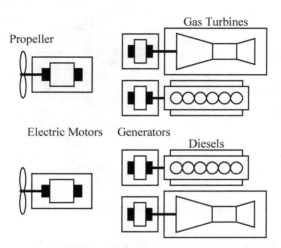

Figure 116 Integrated Electric Propulsion IEP

If the electric motors and propellers are moved outside the hull in an Azimuth Thruster configuration the impact of failure is very high. If and Azimuth Thruster is lost, it is difficult to make repairs and navigation is problematic if there is only one remaining Azimuth Thruster. There is the possibility of using three or four Azimuth Thrusters.

Combined Gas or Gas (COGOG)

Combined Gas or Gas (COGOG) uses gas two gas turbine engines. A high efficiency, low output turbine is used for cruising speeds. A high output turbine is used for high-speed operations. A clutch allows either turbine to be selected, but there is no gearbox to allow operation of both turbines at once. This has the advantage of not requiring heavy, expensive and potentially unreliable gearboxes.

Turbine engines are most efficient when they run at 100% power. A small turbine running at 100% power if more efficient than a large turbine running at 50%. This is that same situation that exists for diesel engines. Diesel engines are most efficient at a particular RPM.

The COGOG is a centralized hybrid architecture design. It is centralized because the engines do not share load. It is hybrid because there is more than one engine type. In this particular case it is the same technology but a different size. So the parts are not interchangeable. The impact of failure is relatively low because most of the key parts are located in the ship hull where there is the possibility of maintenance.

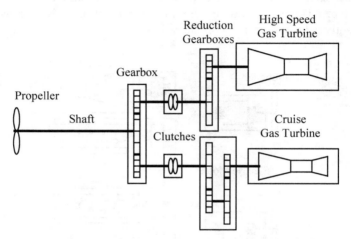

Figure 117 Combined Gas or Gas COGOG

Combined Gas Turbine and Gas Turbine (COGAG)

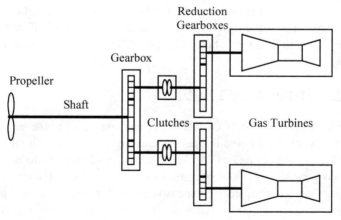

Figure 118 Combined Gas and Gas COGAG

Combined Gas Turbine and Gas Turbine (COGAG) uses two gas turbines connected to a single propeller shaft. A gearbox and clutches allow one or both of the turbines to drive the shaft.

Using one or two gas turbines has the advantage of having two different power settings. Since the fuel efficiency of a gas turbine is best near its maximum power level, a small gas turbine running at its full speed is more efficient compared to a twice as powerful turbine running at half speed, allowing more-economical transit at cruise speeds. Gas turbine engines are smaller than diesel engines with the same power output. So a gas turbine engine only design minimizes the space needs. Also when in high-speed mode the twin gas turbines are more fuel-efficient than a design which includes a diesel engine.

The COGAG is a distributed architecture design. It is distributed because the engines share load. Also there is one engine type and one engine size. So the parts are interchangeable. The impact of failure is relatively low because most of the key parts are located in the ship hull where there is the possibility of maintenance.

Combined Steam and Gas (COSAG)

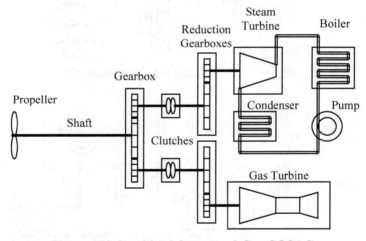

Figure 119 Combined Steam and Gas COSAG

Combined Steam and Gas (COSAG) uses a combination of steam turbines and gas turbines to power the shafts. A gearbox and clutches allow either or both engines to drive the shaft. The steam turbine replaces the diesel engine in other configurations. It combines the reliability of a steam engine with the fast startup time and high speed of a gas turbine. COSAG uses traditional oil-fired boilers for steam turbine. There is no reclamation of the gas turbine heat exhaust.

The COSAG is a distributed hybrid architecture design. It is distributed because the steam and gas turbine engines share load. It is hybrid because there is more than one engine type. The impact of failure is relatively low because most of the key parts are located in the ship hull where there is the possibility of maintenance.

Combined Gas and Steam (COGAS)

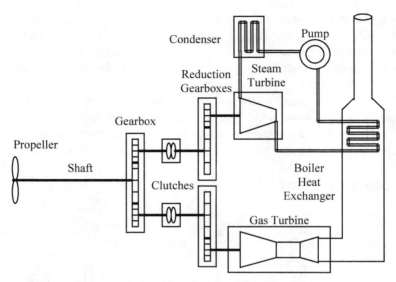

Figure 120 Combined Gas and Steam COGAS

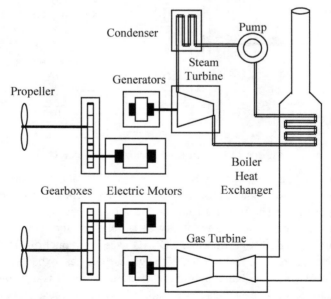

Figure 121 Combined Gas and Steam Electric COGES

Combined Gas and Steam (COGAS) uses a gas turbine and steam turbine. The steam turbine is driven by heat generated from the gas turbine. This increases the efficiency of the design. In this way, some of the otherwise lost energy can be reclaimed and the specific fuel consumption of the plant can be decreased.

If the turbines do not drive the propeller shafts directly and instead a turbo-electric transmission is used, the system is also known as Combined Gas Electric Steam (COGES).

Unlike other designs the COGAS and COGES differ from other propulsion designs because they should not be operated on one engine power source. Although it is possible to operate with one engine, the efficiency benefits are lost. The COGAS and COGES are a centralized architecture design with graceful degradation should one of the power sources fail.

6.15 Early Physical Design Verification and Validation

Before formal verification and validation starts there are early verification and validation activities that are used to further refine the design. This is centered on the process of selecting the physical architecture design and includes formal and informal studies, analysis, and models.

The team points to the information products supporting the final decision and physical design approach. At the highest level the key requirements are used to verify the physical architecture design and the operational concepts are used to validate the physical architecture design. Many times the essence of the operational concepts may be captured in one or more models with various scenarios.

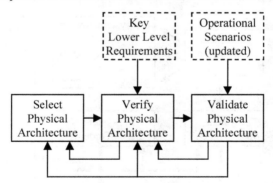

Figure 122 Early Physical Architecture Verification and Validation

6.16 Physical Design Process

Moving from the conceptual to the physical architecture design is about allocations. Typically the allocations are made to segments, elements, subsystems. The lower level allocations are then made by those engaged in designing the subsystem; they engage in implementation architecture design.

The allocations are associated with functions and performance budgets. The performance budgets are quantitative and include timing, reliability, weight, power, heat load, etc. The allocations will change the interface needs, sizes of subsystems, and technology levels.

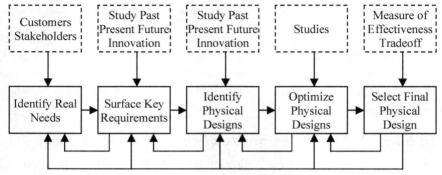

Inner and Outer Feedback and Optimization Loops

Figure 123 Physical Architecture Design Process

The physical architecture design follows the same model as the conceptual architecture design. There are the needs, requirements, alternatives, respect for all stakeholders, key understanding of the past, anticipations of the future and studies.

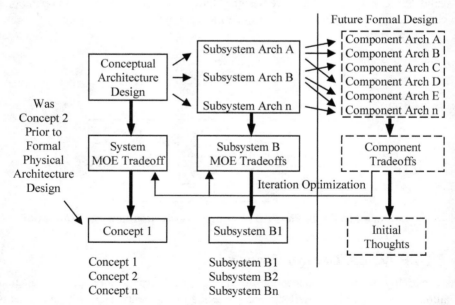

Figure 124 Physical Architecture Design Abstraction Levels

As there is movement down the decomposition tree the lower abstraction level architecture designs may impact the upper level architecture designs. As there is movement down the architecture design tree there is more reliance on existing components that are commercially available. Depending on the solution some of the components, assemblies, subsystems, and systems may not offer sufficient performance even at the state-of-the-art level and so new technologies may need to be developed.

The design needs to balance all the child architecture designs in the system architecture design. That balance includes making sure stress points are found and mitigated. This means understanding the function, performance, and technologies so that they can be effectively allocated into the balanced system architecture design and balanced child architecture designs. This means analysis and models at various levels so that the correct tradeoff choices can be made.

Something as simple as an automobile includes multiple layers of architecture designs. All these architecture designs need to be selected based on reasonable tradeoffs at each architecture design level. As each architecture design level alternative is considered and optimized then selected, it may impact the previous architecture level. Subsystems and components may be purchased as commercial products, modified commercial products, new designs, or state-of-the art designs pushing one or more technologies. These architecture design decisions are made as part of individual tradeoffs at each level.

Example 24 Poor Allocations

Imagine a house where the oven is in the dining room, toilet is in the kitchen, dishes stored in the bathroom, and the bathtub in the dining room. This seems funny but the impact is that the interface load as measured by a person walking between rooms is very high. We also see that the dinning room subsystem needs plumbing, which is redundant to the kitchen and bathroom and thus increases cost. Then we see the dining room subsystem quality and aesthetic level compromised as we eat in the dinning room and look at the dirty bathtub with a mildewed rubber duck.

The allocations are important and they need to be supported with sound logic and quantitative analysis that reduce interface complexity, overhead, and unnecessary technology challenges.

The physical design may impact the conceptual design. This suggests that it start at a low level sometime during the conceptual design. This requires care so that the team does not lose important physical design insights during the conceptual design.

Because of management pressures there may be forces to not update the conceptual design or worse work with a flawed conceptual design based on new knowledge gained with the physical design. This must never be tolerated. Iteration and feedback loops are key ingredients to great designs.

How is this really done, this thing called physical architecture design? Sound familiar? Recall the conceptual architecture design.

One again, when that question is asked many will jump into a process description. Others will fixate on one, two, or a few analysis techniques. All these views are incomplete and when new teams are formed and they are given a vetted process description along with descriptions of how to execute some of the analysis, they fail unless there are designers in the team who have done design in the past.

The designer experience can come at any time in the life of the designer. It does not magically happen to someone after they have completed a formal education as an adult. For example the designs from an individual can be simple designs developed by someone at the young age of 10 or more complex designs developed as professionals in an industry. Designers rely on previous works that are designs. Sometimes others develop the designs and the new designers study these previous bodies of work while at other times the previous designs are works developed by the designer that forms their experience base. Designers may surface as they support other aspects of the project. For example they me engaged in one of the analysis practices or they may be apprentices assigned to existing designers.

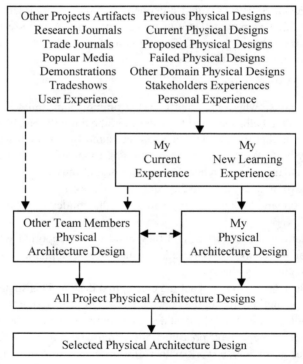

Figure 125 Physical Architecture Design Sources

The following process table is offered as a starting point and an example. It is a guideline that can be used for the physical architecture design portion of the systems engineering design activity.

Table 83 Physical Architecture Design Process Table

Table 83 Physical Architecture Design Process Table

Physical Architecture Design	
• Develop the Physical Architecture Design	
Input	**Output**
• System Conceptual Architecture (SCA) • System Needs Analysis (SNA) • Needs artifacts	• System Physical Architecture (SPA)
Tools	**General Information Products**
• Office Automation: Word Processing, Spreadsheet, Presentation, Email	• Plan Documents • Analysis Documents • Specifications
Activities	**Artifacts**
Update conceptual architecture design	Updated conceptual architecture design
Develop physical architecture description Develop specifications	Physical architecture description Specifications
Additional Information	**Deliverables**
• Physical Architecture Design	• Analysis Documents • Models, Prototypes • Specifications

6.17 Physical Design Socratic Discourse

The following are suggestions of questions to ask as the physical design unfolds. They can be used as a guideline to expand upon the questions that should be asked for each unique project.

- What do you think is the need?
- What do you think are the conceptual architecture design changes?
- Does the conceptual architecture design still satisfy the need?

- What are the current physical design approaches?
- What is wrong with the current physical design approaches?

- What are the new proposed physical design approaches?
- What is the new selected physical design approach?
- Why is the new physical design approach the best solution?
- What are the new function, performance, quality, and aesthetic levels?
- What are the new technologies?

- What are the functional allocations?

- What are the performance allocations?
- What are the interfaces?
- Are the allocations optimized?
- What is the design balance?
- What are the interfaces?
- Are the numbers of interfaces minimized?
- Are the interface complexities minimized?

- What is the growth and expansion strategy?
- What are the maintenance, training, and support philosophy?
- What are the critical functions and how have they been addressed?

- What are the key requirements?
- What are the key issues?

6.18 Physical Design Key Points

➢ The physical design or architecture is captured in the allocated baseline information products

➢ Design synthesis is a creative activity that develops a physical architecture

➢ During concept development, synthesis produces
- System concepts
- Establishes basic relationships among the subsystems

➢ During preliminary and detailed design
- Subsystem and component descriptions are elaborated
- Detailed interfaces between all system components are defined

➢ Design synthesis is what is traditionally viewed as design that happens after concept development

➢ Physical design or architecture activities
- Allocate functions and constraints to physical system elements
- Identify system element alternatives
- Assess technology alternatives
- Define physical interfaces

➢ Physical design or architecture activities
- Define system product Work Break Down Structure (WBS)

- Develop life cycle techniques and procedures
- Select preferred final concept and preliminary physical design

➤ Modular designs are formed by
- Grouping components that perform a single independent function
- Grouping components that perform a single logical task
- Have single entry and exit points
- Are separately testable

➤ Grouping related functions
- Helps enable modular design solutions
- Increases possibility of open-systems approaches in the implementation designs

➤ Desirable attributes of modular units are
- Low coupling and low connectivity
- High cohesion and low coupling

➤ Coupling between modules is a measure of
- Interdependence
- Amount of information shared between two modules

➤ Uncoupling modules
- Eases development risks
- Makes later modifications easier to implement

➤ Cohesion is
- Also called binding
- The similarity of tasks performed within the module

➤ High cohesion is desirable because it
- Enables use of identical or similar components
- Allows use of a single component to perform multiple functions

➤ Connectivity is the relationship of internal elements within one module to internal elements within another module

➤ High connectivity is undesirable because it results in complex interfaces that may impede design development and testing

6.19 Exercises

1. Identify 3 physical architectures, describe the technology issues associated with each of the architectures, and identify the 3-5 key technologies in each of the architectures.
2. Do you think the conceptual architecture design is needed prior to the physical architecture design?
3. Select three products and identify the best design elements of those products.
4. What is meant by characterization of a design?
5. What are key design elements?
6. Identify 3 physical architectures and describe them.

6.20 Additional Reading

1. Designing And Developing Maintainable Products And Systems, DOD Handbook, MIL-HDBK-470A August 1997, MIL-HDBK-470 June 1995, MIL-HDBK-471 June 1995.
2. Discrete Time Systems, James A. Cadzow, Prentice Hall, 1973, ISBN 0132159961.
3. NASA Systems Engineering Handbook, NASA/SP-2007-6105 Rev1, December 2007.
4. National Airspace System Engineering Manual, Federal Aviation Administration, V 3.1, 2006.
5. Practice For System Safety, Department of Defense Standard, MIL-STD-882D, 10 February 2000.
6. Software System Safety Handbook, Joint Services Computer Resources Management Group, US Navy, US Army, And US Air Force, December 1999.
7. Systems Engineering for Intelligent Transportation Systems, Department of Transportation, Federal Highway Administration, Federal Transit Administration, January 2007.
8. Systems Engineering Fundamentals, Supplementary Text, Defense Acquisition University Press, January 2001.
9. Systems Engineering Management Guide, Defense Systems Management College, January 1990.
10. Technology Readiness Assessment (TRA) Deskbook, DOD, May 2005, July 2009.

7 Implementation Architecture Design

Unlike conceptual and physical architecture design the implementation architecture design is product and vendor dependent. The design moves into reality. It is still on paper and in computer databases, but once the paper and computer databases are followed a working physical design is assembled.

7.1 Identifying Implementation Design Alternatives

Identifying implementation design alternatives is about determining if the design will be an unmodified existing design, modified existing design, a new design or any combination. For large complex systems the implementation design includes all these combinations. Additionally, if an existing design is being considered then there is a fundamental decision if the design will come from within the organization or outside the organization.

Table 84 Implementation Design Alternatives

Design Alternatives	Design Source
• New custom design	• Internal to organization
• New product oriented design	• Subcontractor
• Modified custom design	• Vendor
• Modified product oriented design	• Domestic
• Existing custom design	• International
• Existing product design	

As soon as there is pressure to only consider existing designs from within the organization, the system is compromised. The need will be modified to fit the desire to sell a product. This is contrasted with internal product driven design. A compromised situation can be mitigated if the organization is an industry leader and uses the need to transform the product or product line without compromising the need. They view the need as the future and are willing to invest in the future.

7.2 Laboratory Engineering Design

Almost everyone gravitates to the implementation architecture design. That is because we all have knowledge of existing products, companies, solutions, and systems. In many ways this is similar to a garage or basement where someone tinkers and comes up with a weekend project solution. This is sometimes called a garage shop operation.

Sometimes a garage shop solution is all that is needed. However in most cases that is not appropriate. But why, what are the limits of the garage, basement, and perhaps the yard loaded with goodies?

The problem with the garage shop approach is that the design is made of parts that are available on the spot as opposed to the ideal parts. Also the structure of the design may be compromised to fit the availability of the parts on hand. So the mediums, in this case the collection of junk in the basement, garage, and yard significantly influences the final vision. The vision can be brilliant and elegant given the medium available (parts) but it may not be ideal in terms of all the stakeholder needs. However a well stocked garage, basement, and yard may be able to support some great prototypes. This is where R&D with a great lab can start to feed the design process.

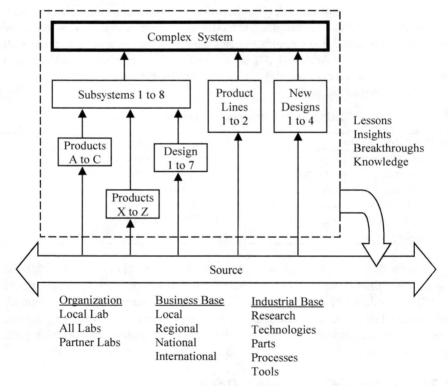

Figure 126 Implementation Architecture Design and Industrial Base

So can the garage shop model be extended to support implementation architecture design? The answer is yes. The garage shop model can be extended to support professional implementation architecture design if we extend the view, broaden our perspective. The perspective should be the entire industrial base. It also can be extended to include intellectual property in patent databases, work at R&D

labs, universities, etc.

This is accomplished by being a participant in the industry. Conferences are attended, trade journals are read, industry surveys are performed, non disclosure agreements are signed, requests for quotes and information are solicited, requests for proposals are offered, vendor visits and demonstrations, product brochures are reviewed etc. This is done to gain access to and understand information that can be used in an implementation architecture design.

7.3 Bench and Catalog Engineering

Bench engineering is a term that became popular with electrical engineering. The idea was that after the device was designed on paper it would undergo final tweaking or adjustment on the bench. This would involve changing different components of one value to another value. For example using a 100 Mega ohm resistor in place of a 50 Mega ohm resistor or a .01 to a .05 Microfarad capacitor. Although the model equations would suggest one set of performance characteristics, the bench measurements would suggest another and so the appropriate bench modifications could be made.

In the case of electrical engineering components became available with sets of standard values. These values were arrived at by the proliferation of designs. For example when working with amplifiers the frequency response would tend to translate into components with the same values. The same is true when working with radios. The AM radio tended to translate into certain component values that were different than for an amplifier or FM radio. In this setting bench engineering was born where there would be no engineering analysis or design with equations. Instead a catalog would be accessed, parts would be ordered, and then prototype assembly would happen on a bench. This would be called bench engineering or catalog engineering.

This is a fascinating scenario because it suggests that the component manufactures were essentially driving engineering solutions. In fact many components were described with a set of performance characteristics and then placed in representative application circuits.

Author Comments: When the apple computer was first created it was created using standard integrated circuits from the chip manufacturers. Many electrical engineers built computers in their basements and garages because the chip manufacturers facilitated it by offering the proper components and representative design schematics in which the components were shown in computer applications. At work these same engineers were providing industrial and government computer based solution. So catalog engineering had become very useful and widely used. It was honed to such a level that non-specialists could design and build a device. The roots of this concept go back to kit radio, television, and stereo sets. Plans would be offered to people who would use or modify the plans and they would use standard components. That could be bought at local stores, including department stores[143] where clothing and other household items were sold.

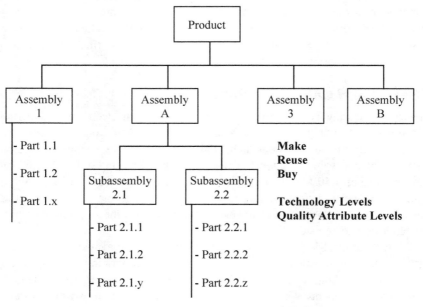

Figure 127 Product Hierarchy

7.4 Different Implementation Designs

There are different implementation architecture designs and they address different needs. These needs are based on the intended use of the design. The design can be targeted for research and development, limited use, final use, with different production quantity levels.

Table 85 Intended Use of Design

Research and Development	Low Production Quantity (tens)
Technology Prototype	Low Production Quantity (hundreds)
Non Production Quality	Medium Production Quantity (thousands)
Production Quality	High Production Quantity (millions)
	Very High Production Quantity (billions)

- **Research and Development Design:** This is a one of a kind system used to

---

[143] WT Grant and Two Guys in Cherry Hill, NJ sold tubes, transistors, resistors, capacitors, transformers, and other electronic components in the same space as clothing, furniture, toys, records, televisions, stereos, and guitars. Building materials and plumbing were in specialty hardware stores however Sears offered many in store hardware supplies.

study one or more aspects of a system. Flexibility is needed so the design can be modified and probed as different questions are addressed. It is typically located in a lab setting with a benign environment.

- **Technology Prototype:** A technology prototype is similar to a research and development design but it is anticipated that it will be placed in an example operational settings. Actual users are able to interact with the design in an uncontrolled setting.
- **Non Production Quality:** This is a final design but it is not a production quality design. This typically arises when a customer sees something in a research and development setting and wants it to be moved to an operational setting. There is little that is done to the original design, so there are quality issues that may be associated with the design that translate to negative levels for many quality attributes. Many times the aesthetics are completely ignored unless it is a key element of the design.
- **Production Quality:** This design is a fully refined design that is considered very high quality by the users. It is also aesthetically complete. It is typically the next step after a non-production quantity design is developed and found to be very useful in a few operational settings.
- **Production Quantity Design:** This design is specifically intended to reduce production costs without compromising the function, performance, quality, or aesthetics of the non production quantity design. The design varies as the expected quantity changes from tens to millions or billions.

A complex system design methodology might use all of the designs just described. The progression might be as follows:

- Research and development prototype
- Prototype
- Pre Production Prototype
- Production Prototype
- Production

7.5 Supply and Demand Driven Design

During implementation architecture design the costs are more of a focus and solidified as technologies, vendors, and design details are being locked down. It is at this time that tough decisions are made with the level of function, performance, and quality. These decisions can be helped with a proper view of supply and demand.

Supply and demand is a multidimensional concept that relates price, quantity, consumers, and producers. It offers several financial metrics and is a fundamental element of modern economics. Supply and demand is based on the following assumptions:

- Consumers behave rationally
- Producers behave rationally
- There are many independent consumers
- There are many independent producers

In this ideal environment of rational behavior and a level playing field of many independent consumers and producers the following relationships logically surface:

- Consumers as a group will buy more product items or service units (quantity) as price decreases
- Producers as a group will increase the number of product items or service units (quantity) as price increases

This relationship is shown in a supply and demand graph. A demand curve represents consumers and shows what price they are willing to pay for an item. As price decreases more consumers enter the market and so more items are sold. The supply curve represents the producers. As prices rise they are motivated as a group to find ways to offer more items. This may be with the introduction of new producers or new processes and or technologies that allow for more items to be made available. In both cases the quantity increases or decreased with price. The intersection of the supply and demand curves is the ideal price where there is no excess quantity or insufficient quantity. It is the point of equilibrium.

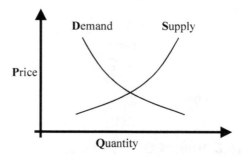

Figure 128 Supply and Demand Graphs

The lines in the supply and demand graph can be various shapes and slopes. Obviously infinite quantity is not possible. Eventually the supply costs start to increase rapidly with each increment in quantity. Eventually as the demand cost becomes very high, sales decrease rapidly with each increment in cost. So the lines are curved as they approach the limits of the market size and the technology.

Elasticity is used to describe the slope levels of the supply and demand curves. The more vertical the supply slope the more inelastic the supply curve. The more vertical the demand slope the more inelastic the demand curve. If the supply curve is perfectly vertical it is perfectly inelastic. This means the quantity is fixed no matter what the price. Many practitioners use land as an example of this scenario. No matter how much someone is willing to pay for additional land more parcels cannot be created.

However the supply and demand model has flaws. As a teaching example the land analogy illustrates the concept, but it is wrong in practice. The reality is that there is always more land if one is willing to look outside the current context or boundary. There are other neighborhoods, towns, cities, regions, etc. There are even alternatives such as artificial islands or land fills and vertical locations such as skyscrapers.

Additionally consumers and producers do not behave rationally. The tulip mania of the 1630's is an example of a speculative bubble[144]. At the peak of the tulip mania in 1637 some tulip bulbs sold for more than the annual income of a skilled craftsman. There have been many economic bubbles in the ensuing centuries. Time and time again consumers convinced themselves that they should pay a price for an item that far exceeds its rational price point as they rode a speculative bubble and hoped not to be the holders of the items once the bubble burst.

Producers when acting in their own interest always try to increase market share. This eventually leads to buying out the last of the remaining weaker competitors. At some point barriers of entry such as capital, branding, regulations or any combination become so significant that essentially oligopoly or monopoly surfaces. The empirical evidence is everywhere in the USA, from GM, Ford, and Chrysler dominating automobiles to Microsoft and its Windows operating system.

So consumers and producers do not behave rationally[145]. Although there are many consumers in this highly automated age, there are not many producers. Also in this age of mass media and mass influence the risk of irrational consumer behavior has risen beyond any expectation for consumers to behave rationally. This is not to say that they are stupid. They are just acting on the information they are offered and if that information is overwhelming and tainted, then there is no other expectation other than irrational behavior. The cottage industry model with consumers that have limited information access fits more appropriately with the supply and demand model; this model disappeared a hundred years ago.

Understanding the supply and demand facts of life was key to introducing new

---

[144] From Mackay, Charles (1841), Memoirs of Extraordinary Popular Delusions and the Madness of Crowds: "In 1634, the rage among the Dutch to possess them was so great that the ordinary industry of the country was neglected, and the population, even to its lowest dregs, embarked in the tulip trade. As the mania increased, prices augmented, until, in the year 1635, many persons were known to invest a fortune of 100,000 florins in the purchase of forty roots."

[145] Irrational human behavior happens in all systems. It needs to be acknowledged and respected. Users will find ways to misuse the system.

products and technologies in the last century. When electricity was first offered the general attitude was why. When the telephone was first offered the same issues surfaced. However realizing that consumers do not act rationally, strategies surfaced that stimulated interest in new products and services. The concept of Veblen[146] goods was applied to many new products and services in hopes of creating new markets.

Veblen goods and services are associated with high social status and exclusivity. Veblen goods and services have a different demand curve from normal goods. In a Veblen good or service, decreasing the price reduces the consumers desire to buy because it is no longer perceived as exclusive or high status. A price increase will increase the consumers' perception of status and exclusivity making the good or service more desirable. There are limits to the price increases and at some point demand will drop even in the exclusive high status market.

Veblen combined sociology with economics in the book "The Theory of the Leisure Class" (1899)[147]. The book suggested that there was a difference between industry, run by engineers, which manufactures goods for the general population, and business, which exists only to make profits for a leisure class. Unlike industry, which is productive, business allows the leisure class to engage in "conspicuous consumption", where the economic contribution is "waste" that contributes nothing to productivity.

So how does this relate to implementation architecture design? System design in the early stages is characterized as groups of ideas and concepts. These ideas and concepts are circulating in what is essentially a small test market with the participating stakeholders. In many ways these stakeholders are an early indication of how the consumers or users will receive the product or system. In this setting many questions can be asked. For example what is the incremental cost of adding a certain feature that separates one design from another and what is the impact on stakeholder acceptability? So conceptually each design approach can have a set of supply and demand curves.

If we replace the x-axis Quantity on the supply and demand chart with Approaches where approaches can be different design features as viewed by consumers then some interesting ideas surface. The features are the function, performance, quality, and aesthetic levels of the design. Further there is a continuum from least costly to produce to most costly to produce based on the features. The project stakeholders can be extrapolated to the broader market consumers and or users. They have a price they are willing to pay for each design

---

[146] Thorstein Bunde Veblen, (July 30, 1857 – August 3, 1929) an American sociologist and economist was the first to introduce the term "conspicuous consumption" and concept of status seeking.

[147] Thorstein Bunde Veblen (1899) The Theory of the Leisure Class, An Economic Study of Institutions, London: Macmillan Publishers.

increment feature block. This is the internal stakeholder demand curve. This demand curve could be augmented with a market study.

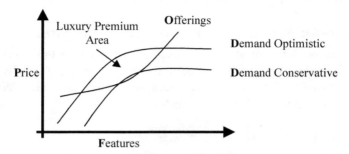

Figure 129 Offerings and Demand

As we examine the demand-offering chart there are several observations. The Offerings curve shows that the cost to produce each design increases with increasing features. It is not linear or smooth. The Demand curve shows that consumers will only pay a certain price for the design regardless of the level of features. It also shows that if the demand intersects the offering at some point, there is an area where a premium price can be charged for some increment of features. These features fall into the luxury category and represent opportunity to increase margins via the offering of luxury features.

Example 25 Value Systems - Early Suburban Housing

Imagine buying and building a house in 1960's suburbia USA. Lets start with the consumer. Here you are living in the city. You have a car and there are new roads to take you into a different world. As you travel these roads you see various farms being sold to developers who are building houses. You stop in, wander through a few sample homes, pick up some brochures, and drive through the new streets. You leave the small development of 50 - 300 houses and drive around the surrounding community. What value system can you use to make your final decision? Are you considering the price with the various features? One developer offers a larger lot at the expense of a smaller house. Another developer offers a large house and large lot but at a different location up the road.

Imagine being a builder. The war is over and you partnered with a brilliant architect you met in the military. You have dreams of building a new world. What features do you offer to separate you from the competition? How do you attempt to speculate what people might want when they themselves are not sure? The Veblen effect does not work. These are people who just lived through a depression and war, they are looking for a different way. What do you do?

Fortunately in this scenario everyone got what they wanted except for the people left behind in the cities. It took decades for the Veblen effect to take hold of the new cities being born after the World War II. Housing bubbles that led to whole communities being bulldozed in some insane frenzy of Veblen effect and massive speculation did not surface until the new century.

7.6 Vendor Product Evaluation and Selection

Vendor product evaluation and selection is a key element to offering designs. If the wrong vendor or product is selected the design can fail. Typically the selection process includes the technical approach, company assessment, and cost. The company assessment includes items such as:

- Years in business
- Size of company and project size relative to company
- Company financial stability
- Company employee turn over rate and layoff history

When a company is viewed from its technical ability to take on a particular job with a particular set of needs, its capabilities are reviewed. This obviously includes listing the unique products and technologies the company offers and its match with the need. There is however a generic approach to view a companies capabilities. The following are ordered lists of company capabilities from the most capable to the least capable:

- Develops and owns successful significant technologies
- Develops and owns successful product lines
- Develops and owns successful products
- Delivers successful projects
- Has a collection of existing people willing to work
- Has a vessel that can employ a collection of people
- Owns its land buildings and equipment
- Leases its buildings owns its equipment
- Leases its buildings leases its equipment

"We agree to support the Apollo 11 mission" is a quote from the movie "The Dish"[148]. It is about how the Parkes Observatory in Australia was used to relay the live television broadcast of man's first steps on the moon, during the Apollo 11 mission in 1969. Six hundred million people witnessed Neil Armstrong's first steps on the Moon through television pictures transmitted to Earth from the lunar module, Eagle. Parkes Radio Telescope pictures were so good that NASA stayed with them for the rest of the 2½-hour moonwalk after 10 minutes of transmission from

---

[148] The Dish, Movie, Director: Rob Sitch, Writing credits: Santo Cilauro, Tom Gleisner, Jane Kennedy, Rob Sitch, Warner Brothers, 27 April 2001.

Honeysuckle Creek tracking station near Canberra, and NASA's Goldstone station in California. During this time there was a violent squall that struck Parkes and the telescope was buffeted by strong winds that swayed the support tower and threatened the integrity of the telescope structure.

Vendor product evaluation and selection is the receiving end of someone's system design practices[149]. It is the successful application of those practices which results in a product, system, component, service, etc that is now being evaluated for inclusion in another system.

The vendor product evaluation and selection is a phased approach where a course tradeoff analysis is performed to narrow the list as time progresses and more is learned. The process begins by reviewing vendor data. This may be followed by a vendor invitation to gather your requirements while they offer a presentation and perhaps a demonstration. There may or may not be a formal request for information (RFI). After the presentation they may leave samples for further evaluation. This may be followed up by visits to the vendor location. At this point a Request for Proposal (RFP) is produced and the vendors respond with a formal proposal.

Prior to final selection there always should be a site visit to validate the information gathered and confirm perceptions by the team. When selecting a vendor there are three broad categories of tradeoff criteria: (1) Technical, (2) Non Technical, and (3) Sustainability.

The non-technical criteria include:

- **Company Stability**: As represented by years in business, gross revenue or size of company, profits, level of research and development, layoff history (brain drain). Layoff history is an extremely serious issue and must be properly explained. If an organization does not value its employees it will not value its customers.
- **Location**: Are there multiple locations, any export import issues, transport issues, access to universities, major metropolitan areas, transportation (roads, airports, railroads, and or ports).
- **Market Share**: Is the market dominated by the vendor, is the vendor a number two, or number three. If not dominant, why.
- **Product Stability**: Years in product business area, maturity of the product, degree of obsolescence, degree of state of the art, proven operations.

The technical criteria include:

- **Features**: Including features not found in other offerings, features with

---

[149] Systems Practices as Common Sense, by Walter Sobkiw, CassBeth, 2011, ISBN 978-0983253082.

possible future applications, features that push the state of the art.

- **Technology Readiness Level**: What is the TRL rating using one of the standard scales described in this text, TRL 1 to 10.
- **Technology Maturity**: What is the technology maturity level as described in this text, bleeding edge, leading edge, state of the art, dated, or obsolete.
- **Performance**: Areas that exceed other offerings, performance that is or exceeds the state of the art.

The sustainability criteria include:

- **Total Energy**: This is a measure of the total energy used in production, shipping, operating, and disposal. Many items consume more energy in production, shipping, and disposal than operation. Examples include personal computers, which consume less energy in operation than production, shipping, and disposal because of its short life. Other examples are items that do not consume energy such as screws. A refrigerator will consume more energy in operation than production because of its long life.
- **Total Carbon Release**: Just like energy, this is the carbon footprint of a product and its allocation to production, transport, operation, and disposal. The carbon footprint will track total energy.
- **Internal Sustainability**: This is a measure of the product, system, services, component, subsystem ability to survive through the years. It is a measure of its own sustainability.
- **External Sustainability**: This is a measure of the impact on other systems. This traditionally is negative environmental impact such as pollution but it also can be impacts on quality of life. Examples include stressing existing educational, health care, transportation, power, water, sanitation, communications and other systems.
- **Cost Shifting**: This is a measure of the degree of cost shifting to other stakeholders. It is most egregious if the stakeholders are not aware of the cost shifting. Examples include fracture gas drilling where gas and or oil may be extracted but surrounding water wells may be destroyed rendering other properties worthless.

In addition the tradeoff criteria identified in the architecture design selection should be considered. Just as in the case of architecture design selection the approach to vendor product selection should be the most effective solution not the lowest cost. So the MOE should be used as described in the formal decision making and architecture section[150].

---

[150] **Author Comment:** You have not yet been introduced to formal decision making and

MOE = Sum of Vendor Criteria / Vendor Cost

Other criteria that may surface include:

- **Product**: performance suitability, transparency (documentation, specifications, etc), functional match (function analysis, % requirements delivered, etc), security, safety, maintainability, update cycle, maturity, upward compatibility, quality, reliability, architectural compatibility, portability, resource utilization efficiency, maintenance costs fees, interoperability (proprietary elements force commitment to vendor)
- **Vendor**: reputation (credibility, stability, longevity, credentials, management), technical support (scope and responsiveness), willingness to negotiate changes, training support, competitive standing, periodic vendor release dates accommodate target systems delivery dates, references
- **Stakeholder Acceptability**: familiarity with candidate, open attitude to new technology offered, training to develop candidate expertise

7.7 Make Buy Modify

Commodity based goods and services available through multiple distribution sources can be handled using a buyer or team of buyers. The products and services are well-known and stable with industry accepted specifications. The costs may vary depending on quantity and need time. A buyer assigned to a class of such commodities can negotiate and make the purchases with little complication. In some cases the buy includes certain quality factors such as full parts inspection or parts screening either by the vendor, the buying organization, or a third part.

A Request for Information (RFI) is a formal request from industry for information about their products, systems, components, subsystems, services, etc. It is used to gather data on the current state of the industrial base so that an effective Request for Proposal (RFP) can be developed.

It involves offering a broad statement of the possibility of a project or program. This statement triggers interest, and information is offered by all parties that may be followed up with formal presentations.

The vendors use the RFI to prepare for a future RFP. This preparation may include soliciting various stakeholder needs, developing internal plans, and even investing in research and development in anticipation of the RFP. It is also an opportunity for the vendors to influence the RFP structure and requirements via an educational interchange that may include white papers, presentations, samples,

---

architecture selection. This topic is addressed later in the text. It was a difficult decision to determine the sequence. I eventually decided that I wanted to move into the lowest levels of design as soon as possible so that the reader does not lose the design big picture.

demonstrations, facility tours, etc.

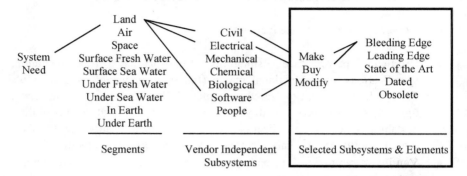

Figure 130 Make versus Buy versus Modify

When buying non-commodity products to fit into a new design there is always a temptation to buy the lowest cost. The problem with this approach is that the item will most likely be obsolete before the final products using the purchased item hits the market or is delivered. The lesson is to always buy the state of the art when it comes time to make purchases.

Once entering the make buy space many design teams realize the fit may not be ideal and so there is an investigation of modifying something that is close to the needed part of the design. This is usually started from a cost schedule perspective rather than from a need point of view and trying to offer the most elegant design. So intentions are important. If the team is instead focused on offering the most elegant design, then there are always issues associated with actually being able to modify the design as desired, especially if the design is outside the primary organizations controls (e.g. subcontractor). In these situations intellectual property and business considerations may get in the way of the design[151].

7.8 Off-The-Shelf Versus In-house Purposeful Design

There comes a time during implementation design when the issue of off-the-shelf designs versus in-house purposeful design needs to be made. Typically as the choice is pushed down the abstraction level to the piece parts level the design tends to be more elegant. That is because function and performance can be finely tuned in the individual designs that form the system. Higher abstraction level units tend to take on functionality and performance that may not apply to the solution. This additional functionality that may never be used comes at the cost of lower performance of functionality that will be used in the off-the-shelf collection.

However, because of the proliferation of so many products at various

---

[151] Hughes Aircraft would deal with these situations by purchasing the company, but only if the company truly had something significant to offer that Hughes could not duplicate.

abstractions, much of today's solutions are an integration of relatively large blocks of the system. This is a cost tradeoff and the primary driver tends to be the non-recurring engineering cost to design the in-house purposeful design. For example it is difficult to justify the design of a new display device when offering a new laptop computer. However when introducing an electronic hand held reader a custom liquid paper display may set a new industry standard while offering a breakthrough new design[152].

7.9 Early Implementation Design Verification and Validation

Before formal verification and validation starts there are early verification and validation activities that are used to further refine the design. This is centered on the process of selecting the implementation architecture design and includes formal and informal studies, analysis, and models.

The team points to the information products supporting the final decision and implementation design approach. At the highest level the key requirements are used to verify the implementation architecture design and the operational concepts are used to validate the implementation architecture design. Many times the essence of the operational concepts may be captured in one or more models with various scenarios.

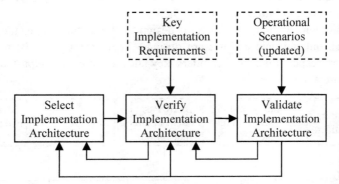

Figure 131 Early Implementation Architecture Verification and Validation

7.10 Implementation Design Process

Design implementation is the process of looking for available parts and subsystems and deciding what can be bought, modified, or needs to be developed. The buy modify model is very similar to catalog engineering. Today we tend to

---

[152] This was the decision faced by many e-book designers when they offered new e-book readers in this century. The first e-book reader was offered by RCA in the early 1980s and it used a LCD almost 30 years before their actual full market acceptance.

refer to it as integration. The suggestion is that additional glue is needed to allow for the buy and modify elements of the system to properly work together. When new design is also needed, the integration glue needs to extend to the new design elements. Design tends to fall into the following categories:

- Commercial
- Industrial
- Military
- Space

These categories tend to define a set of environmental and use conditions that will significantly impact the parts selections. These categories also translate into different design requirements starting at the concept stage, proceeding to the physical stage and now at the implementation stage. Knowledge of these parts and materials are what will impact early design decisions.

The final results of the implementation design are the blue prints, drawings, schematics, design documents, parts lists, product descriptions, and even marketing fliers. The design information products with the parts from the parts list are then used to assemble the system design as part of production. If there will be multiple systems then this is the first article. It can be viewed as a pre production with changes included in future system designs.

The implementation architecture design follows the same model as the conceptual and physical architecture designs. There are the needs, requirements, alternatives, respect for all stakeholders, key understanding of the past, anticipations of the future and studies.

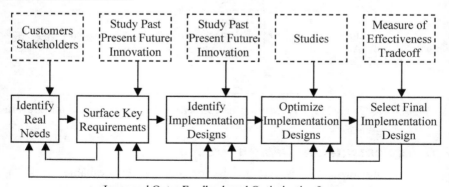

Inner and Outer Feedback and Optimization Loops

Figure 132 Implementation Architecture Design Process

As there is movement down the decomposition tree the lower abstraction level architecture designs may impact the upper level architecture designs. As there is movement down the architecture design tree there is more reliance on existing components that are commercially available. Depending on the solution some of the components, assemblies, subsystems, and systems may not offer sufficient performance even at the state-of-the-art level and so new technologies may need to be developed.

The design needs to balance all the child architecture designs in the system architecture design. That balance includes making sure stress points are found and mitigated. This means understanding the function, performance, and technologies so that they can be effectively allocated into the balanced system architecture design and balanced child architecture designs. This means analysis and models at various levels so that the correct tradeoff choices can be made.

Something as simple as an automobile includes multiple layers of architecture designs. All these architecture designs need to be selected based on reasonable tradeoffs at each architecture design level. As each architecture design level alternative is considered and optimized then selected, it may impact the previous architecture level. Subsystems and components may be purchased as commercial products, modified commercial products, new designs, or state-of-the art designs pushing one or more technologies. These architecture design decisions are made as part of individual tradeoffs at each level.

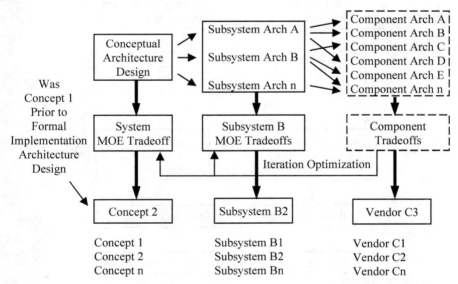

Figure 133 Implementation Architecture Design Abstraction Levels

How is this really done, this thing called implementation architecture design? Sound familiar? Recall the physical architecture design.

One again, when that question is asked many will jump into a process description. Others will fixate on one, two, or a few analysis techniques. All these views are incomplete and when new teams are formed and they are given a vetted process description along with descriptions of how to execute some of the analysis, they fail unless there are designers in the team who have done design in the past.

The designer experience can come at any time in the life of the designer. It does not magically happen to someone after they have completed a formal education as an adult. For example the designs from an individual can be simple designs developed by someone at the young age of 10 or more complex designs developed as professionals in an industry. Designers rely on previous works that are designs. Sometimes others develop the designs and the new designers study these previous bodies of work while at other times the previous designs are works developed by the designer that forms their experience base. Designers may surface as they support other aspects of the project. For example they me engaged in one of the analysis practices or they may be apprentices assigned to existing designers.

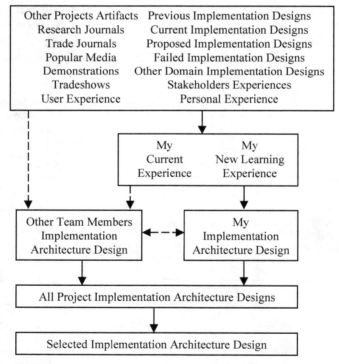

Figure 134 Implementation Architecture Design Sources

The following process table is offered as a starting point and an example. It is a guideline that can be used for the conceptual architecture design portion of the systems engineering design activity.

Table 86 Implementation Architecture Design Process Table

Table 86 Implementation Architecture Design Process Table

Implementation Architecture Design	
• Develop the Implementation Architecture Design	
Input	**Output**
• System Conceptual Architecture (SCA) • System Needs Analysis (SNA) • Needs artifacts	• System Implementation Architecture (SIA)
Tools	**General Information Products**
• Office Automation: Word Processing, Spreadsheet, Presentation, Email	• Plan Documents • Analysis Documents • Specifications
Activities	**Artifacts**
Update conceptual architecture design Update physical architecture design Develop implementation architecture design	Updated conceptual architecture design Updated implementation architecture design Updated specifications Design documents
Additional Information	**Deliverables**
• Implementation Architecture Design	• Analysis Documents • Models, Prototypes • Specifications • Design Documents

7.11 Implementation Design Socratic Discourse

The following are suggestions of questions to ask as the implementation design analysis unfolds. They can be used as a guideline to expand upon the questions that should be asked for each unique project. These questions should be asked for each segment, element, and subsystem.

- What is the subsystem boundary?
- What are the key requirements?
- What are the key functions?
- What are the key issues?
- What are the current implementation approaches?
- What is wrong with the current implementation approaches?
- What are the proposed implementation approaches?
- What are the current possible vendors?
- What is the make buy tradeoff results?
- If buy what are the vendor tradeoff results?
- If buy why was the vendor choice the best choice?

- If build what are the proposed new design alternatives?
- If build what is the selected alternative?
- If build why is the selected alternative the best approach?

- What are the updated key requirements for the subsystem?
- What are the new key requirements for the implementation design?
- What are the key issues?
- What are the technology levels?
- What are the function performance quality and aesthetic levels?

7.12 Implementation Key Points

➢ The conceptual design or architecture is captured in the functional baseline information products

➢ The physical design or architecture is captured in the allocated baseline information products

➢ Implementation design or architecture activities
  - Refine system product WBS
  - Refine life cycle techniques and procedures
  - Select preferred final concept, final physical design, and preliminary implementation designs

➢ The implementation design or architecture is captured in the product baseline information products

➢ During preliminary and detailed design
  - Subsystem and component descriptions are elaborated
  - Detailed interfaces between all system components are defined

➢ Implementation design or architecture activities include
  - Make buy decisions
  - Assessing technology alternatives
  - Designing new elements
  - Modifying existing elements
  - Refining physical interfaces

7.13 Exercises

1. Identify 3 implementation architectures, describe the technology issues associated with each of the architectures, and identify the 3-5 key

technologies in each of the architectures.

2. Do you think the physical architecture is needed prior to the implementation architecture?
3. Do you think the implementation architecture is needed prior to the purchase, modified designs, or new designs of the system elements?
4. Select three products and identify the best design elements of those products.
5. What is meant by characterization of a design?
6. What are key design elements?
7. Identify 3 implementation architectures and describe them.

7.14 Additional Reading

1. NASA Systems Engineering Handbook, NASA/SP-2007-6105 Rev1, December 2007.
2. National Airspace System Engineering Manual, Federal Aviation Administration, V 3.1, 2006.
3. Practice For System Safety, Department of Defense Standard, MIL-STD-882D, 10 February 2000.
4. Systems Engineering for Intelligent Transportation Systems, Department of Transportation, Federal Highway Administration, Federal Transit Administration, January 2007.
5. Systems Engineering Fundamentals, Supplementary Text, Defense Acquisition University Press, January 2001.
6. Systems Engineering Management Guide, Defense Systems Management College, January 1990.
7. Systems Practices as Common Sense, by Walter Sobkiw, CassBeth, 2011, ISBN 978-0983253082.
8. The Dish, Movie, Director: Rob Sitch, Writing credits: Santo Cilauro, Tom Gleisner, Jane Kennedy, Rob Sitch, Warner Brothers, 27 April 2001.
9. Thorstein Bunde Veblen (1899) The Theory of the Leisure Class, An Economic Study of Institutions, London: Macmillan Publishers.

8 Decision Making Selecting Architectures

During the design many decisions need to be made. At the highest level the conceptual, physical, and implementation architectures need to be selected. However each of these architecture views have major issues and decisions points. These decisions will have major impacts on the design and so they need to be treated with the same level of respect as selecting the design architectures. This section will address formal decision making and architecture tradeoff and selection.

8.1 Formal Decision Making

Many of the formal decision making techniques can be traced to Multi-Criteria Decision-Making (MCDM) and Multi-Attribute Utility Theory (MAUT). Many decisions have multiple objectives and involve multiple stakeholders that are affected in different ways by a decision. From a design perspective the decisions might include:

- Level of functionality, performance, quality, aesthetics to provide
- Buy, modify, or develop new designs
- Components, assemblies, subsystem, element technology level selections
- Supplier and subcontractor selections
- Locations of design, integration, manufacturing, distribution, sale, use

8.1.1 Advantages Disadvantages List (ADL)

This formal decision making approach uses a list and identifies the advantages and disadvantages of each approach. It is on a single sheet of paper so that the whole picture can be visualized. If multiple sheets of paper are used they are spread on a physical table so that the full view can be provided[153]. The list is qualitative and identifies items associated with the mind, heart, and stomach[154]. In professional settings the list is usually oriented towards the mind, in anticipation of converting to quantitative measures using other analysis techniques.

The advantage of this approach is that it is fast and stimulates discussion. The

---

[153] This is one of the massive limitations of the computer. A full view cannot be visualized. Using a table or even an entire room with items posted on walls visually immerses the analysts in the problem space.

[154] The mind, heart, and stomach are elements in a phrase referring to logic, compassion, and basic needs. Basics needs are food clothing shelter usually equated to money.

discussion process starts to push the team into a knowledge discovery mode about the problem space.

8.1.2 Alternatives Tradeoff Matrix (ATM)

The tradeoff matrix is a table that has criteria, ratings, and alternatives. It lists the criteria (in rows), assigns ratings for each approach (in columns) to the criteria, and then sums the criteria. The criteria come from different sources but the advantages disadvantages list is usually the starting point for identifying the criteria.

The assignment of numbers uses ad hoc methods decided by the team. This process evokes discussion of how much better one approach is over another approach for each criterion. Occasionally analysis yields quantitative data that is traceable to the values in a particular cell in the matrix. Eventually the values are normalized to some scale such as 1-10, 1-4, 1-3, etc.

To select the best approach a cost is determined for each approach and divided into the total rating of each approach. Arbitrarily setting values to zero or maximum ratings is used to perform sensitivity analysis. Weights are also added to different criteria based on the teams' ad hoc view of the analysis.

The advantage of this approach is the ability to visualize all the alternatives on a single sheet of paper. While assigning values to each cell the team is engaged in intense debate and forced to produce quantitative and qualitative analysis to justify the rating in each cell. Different team members perform analyses of the same areas as they try to justify their original guess and gut level reactions to a rating. Even though the analysis may be based on hard science and engineering it is always modulated by assumptions that originate from different perspectives of the problem.

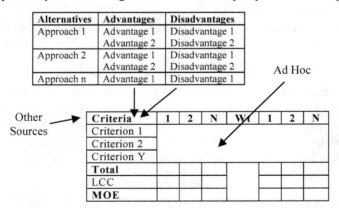

Figure 135 Alternative Lists and Tradeoff Decisions

Eventually the team converges and the matrix and resulting MOE value remain unchanged[155]. There is convergence in a setting where everyone has had a view of the problem, a chance to participate, and the ability to easily view the results captured in the tradeoff matrix. Inclusion and visualization of the decision is key and everyone is able to describe how they arrived at the selected approach by just talking to the matrix and referencing analysis that led to each cell in the matrix.

8.1.3 Probability Based Decisions (PBD)

The best way to discuss Probability Based Decisions (PBD) is through the example of deciding to pursue a contract that requires a proposal submission in a competitive space. Assume there are four possible competitors pursuing a request for proposal (RFP). Also assume there is no other knowledge other than interest in pursuing the contract. So they are all equal. So the probability of win for any one of the four vendors is 25% (1 in 4 or 1:4). This is represented as a probability tree. As marketing starts to investigate the opportunity more information is uncovered that changes the win probability distribution. The Win probability tree starts to decompose into lower levels of information.

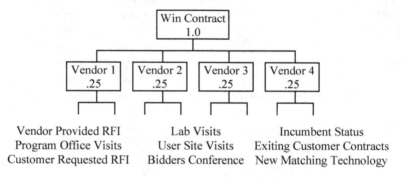

Figure 136 Win probability Tree

This can be converted to a table as an alternative view. The win probability can be calculated by just assigning the number 1 to each item a vendor satisfies (V1-V4), totaling all the columns for each vender, then dividing each vender total by the total for all the vendors. This approach treats all elements of marketing data equally. For example Incumbent status is valued in the same way as Lab Visits.

Table 87 Win Probability

Marketing Data	V1	V2	V3	V4
Customer requested RFI	1		1	

---

[155] It should never be turned off because of money or schedule constraints. The concern should be has the team converged too quickly, should other participants be added to offer new perspectives.

Table 87 Win Probability

Marketing Data	V1	V2	V3	V4
Provided RFI	1	1	1	
Program Office Visits	1	1	1	1
Lab Visits	1		1	
User Site Status Visits	1		1	
Bidders Conference	1		1	
Existing Contracts With Customer	1			
Incumbent	1			
Total	8	2	6	1
Win Probability (Total / 17)	.47 or 47%	.11 or 11%	.35 or 35%	.06 or 6%

8.1.4 Analytical Hierarchy Process (AHP)

Those who have developed probability models, fault trees, reliability models, decomposition trees will recognize the basic approach of using a hierarchy to represent a decision using Analytical Hierarchy Process (AHP). The AHP process is summarized as follows[156]:

1. **Define the problem**. Determine the kind of knowledge sought.
2. **Structure a decision hierarchy**. At the top is the *decision or goal*. Below the decision are the broad *objectives*. Continue the decomposition of the intermediate levels. These are usually *criteria* on which subsequent elements depend. The lowest level is usually the set of *alternatives*.

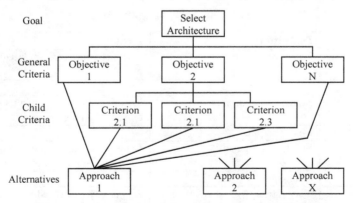

Figure 137 AHP Vertical Hierarchy or Tree Diagram

3. **Develop pair-wise comparison matrices**. Each element in an upper level is used to compare the elements in the level immediately below in the tree.

---

[156] Thomas L. Saaty, Decision Making with the Analytic Hierarchy Process, Int. J. Services Sciences, Vol. 1, No. 1, 2008.

4. **Use priorities obtained from comparisons to weigh priorities in level immediately below.** Do this for every element. Then for each element in the level below add its weighed values and obtain its overall or global priority. Continue this process of weighing and adding until the final priorities of the alternatives in the bottom most level are obtained.

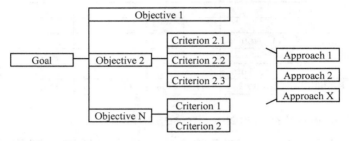

Figure 138 AHP Horizontal Hierarchy or Tree Diagram

The AHP decision hierarchy is a decomposition tree diagram. It can be oriented vertically or horizontally. The more levels in the hierarchy, the more voluminous the calculations because pair-wise matrices are developed for each relationship.

A pair wise matrix is titled using the parent name or designator and the child nodes are rows and columns in the matrix named using the child names or designators. The values assigned in the matrix are based on a scale. The matrix must be consistent so when a whole number is entered in a position its reciprocal is automatically entered in the transpose position.

Table 88 AHP Assignment Scale

Importance	Definition	Explanation
1	Equal Importance	Two activities contribute equally to the objective
2	Weak or slight	
3	Moderate importance	Experience and judgement slightly favor one activity over another
4	Moderate plus	
5	Strong importance	Experience and judgement strongly favor one activity over another
6	Strong plus	
7	Very strong or demonstrated importance	An activity is favored very strongly over another; its dominance demonstrated in practice
8	Very, very strong	
9	Extreme importance	The evidence favoring one activity over another is of the highest possible order of affirmation
Reciprocals	If activity i has one of the above	A reasonable assumption

Table 88 AHP Assignment Scale

Importance	Definition	Explanation
of above	non-zero numbers assigned to it when compared with activity j, then j has the reciprocal value when compared with i	
1.1–1.9	If the activities are very close	May be difficult to assign the best value but when compared with other contrasting activities the size of the small numbers would not be too noticeable, yet they can still indicate the relative importance of the activities.

Example 26 AHP Matrix Calculations

AHP matrix calculations are best illustrated with an example. To keep the example simple only one level of criteria is considered.

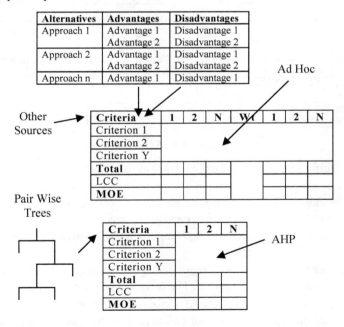

Figure 139 AHP Compared to Alternative List and Tradeoff Matrix

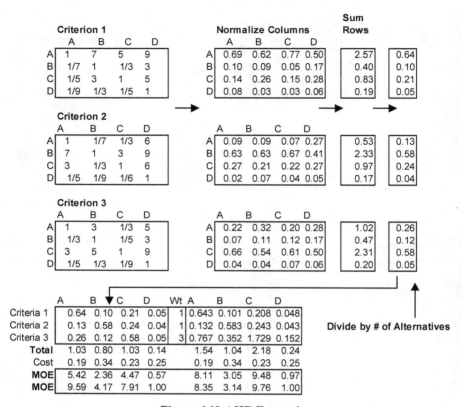

Figure 140 AHP Example

The specific steps for executing AHP are as follows:

- Decompose the goal into its parts, progressing from the general to the specific. At its simplest this consists of a goal, criteria, and alternatives. The more criteria included, the less important each individual criterion becomes as the mix is diluted.
- Create pair-wise matrices representing the decomposition. In this case there is a matrix for each criterion. The rows and columns are the alternatives.
- Populate the cells using the AHP assignment scale.
- Normalize the values in the columns, sum the rows of each matrix, and divide the sum of each row of each matrix with the number of alternatives.
- Sum the criteria for each alternative. This is the value of the alternative. Apply weight to each criterion using lower level AHP analysis if present.
- Find the cost of each alternative and normalized it.
- Divide the value of each approach by its cost. This results in an MOE.

Normalize the MOE to determine level of differences between alternatives.
- Alternatively plot the value versus cost to visualize the degree of separation between the alternatives.

8.1.5 Design to Cost (DTC)

Design to Cost (DTC) is as the name suggests, picking the design that falls within a cost target. The issue is to determine the most effective design attributes. The attributes are function, performance, quality and aesthetics. The trick is to not compromise on offering a great design because of cost restrictions.

This suggests a strategy needs to be established. One approach is to consider that the design can evolve and grow with time, as more funds become available. So the tradeoffs need to consider the most effective function, performance, and athletic levels to offer such that the design is still considered a breakthrough with outstanding attributes.

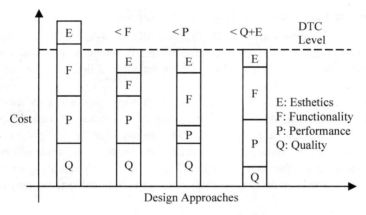

Figure 141 Design to Cost Alternatives

DTC as a decision method on the surface appears to be easy because we are able to determine the costs on our designs or so we think. At the end of a design activity when a complete parts list is available we are able to know the cost of the design. However early in the design when alternatives are being considered the costs are not fully understood and known. If we have an existing design we start from a very well known source of cost data. However as that design is considered for a new application there is the temptation to say there will be no changes but more often than not there will be changes with cost increases.

Once the costs are written down for all to see the next step is to determine the changes in costs as functions are removed, performance is lowered, quality is lowered, and aesthetics are addressed. There are different strategies that can be followed:

- Less functionality
- Lower performance
- Lower Aesthetics
- Lower quality
- Any combination

If it is anticipated that the product and or system will grow then less functionality might be the best approach for reaching a DTC level. If there comes a point where removing the next function translates into a poor design then the next step might be to reduce the performance and maintain a basic minimum level of functionality needed for the design. If both functional an performance reductions are no longer possible then quality and aesthetics become the next possible sources to achieve a DTC target.

8.1.6 Design to Production Cost (DTUPC)

Design to unit production costs (DUPC) is similar to DTC but the view is that of production costs. The issue is to understand the initial, mid term, and final life cycle product production costs. These will vary as a function of time and the number of production level units sold.

An initial design with relatively low production quantity is not as sensitive to DTUPC as an initial design with a higher production quantity. A new design may use a new lower cost part to reduce production run costs but the new part may delay entry into the market because of part availability. So there are tradeoffs between time and cost. There also may be tradeoffs associated with retooling an existing production line that is ready to go with existing parts but unable to support the new parts.

Example 27 DTUPC and Retooling Costs

When surface mount electronic parts became available there were costs associated with retooling the manufacturing facility to support the new parts. The costs were financial associated with new equipment purchases and training. They were also associated with schedule if parallel operations could not be supported. The new surface mount parts were not only superior but they had lower DTUPC levels yet the transitions were challenging to manage.

8.1.7 Design to Schedule (DTS)

Design to Schedule (DTS) is as the name suggests, driving towards a design that falls within a schedule target. The trick is to not compromise on offering a great design because of schedule restrictions.

Unlike DTC where the primary issue is to determine the most effective design attributes, DTS shares those elements but is primarily driven by an additional element usually referred to as reuse. When reuse is considered portions of one or more existing designs are used in the new design solution. The development time for the new design is shortened because information products exist and many unknowns have been addressed.

This suggests a strategy needs to be established. One approach is to consider that the design can evolve and grow with time. So the tradeoffs need to consider the level and target of reuse and how the reuse elements will be upgraded or replaced with new designs.

DTS as a decision method on the surface appears to be easy because we are able to determine the schedule for developing designs or so we think. At the end of a design activity when all the schedule results are available we are able to know the schedule details. However early in the design when alternatives are being considered the schedules are not fully understood and known. If we have an existing design we start from a very well known source of schedule data. However as that design is considered for a new application there is the temptation to say there will be no changes but more often than not there will be design changes and interface challenges associated with reuse that will increase the schedule.

8.1.8 Opportunity Cost Opportunity Lost (OCOL)

Whenever a decision is made, there are one or more lost opportunities associated with the decision. These lost opportunities can be viewed from a financial and non-financial point of view. It is the cost or sacrifice being made as a result of the decision. This decision making approach minimizes the lost opportunity costs. The non-financial costs include:

- Lost Time
- Lost Reputation
- Lost Future
- Lost Capability

8.1.9 Design to Key Discriminators (DKD)

Design to key discriminators is designing to one or more elements of the design that the team believes are key discriminators from previous designs. The following is a list of potential discriminators:

- Maximize Safety, Security, Maintainability, Usability
- Minimize Failures, Wear, Power and Weight, Environmental Impacts
- New function, performance, quality, aesthetic levels

The discriminators can also include the artifacts of the design effort and they include designs that:

- Minimize Risk
- Minimize Design Team Skill Level
- Minimize Team Learning Curves

8.1.10 Formal Autocratic Decision (FAD)

An autocratic decision is made by someone in a position of authority. It should only happen when there is an inability for the team to converge on a decision. It is used to break up a logjam and allow design and analysis to continue.

If it is used to over rule the team, then it must be formally documented and signed by the decision-maker. This document needs to be disclosed to the executive level of all the stakeholder organizations. It should include a description of the alternatives, references to all the analysis with special emphasis disclosing conflicting opinion, and why the decision was made. It should also offer opportunities for revisiting the decision in the future or clearly state this is an end state decision.

8.1.11 Design to Value Systems (DVS)

This design decision method discussion is associated with making design decisions based on value systems. The value systems can be financial and non-financial.

Author Comment: Most believe it is easier to make decisions based on financial metrics because they think it is easy to calculate those metrics. However, that is not the case in complex systems. The numbers associated with a financial analysis of alternative designs is filled with unknowns that can swing the results across most of the design alternatives. The only financial metrics that are accurate are those associated with an existing proven design that is in the market for a reasonable period of time where stability has been reached. However the discussion is still worthy to pursue and the analysis worthy to consider as long as no one makes claims about the superiority of new design decision making based on financial perspectives.

Financial metrics falls under the broad area of economics. They are based on two important economic principles: (1) Fixed and Variable Costs, and (2) Supply Versus Demand. Everyone is familiar with financial metrics and many erroneously believe all decisions should be based exclusively on one or more of these financial metrics. Examples of financial metrics are:

- Lowest Cost
- Highest Profit

- Economic Value Added (EVA)
- Real Option Value (ROV)

- Greatest Return on Investment (ROI)
- Total Cost of Ownership (TCO)
- Internal Rate of Return (IRR)
- Return on Assets (ROA)
- Return on Infrastructure Employed (ROIE)

However, value is not only financial but also non-financial. For example some value a day at the beach more than a day at the mountains. How do you capture the value of a bridge that connects two cities? How do you capture the value of a road that heads into a wilderness? These are interesting questions and they were addressed in the last century.

There is a technique that is based on a simple concept - value is more than apparent financial results. Apparent because it is all relative to your context or view. For example it might make sense to do something because it can translate into thousands of jobs or it can cause people to view a physical land area as attractive so they will move there and buy houses and or open businesses. These can be reduced to dollar numbers but it is more complex[157]. It uses the following elements:

- Life Cycle Costs (LCC)
- Measure of Effectiveness (MOE)

8.1.11.1 Lowest Cost

Cost is the total cost to purchase an item if you are buying it or the total cost to build an item if you are building an item. Most people focus on lowest cost no matter the perspective. However if you are buying an existing item you run the risk of a latent quality issue that does not surface until the product is in use. If you are buying an item yet to be built you run the risk of cost over runs.

The government, when it buys a system based on lowest costs examines multiple bids and looks for cost reasonableness. If a particular proposal comes in at a significantly lower price than the competition, the bid may be tossed out of the competition because of cost reasonableness based on the bids of other vendors and internal cost estimates. The same may be true of a high bid. It should be closely examined to determine if it is the reasonable bid and the others are not reasonable as they try to buy into a contract.

Most people who work on fixed price contracts, based on lowest cost tend to fixate on the "project triangle". The idea is the sides of the triangle are labeled good, fast, and cheap[158] (quality, schedule, and cost). The area of the triangle is project scope. So if you want something at low cost then quality and or schedule must

---

[157] This is a Formal Architecture Tradeoff with Measure of Effectiveness (MOE). Sustainable Development Possible with Creative System Engineering, Walter Sobkiw, 2008, ISBN 0615216307.

[158] Hughes Aircraft defined cheap as a low quality solution while low cost was defined as a solution with no quality loss.

decrease. The alternative is to create a smaller triangle (less area) which is a project with less scope.

However, this is a very myopic view of the problem. Cost is driven by quality, up to a point. There comes a point where no amount of money will increase quality and yet the quality may be too low to field the solution. Cost is driven by schedule, but there comes a point where increasing the cost will not reduce the schedule. This is like trying to give birth to a 9-month baby in 3 days. It is a hilarious but sad situation in an organizational setting to see these ideas taken to unreasonable extremes.

When these ideas surface in an organization most people will start to look for all the hidden costs. Itemized lists are then developed. They try to find the collection of items to cut and yet have the project, organization, system, etc still work. This mindset eventually leads to cost shifting strategies where the burden is moved to another area.

For example if an organization is big enough it may choose to move operations to another country with lower labor and environmental costs. However new costs surface that far exceed the savings to the entity. The entity does not pay for these cost shifted elements. For example a military to protect the assets.

All these views are superficial and unfortunately do not consider traditional economies of scale lessons from the previous century. This typically is a sign of panic or irresponsible behavior. Sometimes it genuinely can be because of a myopic view, which leads to a lack of understanding of the lowest cost. A broader view of cost is to understand what actually drives the cost. Lowest cost is defined as:

Cost ~ (Quality + Features) / (Process + Automated Tools)

So cutting features or reducing quality can reduce cost. Typically that is not possible in a healthy competitive environment. However introducing process and automated tools can reduce the cost. Further tuning the process and automated tools is what will separate a vendor from its competition. The process and automated tools may have such an impact that quality increases and the solution now becomes viable not only from a cost point of view but also from a quality point for view (e.g. chip yields from a foundry). In many ways this simple relationship is the story of the industrial revolution.

Process and automated tools have a cost. However if their cost is less than the cost savings they offer, then they are effective and the indirect costs of the process and automated tools are worth the investment. If the leaders focus on the short term and strip the assets by cutting investment in process and automated tools then the organizations projects will eventually start to fail.

8.1.11.2 Highest Profit

Profit is all the money that comes in minus all the costs. There are typically three types of profit to capture the different categories of costs. They are:

Gross Profit = Sales Revenue - Cost of Goods Sold
Where: Cost of Goods Sold = Production Cost

Operating Profit = Gross Profit - All Operating Expenses
EBIT = Operating Profit
(Earnings before Interest and Taxes)
Operating Expenses = General overhead like Research and Development
(R&D), General and Administrative G&A.

Net Profit = Operating Profit - Tax - Extraordinary Expenses
Net Income = Net Profit

So there are different slices of "profit" that stakeholders use to try to assess and apply value to an organization, project, program, etc. The bottom line is that anyone can show great short term profits while deferring costs such as R&D, G&A, and even taxes. Selling off assets or reducing staff also can increase or maintain profits.

This is relevant in a design discussion about a company, industry, or organization. A design that leads to maximum profits at the expense of no future is not sustainable and is a fatally flawed design.

8.1.11.3 Return on Investment (ROI)

Return on Investment (ROI) is the ratio of the net revenue generated by a business that is divided by the cost to establish and maintain the business. It is also the ratio of cost savings generated by the introduction of a tool, process, method, etc divided by its cost. From an investors point of view it is the rate of return, typically annualized on an investment such as a bank certificate of deposit. The goal is to maximize the ROI.

From a business point of view the ROI is typically associated with a period of time. This is the investment period and the goal is to have the full investment plus additional returns provided back to the investors by the end of the investment period. Depending on the length of the investment period and the inflation rate on the local currency, the cost of money must be factored into the total costs. Typically an ROI plan has the goals of an investment period of 1-3 years with an ROI of 20%.

For complex high stake designs the context of the ROI becomes extremely important. For example, expenditures on one project may not result in planned ROI numbers for that project, but its off shoots are so significant that an entire company, industry, country, or the world is transformed. For example when computers were introduced into air traffic control it was for the purpose of reducing staff. What actually happened is the staff increased as people thought of new ways to use the new system with its new levels of automation. This allowed air transportation to expand beyond anyone's dreams at the time. It gave birth to our modern society of air travel that everyone now takes for granted[159]. How do you calculate the ROI for that investment, especially ahead of time?

Author Comment: Traditionally when engaged with startup companies, the ROI is an important consideration when searching for venture capital funding. Unless responding to a request for proposal or using personal money, when engaged in a startup situation the financial analysis drives the decisions. This is typically captured in a business plan. It is rare when investors are willing to offer money without knowing when and how much they will financially benefit. Many tend to forget that venture capital funding is relatively new surfacing in the 1970s. A Corporation has the ability to issue and sell stock. It can attract funding by selling shares directly to small investors at events that they arrange and sponsor.

8.1.11.4 Total Cost of Ownership (TCO)

Total Cost of Ownership (TCO) is a financial metric that attempts to capture all costs from the perspective of the owner. It typically includes purchase, operation and maintenance. The problem with TCO is that it is from the perspective of the owner. It does not take into account cost shifting or indirect costs, which must be paid by other stakeholders or even non-stakeholders.

For example airline companies are commercial companies and certainly have costs, however the indirect costs of the air traffic control system which includes airports, air traffic control centers, navigational aids, voice communications, satellites, etc are paid for by the tax payer. In addition the indirect costs associated with aircraft include research, development, and technology transfer from military aircraft to the commercial sector. Building and creating maintenance and support mechanisms for something that does not fall from the sky has huge indirect costs.

There are other indirect costs such as pollution that are borne by other elements of society. Noise pollution results in large tracts of land being reserved for special use around airports.

8.1.11.5 Internal Rate of Return (IRR)

Internal Rate of Return (IRR) is similar to ROI. It is the internal rate of return on an investment. It is the annualized effective compounded return rate that can be earned on the invested capital. It does not include the cost of money or inflation.

---

[159] A similar situation is unfolding with the Internet, Tablet Computers, and Smart Phones as of the writing of this textbook.

8.1.11.6 Economic Value Added (EVA)

Economic Value Added (EVA) compares multiple approaches using their respective ROI numbers, however the comparison is with leaving the money in an external investment instrument, such as a bank versus making the investment within the organization. It is essentially adding the cost of money to the investment. So you are asking if it is better to make the investment in the design approach versus another design approach, idea, business, process, method, tool, etc or should you just leave the money in the bank.

8.1.11.7 Real Option Value (ROV)

Real Option Value (ROV) is a modified ROI where the value is not associated with the current project, but with future projects. Essentially the costs are amortized across several projects, programs, business units, etc that stand to benefit from the investment but each alone could not pay for the investment. This is a form of infrastructure investment. The infrastructure investment could have huge benefits for the organization and its current and future projects and programs. This is also a form of investing in the future. The benefit may not surface for several years.

A classic example is the introduction of new tools into an organization. The first project will most likely suffer from a cost and schedule point of view but future projects stand to significantly benefit once the new tools are understood and internalized by the organization.

Another example is the introduction of a capital-intensive machine such as bulldozer into a third world country. The first project cannot pay for itself and using human labor with picks and shovels will yield the most cost-effective approach for the project. However, once the bulldozer is amortized over several projects and the laborers are freed to perform more productive tasks the third world country will transform itself into a first world super power. Buying the first bulldozer is the hard part in any organization without vision.

Investing in the future is exemplified by traditional research and development or deciding to go to a university rather than enter the workforce. In both cases an investment is made with the intent of a large payoff in the future.

8.1.11.8 Return on Assets (ROA)

Return on Assets (ROA) is the net income divided by the value of the assets being used to generate the income. If the income is less than could be derived by the selling off of the assets, then a case can be made to sell off the assets. Coupled in this analysis is time. If the assets can perform for 10 years versus 5 years then the decision to sell at a particular factor of the value of the assets will change. Capital intensive industries have small returns on assets. They also have a large barrier of entry into the market. It is difficult to arrange for the purchase of the "expensive" assets.

For example, it was only a few decades ago that computers were extremely capital intensive. Only governments and extremely large companies were able to purchase computers. The ROA for these machines were very small.

8.1.11.9 Return on Infrastructure Employed (ROIE)

Return on Infrastructure Employed (ROIE) is similar to ROA except it is applied to infrastructure services. For example a computer support department provides services at some cost to various projects, programs, business units, etc. The ROIE may be different for in house versus outsourced computer support services.

8.1.11.10 Life Cycle Costs (LCC)

Unlike traditional financial metrics which are based on artificial system boundaries that attempt to maximize the benefit of one stakeholder at the expense of another stakeholder[160], Life Cycle Costs (LCC) is a broad metric used to capture all the costs from all the stakeholders.

Each generation since World War II has attempted to identify the elements of LCC. Today with the realization of environmental impacts the LCC has become even broader than in the past.

At the highest level of LCC there are direct costs attributed to a project or program and then there are indirect costs that are attributed to infrastructure[161] or other costs not typically allocated to the project or program. Typically it is the indirect costs that significantly impact the selection of the architecture.

The following is a starting point for your LCC analysis:

$$LCC = R+D+P+O+M+S+I+E \text{ or PROMISED}$$

Where:

R = Research	S = Shut Down & Disposal
D = Development	
P = Production	I = Infrastructure
O = Operation	E = Environment & Waste

---

[160] Essentially the total costs in traditional financial metrics are shifted and the true cost burden is hidden or obfuscated.

[161] Executive Order 12803 - Infrastructure Privatization April 30, 1992, (b) "Infrastructure asset" means any asset financed in whole or in part by the Federal Government and needed for the functioning of the economy. Examples of such assets include, but are not limited to: roads, tunnels, bridges, electricity supply facilities, mass transit, rail transportation, airports, ports, waterways, water supply facilities, recycling and wastewater treatment facilities, solid waste disposal facilities, housing, schools, prisons, and hospitals.

M = Maintenance

In the USA the direct costs have typically been borne by commercial companies and indirect costs have been borne by the taxpayer. For example automobiles will not sell unless there is a road infrastructure. Airplanes cannot fly unless there are airports and an air traffic control system. Further airplanes would not exist without defense projects that invested in aircraft. Spaceships carrying satellites that offer commercial services cannot fly without NASA launch and tracking systems.

It is always an interesting moral situation when companies forget that if the true costs of the products and services were passed on to the customer, assuming they could actually implement the infrastructure, they would quickly go out of business. This is a modern political discussion that has resurfaced approximately 40 years after the end of World War II and has not been resolved in the USA at this time.

8.1.11.11 Measure of Effectiveness (MOE)

Minimizing life cycle costs, although extremely beneficial when compared to other financial metrics, still does not offer a true indicator of the value of one architecture design over another architecture design.

Value is not only financial but also non-financial. For example some value a day at the beach more than a day at the mountains.

The Measure of Effectiveness (MOE) is based on the concept that the tradeoff criteria in a design tradeoff matrix should not include cost or requirements. It is a given that all solutions will satisfy the known requirements at some cost.

Cost is used at the bottom of the tradeoff matrix where each approach total rating (sum of all the tradeoff criteria) is divided by cost. This essentially identifies the **goodness of each approach per unit of cost**. This is called the Measure of Effectiveness or MOE. This is expressed as the following equation:

MOE = Sum of tradeoff criteria/cost to produce approach

The MOE equation is the heart of systems engineering. It is fundamental and drives everything. The tradeoff criteria ratings are the result of analysis, which may take years and involve hundreds of stakeholders.

A word of caution, most institutions do not base their decisions on the MOE or measure of goodness of an approach. So there is confusion on what the MOE actually represents. For example some refer to the MOE in terms of what is actually the tradeoff criteria. They state that the MOE is based on operational needs and then are silent on the relationship between the sum of the tradeoff items and cost. So the idea of MOE is obscured and lost. The following is a description of MOEs from NASA:

"MOEs are the "operational" measures of success that are closely related to the achievement of mission or operational objectives in the intended operational environment. MOEs are intended to focus on how well mission or operational objectives are achieved, not on how they are achieved, i.e., MOEs should be independent of any particular solution. As such, MOEs are the standards against which the "goodness" of each proposed solution may be assessed in trade studies and decision analyses. Measuring or calculating MOEs not only makes it possible to compare alternative solutions quantitatively, but sensitivities to key assumptions regarding operational environments... [162]"

Notice the term MOE has become plural, the plural MOEs usage and the description clearly represent tradeoff criteria. However in this ontology the criteria are lost and MOE is obfuscated. Some practitioners are familiar with the subtle distinction between the singular and plural MOE term and use them appropriately in the process[163]. However for clarity, especially in highly controversial settings the MOE term should not be used with the tradeoff criteria for the ontology[164]. Do not use MOE and MOEs together in any process description. Use MOE and tradeoff criteria terminology.

Another potential trap where the MOE could be lost or inappropriately used is if people attempt to equate it to cost benefit analysis. Cost benefit analysis is primarily performed in the financial domain while the MOE with its use of non-financial tradeoff criteria works outside the financial domain. Also cost benefit analysis is typically used to justify an intervention as opposed to picking an architecture approach. The intervention is meant to disrupt the status quo with the intent of reducing future costs.

The MOE is the only value system that uses non-financial variables in the equation. In many ways it is like shifting from the time domain to the frequency domain to perform circuit analysis in electrical engineering. The view that the MOE offers is not possible when using strictly financial variables. Examples of other financial analysis that might be equated with the MOE are:

- Cost-Effectiveness Analysis
- Economic Impact Analysis
- Fiscal Impact Analysis
- Social Return On Investment (SROI) Analysis

---

[162] NASA Systems Engineering Handbook, NASA/SP-2007-6105 Rev1, National Aeronautics and Space Administration NASA Headquarters Washington, D.C. 20546, December 2007.

[163] At Hughes Aircraft I / we used the single MOE to select architecture approaches. This can be referred to as the architecture MOE.

[164] These controversial settings are described in Sustainable Development Possible with Creative System Engineering, Walter Sobkiw, 2008, ISBN 0615216307.

8.2 Gut Level Decisions (GLD)

Many executives in top-level positions of authority are not aware of complex systems engineering and formal decision making techniques[165]. Instead they rely on instinct which leads to poor results. An alternative is to use logic and evidence to eventually help develop a set of internal heuristics. This is evidence-based decision-making and it includes the following elements.

- **Demand Evidence.** Whenever there is a claim, objective quality evidence and data are provided. Here-say and opinion are irrelevant, regardless of the source.
- **Examine Logic.** Evidence is closely examined to ensure the logic is valid. There may be incorrect cause-and-effect reasoning, assumptions, omissions, and other problems with the evidence.
- **Encourage Others.** If there is no evidence, be the first to offer evidence and data. Invite others to do the same and check the viability of potential strategies. Use the resulting data to guide decisions.

Every important decision involves a trade-off. Knowing what can't be pursued is as valuable as what can be pursued. There are some rules that can be used to determine what should be part of a more involved tradeoff:

- **Advantages and Disadvantages Input.** List advantages and disadvantages and ask others for their perspective on which carries the heaviest weight.
- **Balance Short Term with Long Term.** Determine what can be given up in the long run for some important short-term gain? Determine the true cost of this shortsighted strategy?
- **Gauge Support.** While weighing alternatives think about who will support a particular idea and who will oppose it. Ask whose support you can live without, and whose backing and buy-in you absolutely need. This is actually a dangerous anti-system path and suggests that stakeholders are being locked out because of serious divergent stakeholder needs.

There are some decision making common traps that should be avoided.

- **Anchoring.** Many give more weight to the first information they receive. Pursue other lines of thinking, even if the first one seems right.
- **Status Quo.** Change is unsettling and it's easy to favor alternatives that keep things the same. Does the status quo truly serve the objectives? Avoid the urge to stay in your current state.

---

[165] That is why this book exists and the emphasis in this new century on systems thinking and engineering. Much of the high technology wrapped up in a few companies during the last half of the last century need to become ubiquitous across all companies and organizations.

- **Confirming Evidence.** If new information constantly validates existing views, someone needs to rise to argue against these views.

Although this discussion is offered it should not be used in place of the formal decision making practices and architecture selection strategies. It is offered so systems designers can detect decision authorities with missing systems skills. It is also offered, as a strategy to start to provide them with the skill sets needed for serious complex system design activities.

8.3 Architecture Design Selection (ADS)

Architecture design selection and tradeoffs is based on the simple concept that value is more than apparent financial results. Value is relative to your context or view. For example it might make sense to do something because it can translate into thousands of jobs or it can cause people to view an area as attractive so they will move there and buy houses and or open businesses. These can be reduced to dollar numbers but it is more complex and that complexity is captured as a Tradeoff with Measure of Effectiveness (MOE) for each architecture design approach.

Architecture design selection and tradeoff is a series of simple steps that anyone can execute at anytime. The complexity surfaces as science and engineering are applied to the various elements of the steps with all the stakeholders and their views. The steps are:

- Identify the architecture design alternatives
- List the advantages and disadvantages of each approach
- Identify the tradeoff criteria using the list of advantages and disadvantages
- Create a tradeoff matrix listing the tradeoff criteria with the alternatives shown in columns
- Using science and engineering to fill in each cell of the matrix
- Determine the life cycle cost (LCC) of each approach
- Divide the total rating of each approach by the LCC to calculate the measure of effectiveness (MOE) of each approach

8.3.1 Architecture Design Alternatives

Architecture design alternatives come from two primary areas. The first is from current and similar approaches. The second comes from the participants on the team using creativity, innovation, and invention.

There always should be more than one participant involved in identifying the alternatives. It does not matter how simple or complex the design.

The best way to illustrate this is through the concept of metrics. More or less one participant is packed with 100 units of creativity, innovation, and invention - an IQ (invention quotient). There is no way to measure IQ, but if you could measure IQ and compare different participants it would not differ by more than a factor of ten, pick a number, it does not matter. So you could have one participant identifying alternatives or 1000 participants identifying alternatives. At what point do the addition of more participants' result in no new identification of alternatives? That is an interesting question.

In an organizational setting you could start with 3 participants, let them identify alternatives, then start adding more participants over time. At some point diminishing returns start to surface. At some point gestalt surfaces and the IQ of the participants is no longer a simple sum but becomes non-linear. For example 10 participants with an individual IQ of 100 might result in a team IQ of 100,000 rather than 1000.

There always should be more than one alternative being considered. If there is only one alternative you are not engaged in a meaningful activity. Two is not the right answer either. That is normally a sign of someone stacking the solutions towards a vested interest. The universe is more complex than left right, up down, centralized distributed, etc. The issue surfaces when you are engaged in a true system engineering design effort and you are really trying to apply science and engineering principles to each alternative. That costs money. At some point pruning needs to happen in the early studies so that when the serious studies begin not only are costs controlled but also the stakeholders can actually follow the science and engineering. The number seven plus or minus two is the answer. Eventually there are two competing alternatives.

Any of the latter stage design alternatives can be made to work. One design alternative might be strong in one area and weak in another area. Money can be applied to address the weak area. Each architecture design alternative will display this result and each will cost about the same in the end.

This is an extremely powerful observation, and shakes true engineers and scientists engaged in these activities to the core. It usually surfaces in the heat of battle of selecting system architecture designs.

So why go through the process? Why not pick an alternative using one participant and just make it work? Well the alternative from the one participant may not have made the short list once understood by the team because of a fatal flaw. Also the weaknesses of the alternative will not surface because there is no debate. This process forces the team to understand each architecture design alternative and surface their emergent properties.

8.3.2 List of Advantages and Disadvantages

In the beginning of the architecture design trade study there is nothing, just a blank sheet of paper. The first step is to identify alternatives, no matter how bizarre. One of the alternatives should be the current design approach. Another alternative should be the dream design approach. They form two extremes. The other approaches should be everything in between. List the alternatives on a single sheet of paper, create two columns, and label the columns advantages and disadvantages. This is basically the Benjamin Franklin method of decision-making.

Keep this on a single sheet of paper so you can visualize it and cut to the key issues. It is easy to get lost in the noise. This also quickly cuts down on the alternatives. If you only have two alternatives something is wrong. If you have ten alternatives something is wrong. The answer is in between and should include the impossible alternatives.

Table 89 List of Advantages Disadvantages

Architecture	Advantages	Disadvantages
Approach 1	Advantage 1 Advantage 2 Advantage 3	Disadvantage 1 Disadvantage 2
Approach 2	Advantage 1 Advantage 2	Disadvantage 1 Disadvantage 2
Approach n	Advantage 1	Disadvantage 1

The advantages-disadvantages or plusses-minuses tables are very important. It is at this time that the key tradeoff criteria start to surface. These tradeoff criteria will be used in the next phase of the architecture design trade study. At this point we depart the Benjamin Franklin method and start moving into the heart of system engineering.

8.3.3 Tradeoff Criteria

Using the List of Advantages and Disadvantages and input from the stakeholders identify the tradeoff criteria. There is overlap between tradeoff criteria and quality attributes.

The criteria can be general and applicable to any architecture design:

- Resilience, growth, flexibility, technology insertion, maintainability, testability, user acceptance, performance, supportability, transition, fragility, brittleness

They also can include unique items associated with a domain like sustainability:

- Carbon pollution, water pollution, land pollution, air pollution, noise pollution, visual pollution, fuel sustainability

The domain of electronic medical records might be:

- Flexibility, adaptability, interoperability, security, maintainability, transition, user acceptance, etc

8.3.3.1 Traditional Tradeoff Criteria

The following is a list of traditional tradeoff criteria and their descriptions. There is overlap in the list. The intent is to stimulate discussion on the tradeoff criteria that matter for the system being developed.

1. **Resilience**: Resilience to failure is the capability to withstand multiple failures and still offer services. Resilience to change is the ability to accept change and offer current and the new services.
2. **Robustness**: The ability to easily tolerate and recover from unexpected failures and abnormal conditions, strongly constructed, sturdy, durable.
3. **Ruggedness**: Ruggedness is a measure of how tolerant a solution is to its external natural environment. The natural environment includes wind, rain, snow, sleet, humidity, temperature extremes, barometric pressure extremes, dew point, salt fog, mold, mildew, fungus, insects, animals, and radiation (cosmic, etc). The more rugged a system the more survivable it is in a hostile environment.
4. **Survivability**: Survivability is a measure of how a system behaves once the environment exceeds its design requirements. A system is more survivable if it slowly loses capabilities, as the environment becomes more hostile. Sudden loss of all capability with just a small environmental stress level above the design requirement is not a very survivable system. Massive excess in environmental stresses with slow loss of capability is a very survivable system.
5. **Brittleness**: The degree to which something will shatter or completely break down when touched by failure or change. Something that is brittle can be very strong and withstand all assaults, which may otherwise lead to failure. Unfortunately when a failure does happen the system shatters, it is catastrophic.
6. **Flexibility**: The ability to adapt to new, different, or changing requirements or needs.
7. **Reconfigure-ability**: How easy is it to reconfigure the system in the presence of a failure, different load conditions (night time versus daytime operations), training needs, and upgrade needs
8. **Scalability**: This is the building block level. The ability to add more functionality and capacity in small increments. Can the system be sized to support very small operations and very large operations or will the system have over capacity at the small locations.
9. **Stability**: Does the system stop operating, need random human intervention, offer the same performance and response especially to humans

interacting with the system.

10. **Control Ability**: The ability to easily control and reconfigure the system. Is it from a single management source or from multiple dispersed locations? The level of control offered or is the system just on / off with no ability to continue offering services such as during maintenance or upgrade.

11. **Elegance**: Suggests significant effort and refinement to reflect tasteful richness of design, precision, neatness, effectiveness, and simplicity.

12. **Symmetry**: Balanced proportions, harmonious or appropriate proportionality and balance. For example is the load equally distributed across the architecture or is one part of the architecture needlessly stressed.

13. **Beauty**: In balance and harmony, admired, perfection, very good, attractive, or impressive, useful, or satisfying feature, qualities that make something pleasing and impressive, exalts the mind or spirit, graceful.

14. **Simplicity**: Easy to understand or explain, few parts, few connections, believed to have no unexpected behavior, linear, untangled.

15. **Reasonableness**: Not extreme or excessive, moderate, fair, based on sound judgment, logical, sensible, sound, valid, well-founded, well-grounded, coherent, rational, good sense, plausible or acceptable. Some approaches on the surface are immediately viewed as reasonable while others are not. As the approaches are studied and the details surface the level of reasonableness will change.

16. **Transition**: This is a measure of how difficult it is to transition into the new system. For example some approaches may need special throwaway subsystems or elements. Other approach may use the transition supporting elements as part of backup mechanisms. Transition is passage from one state, stage, subject, place, style, concept, etc to another.

17. **Interoperability**: The ability to easily interface and seamlessly operate with existing and new systems.

18. **Usability**: The ability for any operator to easily use the system with little or no training under all load conditions and scenarios.

19. **User Acceptability**: Some approaches may be more acceptable to the users. Care needs to be exercised in this area because users will tend to resist change. They understand the status quo.

20. **Comfort**: Some approaches offer better human factors characteristics. The elements include ergonomics, field of view, reach, tactile feedback, cognitive processing loads, user exposure to temperature, noise, humidity, etc.

21. **Availability**: The percent of time a system is offering services in a system operating 24 hours a day, seven days a week, every day of the year. Availability has little meaning for a system that is permitted to go offline for periods of time.

22. **Fault Tolerance**: The ability to tolerate one or more faults and provide full

or degraded services in the presence of the faults. Ideally all functionality should be preserved with response time being reduced in the presence of a fault. At some point when response time can no longer be reasonably increased then functionality is shed.

23. **Graceful Degradation**: This is a measure of how the system behaves as failures are introduced. Is the loss of function and or performance small or are large pieces of function and performance lost? How many failures does it take before the system completely collapses?

24. **Ability to Meet Requirements**: It is a given that all approaches should be able to satisfy all the requirements. However some approaches are able to meet the requirements with greater ease either because the technology is a better match or an approach is more mature in a particular area.

25. **Performance**: It is a given that all approaches should be able to meet the performance requirements. However some approaches perform better in some areas than other either because the technology is a better match or an approach is more tuned to a particular area.

26. **Model results**: A comparison of various model results from various alternatives under consideration.

27. **Capacity**: The ability to accept more functionality and or more loads without adding new technology or new system elements.

28. **Excess Capacity**: Some approaches use large building block that result in excess capacity, which comes at a cost.

29. **Efficiency**: Minimal or no waste.

30. **Inherent Capacity**: Some approaches have inherent capacity that is provided for free.

31. **Growth**: This ability to accept new system elements of the same type to support new functions and performance.

32. **Technology Insertion**: The ability to accept new technology to support new functions or performance. This includes replacing old equipment with new technology as it ages and becomes failure prone or difficult to maintain.

33. **Produce Ability**: Some approaches may be ideal solutions in limited quantities. As quantities increase the ability to produce the system repeatedly and cost effectively surfaces.

34. **Testability**: Some approaches are inherently more testable than other approaches. This tends to surface when white box testing is needed which means there must be access to the system internals.

35. **Reliability**: This is a measure of how often something breaks in a system. If an approach uses more parts than another approach or if the parts are inherently less reliable in an approach a qualitative assessment can be made before the actual reliability numbers are produced.

36. **Maintainability**: Some approaches are more maintainable than other

approaches. The issues are inherent reliability, access, lowest replaceable parts, skill level, tools, etc. Some approaches may offer better diagnostic tools, other approaches may need special diagnostics.

37. **Training**: Some approaches may have special training needs. Also the skill levels may be different. Even the forms of training may change - class room instruction versus classroom instruction plus simulator training plus on the job training.

38. **Supportability**: This is tied to maintainability but focuses on the logistics elements. Some approaches may need onsite maintenance staff and spares while other approaches will work with a maintenance hub.

39. **Sustainability or Internal Sustainability**: Most systems will stop operating in a very brief period of time without human intervention. Even with human intervention, the system may eventually collapse. This is a measure of each approach to keep working year after year decade after decade, human generation after human generation. The Roman Aqueducts are an example of a very sustainable approach to water delivery. This is exclusive of maintenance. Internal sustainability can be compromised in many ways.

40. **Effectiveness**: This is a measure of how effective the system is once it goes operational. Notice the term system is used rather than approach. It is assumed all the approaches meet the same requirements so they will have the same effectiveness. This is a reality check to see how these approaches compare with the previous system or another possible system.

41. **Safety**: Some approaches are inherently more safe than other approaches. The safety considerations include possible harm to users, maintainers, stakeholders relying on the system, the community where the system is located. For example one approach may blow up and destroy an entire community while another approach may just gracefully shut down.

42. **Security**: Some approaches are inherently more secure than other approaches. Using the commercial open Internet even with sophisticated encryption techniques is less secure than using an inaccessible custom communications network.

43. **Vulnerability**: Some approaches are more vulnerable to external undesired influences that other approaches. A custom computer system with limited knowledge of its structure is less vulnerable than an open system computer system with large numbers of installations and practitioners.

44. **Deployment**: Some approaches are easier to deploy than other approaches. This can be because of the size and or weight of the largest elements, the number of elements and interconnections, physical needs during transition, installation skill levels, etc.

45. **Shutdown**: Some approaches are easier to shut down than others. For example a highly distributed approach may require coordination between

many elements while a centralized approach needs no coordination. There are also issues associated with preparing for a graceful shutdown so that there are no issues. This translates to shutdown time and complexity.

46. **Disposal**: Some approaches may have disposal challenges. For example highly exotic materials in an approach may be unsafe and may require special handling and processing for safe disposal.

47. **Technology Maturity**: Some approaches use less mature technology than other approaches.

48. **Technology Stability**: Some approaches use new technology that is viewed as less stable or old technology that is known to be less stable.

49. **Time to Obsolescence**: Some approaches use older technology than other approaches, which leads to quicker obsolescence.

50. **Degree of Obsolescence**: Some approaches use a higher proportion of obsolete or nearing obsolescence technology than other approaches.

Author Comment: This is a rather large list. How can you prioritize this list? All I can say is that back at Hughes, architecture discussions always eventually revolved around **Elegance, Simplicity, Robustness, Resilience, Fault Tolerance, Efficiency,** and **Effectiveness**. These are highly subjective terms yet people found phrases and analysis data to support or refute them for each architecture approach. The other criteria were also tracked but they were not the discriminators. They tended to be a washout across the architecture approaches in the tradeoff analysis.

8.3.3.2 Sustainability and Regeneration Tradeoff Criteria

The following is a list of Sustainability and Regeneration tradeoff criteria and their descriptions. The intent is to stimulate discussion on the tradeoff criteria that matter for the system being developed.

1. **Sustainability or External Sustainability**: Development that meets the needs of the present without compromising the ability of future generations to meet their own needs[166]. Meet current as well as future mission requirements worldwide, safeguard human health, improve quality of life, and enhance the natural environment[167]. We also see that sustainability was a traditional tradeoff criterion associated with the ability of a system to sustain itself through years of operations. So a qualifier is added to distinguish the difference between internal or system and external or community sustainability.

2. **Ethics:** What are the ethical ramifications of an approach. One approach

---

[166] World Commission on Environment and Development, Brundtland Commission, 1987, Our Common Future.

[167] The Army Strategy for the Environment, October 2004.

may be more ethical than the other approach.

3. **Regeneration**: The ability to re-establish a damaged environment and then improve it beyond its original state before the introduction of a system. For example an approach that is better able to improve water quality than another possible approach.

4. **Integrity**: Does the approach actually work. This is interesting because the approach must meet the stated requirements. However, not all requirements may be captured and a loophole may be found where the system meets the requirements, appears to be verified and validated in some setting[168], but actually does not work. Some might argue this is a failure of systems engineering, however that is irrelevant[169] when an approach is being offered.

5. **Diversity**: The level of diversity possible when offering an approach. A more diverse approach is less brittle and more resilient to stresses. For example can only one company offer the approach or can many companies offer the approach.

6. **Resilience**: Ability to withstand aging or stress and not regress from original levels of regeneration or sustainability.

7. **Acceptability**: The level of acceptance from the regenerative and sustainable community stakeholders.

8. **Growth**: Ability to grow the system in a regenerative or sustainable way.

9. **Technology Insertion**: Ability to accept new technology in a regenerative or sustainable way.

10. **Quality of Life**: Ability of an approach to increase the quality of life for people in a regenerative or sustainable way.

11. **Freedom Liberty**: Ability of an approach to increase freedom and liberty of a people in a regenerative or sustainable way.

12. **Population Growth**: Ability of an approach to allow human population to increase in a regenerative or sustainable way.

13. **Standard of Living**: Ability of an approach to increase the standard of living in a regenerative or sustainable way.

14. **Social Mobility**: Ability of an approach to increase the social mobility in a regenerative or sustainable way.

15. **Pursuit of Happiness**: Happiness is elusive and no one can force someone to be happy. However elements can be established so that people can

---

[168] An incandescent light bulb can be made with two supporting posts or three supporting posts. Both can meet the same lifetime requirements, however a two post light bulb used in a ceiling fixture of a two story wood frame house will fail very quickly from normal floor to roof vibration.

[169] New high efficiency heaters exhaust from the side of a building. In a residential setting the neighbor is exposed to noise and exhaust pollution.

reasonably pursue and find happiness. A reference to Maslow's pyramid[170] is appropriate.

8.3.3.3 Environmental Impact Tradeoff Criteria

The following is a list of Environmental Impact tradeoff criteria and their descriptions. The intent is to stimulate discussion on the tradeoff criteria that matter for the system being developed.

1. **Noise**: Cumulative analysis, single event analysis, noise sensitive area analysis
2. **Compatible Land Use**: Land uses surrounding the facility/ action, future land uses projected in proximity of facility/ action
3. **Social**: Relocation of residences, relocation of businesses, community disruption
4. **Socioeconomic**: Shift in population and growth, public service demands, change in business and economic activity
5. **Air Quality**: Area air quality status, National Ambient Air Quality Standards emissions inventory, conformity with Local and State authorities
6. **Water Quality**: Additional impervious area, requirements for additional water supplies or waste treatment capacity, aquifer or sensitive ecological areas, erosion and sediment control
7. **Laws**: Potential impact, coordination with officials having jurisdiction
8. **Historic**: Includes architectural archaeological and cultural resources, properties in or eligible for inclusion in the National Register of Historic Places, potential impact (e.g. noise, air pollution), coordination with State Historic Preservation and Advisory Councils on Historic Preservation
9. **Flora and Fauna**: Biotic communities, potential for loss of habitat, coordination with wildlife agencies and US Fish and Wildlife Service for streams or other water bodies to be controlled or modified by the project
10. **Endangered and Threatened Species**: Flora and fauna, listed or proposed species and / or designated or proposed critical habitat from US Fish and Wildlife Service and or National Marine Fisheries Service, biological assessment if listed endangered and threatened species are potentially in the area to be disturbed
11. **Wetlands**: Wetland delineation, potential disturbance limits
12. **Floodplain**: Existing floodplain, potential changes to the floodplain limits
13. **Water Table**: Water tables and wells within the area of potential effect,

---

[170] Motivation and Personality, Abraham Harold Maslow, HarperCollins Publishers, 1954, 3d Sub edition January 1987, ISBN 0060419873. Maslow's hierarchy of needs usually shown as a pyramid with the most fundamental levels of needs at the bottom and self-actualization at the top. Usually lower level needs must be satisfied before upper level needs.

consult agencies for consistency

14. **Rivers and Lakes**: Rivers and lakes, within the area of potential effect, consult agencies for consistency

15. **Inter coastal**: Estuaries, inlets, bays, inter coastal water ways, beaches, ocean within the area of potential effect, consult agencies for consistency

16. **Farmlands**: Prime, unique, statewide local importance farmland in area of potential effect, farmland converted to non-agricultural uses, coordinate with local Soil Conservation Service or State Conservationist

17. **Energy Supply and Natural Resources**: Irreversible expenditures of natural resources, fuel, construction materials, cost of the project compared to benefits, energy efficiency

18. **Light Emissions**: Light requirement and location of necessary lights, compatibility of light emissions with existing and future land uses

19. **Solid Waste**: Amount and type of waste to be generated

20. **Construction**: Construction noise, all impacts of construction, sediment control, dust impacts

21. **Visual Impact**: Design art and architectural, areas of natural beauty or historic or architectural significance, aesthetics, design, art and architecture

22. **Environmental Justice**: Disproportionate impacts on selected populations, low income populations, or minority populations, noise, residential relocation

23. **Cumulative and Other Considerations**: Categories with adverse impact, past, present or reasonably foreseeable actions that add to adverse impacts, consistency with state and local plans

8.3.4 Tradeoff Matrix

List the tradeoff criteria in rows and place the alternatives in columns. Rate each criterion for each alternative. You can use 1-3, 1-4, 1-10, or rank each relative to the other. If you start with using high medium low just translate all your word ratings to numbers. In the beginning of the trade study, try to fill in each cell of the matrix with a rating. Literally play with each approach. Do this in one day.

Now comes the hard part. Look at each criterion and architecture alternative (A1, A2, AN). Look at each intersection or cell. Now start to identify studies techniques methods approaches from 5000 plus years of civilization to convert those initial gut-based ratings into ratings backed on sound scientific and engineering principles. Do this as a group and use hard science, soft science, and everything else in that order (your logic) to back up your numbers. Document that logic even if it is just bullets on a chart.

Table 90 Architecture Design Tradeoff Matrix

Criteria	A1	A2	AN	Wt	A1	A2	AN
Criterion 1	5	7	9	1	5	7	9
Criterion 2	5	5	8	5	25	25	40
Criterion 3	5	5	6	1	5	5	6
Criterion 4	5	6	6	2	10	12	12
Criterion 5	5	9	8	3	15	27	24
Criterion Y	5	9	8	1	5	9	8
Total	30	41	45	-	65	85	99

This process may take years. Take snapshots and change the cells of the tradeoff matrix. Add weights to the criteria based on your continued refined analysis of the problem. Some criteria may disappear and others may surface. Don't be afraid to call the team in and have everyone enter their view of the rating for each cell, no matter how detached they may be from the detailed studies. At some point some criteria will become a wash and go away while others become very different or new criterion are added.

Sum the total for each approach. This is the rating for each architecture alternative. Keep it simple at first and do not use weights until you get some initial results. As you gain more insight you can apply different weights to each criterion and change the total.

Develop initial costs and total life cycle costs (LCC) for each approach. Take each rating and divide it by the initial cost. That is your initial MOE. It is a measure of goodness of each approach for each dollar spent. Do the same thing for the life cycle cost and see if they are different. You pick the architecture that has the highest MOE when all costs are considered (the LCC). So you get the biggest advantage for each unit of cost.

Table 91 Architecture Design MOE

Criteria	A1	A2	AN	Wt	A1	A2	AN
Total	30	41	45		65	85	99
LCC	1	1.2	1.4		1	1.2	1.4
MOE	30	34	32		65	71	71
1. The LCC is normalized.							
2. Adding cost shows that Arch 2 is more effective than Arch N.							
3. Including weights shows that Arch 2 becomes less effective and matches Arch N.							

What should your tradeoff criteria include? That is really your call. It is part of the discovery process. However a word of caution. The tradeoff criteria should not include cost or requirements. It is a given that all solutions will satisfy the known requirements at some cost. Cost should be used at the bottom of the tradeoff where each approach total rating is divided by cost. This essentially identifies the goodness of each approach per unit of cost. This is called the measure of effectiveness or MOE.

MOE = Sum of tradeoff criteria/cost to produce approach

Author Comment: This is a terrifying experience for those who want control and have hidden agendas. Vested interests both visible and hidden hate this approach. This is the heart of being Systems Engineering driven and there is management that understands this process and knows how to effectively manage it, but these managers are born only in system engineering driven organizations. This process is based on truth and it is fully transparent so that everyone understands the science and engineering, even the grandparents of the participants. That means that the studies and tradeoffs need to be communicated so that all stakeholders quickly grasp everything[171]. This requires real genius.

Some claim the MOE in many areas but the MOE is actually a measure of goodness per unit cost[172]. That is a significant statement, because it removes cost from the decision and yet considers cost. The decision process is leveled and requested from the people using scientific and engineering principles of analysis when possible, then processed either formally or informally (early in the process) using the MOE.

System engineering is a process for solving problems using system engineers (always more than one in a true system engineering based effort). The system engineers "herd" all the stakeholders (hardware, software, mechanical, civil, chemical, maintenance, training, support, etc) so that all the criteria can be vetted and a reasonable decision can be made by reasonable people always using the MOE. This is like F=MA in physics. It is fundamental - it drives everything. The systems engineering grand unifying equation: MOE = Sum of tradeoff criteria / cost to produce approach[173].

8.3.5 Rating Scale

The rating scale in the tradeoff matrix can be based on a concept. For example AHP offers a suggestion for providing ratings. Alternatively the scale can be even or odd number based. An odd number scale always allows a middle rating to be selected while an even scale forces the raters to make a decision in one of the

---

[171] STOP (Sequential Thematic Organization of Publications) invented at Hughes Aircraft Fullerton in 1963 was first applied to proposals, by the 1980's it was applied to important national and international studies.

[172] Some suggest that the criteria are MOE. However, there is only one MOE for the architecture and a decision needs to be made based on that MOE.

[173] This is how I was taught system engineering at a place that no longer exists - Hughes Aircraft.

directions. In this case the direction is either good or bad. Using four or more rating levels allows the raters to determine the degree to which a particular item is in one direction or the other direction. The following are possible methods of rating each criterion in a tradeoff matrix:

- **Threshold, Acceptable Unacceptable:** This selection scale is binary and the tradeoff criteria is either met or not met. This is problematic because each solution should be able to meet the minimum criteria threshold. So this approach tends to apply very early in the alternative identification and selection process where the unacceptable solutions are removed. Later for the acceptable solutions a more sophisticated decision scale is needed.
- **2 Level Ranking:** Two choices are offered and the 2 choices are treated as a ranking. For example alternative A is better than alternative B. The difficulty arises when there are more than 2 alternatives that need to be ranked.
- **Multi Level Ranking:** The scale matches number of choices. If there are 3 choices then the scale is 1, 2 and 3. Each approach is ranked relative to other approaches. No two approaches can have the same rank. The difficulty arises when two or more solutions are very close and it is not correct to rank them differently while other approaches are vastly different. This then leads to a rating selection approach.
- **3 Choice Rating:** In a rating scale multiple approaches can have the same rating. In this case there are an odd number of choices 1 2 3. Although numbers are used there is a tendency to think in terms of average for choice 2. The middle selection is between the two extremes. This temps the analysts to rate each approach as average.
- **4 Choice Rating:** There are an even number of choices 1 2 3 4. There is no average option available. The four choice rating scale forces the analysts to pick either a good or bad direction. The difficulty is that the gradations between how good or how bad is limited.
- **Multi Odd Rating:** There is a large number of rating items where an average number is possible (e.g. 9). This scale tempts the analysts to move away from the average choice by offering levels of how good or how bad an approach may be for a criterion. Some choices may be very close yet have different ratings while other choices are very far away to either one or the other side of the scale.
- **Multi Even Rating:** There is a large number of rating items where no average number is possible (e.g. 10). This scale removes the temptation to rate all approaches as average and offers different levels of good and bad between the choices. Some choices may be very close yet have different ratings while other choices are very far away to either one or the other side of the scale.

It does not matter which scales are selected when the analysis starts. However as the analysis proceeds there should be the option of changing the scales. Typically the final scale will be even based on more than 4 options.

8.3.6 Sensitivity Analysis

Don't be afraid to perform a sensitivity analysis. Look at the matrix and do sensitivity analysis by changing some values that were previous points of contention. You can then just change values in a big way as part of the sensitivity analysis. It may seem odd but the same architecture tends to surface as part of the answer. If it does not it is because you are missing a key criteria item. Sometimes if you re-list the advantages and disadvantages of each approach new criteria items surface that will help to close the trade study.

Table 92 Architecture Design Tradeoff Sensitivity Analysis

Criteria	A1	A2	AN	Wt	A1	A2	AN
Criterion 2	5	5	8	4	20	20	32
Total	30	41	45		65	85	99
LCC	1	1.2	1.4		1	1.2	1.4
MOE	30	34	32		60	67	65
Criterion 2	5	5	8	6	30	30	48
Total	30	41	45		65	85	99
LCC	1	1.2	1.4		1	1.2	1.4
MOE	30	34	32		70	75	76

The sensitivity analysis can fold into the tradeoff matrix. At some point the studies start to reach a level of diminishing returns and an approach starts to surface.

8.3.7 Architecture Design Selection Big Picture

So architecture selection is a trade study. The most important aspect of the trade study is not the results but the journey. It is during the journey that the stakeholders learn things about the alternatives and ramifications of those alternatives that would normally never surface. Many people try to complicate the architecture tradeoff study because they attempt to document the journey without realizing they are documenting the journey. Once that simple realization sinks in then the documented journey is a pleasure to read and understand.

Author Comment: I would like to offer a personal example, which I believe, hits the nail right on the head relative to all value systems. I will never forget when my new wife and I went on our first trip to a challenged country in 1980. We stayed at a fabulous resort right out of a James Bond Movie. Eventually we took a pink jeep into town and I will never forget what I saw. As far as I could see there were people with picks and shovels digging a trench by the side of the road. The reality is if you just look at traditional financial numbers, you can never justify the cost of a bulldozer over the cost of these poor people digging with a pick and a shovel. This is the trap of third world thinking. Instead of buying a bulldozer and freeing these people to become bulldozer operators they were stuck in the mud and dirt. You need to punch through to another level of thinking.

Author Comment: When you investigate the MOE topic in other documents be aware that some confuse tradeoff criteria with MOE. The MOE is one thing and it is defined as the sum of all the tradeoff criteria numbers divided by the total life cycle cost. This is done for each architecture approach. In these documents they erroneously call the tradeoff criteria the MOE and then they mention it in the plural as MOEs. Then they never really say how you pick an approach. They sprinkle cost into the middle of the tradeoff items. I attribute this to the finance types running amok in the past 30 years.

Author Comment: There are also those that confuse the MOE with cost benefit analysis[174]. The problem with cost benefit analysis is that financial metrics drive the answer rather than function and performance. So when they address a problem they usually get a very low quality solution or a non-working solution.

There should be typically 5 architecture designs tracked for a very long period of time. The LCC people should not be called until the system architecture designs are deeply understood from a functional and performance point of view. The architectures must survive the criteria ratings first. The analysts should not be tainted by early views of the costs until the architectures have been fully understood.

8.3.8 Baseline Reference Method Matrix Ratings

The baseline reference method uses a baseline or legacy design to compare against other designs. Alternatives are evaluated against the baseline design using the evaluation criteria. If an alternative is clearly better than the baseline, it is marked as a plus (+); clearly worse than the baseline (-); same as baseline (S); and unacceptable as the baseline (U). Notes are maintained of the ratings for each relationship. Using numbers or ++/-- may expand the sensitivity of the +/- system. When making the +/- decision, the magnitude of the difference is considered; however, the process of marking an only marginally better feature as + compared to the baseline should be avoided. Generally, alternatives with a U relationship are

---

[174] From the Macnamara wiz kids era.

eliminated. There are exceptions to this rule such as when an alternative is significantly superior in other areas.

Once relationships are defined for each alternative and technical requirement, the overall value of merit of the alternative is calculated. A value of +1 is assigned to each (+) rating, and a -1 to each (-) rating. A relative weight also may be assigned to each evaluation criterion if not all criteria are considered equal.

- Multiply weight and the evaluation. Sum calculation for each alternative. The overall importance rating is a figure of merit for each alternative. The higher the importance rating, the better the alternative for the given need. However, this guide is only relative. Do not differentiate alternatives by closely grouped importance ratings.
- Review each alternative to surface an understanding of the meaning of the final importance rating. Review all negative relationships and enhance the alternatives to eliminate these negatives.

8.3.9 Relative Rank Method

This technique evaluates each alternative against criteria and establishes a ranking for each criterion. Weighting of the criteria is defined for each criterion, while the trade options are graded in their appropriate columns according to the scaling factors over the range 0 to 4. The average ranking for each criterion is multiplied by the weight to determine a score for each criterion. Scores are summed across the criteria for a total.

8.3.10 Cost Assessment Method

This approach is a throwback to financial driven decisions. Rather than use criterion selected and understood by the stakeholders there is a simple minded cost approach used to make a decision. The cost of each alternative is reduced to rough order of magnitude (ROM) estimates of fixed and variable costs. Elements that do not reduce directly to cost (e.g., weight, production time, etc) are translated to cost using ad hoc methods. If risks are present, risk projections are factored into the ROMs. In addition no cost related information is gathered and presented:

- Relative complexity and risk of each candidate system configuration.
- Descriptions of how each approach deals with stringent requirements.
- Analysis of how each approach deals with key requirements such as high level of reliability and availability, quick recovery, growth, support, etc.
- Highlight key factors that result in lower cost and risk. Discuss the factors with the stakeholder, including the option of analyzing a more simple system that addresses only the most critical requirements set. This type of analysis gives the stakeholder a minimum system cost benchmark to assess

cost of the candidate system and functionality of each requirement.
- Include the tradeoffs among hardware, software, and manual operations as part of the cost analysis, and identify the most sensitive cost drivers of each candidate system. If the system has security requirements, also consider security cost drivers.

This approach pushes the non-financial portion of the decision to a gut level or informal decision. This typically allows the financial stakeholders to declare success because their decision portion appears to be more logical and less confusing.

This decision approach should be avoided. It is only offered as an example of how a tradeoff based on the MOE can be compromised. Once the design team goes down this path the design will be poor.

8.4 Profit loss Statement and Valuation

Many times decisions are autocratically made with broad unsubstantiated statements about profits. This is why understanding the simple profit loss statement is so important for all designers. The profit loss statement in many ways is the design of an organization and a close examination of the profit loss statement will quickly show problems with the design of the organization.

There are two key items in a profit loss statement. The first is the line items and the second is the time lines. The time lines include historical entries, the current state, and a prediction of the future. Some of the key financial items to consider are associated with investment, production and distribution, and overhead. Employee costs are associated with costs of goods and services provided while executive compensation is overhead. Overhead is an item that needs to be closely watched and should not be confused with the money used to produce the product or feed the product pipeline in terms of investment such as research and development.

Investments
- Research and Development Investment
- Development Investment
- Tools Machinery Automation Investment
- Employee Training Investment
- Facilities and Infrastructure Investment

Product Costs
- Cost of Goods Sold
- Cost of Services Sold
- Manufacturing Costs
- Distribution Costs
- Transportation Costs

- Employee Costs
- Storage Costs
- Marketing and Sales Costs

Overhead
- Executive Compensation Total Costs
- General and Administrative Costs
- Tools Machinery Automation Investment Maintenance Costs
- Facilities and Infrastructure Maintenance Costs

Financial Results Breakdown
- Total Sales
- Cost of Goods Sold
- Gross Margin
- Operating Expenses
- Sales & Marketing Expenses
- General & Administrative Expenses
- Total Operating Expenses
- Profit Before Interest & Taxes
- Interest Expense
- Taxes Incurred
- Net Profit
- Net Profit/Sales

Before there is a design there are the tools, practices, and process that is used to perform the design. Before there are the tools, practices, and process there is the vessel that is used to establish the tools, practices, and process for the design. So what is the design of the vessel? Is it a Profit Corporation, Partnership, Sole Proprietorship, Non-Profit, Government Organization, or other vessel? Each of these vessels has different systems for evaluating and rewarding employees.

Author Comment: How does a non-profit reward its executives? The Hughes approach was based on the concept of success of the last system. If the individual was successful, they were given a more complex challenge for the next round. The size and complexity of the system the executive was managing and successfully delivered measured success.

After a new company is established what are the items that are used to value the company if there is a desire to sell the company? If the company is publicly traded there are metrics that are used to try and determine the value from a market perspective.

- **Stock Price:** This is the price to buy 1 share of stock in the company
- **Market Capitalization:** This is the price of 1 share of stock multiplied by all the outstanding shares. So this is the price to buy the company from each and every shareholder.
- **Price Earnings Ratio (PE):** This is the Market Capitalization divided by the Earnings. The higher the PE ratio the more overvalued the company.

Author Comment: Executive compensation in for profit vessels is tied to maximizing these metric items in the short term. Unfortunately they are usually in direct conflict with designers that need to produce products and or services and ensure a viable future. The design of the executive package drives everything. If the executive package design does not have a long-term horizon the organization will be in constant turmoil and the designs and or services will be flawed.

Author Comment: One of the major changes that happened in the 1980's was the concept of pushing the profit centers down to the lowest levels in an organization. So each organization needed to justify its existence based on the profits it generated for the quarter. If it could not show profits it was terminated. This transformed organizations and people who were well-versed professionals in their areas and forced them to become bean counters in settings that eventually translated into the loss of the important services provided by an organization. A classic example is delivery of news in media corporations. All of the sudden the news was driven by sales and so newsworthy items important in a democracy took a back seat to sensationalist irrelevant but audience catching content.

Author Comment: Prior to the industrial revolution items varied significantly in quality and performance, so the concept of a negotiated price was reasonable, but there was significant room for abuse. One of the key elements of the industrial revolution was the concept of mass production with no variance in quality and performance between items. Mass production when coupled with the concept of informed consumers led to the same price being charged for the same item. Price stability is a key element that allowed for the industrial revolution to succeed. Today we have people purchasing airline tickets sitting next to each other at significantly different prices. No one likes to be cheated. Technology allowed the bad elements of Old World to seep into the New World. This old flawed approach kept humanity living in the dirt for thousands of years. After the industrial revolution and the price stability it offered humanity started to rise from the dirt. This is a gross misuse of technology that wastes resources and is doing significant harm to our social fabric. Do we really want to return to those dark days?

Some of the more difficult financial metric items to surface are actually some of the most important especially when a company is doing poorly:

- Earnings per employee
- Earnings per employee Minus executives
- Earnings per employee Minus managers
- Earnings per employee Minus executives + managers
- Earnings per employee Minus capital expenditures

As part of preparing a proposal cost estimate the actual costs are subjected to overhead. The overhead is an internal tax within the organization. These items are:

- Overhead
- General and administrative cost
- Cost of money

Prior to the 1980's these additional costs were associated with:

- Employee time between projects
- Employee training
- Employee healthcare
- Employee retirement
- Investments in R&D
- Investment in plant & equipment
- Marketing & new business pursuit

Author Comment: We know that all systems have a duty cycle. Some systems are always running so their duty cycle is 100%. However humans can not support a 100% duty cycle. In the high technology world, the one that gave us our current civilization, it was acknowledged and respected that employees would have time between projects to pursue their interests or official R&D activities with no expectation of results. It was a time to decompress and perhaps learn new things. This is culture lesson 101 for a high technology civilization.

Author Comment: For every dollar an employee makes 2 or 3 dollars is paid as tribute to the employer with the understanding that it does more than just act as a front. It brings something of value to the party. Otherwise employees should just self organize for a project, reap all the rewards, then disband when the project is complete. The employees in this setting are always engaged in new business development. This is very high overhead when the full society is considered where everyone is trying to find the next gig. Also this is not an attractive or stable social setting. So there is benefit to having an employer, but it needs to function in a symbiotic way with its surroundings[175]. It is a system in a sea of other systems.

8.5 Informal Decision Analysis

Informal decision analysis is best described as a random walk through the current thoughts. All the alternatives have been previously described and their names tend to reflect the fundamental element of the approach. Each approach has a description of the current-thoughts but there is care used to ensure that noise is not added to the description. Instead key discriminators of each approach are offered and the impacts of the key discriminators.

Typically this is the first decision analysis approach that is used. As the analysis unfolds other decision analysis approaches are added. They usually start with an advantages disadvantages list and a tradeoff matrix.

There are various formal and informal decision methods. What decision method can be used to select a decision method? The following are some suggestions for using different decision methods. This analysis of the different decision methods is only a guide. It does have what some might consider opinion. References can be added to justify the opinion, but then this would suggest that in a real world setting the analysts should be just as methodical. That is not appropriate. This analysis method does contain opinion and should spur significant discussion and other decision analysis approaches.

Table 93 Selecting a Design Decision Approach

Decision Approach	Primary Stakeholders
Advantages Disadvantages List: This is a simple approach that everyone can understand. However it tends to be superficial and key elements in the analysis may be missed. It is thus a good starting point for future decision analysis.	Customer Organization[176]
Tradeoff Matrix: This is a simple approach that everyone can understand. The difficulty comes in surfacing the tradeoff criteria. This takes time. It is used for major decisions like conceptual and physical architecture alternatives selection.	Customer[177] Organization
Probability Based Decisions: Used primarily to make new business decisions to pursue a contract or collection of contracts in a market area.	Customer Organization
Analytical Hierarchy Process: Tends to be used more by aficionados for formal decision making. Many important insights and details of the decision space can be lost unless someone summarizes the highly detailed	Customer Organization

---

[175] The Internet may remove the overhead and allow this to happen. If companies keep misbehaving the world may quickly shift and make use of the new technologies to put them out of business. There is no reason for someone to pay tribute to a parasite.

[176] Organization includes companies, universities, non-profits, government, and any entity where people are organized to provide products and or services.

[177] Customer is the recipient of what an organization provides.

Table 93 Selecting a Design Decision Approach

Decision Approach	Primary Stakeholders
analysis mechanics. It is good for verifying the less formal tradeoff matrix.	
Design to Cost (DTC): Product development and manufacturing teams in competitive situations use this approach. Its quantitative nature is attractive. The challenge is in the final selection of the correct function, performance, quality, and aesthetic levels that fit the DTC criteria. There may be several alternatives that fit the DTC but some alternatives may lead to market failure. This approach becomes toxic when the DTC is too small to offer a reasonable design solution.	Customer Organization
Design to Production Cost (DTUPC): This is like the DTC except the overriding concern is the production costs. It is important to know the quantity over the product or system life cycle so that appropriate decisions can be made for each stage.	Customer Organization
Design to Schedule (DTS): This is like the DTC except the overriding concern is the design schedule. The trap here is trying to give birth to a 9-month baby in 9 days, a very toxic situation. There is also the issue of selecting the winning combination of function, performance, quality, and aesthetics.	Customer Organization
Opportunity Cost: This is primarily used by business development to determine what price is paid because resources are expended pursuing a particular opportunity. This is also used by executive management as they make strategic decisions, which translate into implementations of one type as opposed to another type. For example a strategic decision may be to dig in and ride the storm in an existing market thinking that it may return in the future.	Customer Organization
Design to Key Discriminators: This is actually the mark of a great design house. They find and understand the key discriminators in a need space and offer the solution. Few engage in this practice.	Customer Organization
Autocratic Decision: This is usually used in highly stressed organizations where they are about to wink out of existence. It rarely succeeds. This can be used to break a logjam within the design team as long as the autocratic decision can be overruled if needed once the logjam is broken and the team is in agreement.	Customer Organization Owners Executives
Design to Value Systems: This is a placeholder for a class of decision methods that are associated with financial and non-financial approaches.	Customer Organization Owners Executives
Lowest Cost: This is typically used in a product setting where there is significant competition. The product tends to be a commodity with no unique discriminators. For example a pipefitting is a pipefitting. It meets the industry-accepted standard, so cost is the driver in sales.	Customer

Table 93 Selecting a Design Decision Approach

Decision Approach	Primary Stakeholders
Highest Profit: Top level senior executives typically use this decision method for 2 primary reasons. The first is to accumulate funds to buy out the competition. The second is to maximize their bonuses, which are based on profits. When there is no more competition to buy they then buy the company shares to reduce the number of outstanding shares. This is also tied to their compensation packages where their bonuses are based on profit and earnings per share. In this setting the common stockholder stakeholders lose significant wealth even though the company may move to a temporary monopoly or oligopoly status.	Executives
Return on Investment: This is used on capital intensive projects. Today real-estate investments are made based on ROI. In the past heavy manufacturing decisions were based on ROI. Angel investors and venture capitalists also use this approach with very high returns in short periods of time.	Owners
Total Cost of Ownership: This is use by capital intensive companies to make major upgrade decisions. For example an airline trying to determine when to upgrade its fleet of airplanes.	Customer
Internal Rate of Return: This is used to determine if an investment should be made internally or externally to an organization. The ROI is calculated for each approach and a decision is made.	Organization Owners
Economic Value Added: This is based on determining ROI numbers for each approach versus leaving money in the bank.	Owners
Real Option Value: This is based on ROI but the ROI is associated with amortizing the costs across several projects. This is a way to justify investment in the future be they tools, training, facilities. So it is an investment in the organizations infrastructure.	Organization
Return on Assets: Return on assets compares the current income using the existing assets versus selling off the assets.	Owners Executives
Return on Infrastructure Employed: This is a specialized case of ROA but it is applied to a service group within an organization. It is used to determine if the operation should be subcontracted to an external organization, this is outsourcing.	Owners Executives
Life Cycle Costs: All of the costs associated with a system are considered including the indirect costs pushed to stakeholders outside the system boundary.	Customer Organization
Measure of Effectiveness: The MOE is the sum of tradeoff criteria divided by the cost to produce approach. It pulls the narrow financial perspective from a decision to include all affected stakeholders.	Customer Organization
Gut Level Decisions: Decision approach of last resort performed by those not versed in decision making.	Customer Organization Owners Executives

Table 93 Selecting a Design Decision Approach

Decision Approach	Primary Stakeholders
Architecture Design Selection: A decision making approach that attempts to address the limitations of all other decision approaches. It is also used to stimulate discussion about the alternatives and the key discriminators between the approaches.	Customer Organization
Informal Decision Analysis: This is a simple approach that everyone can understand. It also has few rules so the decision space can be fully explored. It also allows for expansion and as time evolves other decision methods are added to the initial information product that captured the informal decision analysis. This is used extensively in engineering to select vendors and major components used in designs like the choice of the microprocessor in a device.	Customer Organization Owners Executives

8.6 Decision Analysis Process

The decision analysis process is to select the appropriate decision analysis approach for each unique situation. A guideline has been offered in the previous text. The challenge is that few organizations engage in formal decisions because the decisions will usually not align with employee and organizational incentive systems.

Example 28 Communications Architecture Selection Ramifications

Today we take communications for granted. However when radio and telephones were first being introduced communications was viewed as a marvel that would transform society. One of the major benefits of the telephone was the introduction of the phone book, which not only listed phone numbers of people but also phone numbers of businesses. In major cities it was easy to find businesses that provided needed services. For example if you needed a roofing company to fix a leak a quick look under roofing or other keywords and phrases in phone book would offer all the local companies in the community. An Internet search today results in roofing companies from across the planet but none from the local community.

Communications was always part of the US tradition and the post office was written into the constitution. This communication is guaranteed to be private and should someone illegally access the content it is a felony. The question is why?

Communications carries private information. This information can be business related that a competitor could use to manipulate a situation or private information that someone can use for blackmail. Today we would not consider having the government postal service provide email, web hosting, or other Internet services yet that is the only way to ensure privacy as guaranteed by the constitution. All companies regardless of contractual agreements can and eventually do go out of business. During that time all contracts become academic.

8.7 Decision Analysis Key Points

➤ The tradeoff matrix and MOE can be used to select
- Conceptual architecture
- Physical architecture
- Implementation architecture

➤ Measure of effectiveness is the sum of all the tradeoff criteria divided by life cycle costs for each approach being considered.

➤ The List of Advantages and Disadvantages is the starting point for an architecture design tradeoff

➤ The architecture design with the highest MOE is selected after sensitivity analysis is performed

➤ Architecture design alternatives come from two primary areas. The first is from current and similar approaches. The second comes from the participants on the team using creativity, innovation, and invention.

➤ Architectures based on current concepts have lower variable cost risk than new architectures with little or no previous history

8.8 Exercises

1. Which architecture should be subject to the most rigorous tradeoff analysis: conceptual, physical, or implementation architecture? Please provide rational.
2. Which architecture should be subject to the most rigorous specifications: conceptual, physical, or implementation architecture? Please provide rational.
3. Identify conceptual, physical, and implementation architecture tradeoff criteria. Are they different? If so why if not why not?
4. Identify 3 conceptual, physical, and implementation architectures, describe them, identify key requirements associated with each of the architectures, identify key issues associated with each of the architectures and perform a tradeoff to select the conceptual, physical, and implementation architecture. You can use pervious assignments.
5. Identify 3 implementation architectures and describe them.

8.9 Additional Reading

1. Executive Order 12803 - Infrastructure Privatization, US Government, April 30, 1992.
2. Motivation and Personality, Abraham Harold Maslow, HarperCollins Publishers, 1954, 3d Sub edition January 1987, ISBN 0060419873.
3. NASA Systems Engineering Handbook, NASA/SP-2007-6105 Rev1, December 2007.
4. National Airspace System Engineering Manual, Federal Aviation Administration, V 3.1, 2006.
5. STOP (Sequential Thematic Organization of Publications) invented at Hughes Aircraft Fullerton in 1963 was first applied to proposals, by the 1980's it was applied to important national and international studies.
6. Sustainable Development Possible with Creative System Engineering, Walter Sobkiw, 2008, ISBN 0615216307.
7. Systems Engineering for Intelligent Transportation Systems, Department of Transportation, Federal Highway Administration, Federal Transit Administration, January 2007.
8. Systems Engineering Fundamentals, Supplementary Text, Defense Acquisition University Press, January 2001.
9. Systems Engineering Management Guide, Defense Systems Management College, January 1990.
10. Thomas L. Saaty, Decision Making with the Analytic Hierarchy Process, Int. J. Services Sciences, Vol. 1, No. 1, 2008.
11. World Commission on Environment and Development, Brundtland Commission, 1987, Our Common Future.

9 Artifacts

During design it is important to engage in design. The dilemma is that as the design unfolds it needs to be captured. Otherwise the design team will just engage in endless meetings until one day the meetings will just start to revisit previously covered and what was thought to be closed areas. Then the meetings will degrade. Conversely the danger is that the design team just develops artifacts, meeting all the guidelines, but there is no coherent design. So there is a balance. Ideally the artifacts should be transparently developed as the design unfolds.

The design artifacts are as varied as the design possibilities and needs. They are the result of simple tools such as a writing utensil with paper and complex tools using the most sophisticated machines in existence. The following is a partial list of tools and artifacts that may apply to a design:

- **Office Automation:** word processing graphic text, spreadsheet, drawing, image manipulation, presentation, email, web browser, web conferencing, web authoring
- **Mechanical Drawing:** pencil, paper, ruler, compass, protractor, triangles, templates
- **Computing & Communications:** smart phone, personal computer, tablet computer, laptop, printer, scanner, computer automated design and manufacturing (CAD/CAM)
- **Drawings:** sketch, mechanical drawing, artists rendering, schematic, blueprints, drawings A B C D sizes
- **Free Hand:** draw on napkin and scan into computer, draw on napkin and take picture with smart phone and email to computer, subject hand drawing to image processing tool to find edges and create objects
- **Engineering Tools:** system requirements database, requirements analysis, dynamic modeling, agent based modeling, engineering specific tools hardware software mechanical etc, reliability maintainability availability, problem tracking, version control files, risk analysis, AHP, tradeoffs, decision support tools, visualization tools, tradeoff analysis tools
- **Management Tools:** risk analysis, cost price analysis, project planning, EVMS, decision support tools, visualization tools, tradeoff analysis tools
- **Plans:** program / project management plan, systems engineering plan, systems engineering management plan, install plan, disaster recovery plan
- **Verification and Validation:** system test plan, system test procedures,

system test report
- **Design Artifacts:** analysis documents, models, prototypes, specifications, design documents
- **Design Analysis:** functional, stakeholder, maintenance, RMA, architecture, FTA, FWEA, timing and sizing, training, quality, logistics, support, HMI
- **System Design:** operation concept documents, architecture document, analysis documents, trades study documents, specifications, design documents, drawings, blueprints, test procedure documents, test report documents, maintenance documents, installation documents, training documents, operator documents, certification documents,
- **Simulations and Models:** timing and sizing, heat analysis, load analysis, stress analysis, RMA analysis, power analysis, environment analysis, environmental impact analysis, sustainability analysis, human factors analysis, preliminary engineering analysis, detailed engineering analysis

An important question to ask is - are all these tools and artifacts needed for the design? Are other tools and artifact needed. The answer is yes and dependent on the unique needs and design. What should be noted is that different artifacts and tools are used at different abstraction levels. For example to capture the essence of the design it may be possible to use a simple product flyer. A website with the product flyer may form the start of a new venture.

9.1 Information Products

An information product is as the name suggests a product that conveys information. It can use text, static graphics and or images, animations, movies, and sound in any combination. It can be implemented as a document, slide show, film, sound recording using paper, film, magnetic tape recording, vinyl records, compact disk, or modern digital media using projectors, personal computers or hand held devices.

Some information products are very precise with no room for interpretation. The same message is sent to everyone with no confusion, assuming they understand its content. Other information products are vague, open to interpretation and allow for stimulation dialog. Some information products have complex syntax and ontology where only specialists can read and understand the content. Other information products convey extremely complex and precise information yet they are understood by everyone, including those not versed in the subject area. Finally some are easy to produce while others require a group of media specialists to produce. For example in the previous century drafting departments produced blue prints. Today an individual, such as the originator of the design, can produce blue prints using a computer.

The trick is to realize that information products exist, they have characteristics, and they need to be selected to represent a systems design. The following is a list of potential information products.

Table 94 Information Products and Their Characteristics

Information Products	Characteristics
Mechanical Drawing	Very precise, little interpretation
Blue Prints	Very precise, little interpretation
Schematics	Very precise, little interpretation
Math Equations	Very precise, little interpretation
Logic Equations	Very precise, little interpretation
Chemical Formulas	Very precise, little interpretation
Drawings	Less precise, some interpretation
Sketches	Imprecise, significant interpretation
Set Theory Equations	Very precise, little interpretation
Graphs	Less precise, some interpretation
Ven Diagrams	Less precise, some interpretation
Flow Charts	Very precise, little interpretation
Logic Diagrams	Very precise, little interpretation
Tree Diagrams	Very precise, little interpretation
Functional Block Diagrams	Less precise, some interpretation
Block Diagrams	Imprecise, significant interpretation
Concept Block Diagrams	Imprecise, significant interpretation
Use Cases Diagrams	Imprecise, significant interpretation
Data Flow Diagrams	Less precise, some interpretation
Operational Sequence Diagrams	Less precise, some interpretation
Fish Bone Diagrams	Very precise, little interpretation
Concept Description Document	Very precise to imprecise
Architecture Description Document	Very precise to imprecise
Analysis Document	Very precise to imprecise
Specification Document	Very precise is the goal
Plan Document	Very precise is the goal
Design Document	Very precise is the goal
Test Procedure Document	Very precise is the goal
Test Results Document	Very precise is the goal
Maintenance Document	Very precise is the goal
Training Document	Very precise is the goal
Support Document	Very precise is the goal
System Description Document	Very precise is the goal
Product Brochure	Very precise to imprecise
Report Document	Very precise is the goal
Animations	Very precise to imprecise
Sound	Very precise to imprecise
Videos	Very precise to imprecise
Web Site	Imprecise to very precise

Information products are extremely important from two perspectives. The first is ensuring the correct information products are established with correct and complete content. The second is ensuring that poor or useless information products do not form the final baseline. These information products may have erroneous, old, or confusing information. They also may contain too much information that add so much noise to the situation that they stop progress and analysis of information products that matter.

At some point the system will be subjected to maintenance, modification, upgrade, growth, technology insertion and even movement to a different domain or application with a similar or even perhaps different need. To allow for these activities the original plans, analysis, specification, design, and test information products form the official baseline.

Without the ability to effectively represent the baseline in the information products there is little chance of the system surviving or being used in other areas. In other words the system eventually will be abandoned and discarded. It will be a failed system engineering design.

Information products are designed just like a system and the process used to design the system. They satisfy a need, which is to describe the system such that anyone versed in the art can produce, use, upgrade, maintain, and dispose of the system. That includes providing sufficient analysis so that the system can be tested on paper before significant resources are spent on production.

Example 29 Book Information Product

This book is a product of design. It is trying to fulfill the need of educating the next generation in the art, science, and engineering of systems design. It has a concept, physical structure, and is implemented as part of the authors' process. This book feeds the readers future system development process that then feeds the readers final target system. It is part of each of the transfer functions that is the system.

9.2 Storyboards

Storyboards can be used to capture the design at any abstraction level, including detailed design. Storyboards in this context are associated with the Sequential Thematic organization of Publications (STOP)[178]. The idea[179] is to organize a technical document by two page topics where the left page contains the thesis

---

[178] Sequential Thematic Organization of Publications (STOP): How to Achieve Coherence in Proposals and Reports, Hughes Aircraft Company Ground Systems Group, Fullerton, Calif., J. R. Tracey, D. E. Rugh, W. S. Starkey, Information Media Dept., ID 65-10-10 52092, January 1965.

[179] Created at Hughes Aircraft Fullerton California in 1963.

sentence followed by supporting text, approximately 500 words. On the right page is a supporting graphic. The text and graphic complement and reinforce each other. This obviously leads to other ideas such as how to start the writing process and manage the whole activity. In the middle of this is the STOP storyboard.

The STOP storyboard is similar to other storyboards. They both use a graphic. However, STOP storyboards also contain the topic name, thesis sentence, and text phrases representing main points supporting the thesis sentence. In the STOP format there is less emphasis on a high quality graphic. In some instances it just can be a concept of a graphic showing some but not all the elements. Typically a practitioner should spend between 5 and 15 minutes on a preliminary storyboard.

Book: Sustainable Development Possible with Creative System Engineering
Topic: Introduction
Thesis: The only way we can survive in the next 100 years is through the application of creative systems engineering.

Main Points:

1. It's about sustainable development

2. Sustainable development it not new has always existed

3. The only way to do this is through creative system engineering

4. Creative system engineering is not new

5. What is creative system engineering

6. Creative system engineering transformed the world

Graphic
Table
Image

use proposed book cover
image # 33

Caption: Title

Name: Walt Sobkiw **Date:** 01/31/2008

Figure 142 Storyboard - Book

The storyboards are posted on a wall for the team to casually review. At some point a wall review is scheduled for all the storyboards. These reviews continue and may split the team into separate reviews until everyone is comfortable with the storyboards. At some point writing can begin.

Figure 143 Wall Review[180]

So the STOP storyboard with its strong thesis sentence, text phrases, and supporting graphic can be used anytime to capture any element of the systems engineering effort. It can show:

- Functions and Performance
- Architecture Alternatives
- Selected Architectures
- Study Findings

- Tradeoff Results
- Computer Screen Layouts
- Implementation Details
- Etc

Today many of us can relate to this form of communication when we build or attend power point presentations. However, whereas a power point slide can be deliberately vague, a storyboard should be very precise and accurate.

The elusive thesis sentence is a challenge[181]. It is even more difficult to support the thesis sentence when the analysis has not been performed and understood. When supporting the thesis sentence consider:

- Have a point get to it
- Treat it completely

- Keep out extraneous matter
- Relate graphic to the text

Even though STOP storyboards were created to support the development of technical publications after the analysis is complete and clearly understood, they can be used to convey information as the system analysis unfolds. It's just that the storyboard may be incomplete until the end of the analysis. Also, as in the case of

---

[180] A graphic from STOP Manual - notice free hand drawing, its projected imagery and the number of messages being sent.

[181] Is it any wonder that new people at Hughes were told they would be getting the equivalent of a few Ph.D.'s per year?

STOP, storyboards may be abandoned as dead ends. The thesis may not really have been appropriate and the system went in a totally different direction. This is where storyboards become very valuable. It is much easier to abandon a 1-page storyboard than a 2-page topic or a 25-page white paper. The lesson is never write text until you can draw a picture, establish a point or thesis, and have 5 to 8 supporting word phrases.

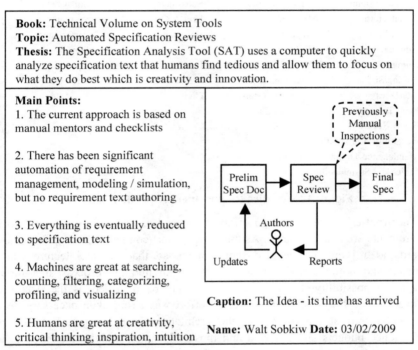

Book: Technical Volume on System Tools
Topic: Automated Specification Reviews
Thesis: The Specification Analysis Tool (SAT) uses a computer to quickly analyze specification text that humans find tedious and allow them to focus on what they do best which is creativity and innovation.

Main Points:
1. The current approach is based on manual mentors and checklists

2. There has been significant automation of requirement management, modeling / simulation, but no requirement text authoring

3. Everything is eventually reduced to specification text

4. Machines are great at searching, counting, filtering, categorizing, profiling, and visualizing

5. Humans are great at creativity, critical thinking, inspiration, intuition

Previously Manual Inspections

Prelim Spec Doc → Spec Review → Final Spec

Authors

Updates   Reports

Caption: The Idea - its time has arrived

Name: Walt Sobkiw **Date:** 03/02/2009

Figure 144 Storyboard - Proposal

9.3 Capturing Requirements

If we examine all the analysis techniques we see that there are common elements. There are inputs and outputs that bound the system. There are operations between the inputs and outputs. There is layering to represent different abstraction levels so humans can focus attention on a layer as needed to understand some aspect of the system. There are words to describe each abstraction level that are qualitative and quantitative. The quantitative words become performance requirements and the qualitative words become the remaining requirements. The requirements are eventually moved to specifications.

There is a tight relationship between studies, requirements, specifications, and tests. Studies help to surface requirements. Requirements are housed in specifications and specification requirements are verified by tests.

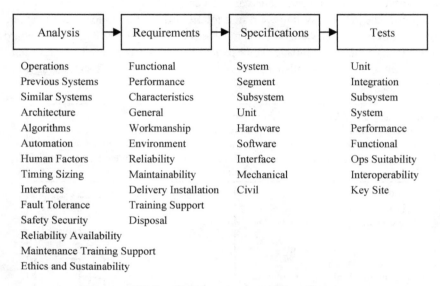

Analysis	Requirements	Specifications	Tests
Operations	Functional	System	Unit
Previous Systems	Performance	Segment	Integration
Similar Systems	Characteristics	Subsystem	Subsystem
Architecture	General	Unit	System
Algorithms	Workmanship	Hardware	Performance
Automation	Environment	Software	Functional
Human Factors	Reliability	Interface	Ops Suitability
Timing Sizing	Maintainability	Mechanical	Interoperability
Interfaces	Delivery Installation	Civil	Key Site
Fault Tolerance	Training Support		
Safety Security	Disposal		
Reliability Availability			
Maintenance Training Support			
Ethics and Sustainability			

Figure 145 Studies Requirements Specifications Tests

The front-end systems design effort is focused on the architecture and so the requirements are at a high level. As the design effort continues the emphasis moves towards identifying the detailed requirements so that the architecture can be designed and implemented. Obviously this is an iterative process and there is always the possibility that the architecture may be modified as the details are surfaced. If the front-end systems design effort was strong then necessary details were uncovered at that time and the architecture will survive. For example, performance budgets are allocated and those allocations should not result in any subsystem being forced to meet an impossible requirement number.

It is reasonable to separate the front-end requirement effort, which is used to develop the architecture from the back end requirement effort, which is used to design and implement the architecture or system. The emphasis is different. The front-end effort is big picture driven while the back end is very detail oriented. The tools for housing and tracking the requirements also will be different. In the back-end effort a relational database is used to track and manage thousands of requirements. This may be unneeded for the front-end effort unless there is a desire to prepare for the back end effort.

The steps for identifying and allocating the requirements are not complex. The complexity is in the performance of the steps. They apply to both the front end and back end system activities. The following is a possible sequence that can be used for requirement and specification development:

- Elicit and gather the requirements

- Identify the key requirements
- Group requirements by functions, performance, and specialty areas
- Allocate requirements to the system architecture
- Allocate requirements to the subsystems
- Create a specification tree based on the architecture and subsystems
- Place requirements in the proper specification tree level
- Allocate requirements to test methods

9.3.1 Key Requirements

Identifying and tracking the key requirements and issues may mean the difference between success and failure. Not all requirements and issues are the same. Some are make or break situations. Key requirements are drivers of the system solutions. They can be technology, performance, cost, schedule, production, maintenance, logistics, support, and other drivers. These drivers may exist because the state-of-the-art is being pushed in an area or previous knowledge shows these requirements and issues are make or break items.

Author Comment: Everyone should know the key requirements. They should never be hidden. It is possible that some requirements and issues are so significant that management will try to hide them, but then no one will be able to use the magic of their abilities to tackle and address these key requirements. In the end the key requirements and issues don't go away, they always remain, but the successful team has addressed and effectively satisfied each of the key requirements and knows how the key issues were closed. It is the essence of the solution.

Key requirements and issues come in layers. There are key requirements and issues at the highest level and are parts of the architecture dialog. There are key requirements and issues at the subsystem levels. There are key requirements and issues at the component levels. There are key requirements and issues at the abstract levels like maintenance, training, support, and other areas that do not make up the physical solution but are part of the system solution. In many ways they are the kickoff of an activity for each new layer of the system development.

9.3.2 Requirement Types

These are some ideas for types of requirements you might consider. Think in terms of form, fit, and function (there is no order to the list):

- Operation, function, interface, transition, growth, upgrade, performance (typically numbers)
- Physical characteristics (weight, size, power, ingress, egress, tie downs, electromagnetic radiation, security, vulnerability), durability, ruggedness,

health and safety
- Design, construction, fabrication, environment (temperature, humidity, dust, fungus, mold, vibration, altitude)
- Human engineering, safety, workmanship, interchangeability
- Reliability, maintainability, maintenance, repair, personnel
- Logistics, materials, parts, support, supply, training
- Transportability, shipping, delivery, installation
- Quality, test (inspection analysis demonstration that you will levy on the contractors that provide the subsystems)
- Product markings / labeling, nameplates
- Chemical, electrical, and physical requirements, dimensions, weight , color, protective coating
- Special tools, work stands, fixtures, dollies, and brackets
- Structural, architectural or operational features
- Raw material (chemical compound), mixtures (cleaning agents, paints), or semi-fabricated material (electrical cable, copper tubing) which are used in the fabrication of a product, toxic products and formulations
- Restraints/constraints, restriction of use of certain materials due to toxicity, dimensional or functional restrictions to assure compatibility with associated equipment

9.3.3 Characteristics of Good Requirements

The authoring of good specification text is not a trivial exercise and has been documented for many years[182]. The following is considered to be a reasonable list of characteristics for good requirements.

- **Complete**: The requirement is fully stated in one place with no missing information. It is atomic it is standalone.
- **Clear**: The requirement is clearly stated using strong unambiguous words. There is no jargon or useless words or phrases. Vague subjects, adjectives, prepositions, verbs and subjective phrases are avoided. Figures and tables can be vague and should be converted to standalone requirement objects.
- **Consistent**: The requirement does not contradict any other requirement in the specification or other specifications associated with the system. For example software requirements specifications must be consistent with the hardware specifications.
- **Accurate**: The requirement is fully vetted and accepted by the stakeholders. The requirement is not obsolete or becomes obsolete. This suggests a

---

[182] In 2005 Carnegie Mellon performed a study, Report CMU/SEI-2005-TR-014, and once again visited the dilemma of poor requirement text.

requirement management mechanism to change requirements as the system unfolds.

- **Feasible**: The requirement can be implemented. Technology is not exceeded, the teams' abilities are not exceeded, and the project cost or schedule is not exceeded. This suggests a requirement management mechanism to track risks associated with key requirements. This also builds the case for identifying the key requirements in the system.

- **Testable**: Do not use negative statements they are not testable. Do not use compound statements, they lead to test confusion and complexity. When a requirement is stated, identify one or more of the traditional test methods: inspection, analysis, demonstration, test, or certification. The stronger methods are test or demonstration and they should be used when practical. Inspection or analysis are weaker test methods and only should be done in special cases.

- **Necessary**: The requirement is fully vetted and all stakeholders agree its absence will result in a deficiency that cannot be ameliorated. This may lead to multiple releases where requirements are pushed to future releases. This suggests a requirement management mechanism where requirements are associated with different releases.

- **Traceable**: The requirement addresses only one thing. Compound requirements lead to traceability and test issues. Figures and tables can house many compound requirements open to interpretation and should be converted to standalone requirement objects.

- **Black Box**: Some believe all requirements should be black box oriented where the requirement specifies externally observable events based on the input and output. Requirements that specify elements within the black box such as internal architecture, algorithms, design, implementation, testing, or other decisions are constraints, and should be articulated in the Constraints section of the requirement specification document. I strongly disagree with this approach. If the details are critical to make sure a particular design and implementation is followed, it should not be buried in the constraint section.

9.3.4 Requirement Style Guide

The need for clear consistent testable specifications is obvious. One approach to help in this area is to develop a requirements style guide[183] that offers guidance to staff when writing the requirements. The style guide offers example sentence syntax and states the preferred imperative. The imperative is the heart of a specification. It is what must be implemented and tested. The imperative is signaled with a key word

---

[183] For Example: CMS Requirements Writer's Guide, Centers for Medicare & Medicaid Services Integrated IT Investment & System Life Cycle Framework, Department of Health and Human Services, V4.11 August 31, 2009.

like shall or must.

9.3.4.1 Requirement Imperatives

Imperatives are words and phrases that command something must be provided. Imperatives are used to signal the presence of a requirement. A requirement is something that must be implemented and tested. The following are different views of imperatives in a specification: NASA, FAA, MIL-STD-490, MIL-STD-463, and my view or Walt's view.

NASA View[184]

Imperatives are words and phrases that command something must be provided. They are in descending order of strength as a forceful statement of a requirement. The order from strongest to weakest is Shall, Must, Must Not, Is Required To, Are Applicable, Responsible For, Will, Should. The NASA requirement documents judged most explicit have a majority of imperative counts associated with the strongest words.

- **Shall**: Dictates provision of a functional capability.
- **Must or must not**: Establishes performance requirements or constraints.
- **Is required to**: Specification statements written in passive voice.
- **Are applicable**: Includes by reference, standards or other documentation as additions to specified requirements.
- **Responsible for**: Systems with predefined architectures e.g. "The XYS function of the ABC subsystem is responsible for responding to PDQ inputs."
- **Will**: Cites operational or development environment things provided to capability being specified e.g. "The building's electrical system will power the XYZ system" In a few instances "shall" and "will" are used interchangeably containing both requirements and descriptions of operational environment system boundaries not always sharply defined.
- **Should**: Not used frequently as imperative. When used, statement is always very weak, e.g. "Within reason, data files should have same time span to facilitate ease of use and data comparison".

FAA View

There was a movement within the FAA to use plain language techniques within the organization. The suggestion was to drop the use of "shall" and replace it with "must".

---

[184] Extracted from Automated Requirement Measurement (ARM) tool description. This is an internal tool used to review specification text.

MIL-STD-490 View[185]

Use "shall" whenever a specification expresses a provision that is binding. Use "should" and "may" wherever it is necessary to express non-mandatory provisions. "Will" may be used to express a declaration of purpose on the part of the contracting agency. It may be necessary to use "will" in cases where the simple future tense is required, i.e., power for the motor will be supplied by the ship.

MIL-STD-963B View[186]

Use "shall" when an instruction is mandatory. "Will" may be used to indicate the Government will do something. Avoid the use of "should" and "may" since Data Item Descriptions (DIDs) normally contain only mandatory instructions.

Walt's View

Keep it Simple. Remove all special cases that need to be remembered. There is no time for fine distinctions of English syntax. Use "shall" for all requirements. Use System Requirements Database (SRDB) attributes like "future" to categorize the requirement statements. Don't try to specify other systems, specify your interface to other systems. Minimize descriptive text to minimize noise in the specification and avoid missing important requirements. Use analysis and design documents to offer descriptive text of the system.

9.3.4.2 Requirement Sentence Structure Suggestions

Obviously there are no absolutes. The following are general rules for writing requirement statements.

- Avoid compound sentences.
- Software processing requirements are stand-alone statements with trigger / action / response as appropriate.
- Requirements are on a single line; use carriage return or line feed consistently to separate requirements. It will simplify exports to other tools.
- Do not embed requirement project unique identifier (PUI) number in requirement statement. Automated tools automatically assign PUI numbers.

Enumerated lists capture sequence. They can be used to capture algorithmic information in English statements rather than flowcharts or other forms of non-text

---

[185] This text is from MIL-STD-490 describing the use of imperatives. Specification Practices, Military Standard, MIL-STD-490 30 October 1968, MIL-STD-490A4 June 1985

[186] This text is from MIL-STD-963B describing the use of imperatives. Standard Practice Data Item Descriptions (DIDs), Department Of Defense MIL-STD-963B 31 August 1997, DOD-STD-963A 15 August 1986.

communication.

Upon power up failure the <device> shall:
1. step 1
2. step 2
3. step n

The numbers are part of the statement. The statement in the list does not need to include the "shall" imperative. An alternative is shown below.

Upon power up failure the <device>:
1. shall step 1
2. shall step 2
3. shall step n

The following are example software requirements:

Request Validation
a. FDP Processing shall reject an <X-request> with an <X-response>, if ... (FDP performs validation checks)

Request Reporting
a. Upon receipt of a valid <X-request>, FDP shall ... (no condition)

b. Upon receipt of a valid <X-request>, FDP shall forward <SS Commands> to the selected SS to ...(if a SS is used)

c. Upon expiration of [X-Timer], FDP shall ... (timed event)

d. Upon receipt of <SS Command Responses> resulting from the successful SS processing of an <X-request>, FDP shall ..

e. Upon receipt of <SS Command Responses> resulting from the successful SS processing of an <X-request>, FDP shall reject the <X-request> with an <X-response> if ... (FDP detects problem that SS can not)

f. Upon detecting an error condition reported in a <SS Command Response> resulting from processing an <X-request>, FDP shall ... (SS detects error FDP can't)

Results Reporting
a. FDP shall return the results of processing an "X" request to the ATC

operator. (Operator notification)

b. FDP shall return the results of processing an <X-request> in a <X-response>. (Computer notification)

Audit Reporting

a. FDP shall store an <FDP Update Msg> in response to processing an <X-request>. (Unconditional reporting)

b. FDP shall store an <FDP Update Msg> in response to processing an <X-request>, if X was selected as an audit event. (Conditional reporting, depending on operator selection)

c. FDP shall store an <FDP Update Msg>, if any errors were encountered in processing an <X-request>. (Conditional reporting, depending on errors)

9.3.4.3 Requirement Words a nd Phrases to Avoid

There are words and phrases that should be avoided in requirement text. They typically suggest problems with the requirements. They are:

- **Buzz Words**: fault tolerant, high fidelity, user friendly
- **Compound**: and, or, with, also
- **Incomplete**: TBD, TBS, TBE, TBC, TBR, ???, huh, not defined, not determined, but not limited to, as a minimum
- **Options**: may, might, could, should, can, optionally, ought, perhaps, probably
- **Unbounded**: all, totally, never, fully
- **Undefined**: any, approximately, near, far, close, back, in front, useful, significant, adequate, fast, slow, versatile, a minimum, as applicable, as appropriate, old, new, future, recent, past, today's, normal, timely, clear, well, easy, strong, weak, good, bad, efficient, low, user-friendly, flexible, effective, usually, generally, often, normally, typically, but, except, unless, eventually, although
- **Unsure**: possible, possibly, eventually, if possible, if needed
- **Weak Words 1**: normal, effective, timely, similar, flexible, adaptable, rapid, fast, adequate, support, maximize, minimize, etc, clear, easy , useful , adequate , good , bad
- **Weak Words 2**: this, these, that, those, it, they, above, below, previous, next, following, last, first
- **Weak Phrases 1**: as appropriate, be able to, be capable of, capability of, capability to, capability of, as required, provide for, easy to, having in mind,

taking into account, as fast as possible
- **Weak Phrases 2**: according to, on the basis of, relative to, compliant with, conform to, but not limited to
- **Untestable**: not

9.3.4.4 Requirement Document Structure

It is important that the document structure is considered and decisions made on where to place certain requirements. The goals are:

- Place logically grouped requirements in the same section
- Make sure there are no duplicate or partial duplicate requirements

The rule is one requirement one place, no exceptions. This can get tricky if the team is very thread oriented. In this case someone must methodically go through the document and remove the duplicates. It is also difficult if a system has multiple modes and states. The mode and state requirements can get duplicated in the functional requirements if the team is not careful.

A requirement document does capture the decomposition characteristics of a system. By counting the number of requirement statements (children) under a paragraph heading it is possible to get some insight into the level of completeness of the requirements.

The number of children at a particular level translates to a document shape. There are different document shapes and each shape has implications. The document shapes are random, rectangle, pyramid, inverted pyramid, trapezoid and diamond.

Item	Count	Prcnt	Shape
1. Level 1 Req	8	4	
2. Level 2 Req	94	54	
3. Level 3 Req	173	100	
4. Level 4 Req	72	41	
5. Level 5 Req	5	2	

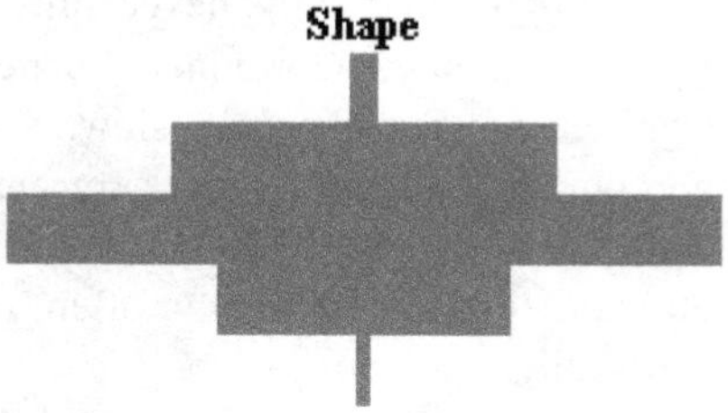

Figure 146 Document Shape

If there are insufficient paragraph levels, either the system is extremely small or there is a problem. The magic rule of 7 +/-2 should be considered when grouping requirements into paragraphs and paragraph levels.

If there are more children at lower document paragraph levels than higher levels, the document shape will be a pyramid, suggesting reasonable decomposition and leveling of requirements. However, it also suggests the team may not have completed their decomposition or they ventured into design[187].

A diamond shape also suggests the decomposition is reasonable and at the lower levels the team did not venture into too much detail suggesting design.

Item	Count	Prcnt	Shape
3.1 Web Portal dsa	5	33	
3.2 Architecture dsa	4	26	
3.3 General Functions dsa	4	26	
3.4 Req Reporting dsa	4	26	
3.5 Rule Processing dsa	13	86	
3.6 Metrics dsa	15	100	

Figure 147 Domain Specific Document Shape

The technique of counting the number of children under a paragraph heading can be expanded to include other views of a document. For example domain specific requirements can be counted. This offers a system view and stimulates dialog on the emphasis in the system. If the domain specific document shape is unexpected, then the team should try to address the issue. Either the team gained new insight or there is work to be done that they are now aware of and can execute.

9.3.5 Review Elements

Typically experts, novices, or some combination produce a specification document. They may or may not use a requirements style guide. At some point the staff decides if they will have a review. If they do not have a review, then they have to deal with the ramifications. If there is a review, then the review is a manual effort needing input from experts. The review includes domain and non-domain experts.

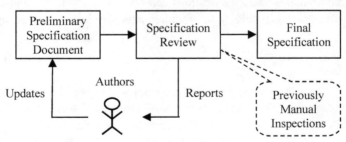

Figure 148 Requirements and Specification Review

The review can be manual or a tool[188] can be used to augment the manual

---

[187] When you look up it is requirements, when you look down it is design. In this case the team may have over achieved.

[188] The Specification Analysis Tool (SAT) was developed as a direct result of the

review. As with all tools, the manual review should not be bypassed by just pressing a few buttons on a tool. Instead the manual and automated review should complement each other to form a full picture not possible with just one approach.

Using a tool does not shorten the review time. The time tends to be arbitrarily set. People will look for possible issues until they get bored or exhausted. The findings from a tool are more consistent. People tend to miss instances in categories while a tool tends to find all problems of a certain type. People tend to miss a whole category of a problem but are better at finding domain specific problems.

When venturing into a tool based review approach let the machines do what they do well such as search, count, filter, categorize, profile, and visualize. Let the humans do what they do well such as creativity, critical thinking, inspiration, and intuition. Also realize there are more findings when a tool is used because the people and machines tend to complement each other.

9.4 Specifications

Specifications are information products that house the requirements. Requirements at the highest abstraction level precisely describe what a system is suppose to do and at the lowest abstraction level describe how the system does it. The lowest level requirements are design and implementation details.

Specifications can take many forms. For example a flyer can list features that are important to a customer. These features can be any abstraction level that someone thinks separates this system or product from another system or product. They can be blue prints, which show design details of a house under construction. They can be text documents, which describe what the system is supposed to do. Low level specifications can be product brochures or even line items in a table of a book listing hundreds of items like pipe fittings.

So requirements and specifications can take on many forms and capture many levels of abstractions. Ideally the requirements should be grouped by abstraction level.

9.4.1 Guiding Principles

Many times in immature settings the team will ignore the requirements and not even produce specifications. This is a serious mistake. Even if a miracle happens and a product is developed, a list of features for marketing and customers is needed. The list is also needed for planning the next generation product. As the product is fielded and customers find problems, the problems are associated with the feature list. Eventually nature will take its natural course. If the product is marginal or fails it does not matter[189]. If the product is successful there will be a reasonable set of

---

Carnegie Mellon, Report CMU/SEI-2005-TR-014 findings.

[189] Study after study has shown project failures are attributed to poor requirements.

specifications housing the requirements following these guiding principals:

- **Precise**: The requirements are written very precisely. The level of precision must be respected and understood. The precise requirements form the foundation for a requirement driven design that yields a solution, which meets the requirements and only the requirements. This precision follows through to the test program where requirements are allocated to test cases that are clearly delineated and easily understood.
- **Accurate**: All the requirements must very accurate because they form the basis of a "proof like" environment that is established during test. Inaccurate requirements will yield an unexpected design. The allocation of requirements must be accurate or the test program will fail to provide a "proof like" environment showing that the design meets the requirements and only the requirements.
- **Rigor**: To establish high levels of precision and accuracy for a design solution a great deal of rigor is needed. For example the introduction of a Systems Requirements Database (SRDB) forces a level of rigor on the organization and allocation of the requirements not possible with a spreadsheet or word processing table. The SRDB is only one example of rigor. Another is the allocation of software requirements to source code.
- **Methodical**: The only way to get to an accurate and precise solution that has the level of rigor to provide for a truly effective system solution is to be very methodical and establish rules that are clear and consistently executed. Simple things like naming conventions become critical to the process. For example, if you use automated test scripts, ensure that the test script names are consistent between the SRDB, test script file names, and test procedure document.

9.4.2 Specifications and Requirement Leveling

There are various approaches to organizing requirements and the internals of a specification. Examples are organization by functional area, operational threads, functional area and operational threads, or a different approach as defined by the team[190]. It is important to realize that different abstraction levels may exist and so different specification documents may be needed that represent those abstraction levels. Many think in terms of upper, middle, and lower levels. However there may be separate groups of upper, middle, and lower level requirements.

---

[190] Although the team may think they may have invented a new breakthrough approach to specifications, before they go down that path they need to study the past including MIL-STD-490 and MIL-STD-1521B.

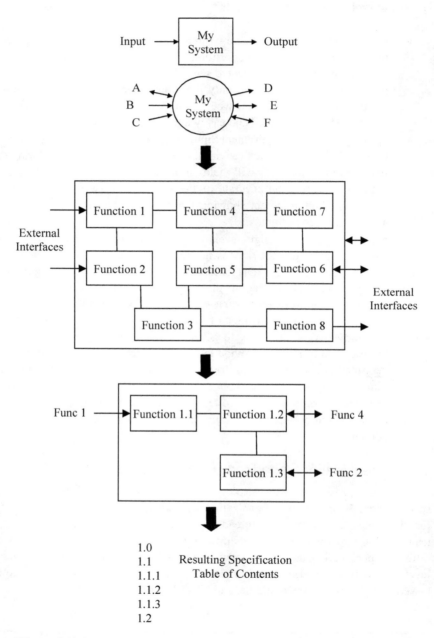

Figure 149 System Boundary Functional Decomposition Specification

If the specification is organized by operational thread, eventually after a few thread requirements are documented, duplicate requirements are created because many operational threads traverse many of the same functions as part of their normal sequence. It is ok to have duplicate requirements in a study such as an operational concept. In fact it is encouraged in studies to spur discussion. However specifications draw the line in the sand, commitment is made and a clear baseline must be articulated.

Duplicate requirements in the specification will lead to serious problems. Duplicate requirements are rarely stated the same way. This can lead to major or minor differences in the requirements. Also as the system evolves and the requirements change, keeping duplicates consistent is a maintenance nightmare. While various requirement alternatives are welcomed in studies, only one requirement clearly stated in one place in the specification is critical to success.

At the highest conceptual level, the possible requirement paragraph numbering scheme can be tree based where the requirements are organized such that logically grouped requirements are stated just once. In the past requirements were written as paragraphs under a logical paragraph title. However with the introduction of requirement management and traceability tools the paragraphs should be parsed into standalone sentences so that they can be easily imported into the tools. These standalone objects are still grouped by paragraph using a number and heading name.

3. REQUIREMENTS
3.1 First Paragraph
    3.1.1 First Subparagraph
3.2 Second Paragraph
    3.2.1 First Subparagraph
    3.2.2 Second Subparagraph
3.3 Third Paragraph
3.4 Fourth Paragraph

As we dig deeper into what may be needed for a specification other text surfaces to support the requirement story[191]. In its simplest form a specification has an introduction, requirements organized by functional area[192], statements associated with test methods, and a verification cross-reference matrix (VCRM) with test methods.

Later versions of the specification show traceability to test procedures and possibly other lower level specifications. This traceability is shown using tables in the child specification documents and child test procedure documents. The parent is the source specification document. So there can be several layers of parent child

---

[191] MIL-STD-490 identified various specifications used to house requirements for different kinds of subsystems and different abstraction levels. It is probably the broadest and deepest description of the topic.

[192] Functional analysis uses cohesion and coupling concepts to group similar items. This removes duplicates from the model or conceptual view.

relationships.

9.4.2.1 Test Methods

There are several test methods, sometimes called verification methods, which can be used to verify the requirements. The test methods are typically identified after the requirement section in a specification using a new standalone section usually called Qualification. The test methods are as follows[193]:

- **Analysis**: Analysis uses mathematical modeling and recognized analytical techniques including computer models to interpret or explain the behavior and performance of a system element and to predict the compliance of a design to its requirements based on calculated data or data derived from lower level component or subsystem testing. It is used when a physical prototype or product is not available or not cost effective. Analysis includes the use of both modeling and simulation.

- **Inspection**: Visual inspection of equipment and evaluation of drawings and other pertinent design data and processes is used to verify physical, material, part and product marking, manufacturer identification, and workmanship requirements.

- **Demonstration**: Demonstration executes a system, subsystem, or component operation to show that a requirement is satisfied. Usually performed with no or minimal instrumentation. Visual observations are the primary means of verification. It is used for a basic confirmation of performance capability and is differentiated from testing by the lack of detailed data gathering.

- **Test**: Test executes a system, subsystem, or component operation to obtain detailed data that is used to verify or to provide sufficient information to verify performance requirements through further analysis. Usually uses special test equipment or instrumentation to obtain very accurate quantitative data for analysis. Testing is the detailed quantifying method of verification.

- **Certification**: This is verification against legal, industrial or other standards by an outside authority, which issues a certificate.

9.4.2.2 Test Verification Cross Reference Matrix

The Verification Cross-Reference Matrix (VCRM) lists each requirement and identifies one or more test methods for each requirement. Preparing the VCRM

---

[193] Systems Engineering Fundamentals, Supplementary Text, Defense Acquisition University Press, January 2001. Defense Acquisition Guidebook, Defense Acquisition University, August 2010.

forces the team to examine the requirements for testability and reasonableness.

Obviously the VCRM must be consistent with the body of the specification. There is no excuse for any disconnect and the specification must be rejected if the Requirement column does not clearly follow the requirement specification paragraphs.

In the past, before the use of a System Requirements Database (SRDB), each specification included a section on Qualification, which had a description of the verification methods. The verification methods still apply however the need to identify them coincident with the initial specification is not as strong as in the past. This is because an SRDB is used in the process where each requirement is linked to one or more tests. The automation and process ensures that each requirement is testable.

Table 95 Test Verification Cross Reference Matrix (VCRM)

Requirement	I	A	D	T	C
3.1 Functional Area 1	-	-	-	-	-
Requirement 1			X		
Requirement 2			X		
Requirement 3				X	X
3.2 Functional Area 2	-	-	-	-	-
Requirement 1	X				
Requirement 2	X	X			

Before the SRDB, the specification also included a VCRM, which showed what test methods or methods are used to verify each requirement. This suggested that each requirement was testable even if the actual test procedure was unknown. Today the VCRM may remain blank until the test planning is started. At that point actual test procedures in the form of test paragraph Headings are shown in the matrix. This tends to make the allocation to test methods overcome by events. However most practitioners still track the allocation to the test methods, along with links to different kinds of tests[194] and the actual test procedure heading number, test PUI[195] and name in the SRDB. This view is then offered, as needed using an SRDB report export.

Although the specification baseline is very strong before test planning is initiated and completed, it is not perfect and changes will happen. Some of the changes include the impacts of test and the final test procedures. Ideally there are no specification changes once test dry runs are completed. However, if dry run testing surfaces changes, those changes must be clearly and methodically addressed in the specification.

---

[194] Different kinds of tests include functional, performance, environmental, reliability, safety, power, durability, etc.

[195] PUI – Project Unique Identifier is a unique number associated with a database object.

9.4.3 Requirements Management

Requirements change as the system is developed and used. These changes need to be understood and tracked. Prior to the release of a specification, requirement changes are easier. The other team members are mostly working with the key requirements and anxiously awaiting the details that are in a specification that they will consume when it is released.

Once a specification is released the consuming team is impacted. Many times it is the consuming team that suggests the changes, as the decomposition is more fully understood. After the specification is released the requirement changes are tracked.

When the design and implementation starts there are also requirement changes. These changes are against the baseline specification so a more formal mechanism needs to be established to propose and either accept or reject the changes.

When the system goes operational there are always suggestions for improvement. These suggestions translate to requirements that need to be managed. Many times a successful system will evolve into a product line. The product line releases need to be managed.

The various requirement changes are best managed with a System Requirements Database Management (SRDB) tool that will capture the history of the changes. One or more attributes and a history of the changes are used to determine how various requirements started and evolved. The SRDB is described in the System Requirements Database Management section of this text.

At the highest level requirement management is established with a specification document, which has a title page that contains the title, sponsor or customer, date, and a version number. This establishes a baseline. As requirements change the specification is released with a new date and version number.

9.4.4 Specification Types and Practices

MIL-STD-490 is an example of grouping requirements at certain abstraction levels and offering a suggestion for placing them in an information product known for that abstraction level. Buried within the standard is not only the notion of abstraction levels but also examples of types of requirements to consider. This list broadens and deepens the thought processes of the stakeholders. It is a significant starting point for making sure things are not missed in the system development[196].

---

[196] Much of this text in this section comes directly from MIL-STD-490. The goal was to extract the most salient points of the standard while minimizing interpretation. The intent is to use this as a universal example of specification practices.

Table 96 MIL-STD-490 Specifications[197]

Type	Title
Type A	System/Segment Specification
Type B	Development Specifications
Bl	Prime Item
B2	Critical Item
B3	Non-Complex Item
B4	Facility or Ship
B5	Software
Type C	Product Specifications
Cla	Prime Item Product Function
Clb	Prime Item Product Fabrication
C2a	Critical Item Product Function
C2b	Critical Item Product Fabrication
C3	Non-Complex Item Product Fabrication
C4	Inventory Item
C5	Software
Type D	Process Specification
Type E	Material Specification

These specifications use common numbered sections. The common sections are Scope, Applicable Documents, Requirements, Qualification Requirements (Software), Quality Assurance Provisions (Hardware), Preparation For Delivery, Notes, and Appendix. For this new generation I have taken the liberty to add Ethics and Sustainability to each information product, including specifications.

9.4.4.1 A Level System Segment Specification

The Type A System Segment Specification states the technical and mission requirements for a system or segment as an entity, allocates requirements to functional areas, documents design constraints, and defines the interfaces between or among the functional areas. Normally, the initial version is based on parameters developed during the Concept Exploration[198] phase.

---

[197] This example is selected because it is the original starting point dating back to October 30, 1968.

[198] This description is based on the approach of Concept Exploration, Demonstration, Validation, Development, and Production phases in a procurement cycle.

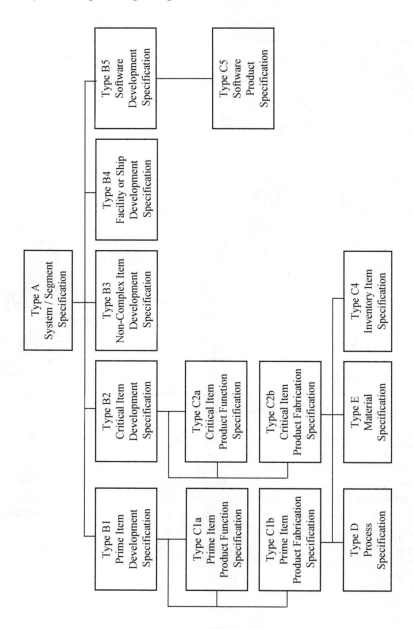

Figure 150 Generic Specification Tree[199]

---

[199] Specification Practices, Military Standard, MIL-STD-490 30 October 1968, MIL-STD-490A4 June 1985.

The initial version is used to establish the general nature of the system that is to be further defined and finalized during the concept Demonstration and Validation[200] phases. This specification is maintained current during the concept Demonstration and Validation phase, culminating in a revision that forms the future performance base for the Development and Production[201] of the prime items and configuration items[202].

1.0 SCOPE
1.1 Scope
1.2 Overview and Definitions
2.0 Applicable Documents

3.0 Requirements
3.1 System (Item) Definition
3.1.1 Functional Layouts
3.1.2 Interfaces
3.1.3 Major Components
3.1.4 Furnished Equipment
3.1.5 States and Modes

3.2 Performance
3.2.1 Operational Performance
3.2.2 Physical
3.2.3 Reliability/Availability
3.2.4 Maintainability

3.2.5 Environment
3.2.5.1 Natural Environments
3.2.5.1.1 Operating
3.2.5.1.1.1 Ambient Pressure
3.2.5.1.1.2 Ambient Air Temperature
3.2.5.1.1.3 Humidity
3.2.5.1.1.4 Fungus
3.2.5.1.1.5 Lightning
3.2.5.1.1.6 Precipitation
3.2.5.1.1.7 Sand and Dust
3.2.5.1.1.8 Wind

3.2.5.1.2.9 Solar Radiation
3.2.5.1.2.10 Corrosive Atmosphere
3.2.5.1.2.11 Magnetic
3.2.5.1.2.12 Fog
3.2.5.1.2.13 Seismic
3.2.5.2 Induced Environments
3.2.5.2.1 Operating
3.2.5.2.1.1 Pressure
3.2.5.2.1.2 Temperature
3.2.5.2.1.3 Humidity
3.2.5.2.1.4 Shock and Vibration
3.2.5.2.1.5 Air Velocity
3.2.5.2.1.6 Acoustic
3.2.5.2.1.7 EMI/EMC
3.2.5.2.2 Non-Operating
3.2.5.2.2.1 Pressure
3.2.5.2.2.2 Temperature
3.2.5.2.2.3 Humidity
3.2.5.2.2.4 Shock and Vibration
3.2.5.2.2.5 Air Velocity
3.2.5.2.2.6 Acoustic
3.2.5.2.2.7 EMI/EMC
3.3 System Characteristics
3.3.1 Safety
3.3.2 Security
3.3.2.1 Physical Security
3.3.2.2 Information Security
3.3.2.3 Personnel Security
3.3.3 Interchangeability
3.3.4 Human Factors

---

[200] MIL-STD-490 consists of four phases: Exploration, Demonstration and Validation, Full Scale Development, and Production and Deployment.

[201] Systems Engineering Fundamentals, Supplementary Text, Defense Acquisition University Press, January 2001 consists of four phases: Concept and Technology Development, System Development and Demonstration, Production and Deployment, Sustainment and Disposal.

[202] Any deliverable designated by the contracting organization for configuration management such as hardware, software, etc.

3.2.5.1.1.9 Solar Radiation
3.2.5.1.1.10 Corrosive Atmosphere
3.2.5.1.1.11 Magnetic
3.2.5.1.1.12 Fog
3.2.5.1.1.13 Seismic
3.2.5.1.2 Non-Operating
3.2.5.1.2.1 Ambient Pressure
3.2.5.1.2.2 Ambient Air Temperature
3.2.5.1.2.3 Humidity
3.2.5.1.2.4 Fungus
3.2.5.1.2.5 Lightning
3.2.5.1.2.6 Precipitation
3.2.5.1.2.7 Sand and Dust
3.2.5.1.2.8 Wind

3.3.5 Miscellaneous

3.4 Logistics
3.5 Personnel and Training
3.6 Documentation
3.7 Major Component Characteristics
3.8 Precedence and Combined Characteristics

4.0 Verification Correlation
5.0 Delivery and Transition
6.0 Ethics
7.0 Sustainability
8.0 Notes

9.4.4.2 B Level Development Specifications

Type B Development Specifications state the requirements for the design or engineering development of a product. Each development specification effectively describes the performance characteristics that each item is to achieve when it evolves into a detail design for production. The development specification should be maintained current during production when it is desired to retain a complete statement of performance requirements. Since the breakdown of a system into its elements may have configuration items of various degrees of complexity which are subject to different engineering disciplines or specification content, there are sub-types: B1, B2, B3, B4, and B5.

9.4.4.2.1 Prime Item Development Specification

A Type B1 Prime Item Development Specification applies to a complex item such as an aircraft, training equipment, etc. A prime item development specification can be used as a functional baseline for a single configuration item development program or as part of the allocated baseline where the configuration item covered is part of a larger system development program. Normally configuration items needing a Type B1 specification meet the following criteria:

- Prime item is received or formally accepted by the contracting organization.
- Provisioning action will be needed.
- Technical manuals or other instructional material covering operation and maintenance of the prime item will be required.
- Quality conformance inspection of each prime item, as opposed to sampling, will be needed.

1.0 SCOPE   3.3.6 Safety

9.4.4.2.2 Critical Item Development Specification

Type B2 Critical Item Development Specifications apply to a configuration item, which is below the level of complexity of a prime item but which is engineering critical, or logistics critical.

Engineering critical occurs when the technical complexity warrants an individual specification. For example reliability of the critical item significantly affects the ability of the system or prime item to perform its overall function, or safety is a consideration. Also when the prime item cannot be adequately evaluated without separate evaluation and application suitability testing.

A critical item is logistics critical when repair parts will be provisioned for the item or the contracting organization has designated the item for multiple source re-procurement.

3.2.6 Transportability
3.3 Design and construction
3.3.1 Materials processes and parts
3.3.2 Electromagnetic radiation
3.3.3 Nameplates and product marking.
3.3.4 Workmanship
3.3.5 Interchangeability

4.1.2 Special tests and examinations
4.2 Quality conformance inspections
5.0 Preparation for delivery
6.0 Ethics
7.0 Sustainability
8.0 Notes
Appendices

9.4.4.2.3 Non-Complex Item Development Specification

A Type B3 Non-Complex Item Development Specification applies to items of relatively simple design. During development, it can be shown the item is suitable for its intended application by inspection or demonstration. Acceptance testing to verify performance is not required. Acceptance can be based on verification that the item, as fabricated, conforms to the drawings. The end product is not software.

Example items are special tools, work stands, fixtures, dollies, and brackets. They can be adequately defined during the development by a sketch and during production by a drawing or set of drawings. If drawings will suffice to cover all requirements, unless a specification is required by the contracting organization, a specification for a particular non-complex item is not needed. However, when it is necessary to specify several performance requirements in a formal manner to ensure development of a satisfactory configuration item or when it is desirable to specify detailed verification procedures, a specification of this type is appropriate.

1.0 SCOPE
2.0 Applicable documents
3.0 Requirements.
3.1 Item Definition
3.2 Characteristics
3.2.1 Performance

3.2.2 Physical characteristics
4.0 Quality assurance provisions
5.0 Preparation for delivery
6.0 Ethics
7.0 Sustainability
8.0 Notes

9.4.4.2.4 Facility or Ship Development Specification

A Type B4 Facility or Ship Development Specification is applicable to each item, which is both a fixed (or floating) installation and an integral part of a system. Basic structural, architectural or operational features designed specifically to accommodate the requirements unique to the system and which must be developed in close coordination with the system. A facility or ship services which form complex interfaces with the system. A facility or ship hardening to decrease the total system's vulnerability; and ship speed, maneuverability, etc. A development specification for a facility or ship establishes the requirements and basic restraints / constraints imposed on the development of an architectural and engineering design for such facility or ship. The product specifications for the facility or ship are prepared by the architectural / engineering activity.

1.0 SCOPE	3.3 Documentation
2.0 Applicable documents	4.0 Quality assurance provisions
3.0 Requirements	5.0 Preparation for delivery
3.1 Facility or ship definition	**6.0 Ethics**
3.1.1 Facility or ship drawings	**7.0 Sustainability**
3.1.2 Interface Definition	8.0 Notes
3.1.3 Major subsystems and component list	Appendices
3.2 Characteristics	

The main emphasis is on 3.2 Characteristics.

a. **Civil:** (1) Axle or wheel loads on roads, (2) Special lane width, (3) Turn and weight provisions for special vehicles, (4) Jack loads transfer requirements, (5) Parking (number of vehicles), (6) Grades on roads types pavement (flexible or rigid) type walks (flexible or rigid), (7) Special water and sewage requirements. Quantity and nature of water and sewage if special, (8) Special fire protection requirements (exterior), (9) Fencing and security, (10) Location and types of existing utilities if any (water gas sewer electrical storm drainage).

b. **Architectural:** (1) Personnel occupancy types hours per day, (2) Designation of use of areas within facility. Partition layout. Hazard areas. Special treatment areas, (3) Types of special doors required, (4) Floor level requirements. Floor drainage, (5) Window requirements if any, (6) Controlling dimension requirements, (7) Clear ceiling heights, (8) Exterior architectural treatment (concrete masonry brick etc.). Indicate whether treatment is to match existing if applicable, (9) Explosive safety requirements for construction.

c. **Structural:** (1) Crane and hoist location and loads. Control requirements. (2) Floor and roof loads. Special loads seismic loads wind loads, (3) Clear span and column-free areas, (4) Blast loads shielding requirements, (5) Personnel ladders elevators, (6) Transfer piers dock loads, (7) General configuration of building number of stories, (8) Barricades and shielding for explosive blast areas.

d. **Mechanical:** (1) Interior potable water. (2) Environment limits temperature humidity ventilation, (3) Compressed air, (4) Fire protection, (5) Vibration and acoustical requirements, (6) Equipment cooling requirements.

e. **Electrical:** (1) Power requirements - types and magnitude. (2) Light intensities, (3) Communications requirements, (4) Grounding.

f. **Equipment:** Provide layout and list each piece of equipment (1) Equipment name. (2) Units required (number), (3) Purpose of equipment, (4) Size of equipment (governing dimensions weight), (5) Power requirements - heat gain BTU's per hour type cooling in-out temperatures relative humidity, (6)

Minimum access requirements - front back sides. Ship characteristics shall include the consideration of the following as necessary.

g. **General:** (1) Limiting dimensions, (2) Weight control, (3) Reliability and maintainability, (4) Environmental conditions, (5) Standardization and interchangeability, (6) Shock noise and vibration, (7) Navy or commercial marine standards including certification of the latter.

h. **Hull structure:** (1) Structural loading and configuration, (2) Basic structural materials, (3) Welding riveting and fastenings, (4) Access features.

i. **Propulsion plant:** (1) Type and number of propulsion units, (2) Type and number of propellers, (3) Propulsion control equipment.

j. **Electric plant:** (1) Type and number of generator units \, (2) Power distribution system, (3) Lighting system.

k. **Communications and control:** (1) Navigation equipment, (2) Interior communication systems and equipment, (3) Electronics systems, (4) Weapon control systems.

l. **Auxiliary system:** (1) Air conditioning system, (2) Fuel systems, (3) Fresh and sea water systems, (4) Steering system, (5) Aircraft handling system, (6) Underway replenishment system, (7) Cargo handling system.

m. **Outfit and furnishings:** (1) Hull fittings boat storage and rigging, (2) Painting deck covering and insulation, (3) Special stowage, (4) Workshops and utility spaces, (5) Living spaces and habitability.

n. **Armament:** (1) Guns and ammunition stowage and handling, (2) Ship-launched weapon systems, (3) Cargo munitions handling and stowage.

9.4.4.2.5 Software Development Specification

Type B5 Software Development Specifications include both software and interface requirement specifications.

Software Requirements Specifications describe in detail the functional, interface, quality factor, special, and qualification requirements necessary to design, develop, test, evaluate and deliver the required software item.

Interface Requirements Specifications describe in detail the requirements for one or more software item interfaces in the system, segment, or prime item. The requirements are those necessary to design, develop, test, evaluate, and deliver the required software. The interface requirements may be included in the associated Software Requirements Specifications under the following conditions: (1) there are few interfaces, (2) few development groups are involved in implementing the interface requirements, (3) the interfaces are simple, or (4) there is one contractor developing the software.

1.0 Scope	3.8 Security requirements
1.1 Identification	3.9 Design constraints

9.4.4.3 C Level Product Specifications

Type C Product Specifications apply to any configuration item below the system level, and may be oriented toward procurement of a product through specification of primarily functional (performance) requirements or primarily fabrication (detailed design) requirements. There are Sub-types of product specifications to cover equipment of various complexities or using different outlines of form.

A product function specification states the complete performance requirements of the product for the intended use, and necessary interface and interchangeability characteristics. It covers form, fit, and function. Complete performance requirements include all essential functional requirements under service environmental conditions or under conditions simulating the service environment. Quality assurance provisions for hardware include one or more of the following inspections: qualification evaluation, pre-production, periodic production, and quality conformance.

A product fabrication specification is normally prepared when both development and production of the hardware are procured. In those cases where a development specification (Type B) has been prepared, specific reference to the document containing the performance requirements for the hardware are made in the product fabrication specification. These specifications state a detailed description of the parts and assemblies of the product, usually by prescribing compliance with a set of drawings, and those performance requirements and corresponding tests and inspections necessary to assure proper fabrication, adjustment, and assembly techniques. Tests normally are limited to acceptance tests in the shop environment. Selected performance requirements in the normal shop or test area environment and verifying tests may be included. Pre-production or periodic tests to be performed on a sampling basis and needing service, or other, environment may reference the associated development specification. Product fabrication specifications may be prepared as Part II of a two-part specification when the contracting organization desires close relationships between the performance and fabrication requirements.

9.4.4.3.1 Prime Item Product Specifications

Type C1 Prime Item Product Specifications apply to items meeting the criteria for prime item development specifications (Type B1). They may be prepared as function or fabrication specifications as determined by the procurement conditions.

9.4.4.3.1.1 Prime Item Product Function Specification

A Type C1a Prime Item Product Function Specification applies to procurement of prime items when a "form, fit and function" description is acceptable. Normally, this type of specification is prepared only when a single procurement is anticipated and training and logistic considerations are unimportant.

1. SCOPE
1.1 Scope
1.2 Classification
2.0 Applicable documents
3.0 Requirements
3.1 Item definition
3.1.1 Prime item diagrams
3.1.2 Interface definition
3.1.3 Major component list
3.1.4 Government-furnished property list
3.2 Characteristics
3.2.1 Performance
3.2.2 Physical characteristics
3.2.3 Reliability
3.2.4 Maintainability
3.2.5 Environmental conditions
3.2.6 Transportability
3.3 Design and construction
3.3.1 Materials processes and parts
3.3.2 Electromagnetic radiation

3.3.3 Identification and marking
3.3.4 Workmanship
3.3.5 Interchangeability
3.3.6 Safety
3.3.7 Human performance/human engineering
3.3.8 Standards of manufacture
3.4 Major component characteristics
3.5 Qualification Preproduction Periodic production inspection
3.6 Standard sample
4.0 Quality Assurance Provisions
4.1 General
4.1.1 Responsibility for inspection
4.1.2 Special tests and examinations
4.2 Quality conformance inspections
5.0 Preparation for delivery
6.0 Ethics
7.0 Sustainability
8.0 Notes

9.4.4.3.1.2 Prime Item Product Fabrication Specification

Type C1b Prime Item Product Fabrication Specifications are normally prepared for procurement of prime items when a detailed design disclosure package needs to be made available, it is desired to control the interchangeability of lower level components and parts, and service maintenance and training are significant factors.

1. SCOPE   3.3.3 Workmanship

1.1. Scope
1.2 Classification
2.0 Applicable documents
3.0 Requirements
3.1 Prime item definition
3.1.1 Major component list
3.1.2 Government furnished property list
3.2 Characteristics
3.2.1 Performance
3.3 Design and construction
3.3.1 Production drawings
3.3.2 Standards of manufacture

3.4 Pre-production sample
4.0 Quality Assurance Provisions.
4.1 General
4.1.1 Responsibility for inspection
4.1.2 Special tests and examinations
4.2 Quality conformance inspections
5.0 Preparation for delivery
6.0 Ethics
7.0 Sustainability
8.0 Notes
8.1 Intended use
8.2 Ordering data

9.4.4.3.2 Critical Item Product Specification

Type C2 Critical Item Product Specifications apply to engineering or logistic critical items and may be prepared as function or fabrication specifications.

9.4.4.3.2.1 Critical Item Product Function Specification

A Type C2a Critical Item Product Function Specification applies to a critical item where the critical item performance characteristics are of greater concern than part interchangeability or control over the details of design, and a "form, fit and function" description is adequate.

1. SCOPE
3.0 Requirements
3.1 Critical item definition
3.2 Characteristics
3.2.1 Performance
3.2.2 Physical characteristics
3.2.3 Reliability
3.2.4 Maintainability
3.2.5 Environmental conditions
3.2.6 Transportability
3.3 Design and construction
3.3.1 Materials processes and parts
3.3.2 Electromagnetic radiation
3.3.3 Identification and marking
3.3.4 Workmanship
3.3.5 Interchangeability

3.3.6 Safety
3.3.7 Human performance/human
engineering 3.3.8 Standards of manufacture
3.4 Qualification (Pre-production) (Periodic
production) inspection
3.5 Standard sample
4.0 Quality Assurance Provisions
4.1 General.
4.1.1 Responsibility for inspection
4.1.2 Special tests and examinations
4.2 Quality conformance inspections
5.0 Preparation for delivery
6.0 Ethics
7.0 Sustainability
8.0 Notes

9.4.4.3.2.2 Critical Item Product Fabrication Specification

A Type C2b Critical Item Product Fabrication Specification applies to a critical item when a detailed design disclosure needs to be made available or where it is considered that adequate performance can be achieved by adherence to a set of detail drawings and required processes.

1. SCOPE	4.1 General
3.0 Requirements	4.1.1 Responsibility for inspection
3.1 Critical item definition	4.1.2 Special tests and examinations
3.1.1 Government furnished property list	4.2 Quality conformance inspections
3.2 Characteristics	5.0 Preparation for delivery
3.2.1 Performance	**6.0 Ethics**
3.3 Design and construction	**7.0 Sustainability**
3.3.1 Production drawings	8.0 Notes
3.3.2 Standards of manufacture	8.1 Intended use
3.3.3 Workmanship	8.2 Ordering data
3.4 Pre-production sample	Appendices
4.0 Quality Assurance Provisions	

9.4.4.3.3 Non-Complex Item Product Fabrication Specification

A Type C3 Non-Complex Item Product Fabrication Specification applies to non-complex items. Where acquisition of a non-complex item is desired against a detailed design, a set of detail drawings may be prepared in lieu of a specification.

1.0 SCOPE	4.0 Quality Assurance Provisions
2.0 Applicable documents	4.1 General
3.0 Requirements	4.1.1 Responsibility for inspection
3.1 Non-complex item definition	4.1.2 Special tests and examinations
3.2 Characteristics	4.2 Quality conformance inspections
3.2.1 Performance	5.0 Preparation for delivery
3.2.2 Physical characteristics	**6.0 Ethics**
3.3 Workmanship	**7.0 Sustainability**
3.4 Qualification inspection and samples	8.0 Notes

9.4.4.3.4 Inventory Item Specification

A Type C4 Inventory Item Specification identifies applicable inventory items including their pertinent characteristics that exist in the inventory and which can be incorporated in a prime item or in a system being developed. The purpose of the inventory specification is to stabilize the configuration of inventory items on the basis of both current capabilities of each inventory item and the requirements of the specific application, or to achieve equipment or component item standardization between or within a system or prime item. This puts the organization on notice for the performance and interface characteristics that are required, so that when changes for an inventory item are evaluated the needs of the various applications may be kept in mind. If this is not done, design changes may make an inventory item unsuitable for the system. A separate inventory item specification should be prepared, as required, for each system, subsystem, prime item or critical item in which inventory items are installed or which require the support of inventory items.

1.0 SCOPE	**6.0 Ethics**
2.0 Applicable documents	**7.0 Sustainability**
3.0 Requirements	8.0 Notes
4.0 Quality Assurance Provisions	Appendixes
5.0 Preparation for Delivery	

9.4.4.3.5 Software Product Specification

A Type C5 Software Product Specification applies to the delivered software item and is sometimes referred to as the "as built" software specification. This specification consists of the final updated version of the Software Top-Level Design Document, the Software Detailed Design Document, the Database Design Document(s), Interface Design Document(s), and the source and object listings of the software.

The Software Top Level Design Document describes how the top-level computer software components (TLCSCs) implement the Software Requirements Specification and the Interface Requirements Specification. The Software Detailed Design Document describes the detailed decomposition of TLCSCs to lower level computer software components and software units.

The Database Design Document describes one or more databases used by the software. If there is more than one database, each database may be described in a separate Document.

The Interface Design Document provides the detailed design of one or more software interfaces. When Interface Requirements Specifications have been prepared, associated Interface Design Documents are prepared as well.

These specifications consist of the final up-dated versions of the Software Top Level Design Document, the Software Detailed Design Document(s), the Database Design Document(s), the Interface Design Document(s) and source and object code listings of the software that has successfully undergone formal testing.

9.4.4.4 D Level Process Specification

A Type D Process Specification applies to a service, which is performed on a product or material. Examples of processes are heat treatment, welding, plating, packing, microfilming, and marking. Process specifications cover manufacturing techniques, which require a specific procedure to achieve satisfactory results. Where specific processes are essential to fabrication or procurement of a product or material, a process specification defines the specific processes. Normally, a process specification applies to production but may be prepared to control the development of a process.

1.0 SCOPE	4.2 Monitoring procedures for equipment
1.1 Scope	used in process

1.2 Classification
2.0 Applicable documents
3.0 Requirements
3.1 Equipment
3.2 Materials
3.3 Required procedures and operations
3.4 Recommended procedures and operations
3.5 Certification
4.0 Quality assurance provisions
4.1 Responsibility for inspection

4.3 Monitoring procedures for materials
4.4 Certification
4.5 Test methods
5.0 Preparation for delivery
6.0 Ethics
7.0 Sustainability
8.0 Notes
8.1 Intended use
8.2 Definitions
Appendices

9.4.4.5 E Level Material Specification

A Type E Material Specification is applies to a raw material (chemical compound), mixtures (cleaning agents, paints), or semi-fabricated material (electrical cable, copper tubing) which are used in the fabrication of a product. Normally, a material specification applies to production but may be prepared to control the development of a material.

1.0 SCOPE
1.1 Scope
1.2 Classification
2.0 Applicable documents
3.0 Requirements
3.1 General material requirements
3.1.1 Character or quality
3.1.2 Formulation
3.1.3 Product characteristics
3.1.4 Chemical, electrical and mechanical properties
3.1.5 Environment conditions.
3.1.6 Stability, Shelf life, aging, etc
3.1.7 Toxic products and safety

3.1.8 Identification and marking
3.1.9 Workmanship
3.2 Qualification (Pre-production)
4.0 Quality assurance provisions.
4.1 Responsibility for inspection
4.2 Special tests and examinations
4.3 Quality conformance inspection
4.4 Test methods
5.0 Preparation for delivery
6.0 Ethics
7.0 Sustainability
8.0 Notes
Appendices

9.4.4.6 Two Part Specification

A Two Part Specification combines both development (performance) and product fabrication (detail design) specifications under a single specification number as Part I and Part II respectively. This practice requires both parts for a complete definition of both performance requirements and detailed design requirements governing fabrication. Under this practice, the development specification remains alive during the life of the hardware as the complete statement of performance requirements. Proposed design changes are evaluated against both the product fabrication and the development parts of the specification. To emphasize that two parts exist, the same specification number identifies both parts and each part is further identified as Part I or Part II. Two-part specifications are not applicable when the product specification is a product function specification or when it is a computer software specification.

9.4.5 Example Specification Trees

Many systems are not massive infrastructure systems. What would a specification tree look like for a smaller project? In many instances someone has done a significant amount of work and captured requirements that need to be understood and converted to a working system.

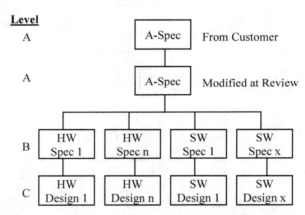

Figure 151 Specification Tree Small Project

A project starts when a vendor receives a specification. The vendor works with the customer to develop a modified A-Level specification. The discussions include feasibility, practical considerations, cost, and schedule. Eventually a modified A-Level specification emerges and becomes the baseline. The vendor proceeds to decompose, design, and implement the system using various B and C level specifications.

C-level specifications provide design detail. Notice this tree does not contain D or E level specifications. Also the B and C levels can be various instances of their respective levels (e.g. B1, C3, etc).

Occasionally a segment specification is introduced. For example there may be the fielded system and then a duplicate system used for simulation, training, and support. The segment specification always presupposes architecture because it includes requirement allocations to its segment and allocates requirements to different subsystems in the segment.

Customers do not want to presuppose an architecture, which might be flawed without input from industry. So segment specifications are A-Level specification but are labeled as "AS" for the special segment characteristic of the architecture being locked down. Who did that allocation how do you know it is correct?

There is some art in trying to determine if a design specification is needed. If you are buying a Commercial-Off-The-Shelf (COTS) item then perhaps all that is needed is a marketing glossy to maintain configuration control. However COTS configuration control is an oxymoron - why bother - in 6 months you will not be able to find the same COTS thing. So this is more of an art.

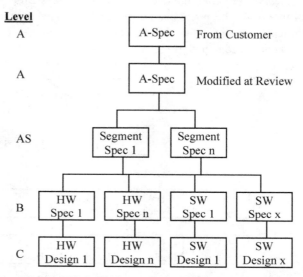

Figure 152 Specification Tree with Segments

So you use A, B, and C to "slice and dice" your system in a way that makes sense for your needs. During the days of MIL-STD-490 the world was very different. There were:

- Engineering notebooks - housed raw information
- Typing pools - created papers and draft documents
- Drafting sections / departments - created blue prints
- Publications departments - created typeset documents / books
- Few computers - no complex models
- Prototypes - no computers to model the details just build a prototype

During that time there was a strong desire to not lose anything. This seemed to apply everywhere. Probably because it was so hard to create everything, things had great value and were not viewed as commodities.

Today with the computer we generate large amounts of paper because we can. So when an important document does need to be created it typically has no meat - it is filled with obvious fluff. This can lead to disaster in the case of specifications. As the years have clicked by, the names have changed and we dropped the requirements for MIL-STD-490 but the fundamentals still need to be present. A rose by any other name is still a rose.

9.5 Traceability

There are two aspects to traceability. The first is allocation to subsystems and links to lower level requirements. The second is the allocation to a test method and links to standalone test procedures, which can use any of the test methods. Requirements always appear in specifications. Studies surface requirements, including the stakeholder needs and requirements. There are different levels of requirement traceability. The levels of traceability are associated with different time frames and different goals. The levels are:

- Very Course Grain
- Course Grain
- Fine Grain
- Very Fine Grain

The terminology was taken from the processing domain where functions and their processing can be broken down into different size chunks. The finer the grain the smaller the chunk. As the numbers of chunks increase, the overhead or amount of effort increases. For traceability the differences between each chunk is very large. For example very course grain traceability might be between ten items. For the same system course grain traceability might jump to hundreds of items, fine grain traceability might jump to thousands of items and very fine grain traceability might jump to tens of thousands of items.

9.5.1 Very Course Grain Traceability

Very course grain traceability is at the <u>document level</u>. This is the simplest form of traceability to implement. It is a connection from a parent specification document to a child specification document. It is a specification tree. The tree can be shown as an indentured list or as a block diagram.

Table 97 Indentured List Specification Tree
1.0 System/Segment Specification

1.1 Prime Item Development Specification
        1.1.1 Prime Item Product Function Specification
        1.1.2 Prime Item Product Fabrication Specification
            1.1.2.1 Process Specification - production
            1.1.2.2 Material Specification - production
        1.1.3 Inventory Item Specification
 	
    1.2 Critical Item Development Specification

Table 97 Indentured List Specification Tree

1.2.1 Critical Item Product Function Specification
1.2.2 Critical Item Product Fabrication Specification
       1.2.2.1 Process Specification - production
       1.2.2.2 Material Specification - production
1.2.3 Inventory Item Specification

1.3 Non-Complex Item Development Specification
       1.3.1 Non-Complex Item Product Fabrication Specification

1.4 Facility or Ship Development Specification
       1.4.1 Inventory Item Specification

1.5 Software Development Specification
       1.5.1 Software Product Specification

1.6 Inventory Item Specification - system
1.7 Process Specification - development
1.8 Material Specification - system

Many times traceability is also needed to other information products. Since the traceability is very course grain, this is not unreasonable. In fact showing how information products tie together is a good way to start to layout a program and understand how different activities interrelate.

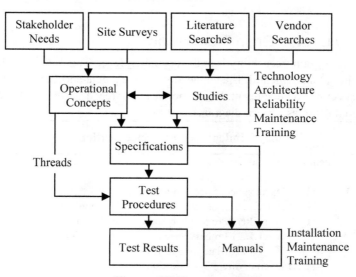

Figure 153 Document Tree

Very course grain traceability is typically used in proposals and plans. It is also used as introductory material to show the context of an information product.

An indentured list specification tree is a decomposition of a specification block in the document tree. Each of the blocks can be decomposed. For example the studies consist of technology, architecture, reliability, maintenance, and training. These studies interrelate and can be shown in their own document tree.

9.5.2 Course Grain Traceability

Course grain traceability is at the <u>paragraph level</u>. It is typically used to show requirement traceability when there are no automated tools such as a System Requirements Database (SRDB). The child document contains a Requirement Traceability Matrix (RTM) as an appendix. The RTM lists the current document paragraph numbers and headings in the left most column of a table. Each paragraph is a separate row. An additional column lists the paragraph number and optionally the heading of the parent document.

Table 98 Requirement Paragraph Level Traceability Matrix

Subsystem Specification	System Specification
3.2.1 Function 10	3.7
3.2.2 Function 11	3.7
3.2.3 Function 12	3.3, 3.4, 3.5
3.2.4 Function 13	3.1
3.2.5 Function 14	3.2

9.5.3 Fine Grain Traceability

Fine grain traceability is at the <u>requirement statement level</u>. It is used to show requirement traceability when there is an automated tool such as a System Requirements Database (SRDB). Projects and programs that use an SRDB have one or more of the following system characteristics:

- Mission and or safety critical[203]
- Must be certified[204] before they can go operational
- Very large with multiple specifications at the same levels
- Anticipate significant growth and change
- Involve goods and services with significant financial risk
- Susceptible to failure due to poor or missing requirements[205]

---

[203] Mission critical systems are systems where there can be loss of life or people can be harmed if the system fails.

[204] Certification usually involves an external authority outside the sponsor and user community that must approve of the system.

[205] Almost all software based systems suffer from this characteristic

- Software intensive

Typically requirements are initially captured in a document using office automation tools such as word processing or spreadsheets. Then the document is imported into the SRDB. As new requirements are developed and other requirements are changed the SRDB is the primary mode of authoring. When a customer delivery is needed or a baseline established the SRDB content is exported into a document format. Various techniques are used to ensure when an SRDB export is performed, a reasonable document is produced with minimal changes in word processing. At no time should a document and SRDB version be manually maintained. This will lead to inconsistencies, which are unacceptable for a project that demands the accuracy of an SRDB in the first place.

Occasionally the requirements are first entered into the SRDB. In these instances office automation tools may be used to create figures and tables, but rather than being imported they are copy and pasted into the SRDB.

Writing requirements destined for the SRDB has a slightly different style. The document headings stay the same, however the content at the paragraph level is parsed into stand-alone lines rather than clumped as one or more paragraphs clustered below a heading. When the document is imported into the SRDB then each line becomes a separate row in the SRDB with its own project unique identified (PUI) number. The PUI items then can be marked for traceability to other PUI items in upper or lower level specifications.

If the paragraphs are not parsed then the entire paragraph becomes a row in the database with one PUI number. The traceability then only is to the paragraph level rather than the requirement level, course grain rather than fine grain traceability. The advantage of the SRDB is then lost.

Table 99 Parent Child Report[206]

PUI	System Text	Subsystem PUI and Text
SSS-14	Requirement A	SRS-77 Requirement
		SRS-81 Requirement
		SRS-22 Requirement
		SRS-23 Requirement
SSS-15	Requirement B	SRS-77 Requirement
		SRS-78 Requirement
SSS-16	Requirement C	SRS-79 Requirement
SSS-17	Requirement D	Missing child
SSS-18	Requirement E	SRS-24 Requirement

---

[206] Notice this table is associated with the parent document rather than just the child document. In fine grain traceability a table is produced for both the parent and child documents.

Specifications using an SRDB include a parent child report in the appendix in place of the Requirement Traceability Matrix (RTM). While the RTM is at the paragraphs level showing the headings of the parent, the parent child report shows the PUI and text of both the parent and child requirements. Just like in the RTM the parent is the left column and the child is the right column. This obviously significantly increases the size of the specification and so the parent child report is typically delivered under a separate cover. The specification in this case just houses a matrix with just the PUI numbers of both the parent and child or the PUI and text of the parent and just the PUI for the child.

Unlike course grain traceability, fine grain traceability includes a report showing that all the parent requirements trace to one or more child requirements. That means the parent document remains alive until the child document is complete. This process ensures that requirements are complete and consistent between levels. This is a critical step that significantly improves the quality of the requirements and attempts to surface all the requirements. A missing child link is a sign of a problem that must be corrected.

Table 100 Child Parent Report

PUI	Subsystem Text	System PUI and Text
SRS-77	Requirement	SSS-14 Requirement SSS-15 Requirement
SRS-78	Requirement	SSS-15 Requirement
SRS-79	Requirement	SSS-16 Requirement
SRS-80	Requirement	Missing parent
SRS-81	Requirement	SSS-14 Requirement

9.5.4 Very Fine Grain Traceability

Very Fine grain traceability starts with fine grain traceability and continues to the implementation level. For example software source code can be compiled and linked into an executable, the final implementation. In these cases the allocation continues to the implementation information products.

The approach is to take the requirement PUI and allocate it into the implementation products as comments. The comments in source code are converted to executable outputs and white box tests are used to verify that the requirements are actually traversed during certification testing.

The requirement claim is placed as close to the end of where the requirement is satisfied as possible. Placing the requirement comment at a higher abstraction level will only obfuscate and defeat the purpose of the allocation to the implementation detail. Also bunching requirements at the end of a long process also defeats the purpose of the allocation.

A-Spec Formal Module View: Export Test w/allocations

ID	Text	IsReq	Alloc	SRSPUI	Test	Rel
SYS -135	3.2.1 The system shall allow users to create a user account.	Yes	Software	SRS-98	12. Acct Mgmt	1.0

SRS Formal Module View: Peer Review

SRS	Text	IsReq	SYSPUI	CPC	File	Rel
SRS -98	3.7.3 Upon receiving an email acknowledgement from the user, account processing shall activate the users account.	Yes	SYS-135	ACCT	reg.cgi	1.0

reg.cgi file

Source code line 1

SRS-98 comment line

Source code line n

Figure 154 Very Fine Grain Traceability Approach

9.5.5 Traceability Reviews

Normally you cannot inspect-in engineering work and quality. However in the case of traceability, verifying the traceability links through inspection is critical. This is a tedious demanding task. A single individual cannot do it. This is a team effort, however the leads of each area must take responsibility. They must know how their products trace from and trace to other products on the project or program.

9.5.5.1 Specification Parent Child Reports

Parent child reports are produced for each specification. If there are holes, this is an indication of missing requirements or requirements not needed for the system. There are two reports produced, parent and child. This cannot be done with a single parent or child report. Both perspectives and views are needed for closure.

The first report lists the parent requirements in the left-hand column and the child requirements in the right hand column. If a right hand column is blank, this is an indication of missing children. This represents forward traceability.

The second report lists the child requirements in the left-hand column and the parent requirements in the right hand column. If a right hand column is blank, this is an indication of a missing parent. This represents backward traceability.

9.5.5.2 Test Parent Child Reports

Just as in the case of specifications, parent child reports are produced to show the forward and backward traceability between a specification and its tests. If there are holes, they must be addressed. Requirements without test links are an indication of insufficient test coverage. Multiple tests with large numbers of common requirement links are a possible indication of repetitive tests that do not add to the test coverage. A test with large a large number of requirement links suggests that the test may be eligible for further decomposition.

9.6 Work Breakdown Structure

A Work Breakdown Structure (WBS) groups work elements to organize and define the total work. Many people erroneously assume that the WBS is another view of the architecture or its functionality. Instead the WBS should be viewed as buckets of money. When a particular activity completes the associated bucket of money is empty. If there is surplus, it gets redistributed to other WBS elements. If there is a shortfall and the bucket will empty before the activity successfully completes, money must be found.

Author Comment: If a WBS element runs out of money or hours and the activity stops, then there is a high probability the work was arbitrarily stopped rather than reaching its natural conclusion. In a proper activity there is always additional money or hours left in a WBS element that is then redistributed when the activity properly completes.

The WBS is not static and can change as the project unfolds. Some changes are trivial with little impact across the WBS. Other changes are the result of project problems and corrective actions must be taken thus impacting the WBS.

A WBS is a tree where each descending[207] level of the WBS is an increased level of detail. The leaves of the tree represent specific work items while the aggregation box (parent) represents the sum of the lower level work items (children). Time and cost is tracked by using a unique charge number for each WBS lowest level (leaf) element. The top level WBS element represents the total sum of all the work.

The WBS may look similar to the architecture at the highest levels in terms of decomposition. However there are important differences between the WBS and architecture decomposition. Also key elements are missing:

- Does not show interfaces

---

[207] Decomposition once again is a key approach to solving a problem.

- Does not capture key requirements
- Does not capture key issues
- Does not show the system boundary
- May not show the key functions
- Does not show key performance elements
- May not show technology and quality breakthroughs

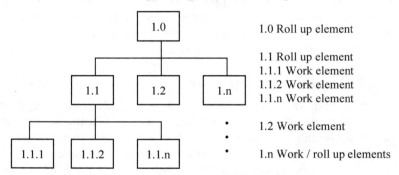

Figure 155 Generic Work Breakdown Structure

Once a WBS is developed it does have some look and feel that is similar to an organizational chart. However just as in the case of architecture and functionality it is distinct and separate from the organization chart. Keeping the concept of collections of money in mind and when the money should be released will yield the most effective WBS.

Author Comment: Some suggest that some projects do not have a WBS. However that is not the case. If money and or work products are being transferred then someone has either a graphical view or an indentured list of the work being performed. It just may not be visible to the participants.

The steps for developing the WBS are broadly associated with deliverables, progress payment, level of detail, and change. The steps and mechanics of developing the WBS are as follows:

- Identify what must be delivered for a successful project.
- Identify the major deliverables. As major deliverables are competed, typically payment is made. These form the progress payments to keep the project funded and move to the next level of work.
- Add additional levels to a WBS to satisfy the customers and projects management and control needs. Each project is different. A WBS can be started with a template but it must be updated to satisfy the customer and project staff.

- Review and refine the WBS until all stakeholders agree. There are planning and reporting elements that surface with a WBS. Just as in the case of micro management a WBS can become too detailed and impede progress.
- If new lower levels are needed for a WBS element, the entire WBS probably will be impacted. The same lower level elements probably will be needed across the WBS, not just the selected elements. This is a restructuring of the WBS and a re-plan where cost tracking and reporting need to be modified.
- If the WBS level of detail is too low, the lower levels can be rolled up to the higher level. In this case there is little impact to the WBS. No restructuring of the WBS or re-planning is needed.

Example 30 Work Breakdown Structures

Some projects have work that is performed in parallel. Other projects have work that is performed in serial. One work activity cannot start without the successful completion of another work activity.

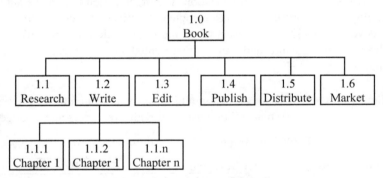

Figure 156 WBS - Writing a Book

Notice that in both cases it is not possible to show the full WBS in graphical format. The approach is to use the same technique that is used to decompose data flow diagrams.

Take an element that needs further decomposition, mark it on the parent diagram as being shown on a child diagram, and decompose it on a separate view. Continue the decomposition until the WBS is fully developed. So the WBS is not a single sheet of paper but a stack of papers.

A WBS dictionary describes the effort needed to accomplish the work and the expected work products. It is written at the leaf level (lowest level) of the WBS. The WBS dictionary is typically used to start the development of a Statement of Work (SOW).

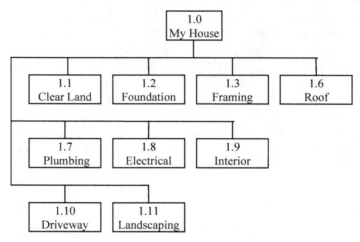

Figure 157 WBS - Building a House

The WBS is executed by an organization. The organization houses the authority, responsibility, and resources needed to complete the WBS project. An organization chart is developed to show the structure of the organization that will execute the WBS. It is a tree structure and can be represented as a graphical figure or an indentured list.

Author Comment: Responsibility should never be allocated to people without authority. Authority and responsibility must be provided resources and a budget.

Table 101 Responsibility Assignment Matrix

Organization	Resp	1.1 Test Plans			1.2 Test Procedures			
		1.1.1	**1.1.2**	**1.1.3**	**1.2.1**	**1.2.2**	**1.2.3**	**1.2.4**
Systems	Walt	X			X			X
RMA	Bill							
Software	Al, Tom		X			X		X
Hardware	Carl, Fred							
Mechanical	Steve			X			X	X
Civil	Claudia				X			
Test	John	X	X	X	X	X	X	X
ILS	Don							
Publications	Starkey	X						
Data Mgmt	Mary	X						
Config Mgmt	Barry	X						
Quality	Bob	X	X	X	X	X	X	X

Links are made between the WBS and the organization chart. A responsibility assignment matrix (RAM) shows these links. The organization indentured list is placed on one axis of the table and the WBS elements are placed on the other axis (rows and columns). Typically the organization is shown in the rows and the columns have the WBS elements. The RAM shows the responsibility of each WBS element with the placement of an X at an intersecting cell. Alternatively each cell can show the planned hours or expected cost in place of each X.

When developing the very first instance of the WBS, previous work (projects, programs, etc) should be reviewed. There are always lessons to be learned from previous work and the architecture of the WBS should be treated with the same level of respect and analysis as the system architecture.

If a common WBS structure exists within the organization then metrics can be gathered and used to support cost estimating for future work. The metrics also can be used to tune and optimize the process. If the WBS is obfuscated and or unique to each project even though the projects have similar cost structures then the chaotic organization will not offer the most effective systems.

When responding to a customer they may offer a WBS as part of the request for proposal. This WBS may not fully match the WBS templates available in the organization. This should be clearly communicated and a common ground negotiated. If needed a translation table can be created so that the customer can have reporting based on their WBS and the organizations common WBS can be preserved for future cost estimates and process tuning. The organization should not sacrifice its future for the unique needs of a customer or group of customers.

The following is a list of common WBS elements that may apply to various systems. These elements start at the second level. The first level is the system to be developed by name.

Table 102 Common Level 2 and 3 WBS Elements

Storage
Planning and Preparation
Storage
Transfer and Transportation
Systems Engineering and Program Management
System Test and Evaluation
Development Test and Evaluation
Operational Test and Evaluation
Mock-ups
Test and Evaluation Support
Test Facilities
Training
Equipment
Services
Facilities
Data
Technical Publications

Table 102 Common Level 2 and 3 WBS Elements

Engineering Data
Management Data
Support Data
Data Depository
Peculiar Support Equipment
Test and Measurement Equipment
Support and Handling Equipment
Common Support Equipment
Test and Measurement Equipment
Support and Handling Equipment
Operational/Site Activation
System Assembly, Installation and Checkout on Site
Contractor Technical Support
Site Construction
Site/Ship/Vehicle Conversion
Industrial Facilities
Construction/Conversion/Expansion
Equipment Acquisition or Modernization
Maintenance (Industrial Facilities)
Initial Spares and Repair Parts

The following is a list of unique WBS elements that may apply to a system. These elements start at the first level. The first level is the system to be developed by name.

Table 103 Unique Level 1 and 2 WBS Elements

Vehicle System
Primary Vehicle
Frame
Suspension and Steering
Power Package and Drive Train
Accessories
Body
Automatic and Remote Piloting
Special Equipment
Navigation
Communications
Integration, Assembly, Test and Checkout
Secondary Vehicle
(Same as Primary Vehicle)
Ship System
Ship
Hull Structure

Table 103 Unique Level 1 and 2 WBS Elements

Propulsion Plant
Electric Plant
Sanitation
Command and Surveillance
Auxiliary Systems
Outfit and Furnishings
Restaurants, Shopping and Entertainment
Integration Engineering
Ship Assembly and Support Services

Electronic and or Automated Software System
Prime Mission Product (PMP)
Subsystem 1...n (Specify Names)
PMP Applications Software
PMP System Software
Integration, Assembly, Test and Checkout
Platform Integration

Aircraft System
Air Vehicle (AV)
Airframe
Propulsion
AV Applications Software
AV System Software
Communications/Identification
Navigation/Guidance
Central Computer
Fire Control
Data Display and Controls
Survivability
Airline Operations Systems
Automatic Flight Control
Central Integrated Checkout
Sanitation
Entertainment
Auxiliary Equipment

Space System
Launch Vehicle
Propulsion (Single Stage Only)
Stage I
Stage II...n (As Required)
Strap-On Units (As Required)
Shroud (Payload Fairing)
Guidance and Control
Integration, Assembly, Test and Checkout
Orbital Transfer Vehicle
Propulsion (Single Stage Only)

Table 103 Unique Level 1 and 2 WBS Elements

Stage I
Stage II...n (As Required)
Strap-On Units (As Required)
Guidance and Control
Integration, Assembly, Test and Checkout
Space Vehicle
Spacecraft
Payload I...n (As Required)
Reentry Vehicle
Orbit Injector/Dispenser
Integration, Assembly, Test and Checkout
Ground Command, Control, Comm and Mission Equipment
Sensor I...n (As Required)
Telemetry, Tracking and Control
External Communications
Data Processing Equipment
Launch Equipment
Auxiliary Equipment
Flight Support Operations and Services
Mate/Checkout/Launch
Mission Control
Tracking and C3
Recovery Operations and Services
Launch Site Maintenance/Refurbishment

9.7 Process

The key to the artifacts is to realize they are only snapshots in time and that they are part of the design process. The production of artifacts is not the design process. Too many times teams establish information products, their expected contents, and then assume that when the information products are produced the design exists and is viable.

However an information product can be viewed as a design than needs to be produced. The same techniques that are used to design and produce the target system also can be used to design and produce the information products that capture the target design.

9.8 Some Key Points

➢ System requirements are allocated to
  • Machines
  • Manual Operations

- ➤ System requirements are allocated to applicable engineering disciplines
  - Hardware
  - Software
  - Mechanical
  - Civil
  - Biological
  - Chemical

- ➤ System requirements are allocated to
  - Maintenance
  - Training
  - Support

- ➤ System requirements are allocated to
  - Segments
  - Subsystems

- ➤ Hardware requirements are allocated to hardware configuration items and or components

- ➤ Software requirements are allocated to software configuration items

- ➤ For certified software intensive systems
  - The software requirements can be allocated to the line of code
  - Will use white box or structural testing

- ➤ All requirements can be allocated or tagged with the following attributes
  - Safety
  - Security
  - Risk
  - Technology level
  - Technology maturity

- ➤ Design requirements
  - Can be offered at any specification level
  - Should be offered at the design level

- ➤ System requirements should be offered at the system level but not below the system level

- ➤ The Detailed System Architecture describes the entire system and includes

- Physical architecture
- Products and services needed for the full life cycle
- Support, maintenance, training
- System Management

➤ A specification clearly and accurately describes the essential technical requirements for items, materials, or services including the quality procedures to determine that the requirements have been met

➤ Specifications
- Help avoid duplication and inconsistencies
- Allow for accurate estimates of necessary work and resources
- Act as a negotiation and reference document for engineering changes
- Provide documentation of configuration
- Allow for consistent communication among those responsible for the systems engineering and design

➤ Specifications allow teams to
- Provide a precise idea of the problem to be solved
- Provide information so teams can efficiently design the system
- Provide information to estimate the cost of design alternatives
- Provide guidance to testers for verification (qualification) of each technical requirement.

➤ Requirement documents express why the development is needed

➤ Specification documents are an intermediate expression of what the needed system has to do in terms of technical requirements (function, performance, and interface)

➤ Design documents (drawings, associated lists, etc.) describe the means by which the design requirements are to be satisfied.

➤ The WBS may look like a portion of the system architecture
- Primarily the segments, subsystems, assemblies, components

➤ The WBS is an incomplete view of the system architecture because it
- Does not show interfaces
- Does not capture key requirements
- Does not capture key issues
- Does not show the system boundary

- May not show the key functions
- Does not show key performance elements
- May not show technology and quality breakthroughs

➤ A WBS groups work elements to organize and define the total work

➤ Many erroneously assume a WBS is a view of architecture or its functionality

➤ The WBS is buckets of money
- When an activity completes associated bucket of money is empty
- If there is surplus, it gets redistributed to other WBS elements
- If there is a shortfall the bucket will empty before the activity successfully completes, money must be found

9.9 Exercises

1. Should requirements be developed for all parts of the system?
2. What is the difference between a system and a design requirement?
3. What are key requirements and why do we care about key requirements?
4. Draw a specification tree.
5. Draw a block diagram of the plans, analysis, specifications, test procedure, and test report documents showing how they all interrelate.

9.10 Additional Reading

1. CMS Requirements Writer's Guide, Centers for Medicare & Medicaid Services Integrated IT Investment & System Life Cycle Framework, Department of Health and Human Services, V4.11 August 31, 2009.
2. Defense Acquisition Guidebook, Defense Acquisition Univ., August 2010.
3. Sequential Thematic Organization of Publications (STOP): How to Achieve Coherence in Proposals and Reports, Hughes Aircraft Company Ground Systems Group, Fullerton, Calif., J. R. Tracey, D. E. Rugh, W. S. Starkey, Information Media Department, ID 65-10-10 52092, January 1965.
4. Specification Practices, Military Standard, MIL-STD-490 30 October 1968, MIL-STD-490A 4 June 1985.
5. Standard Practice Data Item Descriptions (DIDs), DOD, DOD-STD-963A 15 August 1986, MIL-STD-963B 31 August 1997.
6. Systems Engineering Fundamentals, Supplementary Text, Defense Acquisition University Press, January 2001.
7. Technical Reviews And Audits Systems Equipments And Computer Software, MIL-STD-1521A June 1976, MIL-STD-1521B June 1995.
8. Tool for Analyzing Requirements, Carnegie Mellon, Report CMU/SEI-2005-TR-014, 2005.

10 Developing System Element Designs

Eventually the front-end systems engineering activities are complete. The design concept is in place, the physical allocations are complete, and the product vendors have been selected including those that will engage in new designs. It is at this time that the common systems disciplines that were part of the tradeoffs start to design and develop their portions of the system. These are the "ilities" or specialty engineering teams. In addition there are the traditional engineering teams.

Table 104 Specialty and Traditional Engineering[208]

"ilities" or Specially Engineering	Traditional Engineering
Test (Testability)	Civil Engineers
Maintenance (Maintainability)	Mechanical Engineers
Training (Trainability)	Chemical Engineers
Support (Supportability)	Electrical Engineers
Manufacturing (Produceability)	Materials Engineers
Human Factors	Industrial Engineers
Safety	Aerospace Engineers
Quality	Naval Engineers
Configuration Management	Biological Engineers
Security	Environmental Engineers
Packaging	Software Engineers
Shipping	General Engineering
Installation	All Other Engineers

The specialty engineers and traditional engineers use that same model for design as systems engineers. They start with a concept, move to a physical structure, then finalize the details with vendor selections that then offer the designs. The designs can be products or one of a kind designs as either existing, modified, or new design solutions. So the test team develops the test concept, offers the physical structure, then the details which eventually translates into a test lab with test tools, test procedures, and test reports. A similar situation exists for training where it moves from concept to classrooms with students, tools, and instruction. The concepts tend to be captured in the plans and the other information products capture the physical and implementation details.

---

[208] This list is representative and will change with industry and time as new specialty engineering roles surface and others move into traditional engineering with formal degrees. Software is an example.

Author Comment: Once the specialty and traditional engineers are listed it becomes clear why systems engineering exists as a unique discipline. What is interesting is that any of the traditional engineers may move into specialty engineering as their career progresses. Also traditional engineers may move into the systems engineering role. This happens as the need arises in organizations and people decide to fill these roles. The unique knowledge is then gained from on the job exposure, technical conferences, and or additional formal education.

10.1 Systems Engineering Management Plan

The Systems Engineering Management Plan (SEMP)[209] describes the efforts for planning, controlling, and conducting a full integrated engineering effort. It is used to understand and evaluate the engineering work. It is the highest level plan in a project or program that is systems driven. The SEMP contains three parts.

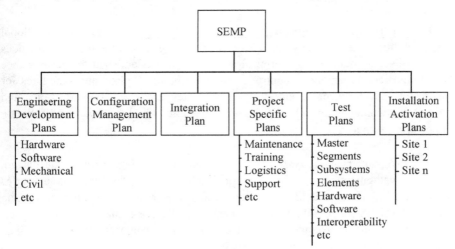

Figure 158 SEMP as Highest Project or Program Plan

Part I System Engineering: describes the system engineering process used for the definition of system design and test requirements. This includes system engineering to define the system performance parameters and the preferred system configuration to satisfy the requirements; Planning and controls of the technical program task; Management of a totally integrated effort of design engineering, (all disciplines), test engineering, logistics engineering and production engineering. A narrative supplemented by graphical presentations describes the plans and procedures for the following elements of the system engineering process:

---

[209] Systems Engineering Management Plan (SEMP), DOD Data Item Description, DI-MGMT-81024 August 1990.

- Analysis and studies including functional allocation, trade studies, design optimization and effective analysis, synthesis, interface compatibility, logistic support analysis, producibility analysis, training for users operators and maintainers.
- Requirements allocation including methods for documenting allocated requirements for designers, integrators, and test personnel as well as for review. Includes how requirement allocation is developed, maintained and used throughout the life of the program.
- Specification generation describing baseline control, including procedures used during requirement allocation, design, configuration management and test with attention on hardware, software, and firmware integration.
- Other system engineering tasks describing the plan and procedures for other system engineering tasks.

Part II Technical Program Planning and Control: identifies organizational responsibilities and authority for system engineering management. This includes control of subcontracted engineering; levels of control established for performance and design requirements and control methods to be used; plans and schedules for the design, development, assembly, integration, test and evaluation functions, and control of documentation. These areas are applicable to both hardware and software engineering activities.

- **Program risk analysis**: Analysis of any risk associated with the design, development, test and evaluation requirements. The analysis identifies critical areas and identifies the need for prototyping, testing or backup development to minimize technical risk. The risk analysis identifies test requirements, technical performance measurement parameters and critical milestones.
- **Engineering program integration**: Describes the planning and control functions for conducting a totally integrated engineering effort.
- **Contract work breakdown structure and specification tree**: Describes how systems engineering develops the technical elements of the contract work breakdown structure (CWBS) and other contractual tasks for a complete CWBS. Provides a complete specification tree and relates it to the CWBS.
- **Assignment of responsibility and authority**: Identifies the key personnel for each of the technical work breakdown structure (WBS) elements, clear definition of their responsibilities, the vehicles or documents used to state these assignments, and their standards or measures of accomplishments. Existing and proposed procedures establishing the authority, lines of

communication and specific functions of these and other organizations associated with engineering policies and their implementation.

- **Program reviews**: Describes the reviews to assess, optimize, and direct the effort.
- **Design reviews**: Plan and schedule for all design reviews under terms of the contract. Describes documentation provided prior to and at the various design reviews and how it relates to other contractually required data. This includes technical manuals, drawings, specifications, software firmware documentation, user's manuals, and how all these final products are related. The total documentation release system is discussed including signoff.
- **Interface control**: Describes the procedures for interface control of the contracted segment or subsystem with other system segments or subsystems developed by other system participants including organizations that furnish equipment, facilities, software and personnel.
- **Documentation control**: Describes methods for controlling change to internal technical data not subject to control by the formal configuration management system. Provides detail to establish its consistency with the configuration management and change control requirements of the project.
- **Engineering testing**: Identifies what engineering efforts lead to the system test documentation. Includes a discussion of test engineering effort not included in the other documentation.
- **Tradeoff studies**: Identifies the major tradeoff studies to be performed and the general plan for their accomplishment. Includes the method for identifying, performing, and documenting the results of tradeoff studies.
- **Technical performance measurement**: Describes the plan for technical performance tracking and reporting including:

  ❑ Identifies technical performance characteristics and technical program achievement parameters for each of the work elements of the CWBS. Identifies routine reporting proposed parameters.
  ❑ The methods, equations or models for transforming parameter values of lower-level elements to higher-level elements and their sensitivities.
  ❑ A planned profile for each of the parameters, the profile being an anticipated and time-phased variation, if any, for these parameters during the design, development, fabrication assembly and testing period. Notes significant technical performance measurement events.
  ❑ A description of how technical performance measurement is related to cost and schedule performance measurement.
  ❑ A sample technical performance report for an out-of-tolerance technical parameter. This includes a planned value, demonstrated value, specification requirement, and current estimate and variance analysis.
  ❑ A proposed list of technical performance reports used for reporting. It

identifies if one report is used for all reportable parameters or if separate reports are used on a subsystem or individual parameter basis or combinations.

❑ Identification of technical performance achievements by developing parameters, which address: subsystem hardware delivery and operation, computer equipment delivery and operation, subsystem software development through each phase of activity. Subsystem hardware software integration, specification and Statement of Work (SOW) requirements, computer programs documentation plan, identification and acquisition of all design critical data.

• Describes the plan and procedures for other technical program planning and control tasks to be accomplished.

Part III Engineering Integration: Describes the methods to integrate the engineering efforts. Includes a summary of each specialty program and cross-references the individual plans covering the specialty programs. Discusses engineering specialty integration and relationships of engineering with overall logistic efforts, including fault isolation methods (automatic, semiautomatic, and manual) and the documentation, and how support equipment is identified.

10.2 Design & Implementation

The original front-end systems team should include representatives from the entire project or program. As the effort unfolds different disciplines increase in staffing size while others shrink. At no time should a particular group go to zero staffing. That is essentially removing a critical stakeholder from the solution and leads to serious problems.

Normally when people think of design and implementation they do not think of systems, systems design practices, or systems staff. Systems personnel and systems design practices become critical during the design and implementation phases of a project or program. Rolling systems staff off the labor plan for the design and implementation phase removes a critical stakeholder form the effort.

The systems staff are not only keepers of the system vision and intent of the requirements, but they are also keepers of the process. That is their stakeholder role. In the pressure to design and implement the solution the team lacking the systems perspective will deviate and cut corners not realizing that their ignorance of a broader picture can lead to complete failure. In addition to the systems stakeholder role, the design and implementation phase of a project or program uses the following system practices:

• Requirement changes, tracking, analysis, management and incorporation

into the baseline
- System Requirements Management Database (SRDB) controlled updates and reissue of new baseline requirements and specifications
- Updates to studies impacted by design and implementation details that surface with this next levels of understanding
- Reviewing design and implementation information products for architecture and requirement deviations or violations
- Developing test plans and procedures for sell off and certifications
- Developing manuals and other information products for maintenance, training, installation, parts, support
- Developing training course material
- Reviewing prototypes, models, and simulations

10.3 System Design Monitoring

At this stage of the design life cycle the systems engineering designers role change. They either move towards one or more specialty engineering roles, a traditional engineering role, or into a design-monitoring role. In the design monitoring role the systems engineering designer is ensuring that the requirements are being properly interpreted, are being met, and are being changed appropriately as design challenges surface. Within this setting is also the role of ensuring that the correct system is being designed. This is a continuation of the early validation activities that were started when the project started. Essentially this is ensuring that the need is being satisfied. The daily activities are filled with:

- Design Reviews
- Technical Interchange Meetings
- Working Groups
- Vendor Visits
- Site Visits
- Sponsor Visits
- Numerous Ad Hoc Information Products

10.3.1 Technical Interchange Meetings

Technical Interchange Meetings (TIMs) are periodic forums on large programs or projects that promote the interchange of views and information regarding different aspects of a system in development. The TIMs are usually organized by different areas and have a periodic schedule, such as monthly. The TIM is a forum to gather diverse stakeholders and educate so that everyone has a similar view at the end of the TIM. Examples of TIMS are:

- Operational sites meetings discuss current and new system capabilities

- Lab meetings of models or prototypes to discuss impacts and approaches
- Developers facility meetings to discuss the system and their progress
- Subcontractors meetings discussing their subsystems and their progress
- Topics include software, hardware, maintenance, human factors, logistics, training, transition, test, etc

10.3.2 Working Groups

Working groups are formed for the express purpose of producing a product, usually a document. They are not meant to educate or include all stakeholders. The working group product may be part of a project or program that also influences or drives a broader industry standard. The working group consists of experts.

10.3.3 Action Items

Action items are a list of things to be done. They are maintained in a table like structure with several attributes such as: number, very descriptive title, origination date, source, close date, and comment.

Action items are usually generated as part of a meeting. They translate to work that may not have been anticipated in the original plan. As a result action items tend to be ignored unless they come directly from a customer.

The problem is if a group of people thinks they need to gather action items and management does not acknowledge the action items. If management continues to follow the plan and what they think is needed to close the project, important work will be missed. An alternative is to acknowledge the action items and assess if a re-plan is needed. If a re-plan is not needed then the action items should be systematically addressed and closed within the existing planned structure.

10.3.4 To Do Lists

A to-do-list is a technique used to bring a project in crisis into stability. It is usually used to get to a milestone that everyone believes will be missed. Many times managers have disappeared from the fray and only dedicated project staff is still engaged and has a strong desire to succeed.

A natural leader that has risen in the crisis usually develops a to-do-list. The list identifies the things that need to be done between the current date and the milestone. It is prioritized and has names assigned to each item on the list. Many times when this happens management reappears and helps to facilitate working off the items on the to do list. Unfortunately the original conditions, which put the project in crisis, remain and the to-do-lists keep reappearing if the natural leaders are still available.

10.3.5 Goals Advanced Concepts

Using goals to manage an effort is similar to formal methids except the detail is significantly reduced and emphasis is shifted away from cost and schedule to producing something of use or value within a pre-defined financial box. A financial box is a defined set of money and schedule. The box rarely is permitted to expand. So the drive is to accomplish the most effective things before the money is exhausted.

Within the box are resources that know the final goal. They establish a prioritized list of goals that lead to the final goal. The prioritized list of goals is usually small and ranges from four to ten goals leading to the final goal.

Goals need to be clearly stated and measurable. They are listed on a single piece of paper or chart with the anticipated completion date. New projects, programs, and products begin with a set of goals. If an individual goal is met within the partitioned financial box, then the next goal is addressed. If however an activity gets stuck at a particular goal, then an assessment is made to increase the size of the financial box, suspend or cancel the project, program, or product.

An activity may be suspended if it is dependent on something that is not available or mature enough to use. This is typically a case where a technology needs to mature and its anticipated maturity level may be reached in a relatively short period of time such as one to two years.

10.4 Design Teams

In the end the goal of an individual or a team is to engage in effective problem solving and innovation. I mix the two together because problem solving can become toxic where the problem is de-scoped to such a level that it goes away. This typically is associated with conservative low risk teams. The context or system boundary keeps shrinking until everyone declares success. The problem with this approach is that all progress stops.

Many times to solve a problem, innovation is needed. Innovation involves increasing the system boundary or scope. It also includes pulling elements from outside the current accepted domain. This typically is associated with progressive high-risk teams.

The trick is to blend individuals from both perspectives to form a well-balanced team that can close on a problem without de-scoping it and yet introduce new and innovative elements.

Table 105 Team Mix Characteristics

Conservative – Less Innovative	Progressive – More Innovative
• Very tightly related focused ideas	• Very loosely related unfocused ideas
• Remove connections to shrink scope	• New connections including external
• Refine the system	• Replace the system
• Incremental change	• Radical change
• Build on assumptions	• Challenge and create new assumptions
• Encourage continuity and stability	• Encourage radical shifts

Table 105 Team Mix Characteristics

Conservative – Less Innovative	Progressive – More Innovative
• Risk averse wants to close	• Thrive on risk wants the challenge

Other individual and team characteristics include consensus building or ignore consensus, detail or non-detail oriented, technical or non-technical. The ideal team is progressive and innovative with emphasis on consensus, detail and non-detail elements, with technical and non-technical perspectives.

Teams have a level of maturity much like people. Many organizations have attempted to measure maturity in people using the Knowledge, Skills, and Abilities (KSA) method. They then sum up the organizations capabilities based on the individual team members' experience and KSA. For example the number of university degrees by category, total number of person years of experience (e.g. 20,000 years), average number of years of experience per person, number of junior experienced and senior staff, etc.

When understanding the maturity level of a person, different categories can be identified. People will exhibit different maturity levels for each category. For example many formally educated engineers from strong universities need little direction and will operate at the highest levels of maturity even if they are junior level engineers. They have very strong work ethics and are self-actuated. That is why principals and executives are able to interact directly with junior level engineers. Some possible maturity categories or curves to consider are:

- General Characteristics
- Technical Responsibilities
- Management Responsibilities
- Direction Received
- Communication Skills

Table 106 General Industry Engineering Maturity Levels[210]

General Characteristics
Engineer Level I Acquires limited knowledge and develops basic skills. Applies techniques and procedures following established criteria to perform assigned tasks. Performs routine technical work that does not need previous experience. Acquires an understanding of professional and ethical responsibilities.
Engineer Level II Acquires basic knowledge and develops skills in a specific practice area. Applies standard techniques, procedures, and criteria to perform

---

[210] This is a composite list from many different sources. It is also a list that is very similar to the lists used in the performance evaluations early in my career.

Table 106 General Industry Engineering Maturity Levels[210]

assigned tasks as part of a broader assignment. Exercises limited judgment on details of work and in application of standard methods for conventional work. **Engineer Level III** Develops broad knowledge and skills in a specific practice area. Evaluates, selects, and applies standard techniques, procedures, and criteria to perform a task or sequence of tasks for conventional projects with few complex features. Collaboratively uses judgment to determine adaptations in methods for non-routine aspects of assignments. Works on small projects or portions of larger projects. **Engineer Level IV** Applies broad knowledge of principles and practices in a specific practice area. Independently evaluates, selects, and adapts standard techniques, procedures, and criteria. Acquires general knowledge of principles and practices of related fields, and ability to function on multi-disciplinary teams. Works on multiple projects of moderate size or portions of major projects. **Engineer Level V** Independently applies extensive and diversified knowledge of principles and practices in broad areas of assignments and related fields. Uses advanced techniques in the modification or extension of theories and practices of sciences and disciplines to complete assignments. Works on a major project or several projects of moderate scope with complex features. **Engineer Level VI** Applies a thorough knowledge of current principles and practices of engineering as related to the variety of aspects affecting their organization. Applies knowledge and expertise acquired through progressive experience to resolve crucial issues and/or unique conditions. Keeps informed of new methods and developments affecting their organization, and recommends new practices or changes in emphasis of programs. Works on programs of limited complexity and scope. **Engineer Level VII** Uses creativity, foresight, and mature judgment in anticipating and solving unprecedented problems. Makes decisions and recommendations that are authoritative and have an important impact on extensive organizational activities. Sets priorities and reconciles directions from competing interests Works on programs with complex features. **Engineer Level VIII** Makes decisions with broad influence on the activities of their organizations. Makes authoritative decisions and conclusive recommendations that have a significant impact on the organization. Demonstrates a high degree of creativity, foresight, and mature judgment in planning, organizing and guiding extensive programs and activities of major consequence.
Technical Responsibilities
Engineer Level I Collects data and gathers information or documents. Performs standard computations or analysis. Prepares drawings and visual aids. Observes development activities. Performs basic engineering work.
Engineer Level II Performs basic design tasks. Assists on other engineering tasks.

Table 106 General Industry Engineering Maturity Levels[210]

Engineer Level III Performs moderate design tasks. Prepares portions of project documents. Edits specifications. Performs research and investigations. **Engineer Level IV** Designs a complete project, system, component, or process. Prepares complete project documents. Designs and conducts experiments, and analyzes and interprets data. Formulates and solves problems. **Engineer Level V** Reviews complete project documents for conformity and quality assurance. Develops new techniques, improved processes, materials, or products. Assists upper level management and staff as a technical specialist or advisor. **Engineer Level VI** Serves as the technical specialist for the organization in the application of advanced concepts, principles, and methods in an assigned area. Keeps informed of new developments and requirements affecting the organization for the purpose of recommending changes in programs or applications. Interprets, organizes, executes and coordinates assignments. **Engineer Level VII** Develops standards and guidelines. Leads the organization in a broad area of specialization or in narrow but intensely specialized field. **Engineer Level VIII** Performs advisory or consulting work for the organization for broad program areas or an intensely specialized area with innovative or important elements. Performs advisory or consulting work for the organization for broad program areas or an intensely specialized area
Management Responsibilities
Engineer Level I No managerial responsibilities at this level. **Engineer Level II** Assigns tasks to and coordinates with technicians or administrative staff. **Engineer Level III** Assigns tasks to and coordinates work with entry level engineers, technicians, or administrative staff. Assists in determining schedule and budget requirements. **Engineer Level IV** Assigns tasks to and directs engineers, technicians and administrative staff. Plans and coordinates detailed elements of engineering work. Prepares scopes, budgets, and schedules for assignments. Assists with proposals to provide professional services or obtain funding for engineering projects or programs. **Engineer Level V** Supervises all staff necessary to complete assignments. Reviews and approves scope, budgets, and schedules for assignments. Prepares proposals to provide professional services or obtain funding for engineering projects or programs. **Engineer Level VI** Supervises staff of engineers and technicians. Plans, schedules, or coordinates the preparation of documents or activities for multiple major projects, or is responsible for an entire program of an organization. Reviews operational procedures to insure compliance with applicable policies and performance measures.

Table 106 General Industry Engineering Maturity Levels[210]

Engineer Level VII Supervises several organizational segments or teams. Recommends facilities, personnel, and funds required to carry out programs. Oversees the technical, legal, and financial issues of an entire program. Determines program objectives and requirements. Develops standards and guidelines. **Engineer Level VIII** Leads an entire program of critical importance. Decides the kind and extent of engineering and related programs needed for accomplishing the objectives of an organization.
Direction Received
Engineer Level I Receives close supervision on all aspects of assignments. **Engineer Level II** Receives close supervision on unusual or difficult problems, and general review of all aspects of work. **Engineer Level III** Receives instruction on specific objectives. Receives direction on unconventional / complex problems, and possible solutions. Receives a thorough review of completed work for application of sound professional judgment. **Engineer Level IV** Receives general direction on key objectives. Receives guidance when necessary on unconventional or complex problems, direction on modified techniques, and new approaches on assignments with conflicting criteria. **Engineer Level V** Receives supervision and guidance relating to overall objectives, critical issues, new concepts, and policy matters. Receives direction on unusual conditions and developments. **Engineer Level VI** Receives administrative supervision with assignments given in terms of broad general objectives and limits. **Engineer Level VII** Receives administrative supervision with assignments given in terms of broad general objectives and limits. **Engineer Level VIII** Receives general administrative direction from a board of directors or regional council.
Communication Skills
Engineer Level I Has basic oral and written communication skills. Interacts with other staff. **Engineer Level II** Interacts with staff, general public, officials, and contractors. **Engineer Level III** Has effective oral and written communication skills. Assists with client, customer, or official contacts and communication pertaining to specific assignments or meetings. **Engineer Level IV** Interacts with clients, customers, officials, contractors, and others. Attends project meetings and presents specific aspects of engineering assignment. **Engineer Level V** Has advanced oral and written communication skills. Represents the organization in communications and conferences pertaining to broad aspects of engineering assignments. **Engineer Level VI** Routinely interacts with clients, customers, officials,

Table 106 General Industry Engineering Maturity Levels[210]

contractors, and others. Leads project meetings and makes presentations. Represents the organization and maintains liaison with individuals and related organizations.

Engineer Level VII Has exceptional oral and written communication skills. Routinely interacts with organization leaders, clients, customers, officials, contractors, and others. Initiates and maintains extensive contacts with key engineers and officials or other organizations and companies and is skilled in persuasion and negotiation of critical issues.

Engineer Level VIII Negotiates critical and controversial issues with top-level engineers and officers of other organizations and companies. Conducts presentations and may participate in media interviews. Represents their organization at important functions or conferences, including media interviews as required.

Typical Titles
Engineer Level I, II, III Engineer in Training, Engineer Intern, Assistant Engineer, Junior Engineer, Staff Engineer, Engineering Instructor; GS-5, GS-7, GS-9, Level-6, Junior Member Engineering Staff
Engineer Level IV Engineer, Associate Engineer, Project Engineer, Resident Engineer, Assistant Professor; GS-11, Level-6, Associate Member Engineering Staff
Engineer Level V Senior Engineer, Project Manager, Associate Professor; GS-12, Level-6, Member Engineering Staff
Engineer Level VI Principal Engineer, District Engineer, Engineering Manager, Professor; GS-13, Level-5, Senior Member Engineering Staff
Engineer Level VII Director, Program Manager, City Engineer, County Engineer, Division Engineer, Department Head, Vice President; GS-14, Level-5, Lead Member Engineering Staff
Engineer Level VIII Bureau Engineer, Director of Public Works, Dean, President; GS-15, SES-1 to SES 4, Level-4 to Level-1, Principal Member Engineering Staff

The following is a list of maturity levels associated with the US Government. Each government organization generates appropriate text for the GS scales. However they tend to follow the concept of maturity levels that are associated with knowledge skills and abilities (KSA).

Table 107 Engineer Maturity Levels GS Scale Detailed Descriptions[211]

GS-7: Makes calculations applying standard formulas; prepares graphs, curves, and tables for other engineers. Records factual data in tests and observation studies. Performs drafting drawing, minor detail design, searches technical reports to obtain information.

---

[211] This is an example of detailed GS descriptions from a US Government organization.

Table 107 Engineer Maturity Levels GS Scale Detailed Descriptions[211]

GS-9: Adapts practices and techniques to specific situations. Adjusts and correlating data. Recognizes discrepancies and deviations in results. Follows operations through a series of related detailed steps or processes. Make tentative and preliminary selections. Adapts engineering alternatives and after approval by the supervisor carries out a sequence of details.
GS-11: Performs assignments where complex features occur infrequently or in isolated, single units. Makes minor deviations to previous work, such as sizes, dimensions, and relationships of details, which can be resolved by engineering calculations; investigating a limited number of variables. Performs experiments in accordance with approaches that have been structured by others. Plans project details based on precedents established in related projects. Recommends methods of standard analysis for solving problems. Makes only minor adaptations or modifications to well-established methods and techniques.
GS-12: Performs assignments that involve combinations of complex features. Plans and conducts work where precedent data, criteria, methods, or techniques are inadequate in some respects, or have narrow gaps. Completes work where the purpose is to improve, extend, or validate currently known precedents, data, methods, or techniques.
GS-13: Performs work characterized by many as having complex features because of the breadth, diversity, or intensity of assignments. Adapts, modifies or makes compromises with standard guides, precedents, methods and techniques. Plans and conducts activities where precedent data, criteria, methods, or techniques are significantly inadequate are controversial or contain critical gaps. Develops new features, in addition to improving, extending, or validating currently known precedents, data, methods, or techniques. Performs staff advisory, consulting, and reviewing services for an engineering organization.
GS-14: Serves as a technical expert on the limitations of proven concepts and practices of a broad and complex subject-matter field or functional area. Successfully takes short cuts or makes compromises that are considered risky or extreme within the context of standard guides, precedents, methods and techniques. Completes assignments that need the ability to anticipate and to take positive action on problems which if not identified in their early stages would likely lead to serious consequences; such as problems involving public safety, key relationships, resource limitations, or performance reliability. Performs staff advisory, consulting, and reviewing services.
GS-15: Conceives, plans, and conducts work in unexplored areas where there is little or no theory to guide experimentation, progress is uncertain, new techniques and approaches need to be devised, and future lines of fruitful experimentation are difficult to determine. Recognized as an authority in their fields, by breaking through the frontier areas and coming up with new knowledge of fundamental

Table 107 Engineer Maturity Levels GS Scale Detailed Descriptions[211]

significance that will influence the procedures and ideas of others. Develops and designs new theoretical treatments, instrumentation, equipment, and procedures for testing and solving the problems. Represents the organization on technical committees develops general plans and procedures for carrying out research and experimental projects. Develops short and long range research and development plans and programs for a large group of research, development, and test activities. Develops and correlates research objectives. Originates new concepts, methods, and techniques for research planning, program guidance, program evaluation, technological forecasting, and resource allocation. Conducts special planning studies to discover, create, and synthesize new approaches to the problems of establishing adequate research and development programs. Coordinates technical planning in installation activities by relating future program plans to projected requirements, available resources, installation responsibilities, related efforts of various laboratories, and scientific discoveries.

Author Comment: There is latitude in the details of describing the maturity levels of an engineer at the various GS levels. However the maturity levels are basically the same. I prefer the shorter description because the essence of the maturity level is captured.

Table 108 Engineer Maturity Levels GS Scale Broad Descriptions[212]

GS-5: Typically an entry-level trainee or developmental level, characterized by work on a limited range of assignments under close supervision.
GS-7: Typically a junior-level employee or advanced entry-level trainee. Work is less limited in scope than the GS-5, and is done more independently, but is still subject to close review and specific guidelines.
GS-9: Generally no longer a trainee level; the scope of work is narrower, and the level of supervision is closer than for a full journeyman, but the employee has considerable latitude in planning and carrying out work.
GS-11: Typically involves a broad scope of responsibility, more variety, and less clear guidelines. Supervisory oversight generally consists of review of completed project to assure compliance with organization policies or regulations.
GS-12: Typically full journey level. It involves a wide range of assignments or a few highly complex assignments, and requires planning and organizing, setting priorities, and working without clear or specific guidelines. Work is typically reviewed only to assess impact on overall organizational objectives.
GS-13: Typically performs multiple, varying, and complex assignments requiring advanced knowledge of engineering principles and limited direction.

---

[212] This is an example of broad GS descriptions from a US Government organization.

Table 108 Engineer Maturity Levels GS Scale Broad Descriptions[212]

Established guidelines exist, but require considerable discretion to select the most appropriate approach or recommend new approaches. Work is typically reviewed at major milestones and at completion for technical compliance and alignment with the requirements of the project. **GS-14:** Typically plans and accomplishes highly complex and challenging projects (often as the principal technical specialist) under the minimal direction of a manager or team leader. Assignments frequently cross the organizational boundaries. Broad policies provide general direction, but discretion is used to develop new and innovative approaches. Work is reviewed through status reports and at project completion for technical compliance and alignment with project requirements and other work activity.

As we take a very broad view of the descriptions of the maturity levels we see that there appears to be maturity levels that transcend disciplines and industries. In many ways these broad maturity levels are associated with the age of a person. By the time a person has raised a family they have been through enough challenges to become strategic thinkers. That is why maturity levels tend to be associated with age and years of experience.

Table 109 Broad Maturity Levels

Engineer Level I GS-5	Learning.
Engineer Level II GS-7	Learning.
Engineer Level III GS-9	Learning.
Engineer Level IV GS-11	Practicing with assistance
Engineer Level V GS-12	Journey person level. Executing plans and mechanisms.
Engineer Level VI GS-13	Journey person level. Setting up plans and mechanisms to implement policy.
Engineer Level VII GS-14	Master level. Senior member affecting policy. Setting up plans and mechanisms to implement policy.
Engineer Level VIII GS-15, SES 1-4	Master level. Executive setting policy

Author Comment: The above lists identifying the maturity levels of engineers have been lost to time. Instead there has been a shift to certifications. In the case of software many ignorant organizations have job applicants take tests. They do not ask fundamental questions like, how many software languages have you learned? What is your approach to coming up to speed on a project quickly? Do you have a demonstrated ability to quickly learn and then innovate for our unique need? This in part is due to the adoption of the concepts associated with Human Capital.

Author Comment: Human capital is a clear example of changing the system boundary and using math and logic for the express purpose of pushing an agenda that is fatally flawed, dangerous, and dehumanizing. People are reduced to the level of a machine, food stock, and slave. This is bad analysis. Humans have infinite potential and at anytime the lowest person in an organization can save a design, project, program, company or industry. The current crop of human resources professionals should be ashamed of themselves for allowing this to happen to our very new great high technology civilization.

Example 31 Infinite Human Potential - PLATO

Prior to World War II education was limited to the few who could afford to attend. In 1944 the GI Bill provided free education to World War II veterans. This was a very different time, where humanity had witnessed incredible horrors and was ready for a new way. This was also the time when Science the Endless Frontier was provided at the request of the president of the United States[213]. In the USSR 1957 launched the Sputnik I satellite and this energized the US Government into spending more on science and engineering education.

So there was a great need to offer higher education to a much larger segment of the population. However there were two challenges that needed to be overcome. The first was capacity and the other was location. Not only was capacity insufficient for all the new students but also many students were located in areas where there were no colleges or universities.

Chalmers Sherwin a physicist at the University of Illinois realized the need and suggested a computer based learning system to William Everett the engineering college dean. William Everett recommended that Daniel Alpert, another physicist, convene a meeting with engineers, administrators, mathematicians, and psychologists. After several meetings they were unable to agree on a single design. Rather than accept failure Alpert mentioned the challenge to a laboratory assistant, Donald Bitzer. Donald had been thinking about the problem, suggesting he could build a demonstration system.

Donald Bitzer is regarded as the Father of Programmed Logic for Automatic Teaching Operations (PLATO). He realized that good graphics were critical to a learning environment. In that time there were only text based displays. He developed the PLASMA display specifically for PLATO. Notice that his Human Capital level would have been rated zero. Also his KSA level once compared to all the experts would have been embarrassingly low, again zero. However because humans have infinite potential Donald transformed our world[214].

---

[213] Science The Endless Frontier, A Report to the President by Vannevar Bush, Director of the Office of Scientific Research and Development, July 1945.

[214] Hughes Aircraft told everyone that their credentials were irrelevant beyond the basic

Many modern concepts in multi-user computing were developed on PLATO, including forums, message boards, online testing, e-mail, chat rooms, picture languages, instant messaging, remote screen sharing, and multi-player games. It was the precursor to the Internet and the Internet would not exist without PLATO.

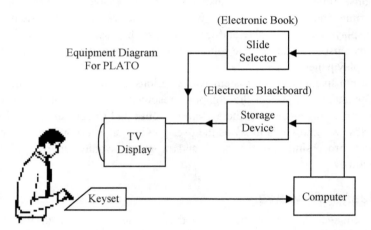

Figure 159 PLATO Bock Diagram 1960

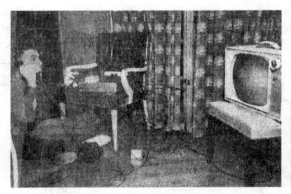

Figure 160 First PLATO Demonstration[215]

Don Bitzer conceived PLATO as a system as shown in a block diagram. The first system was demonstrated March 10, 1960. It used a Television, connected to a graphics generator, keyboard, and dialup modem connected to a computer via long distance telephone wire. Today the concept and equipment are straightforward

---

engineering levels. They clearly stated that you with their infinite potential would have the equivalent of several PhDs very soon. This is a sign of a learning organization.

[215] Don Bitzer Friday March 10, 1961 demonstrates the system at Allerton House. The student indicates their response to a learning exercise by pressing buttons on the keyboard, which is connected to an Illiac computer by long distance telephone wire.

however in 1960 most of the hardware did not exist. Also there were many challenges such as the display and response time.

The display was a big challenge in 1960 because of cost and the ability to offer fast response time. Storage tube displays were expensive and didn't have the response time characteristics needed for an interactive teaching system. Raster graphic displays were expensive and large because they used memory and memory was very expensive and large. The solution was to invent and commercialize the gas plasma display panel.

The responsiveness of the system was a serious challenge. For a student to be properly engaged in a lesson, the computer response had to feel instantaneous. In technical terms, this meant that the system response had to appear in less than 100 milliseconds. We know this today as the user preview area response time. This was when batch processing was the norm and programs would run over night, not instantaneously.

10.5 Design Reviews

When engaged in design monitoring the key element is the design reviews. MIL-STD-1521B is a good starting point for identifying the possible major milestones, their associated design reviews and what should be expected from the various design reviews as the system design matures. Technical interchange meetings occur between the design reviews and are snapshots in time leading to a design review. It is a way to minimize risk of a failed design review.

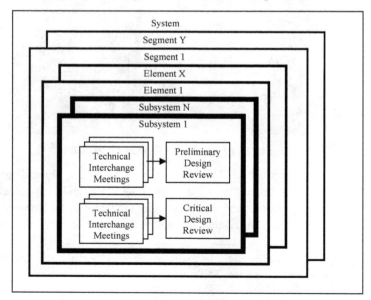

Figure 161 System Monitoring Complexity

It becomes complex with a complex system because there are so many subsystems. As the subsystems vary in traditional engineering disciplines the complexity further increases. As the complexity increases the need for specialty engineering increases, which also then increases the system complexity.

Table 110 Design Review Areas

- Hardware
- Software
- Support Equipment
- Engineering Data
- Detailed Evaluation of Electrical Mechanical Designs
- Detailed Evaluation of Software Designs
- Electromagnetic Compatibility
- Design Reliability
- Design Maintainability
- Human Factors
- System Safety
- Natural Environment
- Equipment and Parts Standardization
- Parts Standardization and Interchangeability
- Assignment of Official Nomenclature
- Value Engineering
- Sustainability
- Ethics
- Transportability
- Test
- Maintenance and Data
- Spare Parts and Externally Furnished Property
- Packaging Special Design Protective Equipment
- Technical Manuals
- System Allocation Document
- Design Producibility and Manufacturing

10.5.1 System Requirements Review (SRR)

The SRR is held very early in the system development. It can happen at anytime but is normally held after the functional analysis and preliminary requirement allocation. It is used to determine initial direction and progress of the effort and its convergence on an optimum and complete system. The functional analysis and allocation includes operations, maintenance, training, hardware, software, facilities, manufacturing, personnel, and human factors.

Since many efforts start with a customer that offers an A-Level specification, the A-Level specification is fully vetted and accepted by both parties based on the analysis. This suggests that requirements have been added, deleted, and modified based on what has been learned to get to the initial architecture concept. A separate SRR can be held for each of the subsystems depending on the nature and complexity of the system.

10.5.2 System Design Review (SDR)

The essence of the SDR is to present the selected functional architecture approach. It is held to evaluate the optimization, traceability, correlation, completeness, and the risk of the allocated requirements, including the corresponding test requirements in meeting the system subsystem requirements, the functional baseline.

The review includes all the system requirements including operations, maintenance, test, training, hardware, computer software, facilities, personnel, and preliminary logistic support considerations. The review also includes the work to date including mission and requirements analysis, functional analysis, requirements allocation, manufacturing methods process selection, program risk analysis, system cost effectiveness analysis, logistics support analysis, trade studies, intra- and inter-system interface studies, integrated test planning, specialty discipline studies, and configuration management. A technical understanding is reached on the validity and the degree of completeness of the following information products:

- System Subsystem Specification(s)
- System Cost
- Preliminary Operational Concept Description(s)
- Preliminary Software Requirements Specification(s)
- Preliminary Interface Requirements Specification(s)
- If appropriate, Prime Item Development Specification(s)
- If appropriate, Critical Item Development Specification(s)

The SDR is the final review before moving to the preliminary design of the system or the detailed requirements analysis of software. The SDR reviews operational mission requirements, system subsystem specification requirements, allocated performance requirements, programming and manufacturing methods, processes planning, and ensures that the information products are necessary and sufficient. The SDR should:

1. Ensure that the System Subsystem Specification is adequate and cost effective in satisfying validated mission requirements.
2. Ensure that the allocated requirements represent a complete and optimal synthesis of the system requirements.
3. Ensure that the technical program risks are identified, ranked, avoided, and reduced through:

    a. Tradeoffs particularly for sensitive mission requirements versus engineering realism and manufacturing feasibility to satisfy the anticipated production quantities of related performance requirements

    b. Subsystem component hardware proofing

    c. A responsive test program

    d. Implementation of comprehensive engineering disciplines such as worst case analysis, failure mode and effects analysis, maintainability analysis, producibility analysis and standardization

4. Identify how the final combination of operations, manufacturing, maintenance, logistics and test and activation requirements have affected overall program concepts, quantities and types of equipment, unit product cost, computer software, personnel, and facilities

5. Ensure that a technical understanding of requirements has been reached and technical direction is provided

10.5.3 Software Specification Review (SSR)

The SSR is a formal review of software requirements in the Software Requirements Specification and the Interface Requirements Specification(s). Normally, it is held after System Design Review but prior to the start of software preliminary design. A collective SSR for a group of software configuration items, treating each configuration item individually, can be held. Its purpose is to establish the allocated baseline for preliminary software design by demonstrating the adequacy of the Software Requirements Specification (SRS), Interface Requirements Specification(s) (IRS), and Operational Concept Description (OCD). The following items are reviewed.

- Functional overview of the software, including inputs, processing, and outputs of each function
- Overall software performance requirements including execution time, storage requirements, and similar constraints
- Internal control and data flow between each of the software functions within the software
- External interface requirements between the internal software configuration items and external to the system
- Qualification requirements that identify applicable levels and methods of testing for the software requirements
- Any special delivery requirements
- Quality factor requirements including correctness, reliability, efficiency, integrity, usability, maintainability, testability, flexibility, portability, reusability, and interoperability
- Mission requirements of the system and its associated operational and

support environments

- Functions and characteristics of the computer
- Milestone schedules
- Updates since the last review to previously delivered software related items including actions or procedures deviating from approved plans

10.5.4 Hardware Requirements Review (HRR)

The HRR[216] is a formal review of hardware requirements in the Hardware Requirements Specification and the Interface Control Document(s). In the past this was done as part of Preliminary Design Review. However with the introduction of high density programmable and application specific hardware devices[217] with resulting massive functionality, an HRR is suggested as part of risk reduction.

The HRR is held after System Design Review but prior to the start of hardware preliminary design. A collective HRR for a group of hardware configuration items, treating each configuration item individually can be held. Its purpose is to establish the allocated baseline for preliminary hardware design by demonstrating the adequacy of the Hardware Requirements Specification (HRS), Interface Control Document(s) (ICD), and Operational Concept Description (OCD).

10.5.5 Preliminary Design Review (PDR)

A Preliminary Design Review (PDR) is a formal technical review of the basic design approach for a configuration item or for a related group of configuration items. The PDR has a long established list of expected items that can be used as guidance for performing preliminary design. It can form the basis of key Socratic questions to ask as the team engages in the preliminary designs of the various lower level abstractions that form the system. The following is a discussion of what may be included in a PDR.

The PDR is held after the Hardware Development Specification(s), the Software Top Level Design Document (STLDD), the Software Test Plan (STP), the Hardware Test Plan, and preliminary versions of the Computer System Operator's Manual (CSOM), Software User's Manual (SUM), Computer System Diagnostic Manual (CSDM), and Computer Resources Integrated Support Document (CRISD) are available, but prior to the start of detailed design.

For each configuration item the review can be performed as a single event, or spread over several events, depending on the nature and the extent of the development of the configuration item and on provisions specified in the contract

---

[216] MIL-STD-1521 is hardware oriented, a separate hardware requirements review is not identified. This is an example of starting with a base and doing what needs to be done.

[217] Field Programmable Gate Arrays (FPGA), Application-Specific Integrated Circuit (ASIC).

Statement of Work.

A collective PDR for a group of configuration items, treating each configuration item individually, can be held; such a collective PDR can be spread over several events, such as for a single configuration item.

The technical program risk associated with each configuration item is reviewed on a technical, cost, and schedule basis. For software, a technical understanding is reached on the validity and the degree of completeness of the STLDD, STP, and the preliminary versions of the CSOM, SUM, CSDM, and CRISD.

The PDR includes many areas of the design. These areas may or may not apply to the unique design being developed by the team. They should all be considered and then used as a starting point for unique areas associated with the new design not offered in the list.

10.5.6 Critical Design Review (CDR)

A Critical Design Review (CDR) is held for each configuration item prior to fabrication production coding release. The CDR has a long established list of expected items that can be used as guidance for performing critical design. It can form the basis of key Socratic questions to ask as the team engages in the critical designs of the various lower level abstractions that form the system. The following is a discussion of what may be included in a CDR.

The CDR ensures that the detail design solutions, as reflected in the Draft Hardware Product Specifications, Software Detailed Design Documents (SDDD), Database Design Documents (DBDD), Interface Design Documents (IDD), and engineering drawings satisfy requirements established by the hardware Development Specification and Software Top Level Design Documents (STLDD).

CDR is held after the Computer Software Operator's Manuals (CSOM), Software User's Manuals (SUM), Computer System Diagnostic Manuals (CSDM), Software Programmer's Manuals (SPM), and Firmware Support Manuals (FSM) have been updated or newly released. For complex large configuration items the CDR may be conducted on an incremental basis where progressive reviews are conducted versus a single CDR.

The overall technical program risks associated with each configuration item are reviewed on a technical (design and manufacturing), cost and schedule basis. For software, a technical understanding is reached on the validity and the degree of completeness of the SDDD, IDD, DBDD, STD, CRISD, SPM, and FSM, and preliminary versions of the CSOM, SUM, and CSDM.

The CDR includes many areas of the design. These areas may or may not apply to the unique design being developed by the team. They should all be considered and then used as a starting point for unique areas associated with the new design not offered in the list.

10.5.7 Design Review Details and Socratic Method

We previously discussed the Socratic method and how it can be used to help the design to emerge. There were generic questions that were offered as examples to use in a design Socratic discourse. The following design review details are essentially lower level questions that should be asked at a design review. They are also questions that can be used at the start of a design activity to help the designers surface the best and complete design. Not all the areas apply and also not all areas may be covered. The team should review these suggestions, modify them as the design unfolds, and use them to engage in meaningful dialog about the design.

Table 111 SRR

Systems Engineering:
a. Mission and Requirements Analysis
b. Functional Flow Analysis
c. Preliminary Requirements Allocation
d. System Cost Effectiveness Analysis
e. Trade studies (addressing system functions in mission and support hardware firmware software).
f. Architecture Synthesis
g. Logistics Support Analysis
h. Specialty Discipline Studies electrical, software, civil, mechanical, chemical, biological, environmental engineering, reliability, maintainability, safety, security, interoperability, compatibility, survivability, vulnerability, test, quality, energy management, environmental considerations, sustainability.
i. System Interface Studies
j. Generation of Specification
k. Program Risk Analysis
l. Integrated Test Planning
m. Producibility Analysis Plans
n. Technical Performance Measurement Planning
o. Engineering Integration
p. Data Management Plans
q. Configuration Management Plans
r. System Safety
s. Human Factors Analysis
t. Value Engineering Studies and Quality Impacts
u. Life Cycle Cost Analysis
v. Preliminary Manufacturing Plans
w. Personnel Requirements Personnel Analysis
x. Milestone Schedules

Describe progress and problems in:
(1) Risk identification and risk ranking (the interrelationship among system effectiveness analysis, technical performance measurement, intended manufacturing methods, and costs are discussed).
(2) Risk avoidance reduction and control (the interrelationships with tradeoff studies, test planning, hardware proofing, and technical performance measurement are discussed).

Table 111 SRR

(3) Significant tradeoffs among stated system subsystem specification requirements constraints and resulting engineering design requirements constraints, manufacturing methods process constraints, and logistic cost of ownership requirements constraints and unit production cost design-to-cost objectives.

(4) Identify computer resources of the system and partitioning the system into hardware and software. Tradeoff studies conducted to evaluate alternative approaches and methods for meeting operational needs and to determine the effects of constraints on the system. Evaluations of logistics, technology, cost, schedule, resource limitations, intelligence estimates, etc., made to determine their impact on the system. Specific tradeoffs related to computer resources are addressed:

a. Candidate programming languages and computer architectures evaluated in light of requirements for approved higher order languages and standard instruction set architectures.

b. Alternative approaches evaluated for implementing security requirements. If an approach has been selected, discuss how it is the most economical balance of elements, which meet the total system requirements.

c. Alternative approaches identified for achieving the operational and support concepts, and for joint operations or opportunities for cross systems support.

(5) Producibility and manufacturing considerations which could impact the program decision such as critical components, materials and processes, tooling and test equipment development, production testing methods, long lead items, and facilities personnel skills requirements.

(6) Significant hazard consideration made to develop requirements and constraints to eliminate or control these system associated hazards.

(7) Specific actions to be performed include evaluations of:

a. System design feasibility and system cost effectiveness

b. Capability of the selected configuration to meet requirements of the System Subsystem Specification

c. Allocations of system requirements to subsystems configuration items

d. Use of commercially available and standard parts

e. Allocated inter and intra system interface requirements

f. Size, weight, and configuration of hardware to permit economical and effective transportation, packaging, and handling consistent with applicable specifications and standards

g. Specific design concepts which may require development toward advancing the state-of-the-art

h. Specific subsystems components which may require "hardware proofing" and high-risk long-lead time items

i. The ability of inventory items to meet overall system requirements and their compatibility with configuration item interfaces

j. Planned system design in view of providing multi-mode functions

k. Considerations given to:

(1) Interference caused by the external environment to the system and the system to the external environment.

(2) Allocated performance characteristics of all system transmitters and receivers to identify potential intra-system electromagnetic (EM) incompatibilities.

(3) Non-design, spurious and harmonic system performance characteristics and their effect on

Table 111 SRR

electromagnetic environments of operational deployments.

l. Value Engineering studies, preliminary Value Engineering Change Proposals (VECPs) and impact on quality.

(8) Review the Preliminary Operational Concept Document, System Subsystem Specification, Hardware Development Specifications, preliminary Software Requirements, and Interface Requirements Specifications for format, content, technical adequacy, completeness and traceability correlation to the validated mission support requirements. All entries marked "not applicable (N/A)" or "to be determined (TBD)" are identified and explained.
(9) Review test documents, including hardware subsystem and system test plans, to ensure that the proposed test program satisfies the test requirements of all applicable specifications. All entries labeled "not applicable (N/A)" or "to be determined (TBD)" in the test section of any applicable specification are identified and explained.
(10) Review the system, hardware, and software design for interaction with the natural environment. If any effect or interaction is not completely understood and further study is required, or it is known but not completely compensated for in the design, the proposed method of resolution shall also be reviewed. All proposed environmental tests are reviewed for compatibility with the specified natural environmental conditions.

(11) Maintenance functions developed to determine that support concepts are valid, technically feasible, and understood. In particular, attention is given to:
a. RMA considerations in the updated System Subsystem Specification
b. Maintenance design characteristics of the system
c. Corrective and preventive maintenance requirements
d. Special equipment, tools, or material required
e. Requirements or planning for automated maintenance analysis
f. Item Maintenance Analysis compatibility with required maintenance program when weapon is deployed
g. Specific configuration item support requirements
h. Forms, procedures, and techniques for maintenance analysis
i. Maintenance related tradeoff studies and findings (includes commercially available equipment, software fault diagnostic techniques)
j. Logistic cost impacts
k. Support procedures and tools for computer software which facilitate software modification, improvements, corrections and updates
l. Hardness critical items processes
m. Support equipment concept.

(12) High-risk areas or design concepts requiring possible advances of the state-of-the-art. Prepared test programs and existing simulation test facilities are reviewed for sufficiency and compatibility.
(13) The optimization, traceability, completeness, and risks associated with the allocation of technical requirements, and the adequacy of allocated system requirements as a basis for proceeding with the development of hardware and software configuration items. Include any available preliminary Software Requirements and Interface Requirements Specifications.

Table 111 SRR

(14) For manufacturing hardware only: a. The production feasibility and risk analyses addressed at the SRR are updated and expanded. This effort should review the progress made in reducing production risk and evaluate the risk remaining for consideration in the Full Scale Development Phase. Estimates of cost and schedule impacts shall be updated. b. Review of the Production Capability Assessment includes: A review of production capability is accomplished which will constitute an assessment of the facilities, materials, methods, processes, equipment and skills necessary to perform the full scale development and production efforts. Identification of requirements to upgrade or develop manufacturing capabilities is made. Requirements for Manufacturing Technology programs are identified as an element of this production assessment. c. Present the management controls and the design manufacturing engineering approach to assure that the equipment is producible. d. Present a review of tradeoff studies for design requirements against the requirement for producibility, facilities, tooling, production test equipment, inspection, and capital equipment for intended production rates and volume. e. The analysis, assessments and tradeoff studies should recommend any additional special studies or development efforts as needed.

Table 112 SDR

(1) Systems Engineering: a. Mission and Requirements Analysis b. Functional Analysis c. Requirements Allocation d. System Cost Effectiveness e. Synthesis f. Survivability Vulnerability g. Reliability Maintainability Availability (RMA) h. Electromagnetic Compatibility i. Logistic Support Analysis, integrated logistics support including maintenance concept, support equipment concept, logistics support concept, maintenance, supply, software support facilities, etc. j. System Safety (emphasis placed on system hazard analysis and identification of safety test requirements) k. Security l. Human Factors m. Transportability including Packaging and Handling n. System Mass Properties o. Standardization p. Electronic Warfare q. Value Engineering and Quality Impacts r. System Growth Capability s. Program Risk Analysis t. Technical Performance Measurement Planning u. Producibility Analysis and Manufacturing v. Life Cycle Cost Design to Cost Goals w. Quality Assurance Program

Table 112 SDR

x. Environmental Conditions, Shock, Vibration, Temperature, Humidity, etc.   y. Training and Training Support   z. Milestone Schedules   aa. Software Development Procedures, Software Development Plan (SDP), Software Test Plan (STP), and other identified plans, etc.   (2) Results of significant trade studies: a. Sensitivity of selected mission requirements versus realistic performance parameters and cost estimates   b. Operations design versus maintenance design, including support equipment impacts   c. System centralization versus decentralization   d. Automated versus manual operation   e. Reliability Maintainability Availability   f. Commercially available items versus new developments   g. Standard items versus new development   h. Testability trade studies (Allocation of fault detection isolation capabilities between elements of built in test, on board on-site fault detection isolation subsystem, separate support equipment, and manual procedures)   i. Size and weight   j. Desired propagation characteristics versus reduction interference to other systems (optimum selection frequencies)   k. Performance logistics trade studies   l. Life cycle cost reduction for different computer programming languages   m. Functional allocation between hardware, software, firmware and personnel procedures   n. Life Cycle Cost system performance trade studies to include sensitivity of performance parameters to cost   o. Sensitivity of performance parameters versus cost   p. Cost versus performance   q. Design versus manufacturing consideration   r. Make versus buy   s. Software development schedule   t. On-equipment versus off-equipment maintenance tasks, including support equipment impacts   u. Common versus peculiar support equipment   (3) Updated design requirements for operations maintenance functions and items.   (4) Updated requirements for manufacturing methods and processes.   (5) Updated operations maintenance requirements for facilities.   (6) Updated requirements for operations maintenance personnel and training.   (7) Specific actions to be performed include evaluations of: a. System design feasibility and system cost effectiveness   b. Capability of the selected configuration to meet requirements of the System Subsystem Specification   c. Allocations of system requirements to subsystems configuration items   d. Use of commercially available and standard parts   e. Allocated inter and intra system interface requirements   f. Size, weight, and configuration of hardware to permit economical and effective

Table 112 SDR

transportation, packaging, and handling consistent with applicable specifications and standards
g. Specific design concepts that may need development toward advancing the state-of-the-art
h. Specific subsystems components which may require "hardware proofing" and high-risk long-lead time items
i. The ability of inventory items to meet overall system requirements and their compatibility with configuration item interfaces
j. Planned system design in view of providing multi-mode functions

k. Considerations given to:
(1) Interference caused by the external environment to the system and the system to the external environment.
(2) Allocated performance characteristics of all system transmitters and receivers to identify potential intra-system electromagnetic (EM) incompatibilities.
(3) Non-design, spurious and harmonic system performance characteristics and their effect on electromagnetic environments of operational deployments.

l. Value Engineering studies, preliminary Value Engineering Change Proposals (VECPs) and impact on quality.

(8) Review the Preliminary Operational Concept Document, System Subsystem Specification, Hardware Development Specifications, preliminary Software Requirements, and Interface Requirements Specifications for format, content, technical adequacy, completeness and traceability correlation to the validated mission support requirements. All entries marked "not applicable (N/A)" or "to be determined (TBD)" are identified and explained.
(9) Review test documents, including hardware subsystem and system test plans, to ensure that the proposed test program satisfies the test requirements of all applicable specifications. All entries labeled "not applicable (N/A)" or "to be determined (TBD)" in the test section of any applicable specification are identified and explained.
(10) Review the system, hardware, and software design for interaction with the natural environment. If any effect or interaction is not completely understood and further study is required, or it is known but not completely compensated for in the design, the proposed method of resolution shall also be reviewed. All proposed environmental tests are reviewed for compatibility with the specified natural environmental conditions.

(11) Maintenance functions developed to determine that support concepts are valid, technically feasible, and understood. In particular, attention is given to:
a. RMA considerations in the updated System Subsystem Specification
b. Maintenance design characteristics of the system
c. Corrective and preventive maintenance requirements
d. Special equipment, tools, or material required
e. Requirements or planning for automated maintenance analysis
f. Item Maintenance Analysis compatibility with required maintenance program when weapon is deployed
g. Specific configuration item support requirements
h. Forms, procedures, and techniques for maintenance analysis
i. Maintenance related tradeoff studies and findings (includes commercially available equipment, software fault diagnostic techniques)

Table 112 SDR

j. Logistic cost impacts
k. Support procedures and tools for computer software which facilitate software modification, improvements, corrections and updates
l. Hardness critical items processes
m. Support equipment concept.

(12) High-risk areas or design concepts requiring possible advances of the state-of-the-art. Prepared test programs and existing simulation test facilities are reviewed for sufficiency and compatibility.
(13) The optimization, traceability, completeness, and risks associated with the allocation of technical requirements, and the adequacy of allocated system requirements as a basis for proceeding with the development of hardware and software configuration items. Include any available preliminary Software Requirements and Interface Requirements Specifications.

(14) For manufacturing hardware only:
a. The production feasibility and risk analyses addressed at the SRR are updated and expanded. This effort should review the progress made in reducing production risk and evaluate the risk remaining for consideration in the Full Scale Development Phase. Estimates of cost and schedule impacts shall be updated.
b. Review of the Production Capability Assessment includes: A review of production capability is accomplished which will constitute an assessment of the facilities, materials, methods, processes, equipment and skills necessary to perform the full scale development and production efforts. Identification of requirements to upgrade or develop manufacturing capabilities is made. Requirements for Manufacturing Technology programs are identified as an element of this production assessment.
c. Present the management controls and the design manufacturing engineering approach to assure that the equipment is producible.
d. Present a review of tradeoff studies for design requirements against the requirement for producibility, facilities, tooling, production test equipment, inspection, and capital equipment for intended production rates and volume.
e. The analysis, assessments and tradeoff studies should recommend any additional special studies or development efforts as needed.

Table 113 PDR CDR Hardware

PDR Hardware
a. Preliminary design synthesis of the hardware Development Specification for the item being reviewed.
b. Trade-studies and design studies results (see SDR for a representative listing).
c. Functional flow, requirements allocation data, and schematic diagrams.
d. Equipment layout drawings and preliminary drawings, including any proprietary or restricted design process components and information.
e. Environment control and thermal design aspects
f. Electromagnetic compatibility
g. Power distribution and grounding design aspects
h. Preliminary mechanical and packaging design of consoles, racks, drawers, printed circuit boards, connectors, etc.
i. Safety engineering considerations

Table 113 PDR CDR Hardware

j. Security engineering considerations
k. Survivability Vulnerability (including nuclear) considerations
l. Preliminary lists of materials, parts, and processes
m. Pertinent reliability maintainability availability data
n. Preliminary weight data
o. Development test data
p. Interface requirements contained in configuration item Development Specifications and interface control data (e.g., interface control drawings) derived from requirements.
q. Configuration item development schedule
r. Mock-ups, models, breadboards, or prototype hardware when appropriate
s. Producibility and Manufacturing Considerations (e.g., materials, tooling, test equipment, processes, facilities, skills, and inspection techniques). Identify single source, sole source, and diminishing source.
t. Value Engineering Considerations and Value Engineering Change Proposals (VECPs) analysis including quality impacts.
u. Transportability, packaging, and handling considerations
v. Human Engineering and Biomedical considerations (including life support and Crew Station Requirements).
w. Standardization considerations
x. Description and characteristics of commercially available equipment, including any optional capabilities such as special features, interface units, special instructions, controls, formats, etc., (include limitations of commercially available equipment such as failure to meet human engineering, safety, and maintainability requirements of the specification and identify deficiencies).
y. Existing documentation (technical orders, commercial manuals, etc.,) for commercially available equipment and copies of contractor specifications used to procure equipment is made available for review.
z. Firmware to be provided with the system: microprogram logic diagrams and reprogramming instruction translation algorithm descriptions, fabrication, packaging (integration technology gate density, device types such as CMOS, PMOS, ASIC, FLASH, FPGA), and special equipment and support software needed for developing, testing, and supporting the firmware and VHDL.
aa. Life Cycle Cost Analysis
ab. Armament compatibility
ac. Corrosion prevention control considerations
ad. Findings Status of Quality Assurance Program
ae. Support equipment requirements.
CDR Hardware
a. Adequacy of the detail design reflected in the draft hardware Product Specification in satisfying the requirements of the Hardware Configuration Items (HWCI) Development Specification for the item being reviewed.
b. Detail engineering drawings for the Hardware including schematic diagrams.
c. Adequacy of the detailed design in the following areas:
(1) Electrical design
(2) Mechanical design
(3) Environmental control and thermal aspects
(4) Electromagnetic compatibility
(5) Power generation and grounding

Table 113 PDR CDR Hardware

(6) Electrical and mechanical interface compatibility
(7) Mass properties
(8) Reliability Maintainability Availability
(9) System Safety Engineering
(10) Security Engineering
(11) Survivability Vulnerability (including nuclear)
(12) Producibility and Manufacturing
(13) Transportability, Packaging and handling
(14) Human Engineering and Biomedical Requirements (including Life Support and Crew Station Requirements)
(15) Standardization
(16) Design versus Logistics Tradeoffs
(17) Support equipment requirements
d. Interface control drawings
e. Mock-ups, breadboards, and or prototype hardware
f. Design analysis and test data
g. System Allocation Document for Hardware inclusion at each scheduled location.
h. Initial Manufacturing Readiness (for example, manufacturing engineering, tooling demonstrations, development and proofing of new materials, processes, methods, tooling, test equipment, procedures, reduction of manufacturing risks to acceptable levels).
i. Preliminary VECPs and or formal VECPs include quality impacts
j. Life cycle costs
k. Detail design information on all firmware to be provided with the system.
l. Verify corrosion prevention control considerations to Ensure materials have been chosen that will be compatible with operating environment.
m. Findings Status of Quality Assurance Program

Table 114 PDR CDR Software

PDR Software
a. Functional flow. The computer software functional flow embodying all of the requirements allocated from the Software Requirements Specifications and Interface Requirements Specifications to the individual Top-Level Software Units (TLSU) of the Software Configuration Items (CSCI).
b. Storage allocation data. This information is presented for each Software item as a whole, describing the manner in which available storage is allocated to individual TL SW Units. Timing, sequencing requirements, and relevant equipment constraints used in determining the allocation are to be included.
c. Control functions description. A description of the executive control and start recovery features of the Software including method of initiating system operation and features enabling recovery from system malfunction.
d. Software structure. Describe the top-level structure of the Software, the reasons for choosing the components described, the development methodology to be used within the constraints of the available computer resources, and any support programs required to develop maintain the Software structure and allocation of data storage.
e. Security. Identify unique security requirements and a description of the techniques to be used for implementing and maintaining security within the Software.

Table 114 PDR CDR Software

f. Special software architecture needs. Identify any special software architecture needs such as re-entrancy requirements and a description of the techniques for implementing.
g. Computer software development facilities. Identify the availability, adequacy, and planned use of computer software development facilities.
h. Computer software development facility versus the operational system. Provide information relative to unique design features which may exist in a TLCSC to allow use within the computer software development facility, but which will not exist in the TLCSC installed in the operational system. Provide information on the design of support programs not explicitly required for the operational system but which will be generated to assist in the development of the Software configuration items. Provide details of the Software Development Library controls.
i. Development tools. Describe any special simulation, data reduction, or utility tools that are not delivered, but which are planned for use during software development.
j. Test tools. Describe any special test systems, test data, data reduction tools, test computer software, or calibration and diagnostic software that are not deliverable, but which are planned for use during product development.
k. Description and characteristics of commercially available computer resources, including any optional capabilities such as special features, interface units, special instructions, controls, formats, etc. Include limitations of commercially available equipment such as failure to meet human engineering, safety and maintainability requirements of the specification and identify deficiencies.
l. Existing documentation (commercial manuals, etc.) for commercially available computer resources and copies of contractor specifications used to procure computer resources are made available for review.
m. Support resources. Describe those resources necessary to support the software and firmware during operational deployment of the system, such as operational and support hardware and software, personnel, special skills, human factors, configuration management, test, and facilities space.
n. Operation and support documents. The preliminary versions of the CSOM, SUM, CSDM, and CRISD are reviewed for technical content and compatibility with the top-level design documentation.
CDR Software
a. Software Detailed Design, Database Design, and Interface Design Documents. In cases where the CDR is conducted in increments, complete documents to support that increment shall be available.
b. Supporting documentation describing results of analyses, testing, etc. as mutually agreed by the contracting agency and the contractor.
c. System Allocation Document for Software inclusion at each scheduled location.
d. Computer Resources Integrated Support Document.
e. Software Programmer's Manual
f. Firmware Support Manual
g. Progress on activities required by Software PDR.
h. Updated operation and support documents (CSOM, SUM, CSDM).
i. Schedules for remaining milestones.
j. Updates since the last review to all previously delivered software related documents.

Table 115 PDR CDR Support Equipment

PDR Support Equipment
a. Review considerations applicable to the Hardware and Software configuration items.
b. Verify testability analysis results. For example, on repairable integrated circuit boards are test points available so that failure can be isolated to the lowest level of repair.
c. Verify that externally furnished SE is planned to be used to the maximum extent possible.
d. Review progress of long-lead time SE items, identified through interim release and SE Requirements Document (SERD) procedures.
e. Review progress toward determining total SE requirements for installation, checkout, and test support requirements.
f. Review the reliability maintainability availability of support equipment items.
g. Identify logistic support requirements for support equipment items and rationale for their selection.
h. Review calibration requirements.
i. Describe technical manuals and data availability for support equipment.
j. Verify compatibility of proposed support equipment with the system maintenance concept.
k. If a Logistic Support Analysis (LSA) is not done, then review the results of SE trade-off studies for each alternative support concept. For existing SE and printed circuit boards testers, review Maintainability data resulting from the field use of the equipment. Review the cost difference between systems using single or multipurpose SE vs. proposed new SE. Examine technical feasibility in using existing, developmental, and proposed new SE. For mobile systems, review mobility requirements of support equipment.
l. Review the relationship of the computer resources in the system subsystem with those in Automatic Test Equipment (ATE). Relate this to the development of Built In Test Equipment (BITE) and try to reduce the need for complex supporting SE.
m. Verify on-equipment versus off-equipment maintenance task trade study results, including support equipment impacts.
n. Review updated list of required support equipment.
CDR Support Equipment
a. Review requirements for SE.
b. Verify maximum considerations externally provided SE
c. Identify existing or potential SE provisioning problems
d. Determine qualitative and quantitative adequacy of provisioning drawings and data
e. Review reliability of SE
f. Review logistic support requirements for SE items
g. Review Calibration requirements
h. Review documentation for SE.

Table 116 PDR CDR Engineering Data

PDR Engineering Data
Review Level 1 engineering drawings for ease of conversion to higher levels and, if available, review Level 2 and 3 drawings for compliance with requirements.
CDR Engineering Data
Continuing from results of Preliminary Design Review (PDR), review data.

Table 117 PDR CDR Electrical Mechanical Designs

PDR Hardware Details
a. Determine that the preliminary detail design provides the capability of satisfying the performance characteristics paragraph of the Hardware Development specifications.   b. Establish compatibility of the Hardware operating characteristics in each mode with overall system design requirements if the Hardware is involved in multi-mode functions.   c. Establish existence and nature of physical and functional interfaces between Hardware and other items of equipment, computer software, and facilities.

CDR Hardware Details
1. Detailed block diagrams, schematics, and logic diagrams are compared with interface control drawings to determine system compatibility. Analytical and available test data shall be reviewed to Ensure the hardware Development Specification has been satisfied.   2. Provide information on firmware, which is included in commercially available equipment or to be included in developed equipment. Firmware in this context includes the microprocessor and associated sequence of microinstructions necessary to perform the allocated tasks.   As a minimum, the information presented during CDR provides descriptions and status for the following: a. Detailed logic flow diagrams   b. Processing algorithms   c. Circuit diagrams   d. Clock and timing data (e.g., timing charts for micro- instructions)   e. Memory (e.g., type (RAM, PROM), word length, size (total and spare capacity))   f. Micro-instruction list and format   g. Device functional instruction set obtained by implementation of firmware.   h. Input output data width (i.e., number of bits for data and control.)   i. Self-test (diagnostics) within firmware.   j. Support software for firmware development: (1) Resident assembler, (2) Loader, (3) Debugging routines, (4) Executive monitor, (5) Non-resident diagnostics, (6) Cross assembler and higher level language on host computer, (7) Instruction simulator

Table 118 PDR CDR Software Designs

PDR Software Details
a. Determine whether all interfaces between the CSCI and all other configuration items both internal and external to the system meet the requirements of the Software Requirements Specification and Interface Requirements Specification(s).   b. Determine whether the top-level design embodies all the requirements of the Software Requirements Specification and Interface Requirements Specification(s).   c. Determine whether approved design methodology has been used for top-level design.   d. Determine is appropriate Human Factors Engineering (HFE) principals have been incorporated in the design.   e. Determine is timing and sizing constraints have been met throughout top-level design.   f. Determine is logic affecting system and nuclear safety has been incorporated in design.

CDR Software Details
Present the detailed design (including rationale) of the CSCI to include:

Table 118 PDR CDR Software Designs

a. The assignment of CSCI requirements to specific Lower- Level Software Units, the criteria and design rules used to accomplish this assignment, and the traceability of Unit and LLSU designs to satisfy CSCI requirements, with emphasis on the necessity and sufficiency of the Units for implementing TLSU design requirements.   b. The overall information flow between software Units, the method(s) by which each Unit gains control, and the sequencing of Units relative to each other.   c. The design details of the CSCI, TLSUs, LLSUs, and Units including data definitions, timing and sizing, data and storage requirements and allocations.   d. The detailed design characteristics of all interfaces, including their data source, destination, interface name and interrelationships; and, if applicable, the design for direct memory access. The contractor shall also give an overview of the key design issues of the interface software design, and indicate whether data flow formats are fixed or subject to extensive dynamic changes.   e. The detailed characteristics of the database. Database structure and detailed design, including all files, records, fields, and items. Access rules, how file sharing will be controlled, procedures for database recovery regeneration from a system failure, rules for database manipulation, rules for maintaining file integrity, rules for usage reporting, and rules governing the types and depth of access shall be defined. Data management rules and algorithms for implementing them shall be described. Details of the language required by the user to access the database shall also be described.

Table 119 PDR CDR Electromagnetic Compatibility

PDR Electromagnetic Compatibility
Review HWCI design for compliance with electromagnetic compatibility electromagnetic interference (EMC EMI) requirements. Use Electromagnetic Compatibility Plan as the basis for this review. Check application of MIL-STDs and MIL-Specs cited by the system equipment specification(s) to the HWCI Subsystem design. Review preliminary EMI test plans to assess adequacy to confirm that EMC requirements have been met.
CDR Electromagnetic Compatibility
a. Review EMC design of all HWCIs. Determine compliance with requirements of the Electromagnetic Compatibility Plan and HWCI specifications.   b. Review system EMC including effects on the electromagnetic environment (inter-system EMC) and intra-system EMC. Determine acceptability of EMC design and progress toward meeting EMC requirements.   c. Review EMC test plans. Determine adequacy to confirm EMC design characteristics of the system HWCI subsystem.

Table 120 PDR CDR Design Reliability

PDR Design Reliability
1. Identify the quantitative reliability requirements specified in the hardware Development and Software Requirements Specification(s), including design allocations, and the complexity of the CSCIs.   2. Review failure rate sources, derating policies, and prediction methods. Review the reliability mathematical models and block diagrams as appropriate.   3. Describe planned actions when predictions are less than specified requirements.

Table 120 PDR CDR Design Reliability

4. Identify and review parts or components which have a critical life or require special consideration, and general plan for handling. Present planned actions to deal with these components or parts.

5. Identify applications of redundant HWCI elements. Evaluate the basis for their use and provisions for "on-line" switching of the redundant element.

6. Review critical signal paths to determine that fail-safe fail-soft design is provided.

7. Review margins of safety for HWCIs between functional requirements and design provisions for elements, such as: power supplies, transmitter modules, motors, and hydraulic pumps. Similarly, review structural elements; i.e., antenna pedestals, dishes, and radomes to determine that adequate margins of safety is provided between operational stresses and design strengths.

8. Review Reliability Design Guidelines for HWCIs to Ensure that design reliability concepts are available and used by equipment designers. Reliability Design Guidelines include, as a minimum, part application guidelines (electrical derating, thermal derating, part parameter tolerances), part selection order of preference, prohibited parts materials, reliability apportionments predictions, and management procedures to ensure compliance with the guidelines.

9. Review for HWCIs preliminary reliability demonstration plan: failure counting ground rules, accept-reject criteria, number of test articles, test location and environment, planned starting date, and test duration.

10. Review elements of reliability program plan to determine that each task has been initiated toward achieving specified requirements.

11. Review the reliability controls.

CDR Design Reliability

1. Review the most recent predictions of hardware and software reliability and compare against requirements specified in hardware Development Specification and Software Requirements Specification. For hardware, predictions are substantiated by review of parts application stress data.

2. Review applications of parts or configuration items with minimum life, or those which require special consideration to Ensure their effect on system performance is minimized.

3. Review completed Reliability Design Review Checklist to Ensure principles have been satisfactorily reflected in the configuration item design.

4. Review applications of redundant configuration item elements or components to establish that expectations have materialized since the PDR.

5. Review detailed HWCI reliability demonstration plan for compatibility with specified test requirements. The number of test articles, schedules, locations, test conditions, and personnel involved are reviewed to Ensure a mutual understanding of the plan and to provide overall planning information to activities concerned.

6. Review failure data reporting procedures and methods for determination of failure trends.

7. Review the thermal analysis of components, printed circuit cards, modules, etc. Determine if these data are used in performing the detailed reliability stress predictions.

8. Review on-line diagnostic programs, off-line diagnostic programs, support equipment, and preliminary technical orders (and or commercial manuals) for compliance with the system maintenance concept and specification requirements.

9. Review software reliability prediction model and its updates based upon test data and refined predictions of component usage rates and complexity factors.

Table 121 PDR CDR Design Maintainability

PDR Design Maintainability
1. Identify the quantitative maintainability requirements specified in the hardware Development and Software Requirements Specifications; if applicable, compare preliminary predictions with specified requirements.
2. Review HWCI preventive maintenance schedules in terms of frequencies, durations, and compatibility with system schedules.
3. Review repair rate sources and prediction methods.
4. Review planned actions when predictions indicate that specified requirements will not be attained.
5. Review planned designs for accessibility, testability, and ease of maintenance characteristics (including provisions for automatic or operator-controlled recovery from failure malfunctions) to determine consistency with specified requirements.
6. Determine if planned HWCI design indicates that parts, assemblies, and components will be so placed that there is sufficient space to use test probes, soldering irons, and other tools without difficulty and that they are placed so that structural members of units do not prevent access to them or their ease of removal.
7. Review provisions for diagnosing cause(s) of failure; means for localizing source to lowest replaceable element; adequacy and locations of planned test points; and planned system diagnostics that provide a means for isolating faults to and within the configuration item. This review encompasses on-line diagnostics, off-line diagnostics, and proposed technical orders and or commercial manuals.
8. Review for HWCIs the Design for Maintainability Checklist to Ensure that listed design principles lead to a mature maintainability design. Determine that design engineers are using the checklist.
9. Evaluate for HWCIs the preliminary maintainability demonstration plan, including number of maintenance tasks that are accomplished; accept-reject criteria; general plans for introducing faults into the HWCI and personnel involved in the demonstration.
10. Review elements of maintainability program plan to determine that each task has been initiated towards achieving specified requirements.
11. Ensure that consideration has been given to optimizing the system item from a maintainability and maintenance viewpoint and that it is supportable within the maintenance concept as developed. Also, for HWCIs ensure that a Repair Level Analysis (RLA) has been considered.
CDR Design Maintainability
1. Review the most recent predictions of quantitative maintainability and compare these against requirements specified in the HWCI Development Specification and Software Requirements Specification.
2. Review preventive maintenance frequencies and durations for compatibility with overall system requirements and planning criteria.
3. Identify unique maintenance procedures required for the configuration item during operational use and evaluate their total effects on system maintenance concepts. Assure that system is optimized from a maintenance and maintainability viewpoint and conforms to the planned maintenance concept. This includes a review of provisions for automatic, semiautomatic, and manual recovery from hardware software failures and malfunctions.
4. Identify design-for-maintainability criteria provided by the checklist in the design detail to Ensure that criteria have, in fact been incorporated.
5. Determine if parts, assemblies, and other items are so placed that there is sufficient space to use test probes, soldering irons, and other tools without difficulty and that they

Table 121 PDR CDR Design Maintainability

are placed so that structural members of units do not prevent access to them or their ease of removal. 6. Review detailed maintainability demonstration plan for compatibility with specified test requirements. Supplemental information is provided and reviewed to Ensure a mutual understanding of the plan and to provide overall planning information to activities concerned.

Table 122 PDR CDR Human Factors

PDR Human Factors
1. Present evidence that substantiates the functional allocation decisions. Cover all operational and maintenance functions of the configuration item, in particular, ensure that the approach to be followed emphasizes the functional integrity of the man with the machine to accomplish a system operation. 2. Review design data, design descriptions and drawings on system operations, equipments, and facilities to Ensure that human performance requirements of the hardware Development and Software Requirements Specifications are met. Examples of the types of design information to be reviewed are: a. Operating modes for each display station, for each mode, functions performed, displays and control used, etc. b. The exact format and content of each display, including data locations, spaces, abbreviations, the number of digits, all special symbols (Pictographic), alert mechanisms (e.g., flashing rates), etc. c. The control and data entry devices and formats including keyboards, special function keys, cursor control, etc. d. The format of all operator inputs, together with provisions for error detection and correction. e. All status, error, and data printouts - including formats, headings, data units, abbreviations, spacing, columns, etc. Present in sufficient detail to allow stakeholders to judge adequacy from a human usability standpoint, and design personnel to know what is required, and test personnel to prepare tests. 3. Make recommendations to update the System Subsystem, or Software Requirements Specification and Interface Requirements Specification(s) in cases where requirements for human performance need to be more detailed. 4. Review man machine functions to Ensure that man's capabilities are utilized and that his limitations are not exceeded.
CDR Human Factors
1. Review detail design presented on drawings, schematics, mockups, or actual hardware to determine that they meet human performance requirements of the HWCI Development Specification and Software Requirements Specification. Interface Requirements Specification(s), and accepted human engineering practices. 2. Demonstrate by checklist or other formal means the adequacy of design for human performance. 3. Review each facet of design for man machine compatibility. Review time cost effectiveness considerations and forced tradeoffs of human engineering design.

Table 122 PDR CDR Human Factors

4. Evaluate the following human engineering biomedical design factors: a. Operator controls b. Operator displays c. Maintenance features d. Anthropometry e. Safety features and emergency equipment f. Work space layout g. Internal environmental conditions (noise, lighting, ventilation, etc.) h. Training equipment i. Personnel accommodations

Table 123 PDR CDR System Safety

PDR System Safety
1. Review results of configuration item safety analyses, and quantitative hazard analyses (if applicable). 2. Review results of system and intra-system safety interfaces and trade-off studies affecting the configuration item. 3. Review safety requirements levied on subcontractors. 4. Review known special areas of safety, peculiar to the nature of the system (e.g., fuel handling, fire protection, high levels of radiated energy, high voltage protection, safety interlocks, etc.). 5. Review results of preliminary safety tests (if appropriate). 6. Review adequacy and completeness of configuration item from design safety viewpoint. 7. Review compliance of commercially available configuration items or configuration item components with system safety requirements and identify modifications to such equipment.
CDR System Safety
1. Review configuration item detail design for compliance to safety design requirements. 2. Review acceptance test requirements to ensure adequate safety requirements are reflected in the system. 3. Evaluate adequacy of detailed design for safety and protective equipment devices. 4. Review configuration item operational maintenance safety analyses and procedures.

Table 124 PDR CDR Natural Environment

PDR Natural Environment
1. Review planned design approach toward meeting climatic conditions (operating and non-operating ranges for temperature, humidity, etc.) that are specified in the HWCI Development Specification. 2. Ensure that the stakeholders clearly understand the effect of, and the interactions between, the natural environment and HWCI design. In cases where the effect and interactions are not known or are ambiguous, ensure that studies are in progress or planned to make these determinations. 3. Current and forecast natural environment parameters may be needed for certain

Table 124 PDR CDR Natural Environment

configuration items; e.g., display of airbase conditions in a command and control system, calculation of impact point for a missile, etc. ensure compatibility between the configuration item design and appropriate meteorological communications by comparing characteristics of the source (teletype, facsimile, or data link) with that of the configuration item. Ensure that arrangements or plans to obtain needed information have been made and that adequate display of natural environmental information is provided.
CDR Natural Environment
1. Review detail design to determine that it meets natural environment requirements of the hardware Development Specification. 2. Ensure that studies have been accomplished concerning effects of the natural environment on, or interactions with, the HWCI. Studies which have been in progress are complete at this time. 3. Determine whether arrangements have been made to obtain current and or forecast natural environment information, when needed for certain HWCIs. Assure compatibility of HWCI and source of information by comparing electrical characteristics and formats for the source and the HWCI.

Table 125 PDR CDR Equipment and Parts Standardization

PDR Equipment & Components
a. Review current and planned actions to determine that equipment or components for which standards or specifications exist are used whenever practical. (Standard items with internal stock numbers should have first preference). b. Review specific tradeoffs or modifications that maybe required of existing designs if existing items are, or will be, in the HWCI. c. Existing designs are reviewed for use or non-use based on potential impact on overall program in following areas: Performance, Cost, Time, Weight, Size, Reliability, Maintainability, Supportability, Producibility, Sustainability d. Review HWCI design to identify areas where a practical design change would materially increase the number of standard items. e. Ensure that Critical Item Specifications are prepared for hardware items identified as engineering or logistics critical.
CDR Equipment & Components
1. Determine that every reasonable action has been taken to fulfill the use of standard items (standard internal part numbers should be first preference) and to obtain approval for use of non-standard or non-preferred items. Accordingly, the following criteria are evaluated: a. Data sources that were reviewed. b. Factors that were considered in the decision to reject known similar or existing designs. c. Factors that were considered in decisions to accept any existing designs which were incorporated, and the tradeoffs, if any, that had to be made.

Table 126 PDR CDR Parts Standardization Interchangeability

PDR Parts Standardization and Interchangeability
a. Review procedures to determine if maximum practical use will be made of parts built to approved standards or specifications. The potential impact on the overall program is to

Table 126 PDR CDR Parts Standardization Interchangeability

PDR Parts Standardization and Interchangeability
be evaluated when a part built to approved standards and specifications cannot be used for any of the following reasons: (1) performance, (2) weight, (3) size, (4) reliability maintainability availability, (5) supportability, (6) survivability (including nuclear), (7) sustainability
b. Identify potential design changes that will permit a greater use of standard or preferred parts and evaluate the tradeoffs.
c. Ensure understanding of parts control program operations for selection and approval of parts in new design or major modifications.
d. Review status of the Program Parts Selection List.
e. Review status of all non-standard parts identified.
f. Review pending parts control actions that may cause program slippage, such as non-availability of tested parts.

CDR Parts Standardization and Interchangeability
a. Determine whether there are any outstanding non-standard or non-preferred parts approval requests and action necessary for approval or disapproval. (Status of parts control program operations).
b. Identify non-standard-non-preferred parts approval problems and status of actions toward resolving the problems.
c. Review potential fabrication production line delays due to non-availability of standard or preferred parts. In such cases, determine whether it is planned to request use of parts, which may be replaced by standard items during subsequent support repair cycles. Assure that appropriate documentation makes note of these items and that standard replacement items are provisioned for support and used for repair.
d. Require certification that maximum practical interchangeability of parts exists among components, assemblies, and HWCIs. Reservations concerning interchangeability are identified, particularly for hardness critical items.
e. Sample preliminary drawings and cross check to Ensure that parts indicated on the drawings are compatible with the Program Parts Selection List.

Table 127 PDR CDR Assignment of Official Nomenclature

PDR Assignment of Official Nomenclature
a. Ensure understanding of procedure for obtaining assignment of nomenclature and approval of nameplates.
b. Determine that a nomenclature conference has been held and agreement has been reached with the stakeholders on the level of nomenclature; i.e., system, set, central, group, component, sub-assembly, unit, etc.

CDR Assignment of Official Nomenclature
a. Determine whether official nomenclature and approval of nameplates have been obtained to extent practical.
b. Determine whether request for Nomenclature, has been processed to the agreed level of indenture.
c. Ensure that approved nomenclature is reflected in the Development and Product Specifications.
d. Identify problems associated with nomenclature requests together with status of actions towards resolving the problems.
e. Ensure that a software inventory numbering system has been agreed to and

Table 127 PDR CDR Assignment of Official Nomenclature

implemented to the CSCI level.

Table 128 PDR CDR Value Engineering

PDR Value Engineering
Review the in-house incentive Value Engineering Program, which may include but not be limited to the following: a. Value Engineering organization, policies and procedures including impact on quality assessments. b. Value Engineering Training Program with emphasis on maintaining or improving quality rather than irresponsible financial application. c. Potential Value Engineering projects, studies and VECPs including impact on quality assessments. d. Schedule of planned Value Engineering tasks events. e. Policies and procedures for subcontractor Value Engineering Programs.
CDR Value Engineering
1. Review status of all VECPs presented per the terms of the contract. 2. Identify the impact on quality for each VECP. 3. Review any new areas of potential Value Engineering considered profitable to challenge. 4. If required by contract (funded VE program), review the actual Value Engineering accomplishments against the planned VE program.

Table 129 PDR CDR Sustainability[218]

Sustainability PDR and CDR
1. Review community sustainability and accountability analysis. 2. Review technology assessment findings. 3. Review key sustainability goals, requirements, and issues. 4. Review sustainability tradeoff criteria and sustainable architecture approaches. 5. Review internal and external sustainability issues and drivers. 6. Review new sustainability performance requirements. 7. Review use of recycled, recovered, or environmentally preferable materials. 8. Review list of and justification of toxic and hazardous materials used in the system. 9. Review list and justification of prohibited materials used in the system. 10. List indirect cost shifting out of the system to external systems and stakeholders. 11. Review maintenance logistics safety reliability quality, etc 12. Review the production and transport sustainability performance results for the selected design: PCF, TCF, CCF, PEC, TEC, CEC, etc. Review the production and transport sustainability performance ratios for the selected design: PCCR, TCCR, PCER, TCER, etc.

---

[218] Sustainability is not part of MIL-STD-1521B, it is being offered in this text.

Table 130 PDR CDR Ethics[219]

Ethics PDR and CDR
1. Review possible technology abuses associated with the system.
2. Review list of possible stakeholders negatively impacted by the system.
3. List indirect cost shifting out of the system in development.
4. Review fundamental ethical questions:
Is there a conflict of interest?
Is a stakeholder getting a hidden benefit?
Is a stakeholder being harmed?
Is there a hidden stakeholder?
Is information being suppressed?
Is the team solving the obvious problems others seem to ignore?
Are checks and balances being removed or made ineffective?
Is a stakeholder being marginalized?
Is staff being marginalized?
Is there a misuse of technology?
Is physical harm being permitted
Is loss of life being permitted
Is physical harm being permitted because it makes financial sense?
Is physical loss of life being permitted because it makes financial sense?
Do the needs of the one out weight the needs of the many and do the needs of the many out weight the needs of the one

Table 131 PDR CDR Transportability

PDR Transportability
1. Review HWCI to determine if the design meets size and weight to permit economical handling, loading, securing, transporting, and disassembly for shipment using in house and commercial carriers. Identify potential outsized and overweight items. Identify system items defined as being hazardous. Ensure packaging afforded hazardous items complies with hazardous materials regulations.
2. Identify HWCIs requiring special temperature and humidity control or those possessing sensitive and shock susceptibility characteristics. Determine special transportation requirements and availability for use with these HWCIs.
3. Review Transportability Analysis to determine that transportation conditions have been evaluated and that these conditions are reflected in the design of protective, shipping, and handling devices. In addition to size and weight characteristics, determine that analysis includes provisions for temperature and humidity controls, minimization of sensitivity, susceptibility to shock, and transit damage.
CDR Transportability
1. Review transportability evaluations accomplished for those items identified as outsized, overweight, sensitive, and or requiring special temperature and humidity controls.
2. Review actions taken as a result of the above evaluation to ensure adequate facilities and military or commercial transporting equipment are available to support system requirements during Production and Deployment Phases.

---

[219] Ethics is not part of MIL-STD-1521B, it is being offered in this text.

Table 131 PDR CDR Transportability

3. Review design of special materials handling equipment, when required, and action taken to acquire equipment. 4. Ensure DOD Certificates of Essentiality for movement of equipment have been obtained for equipment exceeding limitations of criteria established in contract requirements. 5. Ensure transportability approval has been annotated on design documents and remain as long as no design changes are made that modify significant transportability parameters. 6. Identify equipment to be test loaded for air transportability of material in Cargo Aircraft.

Table 132 PDR CDR Test

PDR Test
1. Review all changes to the System Subsystem, HWCI Development, Software Requirements, and Interface Requirements Specifications subsequent to the established Allocated Baseline to determine whether test section of all these specifications adequately reflects these changes.
2. Review test concepts for Development Test and Evaluation (DT&E) testing (both informal and formal). Information includes: a. The organization and responsibilities of the group that will be responsible for test.
b. The management of in-house development test effort provides for: (1) Test Methods (plans procedures) (2) Test Reports (3) Resolution of problems and errors (4) Retest procedure (5) Change control and configuration management (6) Identification of any special test tools not deliverable
c. The methodology to be used to meet quality assurance requirements qualification requirements, including the test repeatability characteristics and approach to regression testing. d. The progress status of the test effort since the previous reporting milestone.
3. Review status of all negative or provisional entries such as "not applicable (N A)" or "to be determined (TBD)" in the test section of the System Subsystem, hardware Development, Software Requirements or Interface Requirements Specifications. Review all positive entries for technical adequacy. Ensure that associated test documentation includes these changes. 4. Review interface test requirements specified in the test section of the hardware Development, Software Requirements, and Interface Requirements Specifications for compatibility, currency, technical adequacy, elimination of redundant test. Ensure that all associated test documents reflect these interface requirements. 5. Ensure that all test planning documentation has been updated to include new test support requirements and provisions for long-lead time support requirements. 6. Review contractor test data from prior testing to determine if such data negates the

Table 132 PDR CDR Test

need for additional testing.
7. Examine all available breadboards, mock-ups, or devices which will be used in implementing the test program or which affect the test program, for program impact.

8. Review plans for software Unit testing to ensure that they:
a. Address Unit level sizing, timing, and accuracy requirements.
b. Present general and specific requirements that will be demonstrated by Unit testing.
c. Describe the required test-unique support software, hardware, and facilities and the interrelationship of these items.
d. Describe how, when, and from where the test-unique support items will be obtained.
e. Provide test schedules consistent with higher level plans.

9. Review plans for CSC integration testing to ensure that they:
a. Define the type of testing required for each level of the software structure above the unit level.
b. Present general and specific requirements that will be demonstrated by CSC integration testing.
c. Describe the required test-unique support software, hardware, and facilities and the interrelationship of these items.
d. Describe how, when, and from where the test-unique support items will be obtained.

e. Describe CSC integration test management, to include:
(1) Organization and responsibilities of the test team
(2) Control procedures to be applied during test
(3) Test reporting
(4) Review of CSC integration test results
(5) Generation of data to be used in CSC integration testing.

f. Provide test schedules consistent with higher level plans.

10. Review plans for formal CSCI testing to ensure that they:
a. Define the objective of each CSCI test, and relate the test to the software requirements being tested.
b. Relate formal CSCI tests to other test phases.
c. Describe support software, hardware, and facilities required for CSCI testing; and how, when, and from where they will be obtained.
d. Describe CSCI test roles and responsibilities.
e. Describe requirements for Government-provided software, hardware, facilities, data, and documentation.
f. Provide CSCI test schedules consistent with higher- level plans.
g. Identify software requirements that will be verified by each formal CSCI test.

CDR Test

1. Review updating changes to all specifications subsequent to the PDR, to determine whether the test section of the specifications adequately reflects these changes.
2. Review all available test documentation for currency, technical adequacy, and compatibility with the test section of all Specification requirements.
3. For any development model, prototype, etc., on which testing may have been performed, examine test results for design compliance with hardware Development,

Table 132 PDR CDR Test

Software Requirements, and Interface Requirements Specification requirements.
4. Review quality assurance provisions qualification requirements in HWCI Product, Software Requirements, or Interface Requirements Specifications for completeness and technical adequacy. The test sections of these specifications include the minimum requirements that the item, materiel, or process must meet to be acceptable.
5. Review all test documentation that supports test requirements of the HWCI Product Specifications for compatibility, technical adequacy, and completeness.
6. Inspect any breadboards, mockups, or prototype hardware available for test program implications.

7. Review Software Test Descriptions to ensure they are consistent with the Software Test Plan and they thoroughly identify necessary parameters and prerequisites to enable execution of each planned software test and monitoring of test results. As a minimum, test descriptions identify the following for each test:
a. Required preset hardware and software conditions and the necessary input data, including the source for all data.
b. Criteria for evaluating test results.
c. Prerequisite conditions to be established or set prior to test execution.
d. Expected or predicted test results.

Table 133 PDR CDR Maintenance and Data

PDR Maintenance and Data
1. Describe System Maintenance concept for impact on design and SE. Review adequacy of maintenance plans. Coverage provided for On Equipment (Organizational), Off Equipment - On Site (Intermediate), Off Equipment - Off Site (Depot) level maintenance of Externally Furnished Equipment, and Internally Furnished Equipment. 2. Determine degree of understanding of the background, purpose, requirements, and usage of Maintenance (failure) Data Collection and Historical Status Records. 3. Describe method of providing Maintenance, Failure, Reliability, Maintainability Data. 4. Describe how requirements are submitted for Equipment Classification (EQ CL) Codes when this requirement exists. 5. Review plans for and status of Work Unit Coding of the equipment. Work Unit codes are available for documenting Maintenance Data commencing with configuration item Subsystem Testing.
CDR Maintenance and Data
1. Review adequacy of maintenance plans. 2. Review status of unresolved maintenance and maintenance data problems since PDR. 3. Review status of compliance with the Reliability, Maintainability Data Reporting and Feedback Failure Summary Reports.

Table 134 PDR CDR Spare Parts and Externally Furnished Property

PDR Spare Parts and Externally Furnished Property
1. Review logistics and provisioning planning to Ensure full understanding of scope of requirements in these areas and that a reasonable time-phased plan has been developed for accomplishment. Of specific concern are the areas of: provisioning requirements, externally provided equipment usage, and spare parts, and support during installation,

Table 134 PDR CDR Spare Parts and Externally Furnished Property

checkout, and test. 2. Review provisioning actions and identify existing or potential provisioning problems - logistic critical and long lead time items are identified and evaluated against use of the interim release requirements. 3. Review plans for maximum screening and usage of externally provided equipment, and extent plans have been implemented. 4. Review progress toward determining and acquiring total installation, checkout, and test support requirements.
CDR Spare Parts and Externally Furnished Property
1. Review provisioning planning through normal logistics channels and Administrative Contracting Officer (ACO) representative (Industrial Specialist) to ensure its compatibility (content and time phasing) with contractual requirements. The end objective is to provision by a method which ensures system supportability at operational date of the first site. Also accomplish the following: a. Ensure understanding of contractual requirements, including time phasing, instructions from logistics support agencies, interim release authority and procedure, and responsibility to deliver spare repair parts by need date. b. Determine that scheduled provisioning actions, such as, guidance meetings, interim release and screening are being accomplished adequately and on time. c. Identify existing or potential provisioning problems. 2. Determine quantitative and qualitative adequacy of provisioning drawings and data. Verify that Logistics Critical items are listed for consideration and that adequate procedures exist for reflecting design change information in provisioning documentation and Technical Orders. 3. Ensure support requirements have been determined for installation, checkout, and test for approval by contracting agency. Ensure screening has been accomplished and results are included into support requirements lists. 4. Determine that adequate storage space requirements have been programmed for on-site handling of Installation and Checkout (I&C), test support material, and a scheme has been developed for down streaming and joint use of insurance (high cost) or catastrophic failure support items.

Table 135 PDR CDR Packaging Special Design Protective Equipment

PDR Packaging SDPE
1. Analyze all available specifications (System Subsystem, HWCI Development, Software Requirements, Interface Requirements, and Critical Items) for packaging requirements for each product fabrication and material specification. 2. Evaluate user operational support requirements and maintenance concepts for effect and influence on package design. 3. Establish that time phased plan for package design development is in consonance with the development of the equipment design. 4. Review planned and or preliminary equipment designs for ease of packaging and simplicity of package design, and identify areas where a practical design change would materially decrease cost, weight, or volume of packaging required. 5. Review requirements for SDPE necessary to effectively support configuration item during transportation, handling and storage processes. Ensure SDPE is categorized as a

Table 135 PDR CDR Packaging Special Design Protective Equipment

configuration item using specifications conforming to the types and forms as prescribed. Review SDPE development product specifications for adequacy of performance interface requirements. 6. Determine initial package design baselines, concepts, parameters, constraints, etc., to the extent possible at this phase of the configuration item development process. 7. Ensure previously developed and approved package design data for like or similar configuration items are being used. 8. Establish plans for trade studies to determine the most economical and desirable packaging design approach needed to satisfy the functional performance and logistic requirements. 9. Verify the adequacy of the prototype package design. 10. Review the packaging section of the Specification to ensure full understanding of the requirements. Identify package specification used for hazardous materials.

CDR Packaging SDPE
1. Review proposed package design to ensure that adequate protection to the HWCI, and the media on which the CSCI is recorded, is provided against natural and induced environments hazards to which the equipment will be subjected throughout its life cycle, and to ensure compliance with contractual requirements. Analysis includes: a. Methods of preservation b. Physical mechanical shock protection including cushioning media, shock mounting and isolation features, load factors, support pads, cushioning devices, blocking and bracing, etc. c. Mounting facilities and securing hold-down provisions d. Interior exterior container designs. e. Handling provisions and compatibility with aircraft materials handling system f. Container marking g. Consideration and identification of dangerous hazardous commodities 2. Review design of SDPE HWCI to determine if a category I container is required. The analysis of the proposed container or handling, shipping equivalent encompasses as a minimum: a. Location and type of internal mounting or attaching provisions b. Vibration - shock isolation features, based on the pre-determined fragility rating (or other constraint of the item to be shipped.) c. Service items (indicators, relief valves, etc.) d. Environmental control features e. External handling, stacking and tie-down provisions with stress ratings. f. Dimensional and weight data (gross and net) g. Bill-of-material h. Marking provisions including the center-of-gravity location i. For wheeled SDPE (self-powered or tractor trailer) the overall length, width, and height with mounted item, turning radius, mobility, number of axles, unit contact load, number of tires, etc. j. Position and travel of adjustable wheels, titling, or other adjustments to facilitate loading. 3. Review the results of trade studies, engineering analyses, etc., to substantiate selected package SDPE design approach, choice of materials, handling provisions, environmental

Table 135 PDR CDR Packaging Special Design Protective Equipment

features, etc.
4. Ensure that package SDPE design provides reasonable balance between cost and desired performance.
5. Review all preproduction test results of the prototype package design to Ensure that the HWCI is afforded the proper degree of protection.
6. Review Packaging Section of the HWCI Product Specification for correct format, accuracy and technical adequacy.
7. Review contractor procedures to assure that the requirements for Preparation for Delivery of the approved HWCI Product Specification, will be incorporated into the package design data for provisioned spares.

Table 136 PDR CDR Technical Manuals

PDR and CDR Technical Manuals
1. Review status of the "Technical Manual Publications Plan" to Ensure that all aspects of the plan have been considered to the extent that all concerned agencies are apprised of the technical manual coverage to be obtained under this procurement. The suitability of available commercial manuals and or modifications thereto shall also be determined.
2. Review the availability of technical manuals for validation verification during the latter phases of DT&E testing.
3. If a Guidance Conference was not accomplished or if open items resulted from it, then review as applicable provisions for accomplishing TO in-process reviews, validation, verification, prepublication, and post publication reviews.

Table 137 PDR CDR System Allocation Document

PDR and CDR System Allocation Document
1. Review the Draft System Allocation Document for completeness and technical adequacy to extent completed.
2. The format provides the following minimum information: a. Drawing Number b. Issue c. Number of Sheets d. Location e. Configuration Item Number f. Title g. Part Number h. Serial Number i. Specification Number j. Equipment Nomenclature k. Configuration Item Quantity l. Assembly Drawing

Table 138 PDR CDR Design Producibility and Manufacturing

PDR Design Producibility and Manufacturing
1. Demonstrate and present evidence that manufacturing engineering will be integrated into the design process.   a. Provide evidence of performing producibility analyses on development hardware trading off design requirements against manufacturing risk, cost, production, volume, and existing capability availability. Evidence of such analyses must conclusively demonstrate that in-depth analyses were performed by qualified organizations individuals and the results of those analyses will be incorporated in the design.   b. Preliminary manufacturing engineering and production planning demonstrations address: material and component selection, preliminary production sequencing, methods and flow concepts, new processes, manufacturing risk, equipment and facility utilization for intended rates and volume, production in-process and acceptance test and inspection concepts. (Efforts to maximize productivity in the above areas should be demonstrated.)   c. Management systems to be used will ensure that producibility and manufacturing considerations are integrated throughout the development effort.   2. The producibility and manufacturing concerns identified in the SRR and the SDR are updated and expanded to: a. Provide evidence that concerns identified in the Manufacturing Feasibility Assessment and the Production Capability Estimate are addressed and that resolutions are planned or have been performed.   b. Make recommendations including manufacturing technology efforts and provide a schedule of necessary actions to resolve open manufacturing concerns and reduce manufacturing risk.
CDR Design Producibility and Manufacturing
1. Review the status of all producibility (and productivity) efforts for cost and schedule considerations.   2. Review the status of efforts to resolve manufacturing concerns identified in previous technical reviews and their cost and schedule impact to the production program.   3. Review the status of Manufacturing Technology programs and other previously recommended actions to reduce cost, manufacturing risk and industrial base concerns.   4. Identify open manufacturing concerns that require additional direction effort to minimize risk to the production program.   5. Review the status of manufacturing engineering efforts, tooling and test equipment demonstrations, proofing of new materials, processes, methods, and special tooling test equipment.   6. Review the intended manufacturing management system and organization for the production program in order to show how their efforts will effect a smooth transition into production.

10.6 Diminishing Manufacturing Sources Material Shortages

Diminishing Manufacturing Sources and Material Shortages (DMSMS) is the loss or expected loss of manufactures of items or raw materials. This includes the loss of remaining items that may be in the supply chain (warehouses of distributors, manufacturers, retailers, and other end users). Although this is usually associated with items that have relatively short life like electronic components, devices, and subsystems it also applies to long lifetime items like infrastructure. Not all systems are worth moving into the DMSMS category. The systems in this category:

- They are useful
- They have parts that are approaching end of life
- The systems have a longer expected life than the diminishing parts

There are various approaches for dealing with systems in this category. They range from being very simple with low costs to complex with high costs where the system is examined for improvement and may result in new functionality and or new performance. The approaches from lowest to highest cost and complexity are:

- Excess stock, least cost, most desired
- Reclamation
- Repair
- Replacement parts
- Replacement supplier
- Emulation
- Complex substitute
- Lifetime buy
- Form fit function assembly redesign
- Technology refresh technology insertion, most cost, least desired

Author Comment: As we continue to build out our high technology society there is more need to develop design solutions from the DMSMS perspective. The needs, functionality, performance, and other system characteristics are well understood. The danger is the desire to reduce the system performance and quality levels such that the system is only tolerated, resulting in massive disruption. For example the analog Television (TV) system was replaced with a digital TV system. As a result users who were able to receive analog TV signals of lower but acceptable quality now get no digital TV signal. The new digital TV system is very brittle and does not gracefully degrade in performance like the analog system. However it is very amenable to a dedicated for cost cable delivery system where cost, quality, and management incentives are tied to bits per second. The end result is poor pixilated cable driven TV signals as the norm rather than the exception.

The DMSMS program might follow:

- **Prepare:** Plan, setup team, setup processes
- **Identify Access:** Logistics, design, and other information products. Identify items with immediate and near term obsolescence.

- **Assess:** Problem areas and prioritize items most at DMSMS risk.
- **Analyze:** Develop a set of potential approaches for the high-risk items.
- **Implement:** Budget, fund, schedule, and execute selected solutions.

10.7 Design Metrics

Once there is a design how might the design be evaluated? It would be easy to count the numbers of things in a design. For example the number of parts, lines of code, fasteners, support studs, number of hardware chips, number of gates per chip number of nails, the amount of concrete poured. But that does not provide the information needed to understand the design and its worthiness. The following is a starting point for possible design metrics.

- Growth and technology insertion ability
- Completeness, Consistency, Correctness, Simplicity
- Attention to details
- Simple effective internal interfaces
- Simple effective external interfaces
- Balanced subsystems and Symmetry
- Appropriate technology readiness levels
- Appropriate technology maturity levels
- Weakest links are more than strong enough
- Commonality to minimize parts training and complexity
- Interoperability

They tend to be qualitative rather than quantitative in nature. Working in a qualitative domain is difficult and contains risks. Unfortunately we are unable to provide other approaches for understanding our systems. If we fall into the trap of counting and tracking items in a design they quickly become useless and are easily compromised. This is the dilemma of management that has no domain knowledge and is part if the discourse of – can managers effectively manage in a situation where they have no knowledge. Infrastructure design metrics might also include:

- Never stops providing services
- Never provides wrong output
- Never provides conflicting output

Author Comment: Consider that electric power is always on, always provides the correct voyage, always provides the correct frequency, and never provides conflicting frequencies (out of phase, always in sync). These might be considered requirements but there are designs that fail to live up to these basic requirements. There are poor designs, there is no excuse other than very bad management that is calling the shots.

Many design metrics appear to be tradeoff criteria when selecting architecture and design alternatives. However in this case the selection has been made and so we are looking for design deficiencies that need to be addressed. If we are unable to find deficiencies then the design can be considered not fatally flawed. If an external reviewer can find design deficiencies using design metrics, it does not reflect well on a team that should have been working the design problems for an extended period.

10.8 Process

At this stage the designs are being reviewed. The process should be driven by the need to identify meaningful reviews and expectations at each review. The difficulty arises when the team is unable to have a successful review. This situation requires special care to ensure the team is not demoralized, yet understands that there are deficiencies that must be addressed. The review process should reflect these basic needs.

10.9 Some Key Points

- ➢ A subsystem has well defined
  - Interfaces
  - Functionality
  - Performance

- ➢ A subsystem may be satisfied by
  - Multiple vendors
  - Unique design
  - A combination of make buy modify reuse

- ➢ A piece part has well defined
  - Interfaces
  - Functionality
  - Performance

- ➢ A piece part may be satisfied by
  - Multiple vendors
  - Unique design
  - A combination of make buy modify reuse

- ➢ Design reviews are held periodically to check on the progress of the design

to ensure
- System requirements are being satisfied
- Design concept is not being compromised
- Architecture concept is not being compromised

➤ The role of systems engineering during preliminary design is to ensure
- System requirements are being satisfied
- Design concept is not being compromised
- Architecture concept is not being compromised

➤ The SRR is a formal review to establish the baseline system requirements

➤ The SDR is a formal review of the system architecture at the highest level

➤ The PDR is a formal technical review of the basic design approach for a
- Configuration item or
- Related group of configuration items

➤ The PDR includes
- Hardware Development Specification(s)
- Software Top Level Design Document(s) (STLDD)
- Software Test Plan (STP)
- Hardware Test Plan
- Preliminary versions of the Computer System Operator's Manual (CSOM)
- Software User's Manual (SUM)
- Computer System Diagnostic Manual (CSDM)
- Computer Resources Integrated Support Document (CRISD) are available
- Prior to the start of detailed design

➤ A CDR is held for each configuration item prior to fabrication, production, coding release

➤ The role of systems engineering during final design is to ensure
- System requirements are being satisfied
- Design concept is not being compromised
- Architecture concept is not being compromised

➤ The CDR includes
- Draft Hardware Product Specifications

- Software Detailed Design Documents (SDDD)
- Database Design Documents (DBDD)
- Interface Design Documents (IDD)
- Engineering drawings

➢ Engineering drawings satisfy requirements established by the hardware Development Specification and Software Top Level Design Documents (STLDD)

➢ The CDR includes
- Computer Software Operator's Manuals (CSOM)
- Software User's Manuals (SUM)
- Computer System Diagnostic Manuals (CSDM)
- Software Programmer's Manuals (SPM)
- Firmware Support Manuals (FSM)

➢ A CDR is the final review and signals that production and implementation can start

➢ After CDR the role of system engineering is to monitor production and implementation to ensure
- System requirements are being satisfied
- Design concept is not being compromised
- Architecture concept is not being compromised

➢ DMSMS is
- The loss or expected loss of manufactures of items or raw materials
- Important as old systems need to be updated rather than replaced

➢ Design metrics
- Are not counts of trivial items in a design
- They are complex qualitative items associated with a domain

10.10 Exercises

1. What is the purpose of the SRR, SDR, PDR and CDR?
2. Should systems be engaged in monitoring the subsystem and element detailed designs? If so why? If Not why not?
3. What can cause a subsystem or element design to fail?
4. What are the activities associated with contract monitoring?
5. Should systems actually perform the detailed design and implementation of

some of the system elements? If so, which ones and why, if not why not?

10.11 Additional Reading

1. Diminishing Manufacturing Sources and Material Shortages A Guidebook of Best Practices and Tools for Implementing a DMSMS Management Program, SD-22, Defense Standardization Program Office, Sep 2009.
2. Systems Engineering Management Plan (SEMP), DOD Data Item Description, DI-MGMT-81024 August 1990.
3. Technical Reviews And Audits Systems Equipments And Computer Software, MIL-STD-1521A June 1976, MIL-STD-1521B June 1995.
4. Anthropometry of US Military Personnel, DOD-HDBK-743A, February 1991.

11 System Design Verification and Validation

The current model for systems testing is based on verification and validation. All testing falls into those two categories. Verification testing ensures that the system meets the specifications. Many restate this as was the system built correctly. Validation testing ensures that the system supports the user needs. Many restate this as was the right system built. This is an interesting model but it does not help to identify all the different tests that might be needed to fully test a system design. In practice there are different kinds of tests with different names addressing some aspect of verification and validation.

There are different views and abstraction levels associated with test. One view is that of development versus production tests. The idea is that production test should not duplicate development test but should focus on the needs of production and what happens when production errors are made. Production tests should be able to detect all possible production errors. If development testing is pushed to production there is a serious problem. Knowing which tests apply in a given development, production, and user setting is fundamental to the design of a test program.

A similar situation exists with verification and validation. It is well known that verification tests are only as good as the specifications. If the specifications are devoid of key content then validation will unfortunately catch the problems. For example, if the specifications have no environmental requirements and the system needs to operate in cold and hot climates validation will catch system failures as the temperature extremes are encountered. That is a bad time to catch these missing requirements because the cost of correction is significant. At the extreme there are no specifications and testers are forced to imagine what they think the requirements might be and they build tests accordingly. In these severely dysfunctional settings everyone typically beats down the testers until the tests have no value. It does not matter because once the system is fielded it will be validated. In that process it will either be accepted or rejected. The big problem arises when the users are forced to live with a really bad system.

Test can be the bearer of bad news resulting from very bad engineering and management. It also can be the bearer of great news where a strong test program shows the system design is truly great. If we are driven by the goal that the primary reason to engage in design is to offer something that is a breakthrough once compared to the status quo then the test program is a key element to that great design.

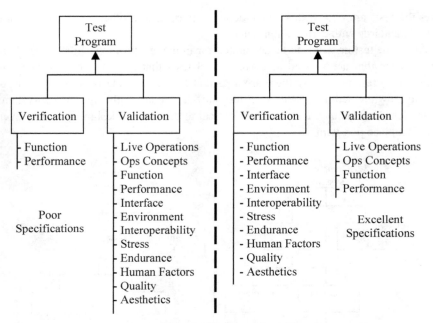

Figure 162 Test Programs and Specification Quality

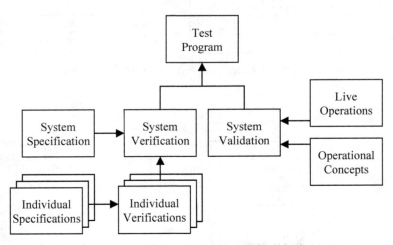

Figure 163 Verification and Validation

11.1 System Test Complexity

The complexity of the system test program is not only driven by the amount of new design in the system it is also driven by the structural complexity of the system. Each system level represents one or more designs that need to be tested. In some cases the tests are new with standalone test reports and in other cases the tests are part of standards with certification letters.

All of the testing needs to be accounted for in the test program. In addition there are the tests that are viewed as system level tests that need to be performed by system level testers. Finally there are tests that are not considered system level but need to be witnessed by system level test staff. These are typically new subsystems or smaller elements that are extremely critical to the system design. This may even include a piece part item.

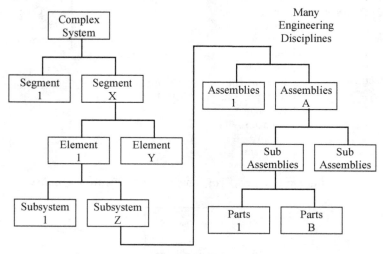

Figure 164 Complex System Test Hierarchy

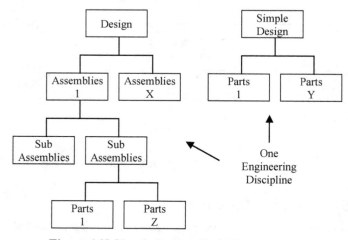

Figure 165 Simple Design Test Hierarchies

The ramification of a complex system is a complex test program. Each of the abstraction levels needs to be tested and accounted for in terms of test results. This puts a huge burden at the system level where all the documents and letters need to be reviewed, managed, and stored.

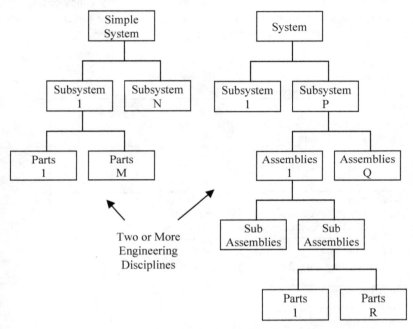

Figure 166 Less Complex Test Hierarchy

When test is involved in the early architecture design decisions especially at the physical architecture design phase they can easily point to the structural complexity leading to test complexity. Some designs will he more difficult to test and manage during the test activities.

11.2 Test Program Design

The design of the test program can use the same model as the design of the system. Initially there is a test concept. Then there is the physical structure of the test activities. There are alternatives in bundling test procedure groups and some groupings make more sense than other groupings. Finally there is the implementation details. This includes who will perform the tests, who will witness the tests, how will findings be captured and fed back into the design team, what are the locations of testing, and what are the test equipment and tools.

On the surface one could suggest that if two elements that form a complete system are individually tested the testing would be complete. However this fails to acknowledge that the two elements interact or interface in the system. That interface or interaction needs to be tested. Also in a system the whole is greater than the sum of its parts. Conversely testing at the system level is also incomplete because there are always element areas that can not be sufficiently accessed for test at the system level. Yet these areas, if they do not behave as expected may cause serious system issues. So a system test program is a combination of complete lower level tests and progressively higher level tests until the system level is reached.

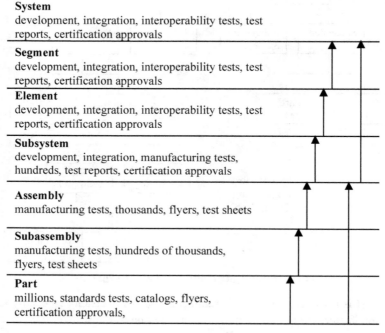

Figure 167 Test Roll Up

The test program includes many tests at different levels of the system decomposition. As the tests move up the decomposition tree there are fewer and fewer test documents housing the test procedures. However all the tests need to be accounted for at the system level. This can be managed by passing authority to the appropriate levels but the authorities must issue formal communications that their levels of testing have been completed. This should also include statements of any risk areas not mitigated. For example a component may be able to meet all requirements except for a vibration requirement. This must be captured as part of official documents, letters of approval, from appropriate members on the team.

The test concept and physical structure is typically captured in the master test plan. The individual child test plans then capture the concept and physical structure at the respective abstraction level. The test procedures capture the implementation details including the test steps and tools.

11.3 Test Approaches

Early in the system development, operational concepts are developed along with a functional decomposition. The tests can be organized using these groupings. So the tests can be based on operational threads, functions, or both threads and functions.

Most test strategies use a combination of thread and functional based test. The context is thread translates to operational sequences or threads and functional translates to requirements. It makes no sense to test something 50 times while ignoring something else, which may result if the dogma of just operational thread based testing is adopted. Also if the dogma of just functional testing is adopted the system will never even be tried in an operational scenario. In theory nothing should be ignored if the tests are traceable to the requirements. However different initial conditions, configuration, and ending conditions not captured in the requirements or operational concepts should result in tests and these tests may uncover significant issues. So there is a third element that many ignore. The element is sequence. A comprehensive test approach can be viewed as:

Strategy = Operational Threads + Functional Tests + Sequence Considerations

11.4 Characteristics of Good Tests

Good tests have certain characteristics. These characteristics are:

- **Atomic**: This means the test procedures are standalone. The test procedures are not dependent on other test procedure or a test sequence.
- **Traceable**: The atomic test procedures are traceable to a reasonable number of requirements. This traceability comes into question if large numbers of requirements are linked to an atomic test case test procedure. Many times it is helpful to encode the requirement text or portions of the requirement text in the test step where the requirement satisfaction is claimed. Obviously this does not mean a copy and paste of the requirements into the test procedures.
- **Thread Oriented**: Test threads may differ from operational threads, although they may appear to be very similar. Test threads try to minimize the number of configuration changes between atomic test procedures. Although each test is atomic, they should take advantage of certain previous tests. For example power cycling and reinstalling software between each test may add several minutes to each test which can translate into hours or days. This wasted time can be used for additional test coverage.
- **Standalone**: Test procedures should be completely standalone. No additional information products should be needed to complete the test. This does not mean that a test procedure does not include other information products such as a product flyer, datasheet, etc. It just means the test

procedure contains everything needed to complete the test.

- **Signature Block**: Each test procedure should end with a signature block for the witnesses to mark that they have seen the test executed as written or as redlined and initialed. The signature block defines the boundary of the atomic test procedure.

Example 32 Test Procedure Document Organization

In a book of 150 test procedures there are 150 signature blocks and any test can be executed in any sequence. However the ideal sequence is organized from beginning to end in the test procedure book. The ideal sequence minimizes the test setup and configuration time as each test builds upon the next test. Just because the ideal test sequence is embedded in the test procedure book, it does not mean that sequence must be followed. The sequence can change as needed with time.

There are different strategies that can be used to select the test execution sequence of any test procedure document or book. One approach is to start with the easy tests and progress to the more complex tests. Another approach is to organize the sequence to minimize the test setup time, the natural order of the test procedure document. Test setup time may be a big issue if it takes hours or even days to setup for a few 10-minute tests. Yet another approach is to start with the complex tests or tests that are suspected to have issues. This allows for time to address these issues while the simple tests are being executed in parallel.

11.5 Test V-Diagram

The Test V-Diagram[220] was created to show a new approach to test and integration for a new system that would start to automate the cognitive processes of its system operators. It was driven by the new challenge to surface latent defects in the software. It was recognized that software could be untested using existing test approaches. So to offer full test coverage of the software the concept of bottom up integration and test was suggested. It was later modified and adopted by others[221] to represent systems engineering at a high level[222].

It is unclear if it originated with the VEE Heuristic[223]. It would make sense

---

[220] Test V-Diagram first appeared at Hughes Aircraft circa 1982 on the Federal Aviation Administration (FAA) Advanced Automation System (AAS) program pre-proposal effort.

[221] The reason the V is such a powerful and enduring image comes from the Hughes culture of coupling all text to powerful multidimensional images. This was the foundation of Sequential Thematic Organization of Publications (STOP) invented at Hughes in 1963.

[222] The Relationship of System Engineering to the Project Cycle, Kevin Forsberg and Harold Mooz, National Council On Systems Engineering (NCOSE) and American Society for Engineering Management (ASEM), 21–23 October 1991.

[223] Educating, Gowin, D.B., Ithaca, N.Y., Cornell University Press. 1981. Gowin

because so many people from education, psychology, cognitive processing, knowledge management, etc were working with computer systems in the 1970's. A side oriented V appeared in DOD-STD-2167 circa 1982 to represent the software development cycle. In this case it showed parallelism between established hardware development and emerging software development. It suggested an approach for building the next generation software systems and showed the different abstraction levels of the design associated with the major milestones used to manage the effort.

Decomposition as a top down activity was fully accepted at that time. Test as a bottom up activity was obvious in most cases but not fully articulated. The thought process was that the bottoms up test approach would complement the top down decomposition and offered an alternative view of the system. Strong traceability would be used between the tests and the associated requirements. Strong bi-directional traceability also would be used between the various specifications.

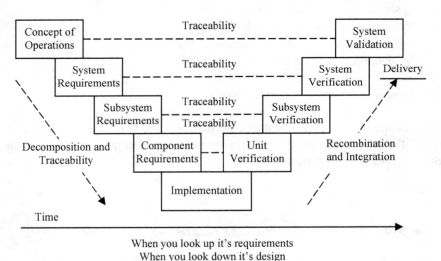

Figure 168 Test V-Diagram

The bottoms up activity blended well with the natural progression of integration. So tests would be performed at the lowest levels so that all conditions and cases could be evaluated and not hidden or prevented from stimulation by a higher level abstraction. Also as the integration continues the interfaces could be fully tested.

developed the VEE heuristic to help students understand knowledge structure (relational networks, hierarchies, and combinations) and understand the process of knowledge construction. It assumes knowledge is not absolute but depends on concepts, theories, and methodologies used to view the world.

11.6 Verification

Verification testing is used to determine if the system is designed and implemented according to the specifications. The requirements are allocated to different test levels and to different test procedures and cases within the procedures. That allocation represents the bi-directional traceable path between each requirement and each atomic test procedure.

The test procedures can be grouped as needed for the unique system but should respect the concept of unit, subsystem, and system level verification. There may be many unit test procedure books, many subsystem test procedure books, but only a few system test procedure books. Examples for splitting the system procedures into separate books are:

- System Environmental Test Procedures
- System Functional Test Procedures
- System Performance Test Procedures
- System Recovery Test Procedures
- System Interoperability Test Procedures
- System Certification Test Procedures

Specifications are imperfect and changes may be made to the specifications as a result of the tests. However these changes should be minimal if a good system engineering activity was performed.

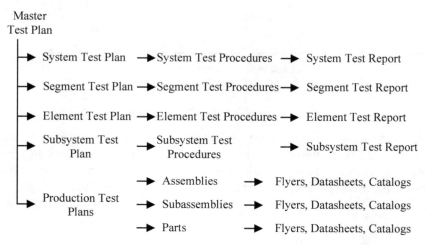

Figure 169 System Roll Up Test Artifacts

As the tests are dry run in preparation for formal test witnessing, defects will surface. These defects and resulting changes need to be formally tracked using a defect-tracking tool. Whenever a defect is detected as much information about the defect should be gathered and documented. This should include an initial assessment of the defect[224].

Table 139 Priorities Used For Classifying Defects

Priority	Applies if a problem could
1 Grave	a. Prevent accomplishment of an operational or mission essential capability b. Jeopardize safety, security, or other requirement designated critical c. Result in loss of life or health
2 Catastrophic	a. Adversely affect the accomplishment of an operational or mission essential capability and no work-around solution is known b. Adversely affect technical, cost, or schedule risks to the project or to life cycle support of the system, and no work-around solution is known
3 Critical	a. Adversely affect the accomplishment of an operational or mission essential capability but a work-around solution is known b. Adversely affect technical, cost, or schedule risks to the project or to life cycle support of the system, but a work-around solution is known
4 Marginal	a. Result in user operator inconvenience or annoyance but does not affect a required operational or mission essential capability b. Result in inconvenience or annoyance for development or support personnel, but does not prevent the accomplishment of those responsibilities
5 Negligible	Any other effect

The key to defects and test is to realize that each defect represents a potential class of a problem. If one problem was uncovered then it is very likely the same problem exists in another area of the design and or implementation. Once this concept is fully understood then it becomes clear that defects should be grouped and treated as a whole with the realization that the entire design and implementation needs to be examined and scrubbed based on these defects.

Author Comment: With the rise of management that is unwilling to learn about the domain they are managing, serious flaws have been introduced into the test defect tracking and closure process. The flaw is centered on the approach that only a specific defect is addressed at any given instant. There is no willingness to accept that this is a learning opportunity to discover all the problems associated with the design and that a defect is a clue that must be pursued. Also, there is no desire to admit that when a single defect is treated as a standalone event, there is enormous overhead associated with it as it is addressed.

This is typically a software scenario. However a good example outside of software is, imagine purchasing a new house. The house has some interior painting

---

[224] MIL-STD-498 Appendix C Category And Priority Classifications For Problem Reporting. There is an overlap with the FMEA categories found in MIL-STD-1629A.

flaws. Rather than the owners offering a few examples, the builder accepting those examples, and then systematically searching for and addressing all paint flaws at once, the painter is only tasked to address the specific flaws pointed out by the new homeowner. Further each flaw is a new scheduled appointment and paint touchup event. This is obviously wrong yet this has become common practice as some view this as a business opportunity in their ignorance dominated situations.

In these situations management will even state that it is perfectly fine if the design has defects that are unknown, buried, lurking in the design. The correct statement is that it is fine to allow a design to have known defects that are placed in a low priority work queue. It is dangerous and stupid to suppress the defect, design understanding, and work off process. This can not be permitted to continue because we live in a complex high technology society that cannot tolerate this type of inefficiency and abuse. We cannot tolerate bad designs.

11.6.1 Verification Plans

The purpose of the verification plan or plans is to capture all the elements of the test program so that personnel, equipment, and facilities can be prepared and made available when needed. The test plan also captures the test philosophy so that the stakeholders can agree on the approach. For example some test programs may be large needing multiple test plans addressing specific areas. Some test approaches are highly automated using state-of-the-art tools while others are manually intensive using large numbers of people. If there are multiple test plans a master test plan introduces the plans and their interrelationships. It also serves as the parent source of common practices and tools such as problem tracking.

Table 140 Test Plan Suggestions

• Master Test Plan (The Plan Of Plans)	• Stress Test Plan
• Hardware, Software, Integration Test Plans	• Interoperability Test Plan
• Safety Test Plan	• System Test Plan
• Security Test Plan	• Production Test Plan
• Environment Test Plan	• Final Acceptance Test Plan

Table 141 Test Plan Outline Suggestion

1.0 Introduction
1.1 Brief description of system under test
1.2 Relationships to other test plans, procedures, and reports
2.0 Reference documents
3.0 Test environment
3.1 Test configuration
3.2 Test tools, data recording, and data reduction approach tools
3.3 Problem tracking approach and tools

Table 141 Test Plan Outline Suggestion

3.4 Requirement traceability
4.0 Test logistics
4.1 Test location and security considerations
4.2 Participating organizations, roles, responsibilities, and personnel (test director, testers, quality assurance, sponsors, customers, etc)
4.3 Orientation and training needs
4.4 Process used to validate tests were executed
4.5 Planned test schedule and relationship to other milestones
5.0 List of planned tests
Appendix - Test Verification Cross Reference Matrix (VCRM) listing tests and requirements verified by each test.

11.6.2 Verification Procedures

The verification procedure takes the verification plan and updates the current plan content with the latest information and then introduces test procedures with test steps in a new section. The VCRM is also updated to reflect the changes surfaced while adding the test procedures and their associated test steps.

The test procedures are atomic or standalone blocks starting with the test purpose or objective and ending with a signature block where all the test witnesses sign off that the procedure as written or as marked up was executed.

Table 142 Test Procedure Outline Suggestion

1.0 - 5.0 Updated from plan
6.1 Test Procedure Name 1 (from test list in section 5.0)
Objective, Requirements verified, Test material, Test configuration settings, Initial conditions, Special test considerations
Test Steps
Test Step 1
Test Step 2
Test Step x
Witness Signatures
6.2 Test Procedure Name 2
6.n Test Procedure Name n
Appendix - Test VCRM

Ideally the tests should be structured so that they are independent and can run in any sequence. However a sequence should be developed that takes advantage of previous configuration setup sequences so that the total test run time for the entire procedure is minimized.

Many latent defects surface as configurations change and sequence changes. Even though the test procedure is optimized for the most efficient formal test run, during dry run the sequences should be naturally permitted to change. This will help to surface sequence and configuration dependent latent defects.

11.6.3 Dry Run Test Execution

Once the procedures are written in the office they need to move from the Ivory Tower to the real test environment. This is known as dry running the test procedures. As part of the dry runs the procedures are updated and defects are uncovered. At some point new defects stop surfacing, old defects have been addressed, and a formal test can be performed. The fully dry run procedures are complete and are submitted for review and acceptance.

As part of the review process requirement traceability is reviewed to ensure all requirements trace to one or more tests. Also, the tests are reviewed to ensure they really verify the requirements. This may be open to interpretation and more test cases may be added to ensure a requirement is verified under all conditions. The conditions might be configuration dependencies, range of values, etc.

Author Comment: Dry run testing is sometimes referred to as exploratory testing. This phrase is inappropriate because it suggests research and study. Test, research, and study may be needed but that is different from maturing and finalizing the test procedures in a controlled setting that is part of multiple dry run sessions. The analogy is actors cleaning up the show before the performance.

11.6.4 Formal Test Execution

The dry runs are rehearsals to get all the bugs out of the design for the final test session. The formal run is the real show with the customer and internal Quality Assurance (QA) witnesses in attendance. The test director[225] typically hosts a Test Readiness Review (TRR) where the artifacts are examined and a determination is made if a test can be started. The items considered in the TRR are open defect reports, test configuration issues, known open requirement issues, etc.

As the tests are executed the steps are typically checked off. If there is a minor problem with a step it is redlined using hand written text and signed, initialed, stamped by QA and the witnesses. At the conclusion of a test all the witnesses sign off the test in the appropriate witness area signature block. If the test fails, it is noted on the procedure, with a note of the failed step or steps. This approach is used to validate that the tests were executed as written.

11.6.5 Test Report

The test report is a log of the formal test run. It includes the as run procedures

---

[225] A test director is associated with a plan, its procedures and the report. They are in charge of the entire test effort and for that body of work. There may be multiple test directors each with their unique set of plans, procedures, and reports.

with redlines, signatures, and new information reporting the test and its results. It is captured in a concise document with the following content.

- **Introduction**: Tests performed and requirements verified at the highest abstraction level. It references the test plan, procedures, and specifications.
- **Summary**: Tests performed by name, test participants, start and end dates, defects written, and a statement if the test session was or was not completed successfully.
- **Test Log**: Organized by date captures the daily events.
- **Detailed Results**: The detailed as run tests, redlines, issues, and defects found for each test. This can point to the appendix.
- **Defects**: List of the defects uncovered during the test.
- **Conclusions and Recommendations**: Statement of the next steps if there are significant redlines, any failed tests, and significant defects.
- **Appendix**: As run test procedures with handwritten checkmarks, redlines, and signatures. The appendix is a way to keep the unique part of the test report small without losing the records of the as run test session.

11.7 Validation

Validation is used to determine if the right or correct system was designed and implemented. This comes from the user perspective. At one level the operational concepts are used to test the system. At another level the community revisits the system mission / need exclusive of any previous notions of the operational concepts and either the system successfully satisfies the mission / need or not.

Validation can start at the development facility where the system is staged before delivery. Operators (includes users and maintainers) can be bought in and the system can be put through various operational scenarios using simulated inputs. Validation can continue at the development facility using some combination of mixed simulation and live data. At some point the system is delivered.

The first site is a key site and is a significant gate. Unlike the operators that may have been used at the development facility, these operators must live with this system. What they say and do is significant. Just like at the development facility, the testing can begin with simulated data, then a combination of simulated and live data, then a session using only live data during an off peak time, such as midnight.

Once confidence is developed, the key site will decide to take the system live with the ability to go back to the previous system[226]. There may be set backs at anytime during this validation sequence, however, eventually all the bugs are worked out and the site goes live with the new system and one or more other sites

---

[226] Some new systems do not have the ability to fall back to a previous system. The decision to remove a fall back approach should never be driven by shortsighted management goals or worse finance. Great system designs have great transition strategies.

are recommended for the new system roll out.

The system is not fully validated until all the sites have been delivered and operating with the new system for a reasonable period of time. This time period may be as long as a year. At some point the old system is phased out as the new system has proven itself. It is validated.

11.8 Accreditation and Certification

Accreditation or certification is given by the organization best positioned to make the judgment that the system is acceptable. The organization may be the operational user or client, program office or sponsor, or a third party entity such as a government agency, depending upon the purposes intended.

Certification usually includes analysis of the process and the solution. It can involve proof like elements. The developers need to show that there was a consistent process that was followed to design and implement the system. Deviation from the process raises concern because it may represent compromises in system. The solution needs to be documented and show strong traceability, especially to the tests. Without the traceability there is concern because once again it may represent compromises in the system.

In many ways the ultimate systems approach needs to be strongly followed with very high levels of accuracy, precision, rigor, and methodical behavior.

11.9 Staging Area Testing

A system should be assembled and tested before it is delivered to the users. For example when purchasing an automobile, the automobile is fully assembled and tested prior to its arrival at a dealer. This testing is performed in a staging area. The staging area is as close to the operational setting as possible. This may not be practical in all instances because interfacing subsystems, elements, segments may be unavailable due to cost or other considerations. In this case these external interfaces are simulated during the staging area testing.

In a manufacturing setting the staging area is typically the quality assurance team that ensures the design was properly manufactured. For a one of a kind system the staging area may be the factory floor at one end of the assembly area or a separate laboratory or other physical location. The point is the design is assembled and tested in a controlled area prior to be shipped and installed.

11.10 Installation and Check Out Testing

Installation and checkout is the final phase of testing where the design team has significant control. The first phase is a preliminary installation and check out where proper installation is verified. This is similar to a manufacturing production test. This is a hectic time and a punch list of things to do on a daily basis is one way to manage the activity. The final phase of the installation and checkout is a set of tests that introduce the new users to the system and begin the transition to validation at an operational fielded site.

Installation and validation begins with site surveys to gather information about the physical location. It continues with training to introduce the users, maintainers, administrators, and managers to the system. It then can proceed with installation and a series of steps that take the system into full-scale operation. This can be captured in a site installation and test procedures plan. The plan elements include:

- Identification of physical locations and roll out sequence
- Site surveys of each location
- Training needs and training rollout sequence

The test procedure elements include:

- **Pre-shakedown Tests**: This is the first step and these tests ensure full installation, check all system elements, ensure proper placement, and make sure the installation meets all safety needs. This can include mechanical and electrical measurements and alignment and adjustments.
- **Shakedown Tests**: This is the next step and these tests ensure that the system meets the performance requirements in the installed environment. Marginal parts and material a replaced.
- **Limited Operational Tests**: These tests are started after everyone agrees the system is correctly installed. These tests are operationally oriented but are performed in a way so that there is minimal disruption to the existing operations. They demonstrate that the system is performing as expected.
- **Onsite Interoperability Tests**: These tests demonstrate that the system interfaces and operates with live external systems as expected. Lab oriented interoperability tests were performed prior to the onsite interoperability tests and all issues were addressed. There is nothing worse than being surprised while onsite.
- **Performance Tests**: These tests demonstrate that the system can handle the full peak operational load once commissioned. This test may not be possible until the system is permitted to be fully used and provide its services. In this instance the previous system remains in place as a backup just incase problems are detected.
- **Full Scale Operations**: The system is allowed to support full-scale operations. If there is a previous system that is being replaced, the previous system is kept in a backup mode just in case it needs to be activated. Once the new system has proven itself over extended operations including several peak load operations, the old system can be removed.

Obviously for a physical structure like a building or a bridge the movement from the Pre-Shakedown tests where everything is physically inspected to full-scale operations is very fast. For a computer-based system the movement is very slow and can take weeks or months.

11.11 Validation Operational Suitability Testing

Validation, operational suitability, and certification is accomplished by following a process that builds confidence in the users and other stakeholders that the system does offer proper services and is operationally acceptable. The elements of the process are:

- Minimize risk by taking small steps by picking one or more key sites, then at the key sites take small steps
- Progressively add more responsibility to the new system in a controlled manner with a fall back position
- Once the system is operational let it work for a period of time so it can prove itself, if available keep the previous system in place as backup
- Commissioning or certification is a stamp of approval given by a body charged with ensuring the system behaves as expected, they provide the approval based on their level of confidence

Obviously the stakeholders will decide the best approach to validation, operational suitability, and commissioning or certification.

11.12 Various Tests, Verifications and Validations

There is a large endless list of tests, verifications and validations. This is just a small sampling of the kinds of tests that may exist in a domain. It is offered to broaden and deepen the perspective on test, verification, and validation.

11.12.1 Highly Accelerated Life Test

Highly Accelerated Life Test (HALT) is used to identify and resolve design weaknesses. It is typically performed during engineering development. It can be performed at the unit, subsystem, or system level. The approach is to progressively apply more environmental stresses in a methodical measured manner until a failure is detected. Obviously this should be beyond the design requirements however surprises do surface when components are integrated into an assembly. There are commercial environmental test chambers available for this type of testing. The environmental stresses are:

- Cold step and Hot step
- Rapid temperature cycles
- Power switch and fluctuation
- Combined stress tests

- Stepped vibration and shock

11.12.2 Safety Tests

Safety tests are used to find unsafe elements in a system. Many times standards are invoked for safety requirements. These standards are highly specialized and typically include many tests with a certificate that is issued when the system or product is shown to meet the standard. A good example is a certificate from Underwriters Labs (UL)[227].

11.12.3 Capacity Stress Testing

Capacity Stress Testing takes selected performance requirements and subjects the system to progressively more stringent performance requirements until a failure is detected. This testing can be isolated to a single performance item or a group of performance requirements that represent a scenario of ever-increasing challenge. Examples include:

- Continuously add more load to a physical structure
- Continuously increase the number of transaction requests into a computer based system until thrashing[228] occurs
- Continuously increase the speed of a motor until it flies apart
- Continuously increase the number of simulated aircraft in an air traffic control system until tracks are dropped
- Continuously increase the number of simulated aircraft in an air traffic control system until the operators are overloaded and near misses increase and more aircraft are placed into holding patterns

11.12.4 Destructive Testing

Tests can be destructive such that the item under test is compromised or destroyed. However fully verifying a requirement may call for a destructive test. This is best described with an example of an electrical fuse. A non-destructive test for a fuse is to check its continuity. A destructive test for a fuse is to continuously increase the current and measure when and how quickly the fuse blows (i.e. works). However once the fuse is blown it is of no value. An approach to destructive testing

---

[227] Found in 1894 Underwriters Labs ® (UL) has been testing products and writing standards for safety for more than a century.

[228] A resource stops doing useful work because there is contention. Once started, thrashing is typically self-sustaining until something occurs to remove the contention. For example, multiple processes accessing a shared resource repeatedly and neither willing to relinquish control so the resource can complete one of the processes while the other patiently waits.

is to sample a production run to verify that an entire batch is working as expected. The implication being that the production run is consistent and the process is not compromised if a selected sample set behaves as expected.

11.12.5 Characterization Tests

Characterization Tests are performed to characterize an existing device, subsystem, system, product, etc. It is used to compare against alternative choices and compare against possible future system upgrades or outright replacement.

Informed consumers are aware of tests and associated resulting specifications for audio products and automobiles. Sometimes when characterization tests are performed the original design specifications are exceeded.

In the past it was common engineering practice to de-rate components and include extra capacity and room for meeting performance requirements in the design. As design has become more precise with miniaturization, automation, and computers many solutions are offered at the specification limits. So a bridge built in the 1960's may catastrophically fail[229] at its expected end of life while a bridge in the same location built at the start of the previous century is still standing and offering service.

11.12.6 Architecture Verification and Validation

This text places great importance on architecture. However can the selected architecture be tested, verified, and validated before it is designed and implemented? Is the architecture tradeoff analysis sufficient evidence to show that the architecture was tested, verified, and validated?

The case for the selected architecture is embodied in the architecture studies and models. The typical studies and models that test and verify the architecture are against the system key requirements and include:

- Timing, sizing, load studies and models
- Reliability, maintainability, availability studies and models
- Functional decomposition and allocation
- Requirements decomposition allocation and allocation

The studies and models that validate the architecture include:

---

[229] I-35W Mississippi River bridge (Bridge 9340) eight-lane, steel truss arch bridge opened in 1967 collapsed during evening rush hour August 1, 2007. Some have suggested modern precise engineering practices were a factor as the bridge reached its original design life. Older bridges with the same design life included less precise over engineering practices, yielding long life.

- Operational sequence diagrams
- Operational simulations
- Operational simulation prototypes, and demonstrations

11.12.7 Software Intensive System Verification

Software intensive systems have a challenge because so many logical and arithmetic elements are within the total software set. All of these elements are suspect until verified. The problem is many of these elements are rarely executed at the system level and if they are executed, their limit conditions and internal paths may be unexercised without inserting computer failures. So software is tested at different abstraction levels and on different environments outside the normal target execution environment.

- **Unit Testing**: This is the smallest atomic test performed. The test might be something as simple as to perform a compile and link. Depending on the application, the testing may include developing unit stubs and drivers to stimulate the inputs and observe the outputs. It may go further and exceed the input limits and or stimulate all possible values in all possible conditions. These exhaustive unit level tests are associated with extremely critical software units.

- **Configuration Item Testing**: Once multiple units are grouped into a configuration item such as a standalone application, it can be tested. The goal is to surface the unexpected emergent behavior associated with multiple unit interactions and their interfaces. This testing may or may not be in the target environment. It also may or may not include a debugger, which can provide white box testing services such as inserting faults and examining internal intermediate values.

- **Integration Testing**: Once all the software configuration items are available they are typically loaded on the final target environment and subjected to integration testing. This may be as simple as verifying that the software executes on the hardware to verifying all the software requirements as specified in the software requirement specification(s).

11.12.8 Interoperability Tests

Interoperability tests are a difficult subject because initially everyone assumes some gold standard test fixture is developed to support interoperability tests of devices and systems from various vendors. However, no one wants the responsibility for validating the gold standard or even paying for its development. So there tends to be a mad rush to be the first out of the gate so that they become the gold standard that everyone else needs to meet. Others will need to make the changes, if needed, not the one who first made it to the gate.

11.12.9 White Box Testing

White box testing is performed on extremely critical software code. This is code where life can be at risk if it does not perform as expected. White box testing is similar to part testing where the test occurs at the lowest level. For software the lowest level of testing is at the instruction processing level. Multiple instructions are used to implement a function and a function can be viewed as a black box with inputs and outputs. As soon as there is a desire to gain visibility into the instructions that implement that function we are performing white box testing. This is also referred to as structural testing. There are two approaches to perform white box testing:

- **Debugger:** The first is to use software debuggers and step through the code. The problem with the software debugger is that it modifies the execution environment. Debuggers can perform some level of white box testing, however because the operating environment is modified some of the tests are suspect.
- **Instrumentation:** The second approach is to instrument the code and have the instrumentation provide outputs that represent paths of execution and content. This also modifies the execution environment. In both cases the Heisenberg principal is present. However this is an acceptable tradeoff in many cases where the code must be certified. There are clever mechanisms that try to minimize the impacts of test activities on the actual operating environment. These include always having the system in a recording mode regardless of status. Another approach is to use a hardware processing architecture where clock cycles are dedicated to instrumentation.

11.12.10 All inputs testing

All inputs testing is also referred to as monkey testing. The idea is that if you have enough monkeys pressing buttons and infinite time, they will be able to generate one of Shakespeare's famous works. In this case it is applied to testing. If all the inputs are stimulated with all possible values and all sequences then defects can be located.

Many equate this testing with software and specifically unit level testing. However it's roots go back to traditional hardware based devices and systems. The following examples are offered.

- **Audio Amplifier:** An audio amplifier is subjected to all frequency inputs from 0 to 30 kHz using a sweep generator that slowly increases the frequency of the input signal then slowly decreases the frequency. At the same time the output is measured to determine the gain level to ensure it is constant. The signal integrity is then examined for all frequencies to ensure the signal output is still a single frequency sinusoidal wave with no distortion (harmonics) where other frequencies magically appear. This is then done for all power levels of the amplifier.

- **Radio Tuner:** Just like in the case of the amplifier the radio tuner is slowly set to all frequencies to ensure that they are all present and that there are no artifacts.

- **Automobile Turning:** The steering wheel is turned all the way in one direction and then the other direction under different suspension loads. The simple check is to look for binding or looseness. The more complex check is to ensure proper alignment is maintained and wheel angle throughout the continuous turning inputs.

- **Automobile Engine:** Acceleration from idle to maximum speed. The output is checked to see if there is stalling or surging.

Author Comment: I performed normal maintenance on a 4-barrel holly carburetor that was mounted on a boat engine. It was part of a collection of other maintenance activities. The engine and boat performed well at low speed but as soon as movement into high speed was initiated the engine would stall. After 3 weeks of troubleshooting the cause was a fuel line filer at the entry if the carburetor. It was cylindrical with mesh on the sides open on one end and closed with plastic on the other end. As the speed was increased gas flow pushed the cylinder up into the housing and closed off the flow. It was installed upside down. The plastic bottom of the filter needed to be facing down, rather than up. The flow was being cut off because of the small opening into the housing.

- **Automobile Driving:** The automobile is accelerated from stop to full speed at different rates and conditions such as straight, turning, low temperature, high temperature, rain, ice, dry etc. There are checks for vibration loss of control and other issues that may surface.

Author Comment: The world is analog not digital. That is why calculus is so great. It provides the complete answer not just some views of some points. It is the same with testing. Spot testing a few points is not a good strategy for determining the performance of a great design. Many in software relinquish the testing to the users citing cost. This is like telling the new owner of an automobile to expect it to have problems on the highway when turning, accelerating, stopping, etc. This is not a responsible position to take. It should translate into lawsuits.

11.12.11 Manufacturing Production Testing

The purpose of manufacturing and production testing is to detect manufacturing and production errors. This is different than trying to surface design errors. So the manufacturing test procedures are different than the verification and validation test procedures. On the one had they should be thorough and on the other hand they must be fast because they are typically applied to each manufactured item. There are instances where spot-checking is performed where a small subset of items from a manufacturing run are subjected to testing.

11.12.12 Free Play Testing

Free play test is as the name suggests. Users are permitted to interact with the system without any limitations or guidance. Typically the users are initially used to perform testing as part of training or familiarization with the system. This approach tends to kill two birds with one stone: full verification and also introducing the users to the new system. This requires relatively sophisticated test procedures and a very effective test director who is able to also act in the role of senior trainer.

One the formal testing and system familiarization sequence is completed the new users are unleashed on the system. This is the start of validation by the users but is typically performed in a sterile lab setting rather that in the operational fielded setting. The free play testing is a way to mitigate validation risks once the system is fielded and then subjected to formal validation.

11.12.13 Children playing with Toys Testing

Children playing with toys is similar to free play testing however in this setting there is no concern associated with any damage that may occur. If the children destroy the toy the information is gathered, analyzed, and factored into the design update.

This is also a scenario that applies in research and development settings where there is a childlike environment of discovery. The primary purpose in this setting is to allow for maximum creativity, imagination, and innovation to occur as something is tested and then analyzed for future design activities.

11.12.14 Test Focus Groups

Test focus groups is similar to free play testing and children playing with toys. In this test setting users totally unfamiliar with the system are asked to interact with the system. Their behavior is recorder and analyzed after the testing. The focus group is also queried in some way to evaluate the design. There may be different focus groups with different characteristics that might include gender, age, education level, geographic regions, etc.

11.12.15 Research & Development Test & Evaluation

Research and development can be performed in a test and evaluation setting. Typically a laboratory setting is established where various elements of a system or multiple systems are established and personnel proceed to perform various test and evaluations to determine the behavior of the system or a new design element in a system[230]. Such facilities exist in organizations where technology tends to change quickly and it is an important element of their setting.

11.13 System Design Verification and Validation Process

A test program needs to be designed just like the target design that will be subjected to the testing. As in every design activity there are the needs, previous works, current thoughts, and challenges.

The need may change depending on the design. In one instance a design that relies on existing highly integrated elements with previous test results may require minimal new testing. For example an existing engine design placed in a new automobile design may be fully tested and so the test program needs to focus on the proven engine interfacing with the new automobile. It may be too heavy, produce too much power, and be too big. This causes the suspension to fail or perform poorly, transmission and axles to fail, and prevent normal maintenance. In another instance the engine may be the focus of the design with a resulting intensive test program. Alternatively both the engine and automobile may be new designs with the focus of a fully integrated solution with no compromises. This is yet another test program.

The test approach design follows the same design evolution as the target system. There is a concept, a physical manifestation, and then an implementation with all the details. There are the needs, requirements, alternatives, respect for all stakeholders, key understanding of the past, anticipations of the future and studies. Although the phrase we may use is "developing the test approach" we also can use "design the test approach". It is the same type of activity and just as important as designing the target system.

Again many will jump into a test process description. Others will fixate on one, two, or a few test techniques. All these views are incomplete and when new teams are formed and they are given a vetted process description along with descriptions of how to execute some of the test techniques, they fail unless there are testers on the team who have developed and executed test programs in the past.

Like all designers the test team relies on previous works. Sometimes others develop the approaches and the new team studies these previous bodies of work while at other times the previous approaches are works developed by the team members that forms their experience base. The team members may surface as they support other aspects of the project. For example they me engaged in analysis or they may be apprentices assigned to existing designers and test specialists.

---

[230] The National Aviation facilities Experimental Center, now called the Federal Aviation Administration Technical Center (FAATC) in Atlantic City, NJ is an example of such a facility. Various portions of the national air traffic control infrastructure are staged at the center and subjected to various tests as new design elements are considered and new issues surface.

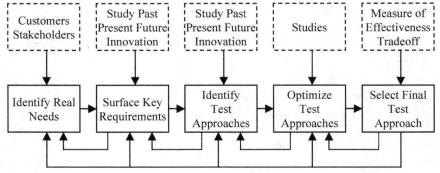

Figure 170 Test Approach Design Process

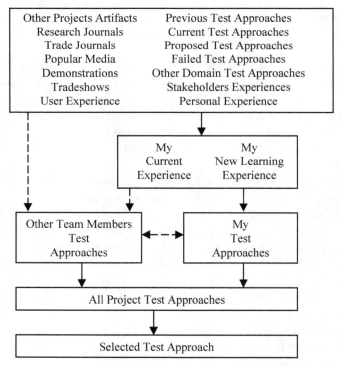

Figure 171 Test Program Design Sources

11.14 Some Key Points

➤ The characteristics of good tests are

- Atomic
- Traceable
- Standalone
- Thread Oriented
- Signature Block

➢ System test procedures can be grouped into separate test procedure books
  - Functional, performance, environmental
  - Recovery, interoperability
  - Certification, safety, security

➢ If there are multiple test plans a master test plan introduces the plans and their interrelationships

➢ Verification checks that the system meets the requirements

➢ Validation checks that the system meets the need / mission

➢ Test is an overloaded term that means many things including verification and validation but there are also many other different kinds of tests such as stress, interoperability, accelerated life

➢ Defects surfaced during test are assigned priorities Grave, Catastrophic, Critical, Marginal, Negligible

➢ In a large system testing is performed for
  - Segments
  - Subsystems
  - Major Components
  - Assemblies
  - Piece Parts

➢ In a large system the systems test team needs to review and understand the lower level
  - Test Plans
  - Test Procedures
  - Test Results

➢ In a large test program
  - Piece part test engineers verify piece part designs
  - Subassembly test engineers verify subassembly designs

- Subsystem engineers verify subsystem designs
- System test engineers verify system designs

➢ Test in many commercial organizations is performed by quality assurance

➢ The system test organization needs to review and in some instances monitor lower level test activities even down to the piece part level

11.15 Exercises

1. If a system consists of multiple segments, subsystems, and elements what does the system test plan look like (e.g. national level weather system with terrestrial and space based assets)?
2. If a mission critical system consists of just one element, what does the system test plan look like (e.g. medical diagnostic device like heart rate monitor)?
3. If a system consists of just one element, what does the system test plan look like (e.g. cell phone)?
4. Who should perform the verification and validation on a system segment?
5. Who should perform the verification and validation on a subsystem segment?
6. Who should perform the verification and validation on a major component?
7. Who should perform the verification and validation on a piece part?
8. Who should keep track of all the tests performed on a system and what are those possible test products?

11.16 Additional Reading

1. CMS Testing Framework Overview, Department of Health and Human Services, Centers for Medicare & Medicaid Services, Office of Information Services, Version: 1.0, January 2009.
2. MIL-STD-498 Appendix C Category And Priority Classifications For Problem Reporting. There is an overlap with the FMEA categories found in MIL-STD-1629A.
3. Test And Evaluation Handbook, Federal Aviation Administration, Version 1.0, August 21, 2008.
4. Test Inspection Reports, DI-NDTI-90909A March 1991, DI-NDTI-90909B January 1997.
5. Test Plan, Data Item Description, DI-NDTI-80566, April 1988.
6. Test Procedure, DI-NDTI-80603, June 1988.

12 Sustainability and Design

Imagine if we found a new civilization that was in need of help. Also imagine if the civilization was fundamentally characterized as:

- They don't respect themselves
- They don't respect others
- They don't respect their planet

The question arises: what benefit do they offer and so why should we help?

This is a question of maturity. However at what point does waiting for maturity and growth eventually become too long and its time to cut ones losses? Irresponsible behavior is one thing in a child it is another in a young adult. What do humans do if they are stuck on a planet where the behavior is toxic and irresponsible because the immature are in control of the situation?

We have the ability to rise to the challenge and offer sustainable designs. There are no excuses. There can be complex discussions of moral hazard, money, resources, etc. It is irrelevant. We must understand and properly manage our technologies. Sustainable development has become a significant topic of discussion in recent years. Some have argued that it is the next great challenge and that we should focus our energies towards sustainability in this new century. There is also some link between technology and sustainability suggesting that the new technologies and their ability to devastate on a massive scale have changed the urgency to address sustainability. So what is sustainable development?

The Brundtland Commission[231] defined sustainable development as development that "meets the needs of the present without compromising the ability of future generations to meet their own needs." Sustainable development is usually divided into social, economic, environmental and institutional. The social, economic, environmental areas address key principles of sustainability, while the institutional area addresses key policy and capacity issues.

It is obvious that a people should try to live well now and in the future. The issue is the mechanisms they have at their disposal to accommodate that life. One of those mechanisms is systems engineering to develop the most effective solution.

---

[231] Brundtland Commission, or the World Commission on Environment and Development, known by its Chair Gro Harlem Brundtland, convened by the United Nations in 1983 published Our Common Future, also known as Brundtland Report, in 1987.

Although it seems obvious to systems engineers that systems design practices should be used to address the sustainability challenges of this new century, others have other views. For example product-oriented people feel that their products are a perfect fit in a particular niche of sustainability. Technology people think they have a magic technology that will solve a challenging sustainability issue. Financial people think that tax incentives or virtual markets will spur innovation and let business rise to the occasion of sustainability needs. Systems practitioners know that none of these will work in isolation. So what systems design practices can start to address the sustainability design challenges?

This section is different from the other sections. There is significantly more opinion and reflection in this section. That is not to say the other sections were purely academic. In many ways the other sections of this book are dedicated to this section. Sustainability and progress is probably the most important task for humanity. The question is how can we maintain our sustainability and progress in an ever more complex and fragile world built on our systems that we must continually design and redesign.

12.1 System Design Big Picture

We know that before we design the target solution we need to identify the tools practices and processes that will be used for the design effort. The tools practices and processes can be as simple as a single individual with a paper and pencil that captures a design in full. For example designing a birdhouse to place in a garden. It also can be as complex as thousands of people working across the planet in almost all industries using the newest tools, practices, and processes to capture the design in full. For example designing the system that will take us to Mars and truly make us an infant space faring civilization.

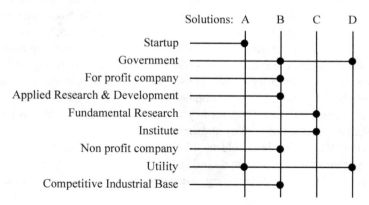

Figure 172 Industrial Matrix

What is rarely discussed is the concept that even before the design of the tools, practices, and processes there is the design of the entity, usually a for profit company, to house all this work. The design of the entity is just like all other designs. It can be new, reuse of something that exists, something that no longer exists but possibly can be recreated, part of many existing entities, or any combination. Once the entity or collection of entities is designed then the organization within the entity or collection of entities needs to be designed. To simplify the discussion the term organization will be used to represent an entity, or its internal structure.

An organization can take many forms and have many characteristics. An organization is filled with Knowledge Skills and Abilities (KSA). It can be the owner of technologies, intellectual property, products, or any combination. It can be a small team in a company or organization or it can be an entire company or organization. It can be a stand alone profit center or mixed with other organizations that form a profit center. It can be an overhead organization with no expected profits. It exists for another purpose. It might even cost significant amounts of money with no clean path to show profits, return in investment, or any other financial benefits but may offer important and critical services.

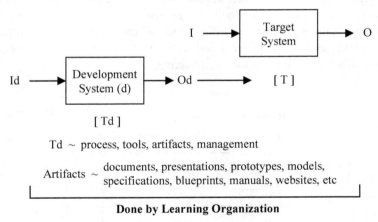

Td ~ process, tools, artifacts, management

Artifacts ~ documents, presentations, prototypes, models, specifications, blueprints, manuals, websites, etc

Done by Learning Organization

Figure 173 System Solution – Learning Organization

Early in this text the thoughts on systems theory suggested that the transfer function is a key element to consider. The transfer function is a result of some body of work that is then used in another body of work. The example was the target system needs a development system. Although not discussed but shown in the figure is the suggestion that this is performed by a learning organization. This is an organization that continually changes and evolves to satisfy the new needs as they arise throughout time.

There are many different organization types that can be used to perform design. The boundary of what is the organization is a consideration and the organizations have different characteristics making this is a complex multidimensional space.

Table 143 Organization Types

Non Profit	Single company	Public	Startup
For Profit	Conglomerate	Private	Established
FFRDC	Consortium		Mature
Government		Local	Obsolete
Utility	Technical standards body	Regional	Broken
	Technical council	National	
Institute		International	Successful
Company	Monopoly		Failing
University	Oligopoly	Small	Collapsing
Laboratory	Competitive Industrial Base	Medium	
		Large	
FFRDC: Federally funded research and development center, an entity in the USA			

Within each organization (or entity) people can be organized differently. The organization can be very hierarchical with official lines of authority and communications like the centralized computer architecture. The organization alternatively can be flat with no official lines of communications or authority but has processing and communicating nodes that work very efficiently and effectively like in a fully distributed computer architecture.

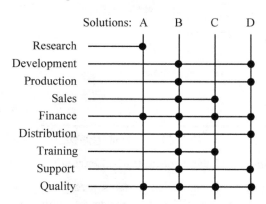

Figure 174 Organizational Matrix

The staffing can be dedicated to a fixed project or allocated as needed to a project via a matrix organization. A matrix exists when there is more than one project in the entity. This allows for the stability and growth of the KSAs (Knowledge Skills Abilities) with time and more diverse project experience. In a project based organization the team leaves the entity once the project is complete (they are given layoff notices). There has been significant debate on the merits and failing of the matrix organization, but it is typically found in learning organizations.

The project-based organization tends to be centralized with distinct lines of authority and control. The matrix organization tends to be more distributed even within the projects, with less centralized control. Many have suggested this is chaotic, however managing chaos is what may be needed in areas of high creativity and proving solutions where none currently exist. The matrix organization is also found in entities with a standalone systems engineering division or group.

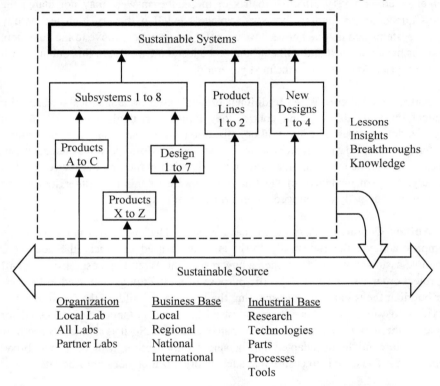

Figure 175 Sustainable System Designs and Industrial Base

Recently the mesh organization has been discussed. The suggestion is that all information nodes (staff) in the organization interact with all other information nodes. In this setting management acts as information node gateways to ensure that no communication bottlenecks arise and that the mesh is working effectively. In many ways when a matrix organization is working at its optimum level the result is a mesh organization. It is easy to see why traditionally educated management has a difficult time working in these settings. It is counter intuitive to their fundamental need to control and manage risk.

Author Comment: This is a challenge moving into this next century because the management theories and techniques used in the non high technology industries of the last century will not work in this new century. Also many of the approaches to organization and management in the very high technology organizations of the last century (e.g. Hughes Aircraft) did not make it back to the universities or technical bodies. So there is a serious knowledge void. Finally the whole issue of control and who controls the desired outcome is key. In a free organization implemented as a very effective matrix or mesh, the answers may not match the status quo or those funding the work. So we are left with very high technology legacy systems and no one knows how we got them or how to move to the next step. Systems have been lost and will continue to be lost until we figure this out and push the appropriate knowledge to the next generation.

Author Comment: When traditional project based organizations surface with distinct lines of authority and control they typically struggle until the informal organization surfaces. The informal organization is as the name suggests, the natural leaders surface and take matters in their own hands while placating management. The concept of the informal organization was detected in the first decades of the last century. Modern managers of the time were aware of this and either looked the other way or actually encouraged the informal organization.

Author Comment: Assume we have a need. The need does not have to be complex and yet the Industrial Matrix is what is used to satisfy the need. For example assume you decide to open a new restaurant. Would you establish and staff a project organization for the specific purpose of all the things that need to be done for building the restaurant from scouting the location to building the furniture? The obvious answer is no. There is an industrial base that is tapped and accessed for building the new restaurant. This is a matrix structure. So it is natural to see how this structure might be adapted into a single organization with deep and broad capabilities. The trick is to ensure that such an organization does not stagnate.

Author Comment: The term ecological organization has been used to suggest that those groups in a large organization not pulling their weight from a financial perspective are allowed to be starved and fade away. This is based on the concept of survival of the fittest, however we know that symbiosis is what allows large ecological systems to thrive. So there is a dilemma. Just because a team can not show profits in an arbitrary window does not mean it is not critical to the organization. A classic example in systems engineering is the test organization. Starve that organization and the entity will soon be faced with litigation and resulting bankruptcy.

Author Comment: Most matrix management discussions revolve around the concept of the power of the manager. This is fatally flawed thinking. It is based on the master slave centralized processing concept. It may have made sense in settings where some nodes needed constant supervision and actualization. However in high technology settings the nodes are self-actuated and need no supervision. Instead they need communications management and facilitation. For example various nodes may be unaware of important work in other areas that will impact their work. They need someone to ensure the tools and operating environment is providing the proper services. Freeing up the people to do what they do at their respective pay grades is key. Having high paid senior engineers make travel arrangements is a waste of precious resources.

Author Comment: In a matrix organization the formal structure becomes less important for getting things done. The managers need to focus on the informal organization that naturally emerges. The structure of networks, communities, teams and groups that need to be set up and maintained to get things done is the driver.

The take away from all of this is that the design of the internal organization is not unlike the design of a computer architecture. Keep in mind that the designs of early computer architectures were based on observations of human organizations and organization theory. Many software programs working to perform an important task are analogous to many people working to perform an important task.

Example 33 Drain Your Swaps First and Establish Infrastructure

The Panama Canal is an engineering wonder. Many may take it for granted and do not realize that it took a while for people to figure out how to actually succeed. Initially the approach was to just go there and start digging a ditch. Using that approach was a failure because people were dying from the hostile environment. So the first step was to recognize that the swamps needed to be drained, mosquitoes addressed, and infrastructure established so that workers could work and not die[232]. The Americans should be given credit for this important insight. The lesson is that the mindset of all new designs should be framed around:

- Layout the infrastructure
- Setup the supply lines
- Get rid of the mentality of I do designs only, this is not my job
- Then proceed to design the target system
- Then build the target system after the infrastructure is in place and sound
- Don't just start to build, especially if some silly manager demands it
- Set up green houses, people need to eat
- Do what you can and do it well
- Do the high technology / push the technology first

---

[232] I was introduced to this in elementary school as part of history. James reminded me of this important history lesson and he stated it much more eloquently than I could in this text.

Design is not a series of steps that if followed will lead to success. Design is a multi dimensional creative process rooted in reason. The combination of art and reason through mathematics, logic, science, and engineering are key to design. For those who must turn to a list to help remind them of some of the concepts suggested in this text, the following is offered:

- Design the organization that will perform the design
- Designed the approach for how the design will be performed
- Design the target system after the organization and approach are established

- Identify the system needs
- Depict architecture design concept for the above
- Allocate functions and performance to concept architecture design
- List external interfaces

- Depict physical architecture design
- Allocate functions and performance to physical architecture design
- Refine concept architecture design based on physical architecture design
- Refine external and list internal interfaces
- Identify performance bottleneck and degradation areas
- Identify inconsistencies, incompleteness
- Identify new technology and quality envelopes

- Depict implementation architecture design
- Allocate functions and performance to implementation architecture design
- Refine concept and physical architecture design based on implementation architecture design
- Refine internal and external interfaces
- Identify performance bottleneck and degradation areas
- Identify inconsistencies, incompleteness
- Identify new technology and quality envelopes

Author Comment: A fundamental question we need to ask is do we have the organizations in place at this time that can actually handle the new sustainable designs that must surface in this century. That is a difficult question because in many ways as I survey the current landscape the answer is no. I claim we have no new learning organizations. Instead we keep creating new special purpose organizations that satisfy an immediate market void that can be financially harvested for a few. If we actually accept that the answer is no, we do not have the organizations capable of developing sustainable designs in this new century then we need designers at all levels to start postulating what these organizations might look like across the society. It broke my heart when I found this out - it is counter to all I was told before deciding to become a high technology contributor.

12.2 Progress and Design

Progress was used extensively in the last century. It was common knowledge that progress was linked to design and technology. It was progress that led to lights in the dark, safe water, sewage, safe abundant food[233], refrigeration, telephones, radio, television, washers, dryers, garbage disposals, automobiles, airplanes, etc. This was extremely difficult and people made enormous sacrifices to put these system designs in place. They significantly benefited the future generation. The question is what progress is this generation making for the future generations.

"Progress is movement in a forward direction. It is a combination of achievement and forward vision, which serves its creator without fear or unforeseen consequence. There can be no progress if these rules are not respected. Technology is not progress unless it is combined in the direction of humanity. Pseudo progress can destroy the natural foundations of human life. It can lead to a society of chaotic beings that can result in global suicide"[234].

Misuse of technology as previously discussed in this text is a serious consideration when addressing progress and sustainability. The Earth has a limited set of resources and one of the most important resources is people. Misusing their abilities and energies is not sustainable. It is critical that we not waste time with useless adventures that may lead to financial fortunes for some in a time of plenty and lose our opportunity to do what must be done before the times get challenging. It was just about 100 years ago that humanity lived in the dark. We should not take our modern world for granted.

12.3 Growth and Design

Many equate and discuss growth in terms of economics and finance such as gross domestic product (GDP). However GDP as a measure of growth is very misleading. For the non-financial stakeholders growth is intimately tied to design and progress. It is the new designs that lead to growth and that growth translates to

---

[233] Many people are still hungry but most have concluded this is a political problem. This may soon change as the population continues to grow and potentially outstrips our ability to provide safe food even in a perfect political situation.

[234] Paraphrased from an interview with Burkhard Heim (February 9, 1925 - January 14, 2001) a German theoretical physicist. He devoted a large portion of his life to the pursuit of a unified field theory. One of his childhood ambitions was to develop a method of space travel, which contributed to his motivation to find such a theory.

progress. So GDP can be misleading towards understanding the nature of the growth and progress in a society.

Money is a method of storing wealth so that a simple common element can be used to exchange goods and services. It does not relate to or show the quality or usefulness of the goods and services. The argument is that the goods and services will always follow the need and quality based on the consumer and their choices. This assumes a rational consumer. However what happens if consumers become irrational either because of their own failings or because of external forces? What happens if the money becomes a means to an end rather than a mechanism to fund useful projects that offer great designs that translate into massive progress[235]?

If the focus is on the quality of life as a market need that can be targeted and filled with the introduction of washers, dryers, toasters, personal transportation, entertainment[236], etc then the introduction of useful goods and services is easily explained. However with massive technology and the ability to produce goods and services anywhere, technology abuse can overcome our sustainable systems, and flood markets with useless products. At this point GDP becomes a useless metric.

12.4 Space Program

The environmental movement started in the 1970's may have never happened without the U.S. space program and its unbelievable mission of going to the moon.

Figure 176 Earth Rising Seen from Moon and Neil Armstrong on Moon

The picture of the fragile Earth in a sea of blackness while seen from a dead space body inspired visionaries to take a whole new view of our world and our

---

[235] In my humble option this is the cause of all depressions. The money gets locked up in the hands of a few and the velocity of money drops to such a low level that all useful work stops. It's not that the few are evil it is just that they cannot duplicate the creativity and innovation of millions of people at the working levels.

[236] Many educational and soul-searching works can be captured on film and in music.

place in the system. This is a classic example of emergence and justification of technological growth for the sake of growth.

The sad part is the space program was an outgrowth of defense. It only grew to its level of performance because of the concept of Dual use Technology and a presidential initiative. It was not viewed as something that made sense and the next step for humanity to follow. So even though we depend on satellites for every aspect of our life, few are willing to fund the fundamentals of trying to survive in the ultimate hostile environment even though that knowledge is easy to equate with us being able to effectively manage our resources on Earth.

12.5 Internal versus External System Sustainability

Internal system sustainability is the ability of a system to sustain itself. Bad systems should fail and disappear, however what should a people do if good systems fail and disappear.

Table 144 Internal Sustainability and Maturity Levels

Food	Water	Waste Management
1. Hunter Gatherers	1. Stream	1. None
2. Family Farmers	2. River	2. Raw into River
3. Regional Farms	3. Well	3. Processed into River except during rain
4. Large Farms	4. Town Square	4. Processed into River
5. Large green houses	5. Piped	5. Effluent watering system
6. Vertical Farms	6. Treated Piped	
Health Care	**Construction**	**Employment**
1. None	1. None	1. None
2. Doctor	2. Mud Hut	2. Investor
3. Clinic	3. Durable Materials	3. Worker
4. Hospital	4. Office Buildings	4. Owner
5. Research Hospital	5. Sky Scrapers	
Education	**Transportation**	**Energy**
1. None	1. Foot	1. None
2. Traditions	2. Animal	2. Individual Intermittent
3. Verbal Apprentice	3. Train	3. Individual Continuos
4. Elementary	4. Public Transit	4. Group Intermittent
5. High School	5. Automobile	5. Group Continuous
6. College	6. Plane	
	7. Space Ship	
Communications	**Security**	**Wealth Exchange Finance Investments**
1. Verbal	1. None	1. Barter
2. Smoke	2. Random	2. Precious items
3. Print	3. Random + Police	3. Money
4. Telegraph	4. Police	4. Equities - Stocks, Mutual Funds
5. Radio	5. Police + Military	5. Interest Bearing - Bonds, Banks
6. Telephone	6. None Needed	6. Trusts - Real-estate Investment Trusts
7. Satellite		7. Taxes Bonds - For infrastructure

Table 144 Internal Sustainability and Maturity Levels

8. Cell Phone		
9. Internet		

There are system designs in every aspect of our society filling key needs. These designs have evolved and matured through the ages. On Earth many of the solutions use designs from all our ages. As we look at our modern world we need to understand it is not a measure of the state of the entire planet. As a result we as a species are not operating at our full potential.

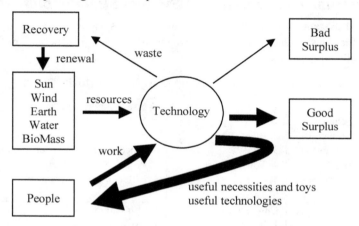

Figure 177 Technology and Sustainability

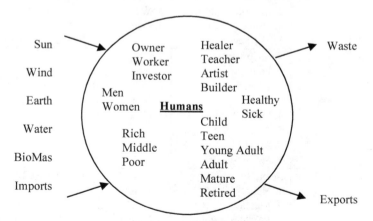

Figure 178 Sustainable Community

Who decides the difference between a good and a bad system? For example what if the clean safe water delivery systems in the U.S. were permitted to fail and go away to be replaced with bottled water? All communities have a maturity level and it should never be assumed that a community can sustain its' current level of existence without serious effort.

External sustainability is a measure of a systems impact on its surrounding community. This is the traditional ecological view of sustainability. Some will point to a scale where one balances the other, however it is not an either or proposition. The easy way out is totally unacceptable. Somehow internal and external sustainability must be addressed.

It is easy to slip into simple economic views of the problem. However stepping back and doing things like drawing simple context diagrams and then attempting to go into the context diagrams may yield important insights.

12.6 Sustainability V-Diagram

The System V-Diagram has been used to communicate some aspect of systems engineering to systems practitioners and non-system practitioners. It shows traceability through the various specification levels and the links to the associated, verification, validation and integration levels.

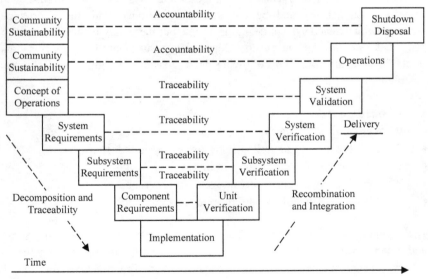

Figure 179 Sustainable System V-Diagram

One of the primary messages is that decomposition is from the top down while test and integration is from the bottom up. It also shows when system handoff or delivery occurs so that system validation can proceed. It tends to be modified to show some particular aspect of systems engineering. So what might we say about the V-Model if we start to introduce sustainability into the picture?

At one level it is obvious that sustainability would find itself moving into each of the individual blocks. However once the system becomes operational, eventually is shutdown, and is disposed of, the traditional System V-Diagram does not fully address sustainability. A suggestion is to modify it to include sustainability for the full life cycle of a system and not limit it to just development, verification, and validation.

In this extended life cycle system view the operations, shutdown and disposal are added resulting in the Sustainable System V-Diagram. This extended view suggests a need for one or more information products associated with "community sustainability". This is not unlike what happened with the rise of the environmental movement and the introduction of environmental impact studies when new or modified structures are proposed in a community[237].

12.7 Community Sustainability and Accountability

In the past many system design efforts started with the Operational Concept. The Sustainable Systems V-Diagram suggests that system designs start with Community Sustainability and be concurrently developed with the operational concepts. Obviously each system design is unique but there may be generic items of interest that should be in each Community Sustainability Concept and Accountability document. The following is a possible list for these common sustainable items of interest:

- Who are the stakeholders
- What are the stakeholder needs
- What are the key sustainability issues in this system design
- What are the sustainability goals in this system design
- What are the key sustainability and stakeholder requirements
- What is the accountability path for poor sustainability

The community sustainability concept can suggest where sustainability issues are addressed in various systems design practices during the development stages of the system design. Some of the common systems design practices that should address sustainability are:

- Sustainable Requirements
- Technology Assessment, Innovation, and Stability
- Modeling and Prototyping
- Maintainability, Logistics, Safety, Reliability, Quality

---

[237] Community is the collection of stakeholders that are impacted by the system.

- Life Cycle Cost
- Architecture Identification, Tradeoff, and Selection

Although this list is logically sequenced, the greatest impact that systems design practices can have are in the areas of architecture and technology. This is the role of the systems integrator, to pick the most effective architecture and technology for the system and then integrate the system. The question is can current systems integrators start to stimulate technology growth in these areas.

12.8 The Search for Sustainable Requirements

Systems designers are good at surfacing new kinds of metrics and ways of characterising performance. This is after a long process of surfacing functional requirements and characteristics. But at some point performance surfaces.

In this particular case our challenge is to perform literature searches, vendor searches, and vendor assessments of current offerings in alternative energy sources, transportation vehicles, fuels, etc. Once the vendors and their offerings are identified the next step is to start to find discriminators between these various offerings. These discriminators start to surface new performance specification categories. For example in the simple case of wind turbines the following performance may be identified and compared:

- Minimum Useful Wind Speed or Cut In Speed
- Maximum Useful Wind Speed or Cut Out Speed
- Peak Theoretical Power Per Day, Week, Month, Season, Year
- Average Power Per Day, Week, Month, Season, Year
- Power Distribution Per Day, Week, Month, Season, Year
- Power Per Footprint Area, Per Linear Height, Per Unit Of Weight
- Set Up Time In Transportable Settings

At one level the broad choices of wind turbines include Horizontal-Axis Wind Turbines (HAWT), Vertical-Axis Wind Turbines (VAWT). They come in different sizes and in the case of VAWT the wind capture approaches vary. At another level there is the choice of Micro Turbines and a massively distributed system

The same process needs to be applied to solar photo voltaic, solar thermal, alternative transportation, alternative fuels, and other traditional system elements now subjected to sustainability needs. What are the performance characteristics of existing products, are these measures capturing what is really needed or should new performance metrics or requirements be created to effectively represent what is actually needed?

The simpler case of sustainability and requirements is probably associated with functionality and characteristics. The following is a small set of possible requirements to consider:

- Use recycled, recovered, or environmentally preferable materials
- Toxic and Hazardous materials are not used
- Avoid prohibited materials: lead, radioactive material, glass fibers, ozone depleting chemicals or substances, toxic materials that give off toxic fumes when burned or exposed to high temperatures. Registry of Toxic Effects of Chemical Substances (RTECS)[238], 29 CFR 1910 OSHA standards [OSHA].
- Avoid materials on EPA 17[239] list [EPA 1999]:

1.	Benzene	10.	Trichloroethylene
2.	Carbon tetrachloride	11.	Xylenes
3.	Chloroform	12.	Cadmium and cadmium compounds
4.	Dichloromethane	13.	Chromium and chromium compounds
5.	Methyl ethyl ketone	14.	Cyanide compounds
6.	Methyl isobutyl ketone	15.	Lead and lead compounds
7.	Tetrachloroethylene	16.	Mercury and mercury compounds
8.	Toluene	17.	Nickel and nickel compounds
9.	1,1,1-Trichloroethane		

Once various vendor solutions are identified and characterised, the next steps might be to start to identify the performance requirements that are a candidate for improvement. At this point the systems integrator moves from commercial product consumer to technology developer while attempting to encourage or push technology development and growth.

12.9 New Sustainability Performance Requirements

In keeping with the system practice of identifying new measures of performance for new systems or new views of systems, new performance requirements should be surfaced when addressing sustainability. The following is a suggested list of new sustainability performance requirements. They are based on key ratios associated with any product or system. The ratios use the expected load on the system. So first the loads are calculated, then the key ratios are determined. The sustainability performance loads are as follows:

---

[238] Registry of Toxic Effects of Chemical Substances (RTECS) toxicity database compiled without reference to validity or usefulness of studies. Center for Disease Control, The National Institute for Occupational Safety and Health (NIOSH) maintained it as a freely available publication until 2001.

[239] The 33/50 Program targeted 17 priority chemicals and set as its goal a 33% reduction in releases and transfers by 1992 and a 50% reduction by 1995 measured against a 1988 baseline.

- **Packaging Carbon Footprint (PCF):** The package carbon load calculation includes production, recycling, and disposal.
- **Transport Carbon Footprint (TCF):** The transport carbon load includes the fuel during transport, the building and maintenance of the transport vehicles, and the infrastructure to support the vehicles.
- **Content Carbon Footprint (CCF):** The content carbon load includes production, recycling, and disposal.
- **Packaging Energy Consumption (PEC):** The package energy load calculation includes production, recycling, and disposal.
- **Transport Energy Consumption (TEC):** The transport energy load includes the fuel during transport, the building and maintenance of the transport vehicles, and the infrastructure to support the vehicles.
- **Content Energy Consumption (CEC):** The content energy load includes production, recycling, and disposal.

These loads should be minimized in the system. In addition the system should be in balance. To maintain this balance key ratios also should be minimized. The sustainability performance ratios are:

- **Packaging / Content Carbon Ratio (PCCR):** This is the ratio of Packaging Carbon Footprint (PCF) versus Content Carbon Footprint (CCF). This can be expressed as carbon ratio of package versus content or PCCR = PCF/CCF.
- **Transport / Content Carbon Ratio (TCCR):** This is the ratio of Transport Carbon Footprint (TCF) versus Content Carbon Footprint (CCF). This can be expressed as carbon ratio of package versus content or TCCR = TCF/CCF.
- **Packaging / Content Energy Ratio (PCER):** This is the ratio of Packaging Energy Content (PEC) versus Content Energy Content (CEC). This can be expressed as carbon ratio of package versus content or PCCR = PEC/CEC.
- **Transport / Content Energy Ratio (TCER):** This is the ratio of Transport Energy Content (TEC) versus Content Energy Content (CEC). This can be expressed as carbon ratio of package versus content or TCER = PEC/CEC.

Example 34 Unsustainable Packaging

The goal is to minimize the total sustainability performance loads and the sustainability performance ratios in the system. For example, if the total load of PEC + TEC + CEC is minimized and yet the packaging is so small that the content is "less" than the package, then the question must be asked - is system violating basic common sense related to sustainability? The following is a list of packaging practices and their characteristics:

- Does it make sense to place 3 machine screws in a package? Wouldn't a bin of screws and nuts be more effective? Does every product item need a bar code at the final point of sale? Would a bar-coded bag of 100 nuts sold to the retailer preserve the same metrics for both the wholesaler and retailer?
- It is not unusual to shrink packages and keep prices the same during difficult economic times. Is this reasonable, sustainable, or even ethical in a time of stress?
- Cross packaging of dependent products leads to similar inefficiencies. Does it make sense to place 3 machine screws in one package and 4 complementary nuts in another package?

Once multiplied by millions or hundreds of millions this translates into enormous waste of resources and can be measured as high PCER and PCCR ratios.

Example 35 Unsustainable Transport

Does it make sense to manufacture an item and transport it across a continent or around the world? The high TCER and TCCR ratios clearly show the sustainable approach. So how did we get into a situation where products are constantly moving across the planet? This is a difficult question and fundamental to the question of being systems driven or finance driven.

In the U.S. during the early 1970's there was a significant argument against the new Environmental Protection Agency (EPA) because the new environmental regulations the EPA needed to enforce were encouraging rust belt industries to relocate to countries with little or no environmental regulations. This was the start of offshore production and one of the major reasons for new trends against government bureaucracy and its role in U.S. society[240].

In a perfect world the financial analysis results would match the system analysis results. However in an imperfect world with artificial markets and indirect cost shifting we see our current state of affairs. The system analysts can build the models, perform the analysis and show the inefficiency in the markets and its impact on sustainability. It is then up to policy makers to determine how to proceed.

Example 36 Think Local Production and Distribution

Reducing energy and carbon ratios translates into local production and distribution of products. The issue is how to factor the true costs of producing a product into a mechanism so that location and distribution is not driven by the most clever scheme of offsetting indirect costs but the lowest impact on the whole system. This is an example of making sure the context diagram is large enough to represent the true system and not some artificial boundary driven by a limited set of

---

[240] Author perception of the current events of the time.

stakeholders.

One approach is to clearly attempt to measure the performance of a product and its impact on the whole system. The TCER, TCCR, PCER, and PCCR are relatively easy to calculate. The issue is what to do once the performance numbers are produced. Policy makers may force a tax or consumers might choose to purchase based on the ratios. Then there is the question of how to validate the claimed ratios.

The simple act of just thinking local might be all that is needed, but that does not necessarily mean a local production facility has the lowest ratios. It may help a people with regulations such as the U.S. but it is of little use to a people with little or no regulations.

12.10 Technology Assessment, Innovation, Stability

An interesting question is can systems design practices spur innovation. Perhaps some simple thought experiments not uncommon in systems design might answer that question. Thought Experiment 1: Why do wind turbines use propellers?

- What does it mean if a 200-foot propeller is used on a 300-foot wind turbine
- What about using a ducted fan or a centrifugal (squirrel-cage) fan or other methods of capturing the wind
- Should it be just one fan on the 400-foot tower or multiple fans
- Are there wind gradients across the diameter of the fan and what do those wind gradients do to efficiency
- In a wind turbine farm, should only one type of wind turbine be used
- What is the ideal physical placement of each turbine in a large wind farm

Clearly someone should be modeling the different wind turbine architectures and characterizing them for different environments. Perhaps there even should be simulation test facilities using large wind tunnels to try these different wind turbine architectures in semi live settings but under controlled conditions. Thought Experiment 2: How should a wind turbine interface to the grid?

- Use fixed rotation wind turbines but then what are the lost opportunities
- Use solid state electronics but what about extremely large wind turbines
- Use motor generators, rotary converters, or double fed induction generators to interface to the power grid but what about losses

These issues are associated with technology assessment. Technology assessment includes identifying the Technology Maturity Levels and Technology Readiness Levels[241] of system elements. These assessments tie in closely with modeling and

---

[241] As previously discussed in this text.

prototyping, the primary goals being to mature technologies that have promise of positively impacting a system with one or more sustainability challenges.

12.11 Maintenance Logistics Safety Reliability Quality

Current systems are extremely maintainable, supportable, safe, reliable, and of high quality. Decades of evolution bought them to this state. New systems based on displacement technology that do not have the luxury of decades of evolution also must be highly maintainable, supportable, safe, reliable, and of high quality.

Although many systems design practitioners are very familiar with Maintainability, Logistics, Safety, Reliability, and Quality many sustainability practitioners lack these basic understandings. Many solutions offered by the sustainability community are non-starters because they are not maintainable. For example solar blankets have been proposed to slow down glacier melt. However it is obvious the approach did not consider maintainability or production. The lesson is that sustainable solutions must not compromise standards of Maintainability, Logistics, Safety, Reliability, and Quality.

12.12 Life Cycle Cost

Cost shifting is a prctice where the true system costs are shifted to other stakeholers who may be unaware of their new found responsibility. The Life Cycle Cost (LCC) equation is modified to remove any possibility of cost shifting. A suggestion is to consider the followng cost elements to repersent total cost.

LCC = R+D+P+O+M+W+S+T Where:

R = Research	M = Maintenance
D = Development	W = Waste
P = Production	S = Shut Down and Decommissioning
O = Operation	T = Disposal

An alternative view is: LCC = R+D+P+O+M+S+I+E or PROMISED Where:

R = Research	M = Maintenance
D = Development	S = Shut Down & Disposal
P = Production	I = Infrastructure
O = Operation	E = Environment & Waste

Author Comment: Infrastructure (I) represents the cost of establishing the infrastructure so that others can offer system solutions. Examples are government funded research, development, and operations of air traffic control systems and research and development of air planes for defense that are then transferred to civilian use. In this setting it is absurd to think a commercial airline company is a real business that funds all its costs. It becomes even more absurd when managers of these entities think they should derive revenue by charging for toilet services while in flight. It would be impossible for these companies to exist if the true cost of flying were factored into the business. They could not exist. The same is true of all the businesses that benefit from the rural electrification program, interstate highways, roads, space satellite systems and a plethora of other infrastructure projects that no business could justify in a reasonable business model. But that does not mean the Infrastructure costs should not be identified for various system solutions. To the contrary they should be clearly identified so that a system does not become a burden on the people[242].

12.13 Architecture Identification Tradeoff Selection

At some point architecture alternatives, tradeoffs, and selection need to be addressed. Are there any unique tradeoff criteria to consider when selecting an architecture? How can the architectures be depicted? What process can be reasonably followed to select the architecture especially when sustainability surfaces? The following is a list of possible new sustainable related criteria to consider in architecture development:

- Sustainability
- Short Term and Long Environmental Impact: Air, land, water, sea, space, and outer atmosphere
- Air, water, and land pollution
- Noise[243] and visual pollution
- Cost Shifting
- Technology Maturity, Stability, Growth Potential
- Maintainability, Producibility, Supportability
- Aesthetics, form, user acceptability

To start the process, identify the architecture alternatives. The identification includes the name of the architecture, a simple picture and a few words that capture the essence of the architecture approach. This is limited to a single page for each architecture approach.

What should be considered in the architecture of a power generation system for a community[244]? If the focus is on a new wind farm that will produce power does it make sense to use one type of wind turbine in a homogeneous system or should the

---

[242] What is the Infrastructure cost of a catastrophic Nuclear Power Plant disaster?

[243] Noise pollution has been addressed by air traffic control systems for decades.

[244] The Rural Electrification Act of 1936, supplied the infrastructure and funding to electrify isolated U.S. farms. May 20, 1936, S. 3483, Public, No. 605.

system solution use multiple sizes and types of wind turbines in a heterogeneous architecture arrangement? Should the architecture use different energy generation technologies? What are the maintenance and support impacts of heterogeneous architectures and are they mitigated by the advantages?

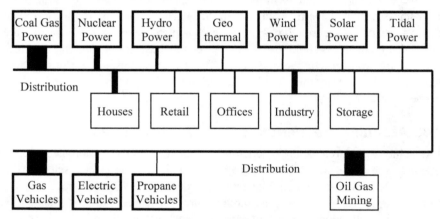

Figure 180 Sustainable Architecture Depiction

Identifying the architecture alternatives, surfacing the tradeoff criteria and selecting the most effective architecture is one of the most important practices in systems engineering. It is especially important when questions of sustainability surface.

12.14 Value Systems

When there are different architecture alternatives what methods can be used to pick the best approach? Within this question is the concept of value systems. There are different value systems that can be used to make a selection; most of them based on financial metrics. However there is an alternative to using strictly financial metrics to make a selection. Except for the MOE, the following is a list of financial value systems.

Lowest Cost	EVA - Economic Value Added
Highest Profit	ROV - Real Option Value
ROI - Greatest Return on Investment	ROA - Return on Assets
TCO - Total Cost of Ownership	ROIE - Return on Infrastructure Employed
IRR - Internal Rate of Return	MOE - Measure of Effectiveness

Although we are familiar with various value systems, many outside the systems engineering community are not familiar with the Measure of Effectiveness (MOE) that can be calculated with each architecture approach. The Architecture MOE is the sum of the tradeoff ratings divided by the total cost or LCC.

MOE = Sum of Tradeoff Criteria / Total Cost or LCC

The Architecture MOE moves the architecture selection discussion to a different level. One solution might be lowest cost, another highest cost, and yet a third with a mid-level cost. The same applies to the tradeoff rating where one solution might have the highest rating, another the lowest, and yet a third with a middle rating. The most effective solution is the one with the best Architecture MOE.

12.15 Advantages Disadvantages List

In the beginning of the architecture trade study there is nothing, just a blank sheet of paper. The first step is to identify architecture alternatives, no matter how bizarre. One of the alternatives is the current approach. Another alternative is the dream approach. They form two extremes. The other approaches are everything in between. The alternatives are listed on a single sheet of paper and two columns are added. They are labeled advantages and disadvantages.

This is kept on a single sheet of paper so it can be easily visualized allowing the analysts to quickly get to the key issues. The objective is to minimize irrelevant information and quickly cut down on the alternatives. If there are only two alternatives, something is wrong. If there are ten alternatives, something is wrong. The answer is in between, and should include the impossible alternatives.

Table 145 List of Advantages Disadvantages

Architecture	Advantages	Disadvantages
Approach 1	Advantage 1 Advantage 2 Advantage 3	Disadvantage 1 Disadvantage 2
Approach 2	Advantage 1 Advantage 2	Disadvantage 1 Disadvantage 2
Approach n	Advantage 1	Disadvantage 1

The advantages-disadvantages or plusses-minuses tables are very important. It is at this time that the key tradeoff criteria start to surface. These tradeoff criteria are used in the next phase of the architecture trade study.

12.16 Sustainability Tradeoff Criteria

The advantages and disadvantages table can be used to surface tradeoff criteria that naturally flow into the tradeoff matrix. Although there are tradeoff criteria unique to sustainability, the architecture tradeoff should still consider system relevant criteria. The criteria can be general and apply to any architecture design.

Table 146 General Tradeoff Criteria

Table 146 General Tradeoff Criteria

Resilience	Transition	Reliability
Robustness	Interoperability	Maintainability
Ruggedness	Usability	Training
Survivability	Availability	Supportability
Brittleness	Fault tolerance	Survivability
Flexibility	Graceful degradation	Comfort
Reconfigureability	Performance	Sustainability
Scalability	Capacity	Effectiveness
Stability	Growth	Safety
Controllability	Technology insertion	Security
Elegance	Ability to meet requirements	Vulnerability
Symmetry	Performance	Deployment
Beauty	User acceptability	Shutdown
Simplicity	Produce-ability	Disposal
Reasonableness	Testability	

They also can include unique items associated with a domain like sustainability:

Table 147 Sustainability Tradeoff Criteria

Carbon Pollution	Visual Pollution	Internal Sustainability	Social Mobility
Water Pollution	Fuel Sustainability	External Sustainability	Freedom and Liberty
Land Pollution	Regeneration	Survivability	Quality Of Life
Air Pollution	Progress	Population Growth	Happiness
Noise Pollution	Model Results	Standard Of Living	

12.17 Sustainability Tradeoff Matrix

When developing the sustainability tradeoff matrix list the tradeoff criteria in rows and place the alternatives in columns. Rate each criterion for each alternative. The values can be 1-3, 1-4, 1-10, or a ranking of each alternative relative to the other alternatives. If using high, medium, or low, they can be translated to numbers. In the beginning of the trade study, fill in each cell of the matrix with a rating even if there is no supporting data. It is an educated guess based on current knowledge and perceptions. Play with each approach. Do this in one day.

Now comes the hard part of moving the content of the tradeoff matrix to fully vetted content approved by all the stakeholders. Examine the criterion and architecture alternatives. Examine each intersection or cell. Identify studies, techniques, methods and approaches to convert the initial gut-based ratings into ratings backed by sound scientific and engineering principles. This is performed as a group using hard science, soft science, and everything else in that order to back up the numbers. Document the logic even if it is just bullets on a chart.

Table 148 Architecture Tradeoff Matrix

Criteria	A1	A2	AN	Wt	A1	A2	AN

Table 148 Architecture Tradeoff Matrix

Criteria	A1	A2	AN	Wt	A1	A2	AN
Criterion 1	5	7	9	1	5	7	9
Criterion 2	5	5	8	5	25	25	40
Criterion 3	5	5	6	1	5	5	6
Criterion 4	5	6	6	2	10	12	12
Criterion 5	5	9	8	3	15	27	24
Criterion Y	5	9	8	1	5	9	8
Total	30	41	45	-	65	85	99

Take snapshots and change the cells of the tradeoff matrix. Add weights to the criteria based on continued refined analysis of the problem. Some criteria may disappear and others may surface. Don't be afraid to call the team in and have everyone enter their view of the rating for each cell, no matter how detached they may be from the detailed studies. At some point some criteria will become a wash and go away while others become very different or new criterion are added.

Sum the total for each approach. This is the rating for each architecture alternative. Keep it simple at first and do not use weights until there are some initial results. As more insight is gained apply a different weight to each criterion and change the total.

Develop initial costs and total life cycle costs (LCC) for each approach. Take each rating and divide it by the initial cost. That is the initial Architecture MOE. It is a measure of goodness of each approach for each dollar spent. Do the same thing for the life cycle cost and see if they are different. Pick the architecture that has the highest MOE when all costs are considered (the LCC). This yields the biggest advantage for each unit of cost.

Table 149 Architecture MOE

Criteria	A1	A2	AN	Wt	A1	A2	AN
Total	30	41	45		65	85	99
LCC	1	1.2	1.4		1	1.2	1.4
MOE	30	34	32		65	71	71
The LCC is normalized.							
Adding cost shows that Arch 2 is more effective than Arch N.							
Weights shows Arch 2 becomes less effective and matches Arch N.							

What should the tradeoff criteria include? That is really something the team decides. It is part of the discovery process. However, a word of caution: the tradeoff criteria should not include cost or requirements. It is a given that all solutions will satisfy the known requirements at some cost. Cost should be used at the bottom of the tradeoff where each approach's total rating is divided by cost. This essentially identifies the goodness of each approach per unit of cost: this is called the

Architecture Measure of Effectiveness or Architecture MOE.

The tradeoff study is not about the numbers in the matrix. It is about the journey to populate the matrix. Anyone can go into a closed room, fill in a matrix, and emerge to dictate that this is the answer. That is a failed effort.

A team populates the tradeoff matrix where each architecture camp makes their position. As they find weakness in their architecture alternative, they then proceed to modify it until the weakness is mitigated or completely removed. As long as the architecture concept remains in place it matures and moves from a straw man approach that is easy to knock down to an iron man then stone man architecture that is difficult to knock down. This holds for all the architecture approaches considered in the tradeoff matrix. So the tradeoff matrix is a framework to capture the quantitative study results and the qualitative arguments. It summarizes the arguments, positions, and journey that are captured in the architecture study.

12.18 Sustainability Push Versus Pull

Things either can be pushed into the mainstream or pulled in by the mainstream. This applies to new ideas, technologies, architectures, processes, methods, products, etc. The problem arises when a new technology that is good surfaces and the mainstream rejects it in favor of the status quo especially if the status quo is less effective and everyone knows it, this is displacement technology[245]. There are also cases where new technologies arrive and there is no status quo but the stakeholders still reject the technology. The following are examples of challenges faced by previous generations to establish new technologies that are now the mainstream:

Table 150 Displacement Technologies and Designs

• Electricity versus gas	• Television versus movie house
• AC versus DC electricity	• Automobile versus public transit
• Automobile versus horse	• Airplane cargo carrier versus truck
• Telephone versus letter	• Cell phone versus land line phone
• Radio versus telegraph	• Internet versus print media versus retail versus sales staff, etc
• Airplane versus railroad	
• Airplane oceanic versus ship	

It is interesting to list home appliances and entertainment:

Table 151 Design Evolutions

• Indoor water	• Reel to reel tape recorder
• Indoor sewage	• Cassette tape recorder
• Electricity	• Video tape recorder
• Telephone	• Laser video player

---

[245] The early Internet was an example of a massive displacement technology.

Table 151 Design Evolutions

• Radio	• Cell phone
• Automobile	• Compact disk (CD) player
• Washer	• Digital video disk (DVD) player
• Television	• Personal computer
• Dryer	• Internet
• Garbage disposal	• MP3 player
• Dish washer	• Global Positioning System (GPS)
• Stereo record player	• Internet phone
• Stereo FM radio and record player	

So what tools, techniques, strategies can be used to convert from push to pull and if the conversion is not happening what can be done to enable that conversion. The following are some possibilities:

- Great marketing campaign, but what does that mean? Use the Veblen effect[246]; appeal to the ego and exclusivity of the less enlightened.
- Broadcast the Measure of Effectiveness (MOE) findings far and wide. This was a technique used for new systems such as satellites.
- Establish small example and point to the exceptional advantages. Niagara Falls provided AC electric power for the first time on a large scale[247]. This was used to show the benefits of AC electricity.
- Educate the stakeholders. This was a technique used to successfully introduce computers in the last century.
- Use the Socratic method of discourse where questions and answers stimulate critical thinking and illuminate ideas. The goal is to lead to the obvious conclusions.

The alternative to converting from a push to a pull scenario is to force the push. Some of the techniques are:

- Convert a waste element to a revenue producer. This is a form of recycling that happens at the production level.
- Legislation which forces the new technology to be adopted or makes the old technology illegal or tightly controlled.
- Tax incentives in the form of reduced taxes or tax credits.
- Create a virtual market. Sulfur dioxide is used as an example to establish

---

[246] The Veblen effect is described in this text.

[247] The Electrical World, A weekly Review of Current Progress in Electricity and Its Practical Applications, Volume 29, WJJC (The W.J. Johnston Company), Library of Princeton University, January 2 to June 26 1897.

other commodity markets for harmful by products such as carbon dioxide.

Author Comment: With the introduction of mass media there is information overload so demonstrations of new technology may not move the technology from a push to a pull. A classic example is the manned space program which resulted in humans stepping foot on the moon. Even though that was a spectacular demonstration of technologies, it was soon abandoned. Six Apollo missions landed astronauts on the Moon, the last in December 1972. In these six Apollo space flights, 12 men walked on the Moon. Apollo began after President John F. Kennedy's 1961 address to Congress declaring a national goal of landing a man on the Moon by the end of the decade.

12.19 Moving Forward

After World War II the USA fell into the cold war. This led to massive defense spending and the space race. To justify some of this expenditure the people convinced themselves of the concept of dual use[248]. Although inefficient, dual use did lead to practical systems needed for the emerging modern society. Interstate freeways became the backbone of the country as new cities emerged along its corridors. Defense RADAR was applied to civilian air traffic control and weather services. Computers and massive communications from the SAGE system gave birth to our highly automated and interconnected way of life. And certainly the space race yielded satellites and other technologies that transformed our world.

The problem is dual use has become a dated concept. There is little flowing into practical applications of everyday life as defense has taken on the concept of using commercial elements and the space program has turned into low level activities[249] that are not pushing any technologies to their limits. So the dilemma is who will pay for the new technologies and systems needed for our sustainable future?

The argument starting in the 1980's has been that the markets will provide for new technologies and systems, as they are needed. The idea is that the financial sector, which stores capital, would make capital investments available for new ventures. However, currently capital is not released for investment in new technology, development, and systems. Instead capital is being used to chase other capital via various financial investment products[250].

---

[248] Dual Use Technology, Dual Use Processes, Dual Use Products all refer to Dual Use where peaceful and military use is possible. It became part of the national dialog after World War II. Early references are not easily found. A Survey of Dual-Use Issues, IDA Paper P-3176 Prepared for Defense Advanced Research Projects Agency (DARPA).

[249] The Space Shuttle has been flying since 1981, some suggest NASA has turned into a taxi service for satellites rather than a technology driver and developer.

[250] My Life as a Quant: Reflections on Physics and Finance, Emanuel Derman, Wiley, 2007, SBN 0470192739. How I Became a Quant: Insights from 25 of Wall Street's Elite,

Infrastructure	Manufacturing	Services
Housing		
Water	Durable Goods	Value Added
Sewage	Automobiles	Education
Lighting	Computers	Health Care
Power	Televisions	Restaurants
Roads		Intellectual Prop
Trains	Non-Durable Goods	
Automobiles	Toilet paper	Overhead
Planes	Detergent	Insurance
Satellites	Food	Investments
Space Ships		

Figure 181 Infrastructure Manufacturing Services

So where is the intelligent application of capital? Who decides who gets funded and under what conditions?

Outside the free market another approach is to use government funds to support projects people think are needed for their society. An example is government provided healthcare in some countries. As the details are uncovered it becomes more complex and many people immediately point to socialism as the approach with a negative connotation.

So the argument is socialism versus capitalism when deciding how to apply capital to a problem. Whether it is taxes and a politician deciding where to apply the money or investments and savings with a financial executive deciding where to apply the money the result is the same. Projects that must be funded for sustainability are not funded. The only way out of this intellectual box is to accept the following:

- Dual use technology no longer exists
- It's not about socialism or capitalism
- Someone needs to pay for indirect costs that no business can ever justify

A bold approach is to get government back into the research business and directly fund sustainable projects in much the same way government funded defense and space in the dual use technology days. There even may be resurgence in dual use as defense realizes some of the sustainable projects may directly impact their needs. Also, perhaps NASA should return back to manned space missions. After all, not only is the extremely hostile space environment the ultimate teacher for sustainability but humanities future also may lie in the stars.

Richard R. Lindsey, Wiley, 2009 ISBN 0470452579. The Quants: How a New Breed of Math Whizzes Conquered Wall Street and Nearly Destroyed It, Scott Patterson, Crown Business, 2010, ISBN 0307453375.

12.20 Going Backward

The fundamental element of the Earth is dirt. There is nothing wrong with dirt. There are billions of organisms living on dirt, in dirt, within dirt, between dirt, at one with the dirt. Humans at one time lived in the dirt and they certainly can return back to living in the dirt. The problem is billions of existing people cannot survive on a dirt-based system.

So what uplifted humanity away from the dirt and allowed 6 billion people to survive? The answer is technology applied in our systems.

The problem is our current technologies in our systems have reached their limits and our technologies and systems are causing long-term problems for our Planet. Some think that we should consciously reduce our population or the Earth will reduce our population involuntarily. However who gets to decide whom goes and who stays and under what conditions should all this devolution happen?

It's time to grow up. Asking for a conscious reduction in population is wrong. At what point do we stop our devolution and say everything is now in balance? Perhaps there is a reason for 6 billion people that may not become apparent until a small asteroid hit makes 5.5 billion people go away.

Necessities	Transportation	Entertainment	Luxuries
Food	Cars	Movies	Jewelry
Clothing	Trains	Concerts	
Shelter	Planes	Theatre	
Infrastructure			
	Information	Services	
	Computers	Health Care	
	Televisions	Education	
	Radios		

Figure 182 From Necessities to Luxuries

It is obvious that dual use practiced after World War II yielded technologies that allowed 6 billion people to emerge. However dual use was never very efficient and has been abandoned. So the issue is who funds the projects needed for our sustainability - survival?

Business does not care about large-scale technology or the long term survival and growth of humanity. They only care about profits, which tend to be tied to short term needs - and that is perfectly appropriate. There is no relationship between profit and large-scale sustainability projects.

So the question is who will make the investments needed for a future that not only gracefully supports 6 billion people today but also allows for reasonable growth and a happy healthy future?

Table 152 Our Progress to Date

Tech Level	Waste	Surplus	People
Hunter Gatherers	None	None	0.1 million
Agricultural	None	Food, Clothing	1 million
Industrial	1 Earth	Food, Clothing, Infrastructure	200 million
Technological	4 Earth's	Food, Clothing, Infrastructure, Information	6000 million

12.21 Sustainability Practitio ners

Although sustainable development is not new and it is obvious that we practiced some form of sustainable development to get us to this point in our history, it appears that something new has surfaced to cause such interest. Perhaps it is our increasing sensitivity to our technologies and systems and their impact on our world. Perhaps we are detecting that our current systems and technologies have reached their limits and it is time for the next step.

This text has suggested the next step in this quest for sustainability must include systems design practices. It offers some suggestions to systems design practitioners as they attempt to address sustainability in their design solutions. Although system design practices are known in the systems community and the community gets very exited over small details of some aspect of a systems design practice, the reality is that many outside the community need basic introduction to the field, especially those attempting to offer sustainable solutions.

12.22 Sustainable Air Traffic Control Example

In the early 1980's the FAA had concluded that the current Air Traffic Control (ATC) System would start to saturate; reach capacity limits in certain parts of the country that would then affect all flights. The National Air Space (NAS) Plan or Brown Book was developed in response to this future projection of capacity limits. The Office of Technology Assessment (OTA)[251] performed a review of the NAS plan in 1982 and concluded that it was primarily technology driven and emphasized Enroute ATC[252]. According to the OTA: "The national air space system is a three-legged stool made up of airports, the ATC system, and procedures for using the airspace".

The original FAA intent was to significantly raise the automation level of the Enroute systems while the planes were within Enroute airspace. Effectively the planes would be metered and spaced so that the airport peak loads could be spread out in time[253]. It was a continuation of the flow control concepts at the national level

---

[251] The OTA was established with The Technology Assessment Act of 1972. It was de-funded in 1995 as part of the 104th Congress "Contract with America".

[252] Review of the FAA 1982 National Airspace System Plan, August 1982, NTIS order #PB83-102772. Library of Congress Catalog Card Number 82-600595, U.S. Government Printing Office, Washington, D.C.

[253] In the early 1970's the FAA established a Central Flow Control Facility to prevent

that were found to be very effective.

It did not matter that the OTA may not have fully understood the impact of the planned automation. It was reasonable to add the other two legs of the ATC system (Airports and Procedures) to the NAS plan. A revised plan was issued the following year in 1983. Many years ago I concluded there are only a few ways to increase capacity of an ATC system.

- **Cities:** The first is to build new cities away from existing cities with new airports some distances away from existing cities. The FAA has no control over how and where cities should be built. This is a bigger issue and may actually be the source of the ATC capacity problem and other problems. So the only answer might be to start to think broader and bigger and realize new cities are needed.

- **Bigger Planes:** The second is to build bigger airplanes and make sure they are filled to capacity. The FAA could encourage the airlines to buy bigger airplanes and increase seating capacity. However, some airports may be unable to handle the bigger airplanes and huge numbers of people arriving and departing. History suggests that is what may have actually happened as the casual traveler compares air travel of the 1970's and early 1980's with air travel today.

- **Procedures:** The third is to change the procedures. The procedures could be modified. Approach departure routes could abandon sound abatement rules and subject ground neighborhoods to the stresses of loud noise and possible fear of airplane accidents. Some might even suggest changes to reduce minimum separation standards. Others might suggest removing airplanes from standard air routes[254] to significantly improve capacity. However removing airplanes from air routes would require new navigational aids like Global Positioning System (GPS)[255] and a new control system. Basic things like Flight Plan Aided Tracking, Fix Posting Determination, etc all embedded within the existing automated system would need changes.

- **Automation:** The fourth is to increase automation to allow more airplanes

---

clusters of congestion from disrupting the nationwide air traffic flow.

[254] Air routes are like railroad tracks in the sky. It makes sense given that railroads existed before airplanes. It is easy to see how people from the previous century would adopt this approach for order, efficiency, and safety. Flying from visual point to visual point or navigation beacon to navigation beacon made perfect sense.

[255] First experimental Block-I GPS satellite was launched in 1978. In 1996, U.S. President Bill Clinton issued a policy directive declaring GPS to be a dual-use system. The policy presents a vision for management and use of GPS for military, civil, commercial, and scientific interests, both national and international where the Department of Defense, Department of Transportation, and Department of State manage it as a national asset.

to be pumped through the system. The reality is the system was very automated circa 1980. Many of the manual activities had been addressed with the introduction of the computer. Also automation is most effective where the airplanes have time to respond and maneuver.

The job at the tower is to basically watch the airplane on the taxiway and get it safely and quickly to and from the runway via the taxiways. Some airports can be expanded with additional runways, more taxiways, and larger physical terminals. However many airports that mattered reached their capacity limits.

The Terminal RADAR Approach Control Facility (TRACON) also has little options to increase capacity. The airplanes fly fast and 30 miles away from an airport does not leave much time for metering or other techniques to increase capacity.

If the airport peak loads could be spread out where there was time to respond, such as when the airplane is Enroute, then the system capacity could increase. So the automation was most appropriate for the Enroute centers.

The problem is the automation of the Enroute centers was captured within the Advanced Automation System Program (AAS) and the Automated En Route ATC (AERA) system concept. From the beginning, the GAO[256] report found the AERA concept was flawed. So the ambitious goal of automation failed as AAS was restructured to just replace the existing hardware and software with new technology while essentially staying within the same levels of automation. The GAO report findings are summarized as follows.

From Executive Summary

- *"Growth.* —FAA's traffic forecasts have been too high in the past and there are questions about the methodologies and assumptions underlying the projections on which the NAS Plan is based. Overestimation may have led FAA to foreclose technological options and accelerate the implementation schedule unnecessarily. It may also have led FAA to overestimate the user-fee revenues that will be available to pay for the proposed improvements."

Author Comment: Growth is an interesting concept. It is unclear how aviation may have changed if the original AAS program were permitted to evolve. Everyone in the community at the time knew that the introduction of the computer into air traffic control was sold as a labor saving device. However what really happened is the system was transformed to a new level allowing more people to fly while at the same time increasing the labor force as new kinds of activities surfaced. This not

---

[256] Review of the FAA 1982 National Airspace System Plan, August 1982, NTIS order #PB83-102772. Library of Congress Catalog Card Number 82-600595, U.S. Government Printing Office, Washington, D.C.

only happened in air traffic control but also in every segment of the world that adopted computer technology. What would have happened if AAS as originally envisioned emerged? We may never know.

- *"En Route Computer Replacement.* —FAA's option analysis issued in January 1982 supports upgrading the 10 en route computers that face capacity problems.[257] The NAS Plan, released at about the same time, calls instead for replacing the computer hardware (called rehosting the software) in all 20 centers as a part of a long-term plan to increase productivity and reliability as well as capacity. OTA does not find persuasive the reasons advanced by FAA for rejecting the previously preferred option of upgrading only selected en route centers. In addition, the choice of a host computer now may limit the options available to the contractor for the sector suite and software. OTA conferees were sharply divided in their views on this question. Some felt that the choice of a host computer now might limit future ability to benefit from a distributed computer architecture, local area networking, and new techniques in software development. Others believed that, if the host is chosen judiciously, the transition to a new system embodying these advanced and desirable features could be made without difficulty."

Author Comment: The proposed Hughes architecture was highly distributed in anticipation of the coming automation. Hughes was concerned that the cost of the rehost program would eventually stop AAS and the full-scale automation envisioned with AERA. In hindsight they were probably correct.

- *"Automation.* —While the NAS Plan envisions substantial cost savings due to extensive automation, supporting analysis is not provided in the plan. This analysis is probably still in progress and may take some time to complete, but it would be useful for the interim results to be made available to assist in congressional review of the automation portions of the overall plan. In addition, there is concern on the part of some experts about the ability of human operators to participate effectively in such a highly automated system and to intervene in the event of system error or failure."

Author Comment: Hughes was very aware of the role of automation in air defense systems. It was common knowledge that moving from a manual system to an automated system significantly reduced fighter intercept time and could mean the difference between winning and losing a battle. Everyone was also aware of the manual air defense and air traffic control system prior to RADAR and its affect on aircraft separation. So the practitioners in the business did not need to be sold on the

---

[257] Federal Aviation Administration, "Response to Congressional Recommendations Regarding the FM's En Route Air Traffic Control Computer System, " report to the Senate and House Appropriations Committees pursuant to Senate report 96-932, DOT/FAA/ AAP-823, January 1982.

concept of AERA. It was intuitively obvious that using machines to find ideal trajectories was significantly safer and faster than using humans. This was all lost in the politics of the day, as air traffic controllers feared losing their jobs and existing companies feared losing their contracts.

- *"Satellites.* —Satellite technology has significant potential applications for communication, and eventually for surveillance and navigation. FAA does not see a role for satellites in the period covered by the NAS Plan. FAA's decision against satellites appears to have been driven by timing and present cost effectiveness, rather than technology readiness or long-term system advantages."

Author Comment: Satellites were interesting and exciting. However no one at the time could figure out how satellites could allow more aircraft to be pumped through the system. The USA fortunately spent the money to provide RADAR coverage down to the ground level using gap filler RADARs where they were needed. Hughes had more satellite experience than anyone, but they were unable to see an application to address the ATC capacity problem. Hughes was extremely technology driven, with no real interest in products, so rather than trying to sell unneeded satellites, which they easily could have, the team continued to work the AAS program. While some were concerned about machines failing when offering advanced automation no one seemed concerned about satellite failure.

- *"User Effects.* —A great many of the proposed ATC system improvements are directed to the needs of traffic operating under the instrument flight rules (IFR), particularly while en route at cruise altitude. These improvements will benefit FAA itself by automating functions and reducing labor costs. The principal beneficiaries among users will be air carriers and larger business aircraft. Personal general aviation (GA) users could receive improved weather information, an important benefit; but in order to obtain this benefit and other operational advantages of the new system, more avionics will be required, and there would be restrictions on access to airspace by aircraft not so equipped. The Department of Defense (DOD) too, is concerned about the cost of new ATC avionics and feels that the new plan must be carefully coordinated with the military services to ensure that their mission needs and responsibilities for administration of the airspace are integrated with those of FAA."

Author Comment: The problem was system capacity. Some radicals were even suggesting taking GA out of the equation entirely so that the system could be sustainable in the future. The cost of avionics for DOD was a red hearing. The DOD budget at the time was at least 10 times more than the FAA budget. This cost would have been trivial compared to the cost of a typical DOD aircraft.

- *"Cost and Funding.* —Implementing the improvements proposed in the 1982 NAS Plan would more than double FAA's facilities and equipment budget through 1987, compared to the last 10 years. FAA has not yet released cost estimates for completing the proposed programs, but it seems likely that expenditures of like magnitude will be needed in the years beyond 1987. FAA proposes to recover 85 percent of its total budget through user fee revenues and a drawdown of the uncommitted Trust Fund balance. The user fee schedule would perpetuate the existing crosssubsidy from airline passengers and shippers of air cargo to GA. Business aviation would benefit particularly because of the extensive use these aircraft make of the IFR system. In addition, higher user fees may dampen the growth of aviation, thereby reducing the revenues expected to pay for the proposed improvements."

Author Comment: Many organizations were after the FAA trust fund coming from the gate fees in the 1980's and 1990's. For years there were movements to privatize the FAA while shifting all the indirect costs to the taxpayers via various privatization schemes. The reality is air travel is very high technology with huge indirect costs paid for by the taxpayer. From research for new aircraft via DOD to RADAR and other such systems that have no commercial equivalents that business can justify as investment.

From Technologies

- "Rand's principal conclusion is that the goal of full automation sought under AERA is a questionable research and development strategy that may present serious problems with regard to safety, efficiency, and increased productivity. An ATC system in which computers make most of the time-critical decisions in controlling aircraft, while the human operator serves in a managerial and back-up role, implies a needlessly complete and irrevocable commitment to automation. Rand argues for an alternative approach, called "shared control, " that would construct the future ATC system as a series of independently operable, serially deployable modules that would aid—not replace— the human controller and keep him routinely involved in the minute-to-minute operation of the system."

Author Comment: This killed the automation program. Placing the human in the minute-to-minute operation of the system would have been like placing people on the ground with binoculars to radio in positions (like they did at one time) rather than use RADAR. It would have been like not digitizing RADAR and using a computer to generate tracks, instead just staying with the proven broad band system and letting everyone use grease pencils and shrimp boats (like they did at one time).

AERA was represented as a phased implementation of progressively more elaborate automation and was structured as AERA I, II, and III.

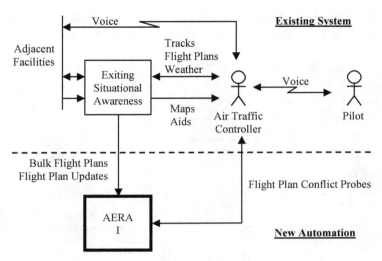

Figure 183 AERA I

The AERA I goal is to access the flight plan database and use it to perform flight plan conflict probes prior to providing a clearance that would need an update to a flight plan. This automation is of a strategic nature because the database is slowly updated, on the order of minutes. The automation includes graphical projections of the trajectories of the aircraft.

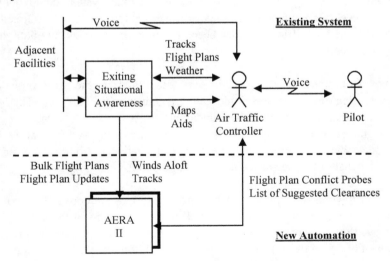

Figure 184 AERA II

In AERA II the goal is to access the tactical database populated by tracks (from RADAR) and winds aloft data to work with the flight plan database and offer a list of suggested clearances. The graphical projections of the trajectories of the aircraft now include the tactical information associated with the tracks. With this real time information a list of possible clearances is offered to a controller.

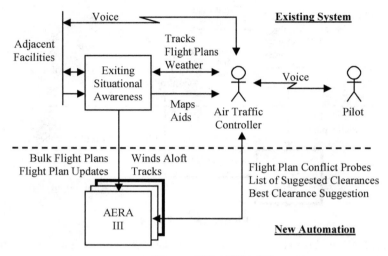

Figure 185 AERA III

In AERA III additional automation is added to offer a best clearance suggestion from the list of clearances. It is the choice of the controller to use or not use the information provided by the automation system. If the system could actually achieve this level of automation then the clearances could be data linked directly to the pilot with the air traffic controller becoming more of a system monitor rather than an active decision maker in the system.

Author Comment: It is obviously very easy to draw the AERA pictures. However turning these pictures into reality is much more difficult. The AAS program was supposed to provide the foundation for AERA. But AAS failed, in part because of the complexities of not only replacing an existing system that evolved over decades, but also because of the technical challenges of AERA, and the political challenges of its suggested levels of automation.

Today air travel is not a pleasant experience. All flights are booked to maximum capacity. There are no open seats as existed in the 1980's. Even the galleys have been removed to add more seating. Delays were common in the past but today we see delays of hours on the Tarmac. This was unheard of in the past. The bottom line is the system has reached its limits. The question now is will there be restrictions to reduce the number of passengers (airplanes in the sky) or will there be a new system[258]? The following is a summary of the SE2020 solicitation:

---

[258] SE2020 and NextGen are the FAA's new initiative to build a new air traffic control

"December 4, 2009. The FAA is soliciting bids from companies interested in competing for NextGen support contracts with an approximate combined value of $7 billion, the largest award in the agency's history. Under the umbrella awards, called System Engineering 2020 (SE2020), the FAA will award as many as five separate contracts for research and development and systems engineering work that will help the agency deliver NextGen.

The SE2020 contracts will be awarded to teams of companies, up to three of which will perform research and development work and two of which will perform systems engineering work. This work will complement and enhance major NextGen initiatives already under way, such as Automatic Dependent Surveillance - Broadcast, System Wide Information Management and Data Communications. Contract teams will focus on a series of operational capabilities, including Trajectory Based Operations, Collaborative Air Traffic Management and Reduced Weather Impact. The goal is to achieve early NextGen successes to improve safety and bring greater efficiencies to the nation's airspace system."

The following is a summary description of the NextGen program:

"NextGen is an umbrella term for the ongoing, wide-ranging transformation of the National Airspace System (NAS). At its most basic level, NextGen represents an evolution from a ground-based system of air traffic control to a satellite-based system of air traffic management. This evolution is vital to meeting future demand, and to avoiding gridlock in the sky and at our nation's airports.

NextGen will open America's skies to continued growth and increased safety while reducing aviation's environmental impact.

We will realize these goals through the development of aviation-specific applications for existing, widely-used technologies, such as the Global Positioning System (GPS) and technological innovation in areas such as weather forecasting, data networking and digital communications. Hand in hand with state-of-the-art technology will be new airport infrastructure and new procedures, including the shift of certain decision-making responsibility from the ground to the cockpit.

When fully implemented, NextGen will allow more aircraft to safely fly closer together on more direct routes, reducing delays and providing unprecedented benefits for the environment and the economy through reductions in carbon emissions, fuel consumption and noise."

Hindsight is always 20/20. That was a common saying in the ATC community circa 1980. However the GAO report, which rejected the AERA concept because it was too risky, was the wrong answer. It is interesting they did not give a history of air traffic control and reference the SAGE system. Without that context no one would realize that air traffic control advances were always driven with new and innovative technologies. Certainly satellites were new and innovative and GAO pointed out that the FAA ignored satellites in the plans. However GAO and others

---

system.

failed to identify how satellites could translate to increased capacity[259].

Perhaps the most significant failure of the GAO report was to realize that air traffic control is a classic control loop with the human in the feedback loop. There were many automated control loops in everyday practice by 1982. For example radios used automatic frequency and gain control circuits so that they would not drift off frequency and the sound not vary in loudness. Television used these same closed loop control mechanisms to make sure the picture maintained correct brightness, contrast, and color. A simple example of removing any of these automated control systems and placing the human in the loop to control and balance the sound or video by turning knobs would have clearly demonstrated how the current air traffic control system was limited by the human. The poor air traffic controller continuously turns knobs to provide safe and efficient separation services.

The real tragedy is the option offered was an all or nothing option for AERA. Rather than allowing the AERA technology to continue to evolve with limited operational tests, it was abandoned. Hughes with their air defense intercept algorithms could have substantially moved the AERA concept forward. A simple approach of awarding production to IBM for the status quo and a new research and development activity associated with AERA concepts would have been interesting.

Few are aware that at that time there were proponents of moving the entire air traffic control function into the airplane cockpit. The idea was to provide full situational awareness in the cockpit and let the pilots negotiate the airspace.

The AERA technology was the next logical step in automation. It did not propose moving the function into the cockpit. It is unclear how AERA compared to the SAGE system, which introduced the computer into the system with incredible levels of automation and communications networking. It is unclear how it compared with the manned space program and the mission to the moon.

What is clear is that with the removal of AERA from the system goals many challenges disappeared. It is possible that with AERA many of the computer companies that went out of business in the late 1980's could have remained and perhaps new forms of computing could have surfaced. Perhaps the Internet could have arrived 10 years earlier. So the impact of this decision had far ranging consequences that no one can really identify except to say that progress certainly stopped and the current system internal sustainability is now in question.

12.23 Sustainable Air Traffic Control Lesson

AAS is a very important lesson for all sustainability practitioners. In this case the institutions were in place, they were very effective, the money was there, and everyone had the best of intentions. Yet the big goal was never achieved and the

---

[259] Satellites were great for countries with no infrastructure, hostile environments, or spread out over vast bodies of water. It is like cellular phone communications, the infrastructure can be quickly and easily established.

system stagnated.

What happened was the age-old battle of the status quo and the new. Eventually the status quo won and the new was abandoned. There were actually camps that formed. IBM and the air traffic controllers represented the status quo. IBM was awarded the AAS production contract. Hughes and many engineers represented the new. Hughes lost the AAS production contract and moved on to field air traffic control systems in Canada and the Pacific Rim. The Pacific Rim shortly followed by Canada were the first to embrace satellites both for data link and position keeping.

So the status quo is extremely powerful and at times dangerous. In the 1980's it was not uncommon for older people to always refer to status quo and the bureaucracy. The bureaucracy was a thing to be avoided. However that is easier said than done.

In the 1980's there was a huge gap between technologists and everyone else in society. Today that gap is significantly smaller partly because the engineers have abandoned much of their high tech views with downsizing[260] and partly because everyone else has become more technically literate with the Personal Computer, Cell Phones, and the Internet. Most are now familiar with their version of SAGE. The sad part is the system that everyone thought was high risk, developed by extremely high tech people, was dwarfed by what was to come and is now common in this century. The following points summarize the whole sad situation:

- In the early 80's they were asked to create a new architecture that would not fail and support growth and technology insertion into the next century.
- The solution was a highly distributed system with over 300 computers per facility with 30 facilities across the USA.
- Never did they visualize hundreds of millions of computers connected together into a single machine, the Internet.

12.24 Beyond Sustainability Regenerative Systems

Regenerative systems go beyond sustainability. As part of their normal operations they improve the environment while operating and leave the environment in a better state after their operation. The following are examples of regenerative systems:

- Systems that are absolutely waste free and consume waste
- Systems that use water and return it back to the environment cleaner than when it arrived into the system
- Systems that add back the original bio-diversity to land and then add more bio-diversity to land than what was possible before the system introduction

---

[260] Sustainable Development Possible with Creative System Engineering, Walter Sobkiw, 2008, ISBN 0615216307.

The concept of regenerative systems was started in the late 1970's by professor John T. Lyle[261] who challenged graduate students to envision a community based on living within the limits of available renewable resources without environmental degradation.

12.25 Stakeholders and Benefits

The Space Act of 1958 included the forces of defense, control with ownership, and the elusive "for all mankind" idea. I remember the space race like yesterday. Many people including myself only believed in the "for all mankind" part of the equation. People were very excited about the early space walks and the first moon landing. But as time passed people started to believe that this was easy. Meanwhile we had enormous problems of war and hunger on Earth. So many people started asking the fundamental question of why we were spending so much energy and resources on space when there were needs here on Earth.

Going into space required enormous intellect, will power, resources, etc. Few realized that shutting it down would be a huge act of hubris. Today few realize that if you shutdown something you never may be able to recreate it regardless of our desires. This is emergence at its most significant level.

There is no question that the military used space funding to further their needs. There is also no question that those who think they have a right to own everything furthered their needs. The problem is where does the "for all mankind" fit into the equation and what does it really mean.

Today when we point to hunger, want, and other ills we immediately shift to the idea that this is all rooted in our politics. We think our technologies and systems are mature enough to feed and provide for everyone. However what if that is not the case. What if we use politics as an excuse and in reality we are engaged in an act of hubris. What if we really are lacking the technologies, know how, and systems to beat the elements and live well on Earth.

We witnessed the earthquake and tsunami in Japan with the resulting nuclear disaster. Not only were we not able to gracefully deal with the earthquake and tsunami[262] but the nuclear disaster was also beyond our control. This is a classic case of being humbled by Mother Nature and our best technologies failing.

12.26 User Sustainability Responsibilities

All designs must be internally and externally sustainable. However a design can

---

[261] Regenerative Design for Sustainable Development, John Tillman Lyle, Wiley Professional, December 1 2008, ISBN 0471178438

[262] Even though the Japanese earthquake preparedness was state-of-the-art and an example to the rest of the world.

only go so far. At some point the users must take responsibility. This discussion initially focuses on internal sustainability, but the impacts and analogies are easily related to external sustainability. There are four types of users:

- **Insensitive:** The insensitive users damage the system because of their insensitive self-centered behavior. The result is damaged paint surfaces, physically damaged surfaces, broken attachments, dirt grease goo, etc. This is typically behavior associated with a child, some teenagers and a few adults. They are unaware of their damage and if confronted will just ignore the discussion.

- **Sensitive:** These users realize the damage they have done in the past and become sensitive. They develop techniques to interact with systems where there is minimal damage. However accidents do happen and they feel bad. Even though they are sensitive, they are helpless to fix the system once damaged. They don't know what to do. This is typically behavior associated with teenagers, young adults, and a few adults. Notice a maturity trend is surfacing.

- **Sensitive Dependent:** This is a sensitive user that realizes when the system is damaged it needs to be repaired. However the user is unable to repair it and calls in an expert to perform the repair. This condition can be present either because the user is too busy to learn and perform the repair, too lazy to learn and perform the repair, or the system design is predatory preventing easy repair by anyone with some initiative.

- **Sensitive Independent:** This is a sensitive user that realizes when the system is damaged it needs to be repaired and they are able to easily perform the repair. They are self-sufficient people and the system design is not predatory, thus allowing the users to constantly maintain the system at peak performance and aesthetic levels.

Author Comment: Getting a society to the level of Sensitive Independence is a serious challenge. There has been a general trend of devolution and it is not uncommon to see many adults operating at the Insensitive Level. Some might suggest the source is the complexity of our high technology designs. I disagree. Instead our systems have become very successful allowing many user to abdicate their responsibilities. However there is a price to be paid for that abdication of responsibility. The price ranges from potential predatory labor practices in other countries to massive external sustainability failures.

12.27 A Business and Management Story

This discussion of business and management is different from other text book business management discussions because it is based on over 50 years of personal experience. These are my observations and opinions I have formed, so it is an isolated case history[263].

I was fortunate to have been bought up in a family that started a small business and successfully operated it for over 35 years. People who had small businesses back then (circa 1960 to perhaps the late 1980's)[264] were driven by their passions and satisfying their customers needs. The customers are important because they provide the cash to support the business and allow the owners to pursue their passions. There is great pride in serving the customers and providing the best quality possible. However there are times when some customers are unreasonable and they are asked to leave the business establishment. The money is returned and the relationship is severed. These are free people who enjoy liberty and are completely unencumbered by class, social status, rank, or wealth. There is a close relationship between their passion their view of their business and the customers.

I like to offer the example of hardboiled eggs when describing the small business environment. One day we became interested in hardboiled eggs. The idea was to boil eggs and offer them to the customers using a nice daily fresh display of fresh hardboiled eggs. When the eggs appeared the customers initially thought it was odd, but then became interested and eventually splurged for a hardboiled egg. In this simple example a new product was established in a new market for the existing business. Not only would hardboiled eggs bring excitement to the customers it also would get them thirsty for another glass of beer.

So small business is about hardboiled eggs. If you have an interest, try it. If you like it, keep doing it, unless it costs you extra money. As soon as you stop liking it, or it costs you money, stop.

I decided to leave the small family business world to pursue high technology engineering, which at the time was electrical engineering. I picked high technology engineering because I did not want to work for a traditional corporation. At the time my perception was that the traditional corporate driving factors were to constantly pursue increased financial earnings and profits rather that to pursue sustainable passions[265].

Many use the corporate charter as an excuse for a corporation to exclusively pursue increased earnings and profit regardless of the impacts. The boards and their selected executives claim they have a fiduciary responsibility to the current (not

---

[263] The Egyptian is a 1954 Hollywood film based on The Tale of Sinuhe, considered one of the finest works of Ancient Egyptian literature. It is the life story of Sinuhe that he writes on scrolls towards the end of his life for others to read. It includes the massive forces he has experienced and their impact on the world and his life. Published in 1945 by Mika Waltari in Finnish then Naomi Walford in 1949 in an abridged English translation from Swedish.

[264] As the society changed and money became the primary focus many small businesses may have abandoned this approach to business either because of survival or the desire to exclusively pursue significant wealth. Many were converted to medium or large size businesses, no longer owed and controlled by a small team of partners or a family.

[265] Sustainable passions - this is a loaded phrase and was fundamental in small business.

future) stockholders. So they suggest the corporate charter follow these requirements in priority order:

- Principal investors
- Current stockholders
- Customers
- Employees
- Community

However a corporate charter can include many items, different priority order, and still clearly show a case that current and future stockholder interests are protected. The following is an example of an alternative corporate charter in priority order:

- Customers
- Employees
- Community

Notice there is no mention of principal investors, current, or future stockholders. That is because if the interests of the customers, employees, and community are maintained the business is sustainable. There is no loss of customers, brain drain, or lawsuits from harmed community members. Further, increasing the customer base via new products, technologies, better products and or services, and even lower prices immediately translate to greater value to the investors and stockholders.

The big ugly issue about a large business is that there are enormous assets that can be stripped to show high profits for the principal investors and current stockholders. However it is not sustainable. Once the inheritance is blown by the irresponsible lazy offspring, it is gone. So I decided to enter and participate in high technology companies and industries. These entities were driven by passion and common sense financial needs much like a small family business.

I am sad to say that the high technology business model and enlightened thinking that accompanied this world has been replaced by what I viewed was a traditional corporation. At the time I did not know that these traditional corporations were in the last stages of their life cycles. The products, technologies, processes, management styles, were all completely obsolete. The problem was that once these corporations closed, their managers entered my high technology industries and companies. As they practiced what they learned in the dying companies they eviscerated and destroyed the high technology industries, companies, and ways of doing business and thinking. It was like a cancer.

There is a term called breakaway civilization. Many of the old high technology companies were so advanced in every aspect of everything that they did, everything outside was considered slow, behind the times, primitive native life. This may sound arrogant but the people were not arrogant. They did not abuse their extreme power and privilege on the less fortunate. Instead they would continuously educate and try to elevate anyone who was interested in the high technology way.

During one of my job assignments circa 2011 a young engineer was having difficulty understanding the primitive company behavior and bad technical team. I remarked to this young brilliant engineer that circa 1980 Hughes Aircraft was 50 years ahead of where we are here now at this company (2011) in every aspect of business, products, technologies, practices, management, thinking, etc. He intuitively knew I was correct and asked what was the answer. I was unable to offer an answer other than he consider starting his own company or take some overseas assignments.

Many tend to forget that a corporate charter is a privilege granted by the people via the state. In the US, the government has no power except that which the people decide to provide to the state. So a corporate charter can be revoked at any time. This is an incredible design that is unique in history. This design is the product of some serious systems thinking and engineering.

Whether you agree with this case history or not is irrelevant, this history exists. What matters is that there always will be a future and the content of this text tried to help make a better future.

12.28 Some Key Points

> Internal system sustainability is the ability of a system to sustain itself

> External sustainability is a measure of a systems impact on its surrounding community

> Sustainable development is development that "meets the needs of the present without compromising the ability of future generations to meet their own needs"

> Addressing shutdown and disposal is an element of system sustainability and design

> A Community Sustainability and Accountability plan includes
> - Who are the stakeholders
> - What are the stakeholder needs
> - What are the key sustainability issues in this system
> - What are the sustainability goals in this system
> - What are the key sustainability and stakeholder requirements
> - What is the accountability path for poor sustainability

➢ Some of the common systems design practices that should address sustainability are:
- Sustainable Requirements
- Technology Assessment, Innovation, and Stability
- Modeling and Prototyping
- Maintainability, Logistics, Safety, Reliability, Quality
- Life Cycle Cost
- Architecture Identification, Tradeoff, and Selection

➢ The role of the systems integrator
- Pick the most effective architecture and technology
- Integrate the system

➢ Example sustainability performance requirements
- Packaging Carbon Footprint
- Transport Carbon Footprint
- Content Carbon Footprint

➢ Example sustainability performance requirements
- Packaging Energy Consumption
- Transport Energy Consumption
- Content Energy Consumption

➢ Example sustainability performance requirements
- Packaging / Content Carbon Ratio
- Transport / Content Carbon Ratio

➢ Example sustainability performance requirements
- Packaging / Content Energy Consumption Ratio
- Transport / Content Energy Consumption Ratio

12.29 Exercises

1. Is sustainability an important element to consider in all designs? If so why, if not why not?
2. How can you balance external and internal sustainability?
3. What is the role of esthetics in sustainable designs?
4. What are the 3 key issues associated with sustainability and design?

12.30 Additional Reading

1. A Survey of Dual-Use Issues, IDA Paper P-3176 Prepared for Defense

Advanced Research Projects Agency (DARPA), March 1996.

2. Brundtland Commission, or the World Commission on Environment and Development, known by its Chair Gro Harlem Brundtland, convened by the United Nations in 1983 published Our Common Future, also known as Brundtland Report, in 1987.

3. Federal Aviation Administration, "Response to Congressional Recommendations Regarding the FM's En Route Air Traffic Control Computer System, " report to the Senate and House Appropriations Committees pursuant to Senate report 96-932, DOT/FAA/ AAP-823, January 1982.

4. How I Became a Quant: Insights from 25 of Wall Street's Elite, Richard R. Lindsey, Wiley, 2009 ISBN 0470452579.

5. My Life as a Quant: Reflections on Physics and Finance, Emanuel Derman, Wiley, 2007, SBN 0470192739.

6. Regenerative Design for Sustainable Development, John Tillman Lyle, Wiley Professional, December 1 2008, ISBN 0471178438.

7. Response to Congressional Recommendations Regarding the FM's En Route Air Traffic Control Computer System, report to the Senate and House Appropriations Committees pursuant to Senate report 96-932, Federal Aviation Administration, DOT/ FAA/ AAP-823, January 1982.

8. Review of the FAA 1982 National Airspace System Plan, August 1982, NTIS order #PB83-102772. Library of Congress Catalog Card Number 82-600595, U.S. Government Printing Office, Washington, D.C.

9. Sustainable Development Possible with Creative System Engineering, Walter Sobkiw, 2008, ISBN 0615216307.

10. The Electrical World, A weekly Review of Current Progress in Electricity and Its Practical Applications, Volume 29, WJJC (The W.J. Johnston Company), Library of Princeton University, January 2 to June 26 1897.

11. The Quants: How a New Breed of Math Whizzes Conquered Wall Street and Nearly Destroyed It, Scott Patterson, Crown Business, 2010, ISBN 0307453375.

12. The Rural Electrification Act of 1936, S. 3483, Public, No. 605.

13. Thorstein Bunde Veblen (1899) The Theory of the Leisure Class, An Economic Study of Institutions, London: Macmillan Publishers.

13 Bibliography

1. A Logical Approach to Requirements Analysis, Dr. Peter Crosby Scott, A Dissertation in Systems, Presented to the Faculties of the University of Pennsylvania in Partial Fulfillment of the Requirements for the Degree of Doctor of Philosophy, 1993.
2. A Survey of Dual-Use Issues, IDA Paper P-3176 Prepared for Defense Advanced Research Projects Agency (DARPA), March 1996.
3. A Systems Engineering Capability Maturity, Version 1.1, SECMM-95-01, CMU/SEI-95-MM-003, November 1995.
4. A Theory of Human Motivation, A.H. Maslow, Psychological Review 50(4), 1943.
5. Anthropometry of US Military Personnel, DOD-HDBK-743A, February 1991.
6. Applied Imagination: Principles and Procedures of Creative Problem Solving, A.F. Osborn, New York, NY: Charles Scribner's Son, Third Revised Edition 1963.
7. Art of Thought, Wallas, 1926.
8. Brundtland Commission, or the World Commission on Environment and Development, known by its Chair Gro Harlem Brundtland, convened by the United Nations in 1983 published Our Common Future, also known as Brundtland Report, in 1987.
9. CMS Requirements Writer's Guide, Centers for Medicare & Medicaid Services Integrated IT Investment & System Life Cycle Framework, Department of Health and Human Services, V4.11 August 31, 2009.
10. CMS Testing Framework Overview, Department of Health and Human Services, Centers for Medicare & Medicaid Services, Office of Information Services, Version: 1.0, January 2009.
11. Colossus: The Forbin Project, movie, writers: James Bridges (screenplay), D.F. Jones (novel), 1970.
12. Configuration Management Guidance, Military Handbook, MIL-HDBK-61 30 September 1997, MIL-HDBK-61A (SE) 7 February 2001.
13. Connections, TV Series, Writer Presenter: James Burke, Producer Director: Mick Jackson , Production Co: British Broadcasting Corporation (BBC), 1978.
14. Decision Making with the Analytic Hierarchy Process, Thomas L. Saaty, Int. J. Services Sciences, Vol. 1, No. 1, 2008.
15. Defense Acquisition Guidebook, Defense Acquisition University, August

2010.

16. Design Submission Requirements Manual, US Army Corps of Engineers New York District, NANP-1110-1-1, August 2009.

17. Designing And Developing Maintainable Products And Systems, DOD Handbook, MIL-HDBK-470A August 1997, MIL-HDBK-470 June 1995, MIL-HDBK-471 June 1995.

18. Diffusion of Innovations, Everett Rogers, 1962.

19. Diminishing Manufacturing Sources and Material Shortages A Guidebook of Best Practices and Tools for Implementing a DMSMS Management Program, SD-22, Defense Standardization Program Office, September 2009.

20. Discrete Time Systems, James A. Cadzow, Prentice Hall, 1973, ISBN 0132159961.

21. Earned Value Management Implementation Guide, DOD, Defense Contract Management Agency, October 2006.

22. Earned Value Management System (EVMS), DOE G 413.3-10, U.S. Department of Energy, EVMS Gold Card May 06 2008.

23. Educating, Gowin, D.B., Ithaca, N.Y., Cornell University Press. 1981.

24. Energy Efficiency and Renewable Energy, U.S. Department of Energy, February 2011.

25. Engineering Graphics, James S Rising, M. W. Almfeldt, P. S. DeJong, W. C. Brown Co; 4th edition (1970), ISBN 0-697-08601-1, 1970.

26. Executive Order 12803 - Infrastructure Privatization, US Government, April 30, 1992.

27. Federal Aviation Administration, "Response to Congressional Recommendations Regarding the FM's En Route Air Traffic Control Computer System, " report to the Senate and House Appropriations Committees pursuant to Senate report 96-932, DOT/FAA/ AAP-823, January 1982.

28. Fundamentals of Physics, David Halliday and Robert Resnick, John Wiley & Sons Inc; Revised edition (January 1, 1974), ISBN 0471344311.

29. Generic TRL descriptions found in NPR 7123.1, NASA Systems Engineering Processes and Requirements, Table G-19.

30. High Performance Computing and Communications Act of 1991 (HPCA) Public Law 102-194, the Gore Bill.

31. How I Became a Quant: Insights from 25 of Wall Street's Elite, Richard R. Lindsey, Wiley, 2009 ISBN 0470452579.

32. Human Engineering Design Criteria, DOD, MIL-STD-1472C May 1981, MIL-STD-1472D March 1989, MIL-STD-1472E October 1996, MIL-STD-1472F August 1999.

33. Human Factors for Evolving Environments: Human Factors Attributes and Technology Readiness Levels, DOT/FAA/AR-03/43, FAA/NASA Human

Factors Research and Engineering Division, FAA, 2003.

34. IBM's Early Computers, Charles Bashe, MIT Press, 1986.

35. Improving R&D Productivity: A Study Program and Its Applications, Robert M Ranftl, National Conference on Productivity and Effectiveness in Educational Research and Development, December 1977.

36. International Council on Systems Engineering (INCOSE) Systems Engineering Handbook 2011.

37. Managing The Development Of Large Software Systems, Winston W. Royce, Technical Papers of Western Electronic Show and Convention (WesCon), Los Angeles, USA, 1970.

38. Modern Control Systems, Richard C. Dorf, Addison-Wesley Publishing Company, 1967, 1974, Library of Congress CCN 67-15660, ISBN 0201016060.

39. Motivation and Personality, Abraham Harold Maslow, HarperCollins Publishers, 1954, 3d Sub edition January 1987, ISBN 0060419873.

40. My Life as a Quant: Reflections on Physics and Finance, Emanuel Derman, Wiley, 2007, SBN 0470192739.

41. NASA Appendix G Technology Assessment, NASA Systems Engineering Handbook, NASA/SP-2007-6105 Rev1, National Aeronautics and Space Administration NASA Headquarters Washington, D.C. 20546, December 2007.

42. NASA Procedural Requirements NASA Systems Engineering Processes and Requirements w/Change 1 (11/04/09), NPR 7123.1A, March 26, 2007.

43. NASA Research and Technology Program and Project Management Requirements, NASA Procedural Requirements, NPR 7120.8, February 05, 2008.

44. NASA Systems Engineering Handbook (DRAFT), September 1992.

45. NASA Systems Engineering Handbook, NASA/SP-2007-6105 Rev1, December 2007.

46. NASA Systems Engineering Handbook, SP-6105, June 1995.

47. National Airspace System Engineering Manual, Federal Aviation Administration, V 3.1, 2006.

48. Peopleware, DeMarco, Tom, Yourdon Press, 1987. Second edition, Dorset House Publishing Company, Inc, ISBN: 0932633439

49. Physical and Quantum Electronics Series, Demetrius T. Paris, F. Kenneth Hard, McGraw-Hill Book Company, 1969, Library of Congress CCN 68-8775, ISBN 070484708.

50. Pierre François Verhulst (1845) studied the logistic curve in relation to population growth. The S-

51. Practice For System Safety, Department of Defense Standard, MIL-STD-882D, 10 February 2000.

52. Quality Assurance Terms And Definitions, DOD, MIL-STD–109C 2

September 1994, MIL-STD-109B 4 April 1969.

53. Quality Program Requirements, DOD, MIL–Q-9858A 16 December 1963, MIL–Q-9858 April 1959.

54. R&D Productivity Second Edition; Hughes Aircraft, June 1978, AD Number A075387, Ranftl, R.M., Carver City, CA: Hughes Aircraft Co., Second Edition, 1978, OCLC Number: 4224641 or 16945892. ASIN: B000716B96.

55. Regenerative Design for Sustainable Development, John Tillman Lyle, Wiley Professional, December 1 2008, ISBN 0471178438

56. Registry of Toxic Effects of Chemical Substances (RTECS) toxicity database compiled without reference to validity or usefulness of studies. Center for Disease Control, The National Institute for Occupational Safety and Health (NIOSH) maintained it as a freely available publication until 2001.

57. Reliability Program For System and Equipment, Military Standard, MIL-STD-785B, 15 September 1980.

58. Research & Development Degree Of Difficulty (R&D3) A White Paper, John C. Mankins, Advanced Projects Office of Space Flight NASA Headquarters, March 10, 1998.

59. Response to Congressional Recommendations Regarding the FM's En Route Air Traffic Control Computer System, report to the Senate and House Appropriations Committees pursuant to Senate report 96-932, Federal Aviation Administration, DOT/ FAA/ AAP-823, January 1982.

60. Review of the FAA 1982 National Airspace System Plan, August 1982, NTIS order #PB83-102772. Library of Congress Catalog Card Number 82-600595, U.S. Government Printing Office, Washington, D.C.

61. Sandia Software Guidelines Volume 5; Tools, Techniques, and Methodologies; Sandia Report, SAND85–2348 1 UC–32, Reprinted September 1992.

62. Sequential Thematic Organization of Publications (STOP): How to Achieve Coherence in Proposals and Reports, Hughes Aircraft Company Ground Systems Group, Fullerton, Calif., J. R. Tracey, D. E. Rugh, W. S. Starkey, Information Media Dept., ID 65-10-10 52092, January 1965.

63. Software Development And Documentation, MIL-STD-498, Military Standard, 5 December 1994.

64. Software System Safety Handbook, Joint Services Computer Resources Management Group, US Navy, US Army, And US Air Force, December 1999.

65. Specification Practices, Military Standard, MIL-STD-490 30 October 1968, MIL-STD-490A4 June 1985.

66. Standard Practice Data Item Descriptions (DIDs), Department Of Defense MIL-STD-963B 31 August 1997, DOD-STD-963A 15 August 1986.

67. Strategic Management: A stakeholder approach, Freeman, R. Edward, Pitman Publishing, 1984, ISBN 0273019139.
68. Structured Analysis and System Specification, Tom DeMarco, Englewood Cliffs, NJ: Yourdon Press, 1978, ISBN 0917072073.
69. Sustainable Development Possible with Creative System Engineering, Walter Sobkiw, 2008, ISBN 0615216307.
70. System / Segment Specification, DOD Data Item Description DI-CMAN-80008A, June 1986.
71. System Engineering Management, Military Standard, MIL-STD-499 17 July 1969, MIL-STD-499A 1 May 1974.
72. Systems Engineering for Intelligent Transportation Systems, Department of Transportation, Federal Highway Administration, Federal Transit Administration, January 2007.
73. Systems Engineering Fundamentals, Supplementary Text, Defense Acquisition University Press, January 2001. Defense Acquisition Guidebook, Defense Acquisition University, August 2010.
74. Systems Engineering Management Guide, Defense Systems Management College, January 1990.
75. Systems Engineering Management Plan (SEMP), DOD Data Item Description, DI-MGMT-81024 August 1990.
76. Systems Practices as Common Sense, by Walter Sobkiw, CassBeth, 2011, ISBN 978-0983253082.
77. Technical Reviews And Audits Systems Equipments And Computer Software, MIL-STD-1521A June 1976, MIL-STD-1521B June 1995.
78. Technology Readiness Assessment (TRA) Deskbook, DOD, May 2005, July 2009.
79. Test And Evaluation Handbook, Federal Aviation Administration, Version 1.0, August 21, 2008.
80. Test Inspection Reports, DI-NDTI-90909A March 1991, DI-NDTI-90909B January 1997.
81. Test Plan, Data Item Description, DI-NDTI-80566, April 1988.
82. Test Procedure, DI-NDTI-80603, June 1988
83. The Analytic Hierarchy Process: Planning, Priority Setting, Resource Allocation (Decision-Making Series), Thomas L. Saaty, Mcgraw-Hill, January 1980, ISBN 0070543712.
84. The Dish, Movie, Director: Rob Sitch, Writing credits: Santo Cilauro, Tom Gleisner, Jane Kennedy, Rob Sitch, Warner Brothers, 27 April 2001.
85. The Egyptian, Mika Waltari 1945, Finnish then Naomi Walford in 1949 abridged English translation from Swedish.
86. The Egyptian, Movie, Director: Michael Curtiz, Writers: Philip Dunne (screenplay), Casey Robinson (screenplay) Mika Waltari, Production Co: Twentieth Century Fox Film Corporation 1954.

87. The Electrical World, A weekly Review of Current Progress in Electricity and Its Practical Applications, Volume 29, WJJC (The W.J. Johnston Company), Library of Princeton University, January 2 to June 26 1897.
88. The Golden Arrow, Movie, released 1964, Distribution: Metro-Goldwyn-Mayer, Production: Titanus.
89. The Magical Number Seven, Plus or Minus Two, George A. Miller, 1950.
90. The Magical Number Seven, Plus or Minus Two: Some Limits on Our Capacity for Processing Information, G.A Miller, The Psychological Review, 63, 2 (March): 81-97, 1956.
91. The Quants: How a New Breed of Math Whizzes Conquered Wall Street and Nearly Destroyed It, Scott Patterson, Crown Business, 2010, ISBN 0307453375
92. The Relationship of System Engineering to the Project Cycle, Kevin Forsberg and Harold Mooz, National Council On Systems Engineering (NCOSE) and American Society for Engineering Management (ASEM), 21–23 October 1991.
93. The Rural Electrification Act of 1936, May 20, 1936, S. 3483, Public, No. 605.
94. The Rural Electrification Act of 1936, S. 3483, Public, No. 605.
95. The Theory of the Leisure Class, An Economic Study of Institutions, Thorstein Bunde Veblen, London: Macmillan Publishers, 1899.
96. Tool for Analyzing Requirements, Carnegie Mellon, Report CMU/SEI-2005-TR-014, 2005.
97. Vitruvius The Ten Books on Architecture, Herbert Langford Warren (Illustrator), Morris Hickey Morgan (Translator) Courier Dover Publications, 1960, ISBN 0486206459.
98. Vitruvius, Fra Giocondo, Venice, 1511.
99. Vitruvius: Ten Books on Architecture, Cambridge University Press, Cambridge 1999, Editors D. Rowland, T.N. Howe, 2001 ISBN 0521002923.
100. WarGames, movie, writers: Lawrence Lasker, Walter F. Parkes, Walon Green, 1983. Film is about a fully automated defense system that decides to play the ultimate game as the humans try to stop it before its too late.
101. Webster's New World Dictionary, 1982, Simon & Schuster, ISBN 0-671-41816-5 (edged) or ISBN 0-671-41816-3 (indexed)
102. White Paper, Systematic Assessment of the Program / Project Impacts of Technological Advancement and Insertion, James W. Bilbro George C. Marshall Space Flight Center, December 2006, with acknowledgements: Dale Thomas, Jack Stocky, Dave Harris, Jay Dryer, Bill Nolte, James Cannon, Uwe Hueter, Mike May, Joel Best, Steve Newton, Richard Stutts, Wendel Coberg, Pravin Aggarwal, Endwell Daso, and Steve Pearson.

14 Index

B

C

D

E

F

G

H

I

K

L

M

O

P

Q

S

T

U

V

W